LINEAR PROGRAMMING AND
EXTENSIONS

LINEAR PROGRAMMING AND EXTENSIONS

by GEORGE B. DANTZIG

THE RAND CORPORATION

and

UNIVERSITY OF CALIFORNIA, BERKELEY

1963

PRINCETON UNIVERSITY PRESS

PRINCETON, NEW JERSEY

DEDICATED TO

Tobias Dantzig, my father, *in memoriam*

and to

John D. Williams, A. W. Tucker, and Anne S. Dantzig

PREFACE

The final test of a theory is its capacity to solve the problems which originated it.

This book is concerned with the theory and solution of linear inequality systems. On the surface, this field should be just as interesting to mathematicians as its special case, linear equation systems. Curiously enough, until 1947 linear inequality theory generated only a handful of isolated papers, while linear equations and the related subjects of linear algebra and approximation theory had developed a vast literature. Perhaps this disproportionate interest in linear equation theory was motivated more than mathematicians care to admit by its use as an important tool in theories concerned with the understanding of the physical universe.

Since 1947, however, there have appeared thousands of papers concerned with problems of deciding between alternative courses of action. There can be little doubt that it was the concurrent advances in electronic computers which have made it attractive to use mathematical models in decision-making. Therefore it is not surprising that this field has become, like physics before it, an important source for mathematical problems.

When a decision problem requires the minimization of a linear form subject to linear inequality constraints, it is called a linear program. By natural extension, its study provides further insight into the problem of minimizing a convex function whose variables must satisfy a system of convex inequality constraints. It may be used to study topological and combinatorial problems which may be couched in the form of a system of linear inequalities in discrete-valued variables. It provides a framework for extending many problems of mathematical statistics. This, in brief, is the mathematical scope of the book.

To provide motivation, the first three chapters have been devoted to concepts, origins, and formulation of linear programs. To provide insight into application in a "real" environment, two chapters on application conclude the book.

The viewpoint of this work is constructive. It reflects the beginning of a theory sufficiently powerful to cope with some of the challenging decision problems upon which it was founded.

Many individuals have contributed, each in an important way, to the preparation of this volume. John D. Williams of The RAND Corporation, in his former capacity as head of the Mathematics Department and in his present position as member of the Research Council, has been a constant source of encouragement. At his suggestion, the writing of this book was

[vii]

initiated as an answer to the many requests that flowed into RAND for information on linear programming.

Much of the theoretical foundation of the field of linear programming has been developed by Professor A. W. Tucker and his associates at Princeton University. Professor Tucker, who took a personal interest in the book, was instrumental in having the manuscript critically reviewed by a committee consisting of leading contributors to the field. Dr. Alan Hoffman of IBM Research reviewed Chapter 10, which deals with a perturbation method to avoid degenerate solutions; here the reader will find Hoffman's famous example that demonstrates the possibility of circling in the simplex algorithm. Professor W. Baumol of the Princeton Economics Department was asked to read Chapter 12 on prices, since he has written many papers and books using linear programming as a tool for the solution of economic problems. Professor Harold Kuhn of the Princeton Mathematics and Economics Departments reviewed Chapters 14, 15, and 16, which deal with the transportation problem. Throughout the book there are frequent references to Professor Kuhn's fundamental contributions to the field. Dr. Ralph Gomory of IBM Research attended to Chapter 26, in which his recent, exciting theory of integer programming is presented. The final member of the review committee was Dr. Michel Balinski, a member of the staff of *Mathematica*. Dr. Balinski has a fine grasp of the entire field and worked closely with Professor Tucker on a careful, general review of the volume.

The present content of Chapters 14–21 on transportation and network theory reflects the suggestions of Dr. D. R. Fulkerson of RAND, who kindly reviewed each of the drafts. This particular area has been undergoing rapid development, with Fulkerson a ranking contributor to its elegant theory. I am also pleased to acknowledge indebtedness to Julien Borden, graduate student in mathematics, for his aid in rewriting these chapters.

Individuals who combine a high theoretical ability with a desire to exploit the capabilities of electronic computers contribute in a basic way to the development of the programming field. Such a person is Dr. Philip Wolfe of RAND, who has made fundamental contributions to quadratic, nonlinear, and generalized programming. I am indebted to him for his many constructive suggestions and for his undertaking to rewrite the very important Chapter 3 on formulation, which serves as the key motivation chapter.

Dr. Tibor Fabian, an economist by training, formerly Chief of the Lybrand, Ross Brothers, and Montgomery operations-research team, assisted in the development of the first two chapters on concepts and origins. Professor Paul Randolph of Purdue University played an important role in the development of the earlier drafts of Chapter 5 on the simplex method and of the material on vectors and matrices. At the suggestion of Professor R. Dorfman of Harvard University, Clopper Almon, graduate student in economics at Harvard, undertook to read Chapter 12 on prices and Chapter 23 on the decomposition principle; he kindly contributed § 23-3 and part of § 12-1 illustrating the application of pricing concepts in planning. Similarly William Blattner of U.S. Steel, as part of his graduate studies at the University of California, Berkeley, contributed § 12-4 on sensitivity analysis.

I am grateful to my colleagues at RAND, Dr. Melvin Dresher and Dr. Lloyd Shapley, both experts on game theory, for their suggestions regarding Chapter 13; Dr. Albert Madansky for his many contributions to Chapter 25; and Frank H. Trinkl for his assistance in the organization of Chapter 12.

Marvin Shapiro, formerly of RAND's Computer Sciences Department, and my students, particularly R. Van Slyke, J. Clark, and H. Einstein, carefully read the manuscript and furnished detailed constructive comments. I am grateful to Miss Leola Cutler of RAND for her critical reading of Chapter 18 on bounded variables. The numerical calculations in Chapter 28 were made on RAND's electronic computer, the "Johnniac," by means of a linear programming code developed by W. Orchard-Hays and Miss Cutler.

The administration of the final preparation of the book was done by my very capable assistant, Mrs. Margaret Ryan, who formulated the layout, pre-edited, developed references, and prepared the index. Because of the technical character of the material and the size of the volume, these tasks involved great responsibility. Without her help, the book in its present form would not have been realized.

I am most grateful to Miss Ruth Burns, Chief Secretary of the RAND Mathematics Department, and to her able staff for their full support during the preparation of the manuscript, and to Mrs. Elaine Barth and Mrs. Ella Nachtigal for their work on earlier drafts. It is with great pleasure that I express my gratitude to my secretary, Mrs. Marjorie Romine Marckx, who did much of the final typing and with patience endured my numerous changes in the text.

The editing of the galley and the final page proof was under the jurisdiction of Miss Dorothy Stewart, her assistants at RAND, and my graduate students at the Operations Research Center, University of California, Berkeley: Richard Van Slyke, Donald Steinberg, Earl Bell, Roger Wets, and Mostafa El-Agizy, with Richard Cottle in charge. The detailed index was prepared by Bernard Sussman with the aid of Mrs. Barbara Wade, secretary of the O.R. Center. This team of people uncovered many technical flaws and have contributed in a positive manner to the final polish of the book.

Dr. T. E. Harris, Head, Dr. E. S. Quade, Deputy Head, and Professor E. F. Beckenbach, Editor, of the RAND Mathematics Department kindly provided me with full administrative and editorial support. Likewise, Brownlee W. Haydon, Assistant to the President for Communications at RAND, and John C. Hogan, in charge of RAND publication contracts, gave their full cooperation.

Finally, I am especially grateful to my wife, Anne S. Dantzig, for patience beyond the call of duty. She not only cheerfully suffered my continuous involvement, but even participated actively in various phases of the writing. Many of the better passages of the book reflect her acute rhetorical sense.

This study was undertaken by The RAND Corporation as a part of its research program for the United States Air Force.

GEORGE B. DANTZIG

The RAND Corporation

CONTENTS

[xi]

CONTENTS

CHAPTER 5

THE SIMPLEX METHOD

CHAPTER 6

PROOF OF THE SIMPLEX ALGORITHM AND THE DUALITY THEOREM

CHAPTER 7

THE GEOMETRY OF LINEAR PROGRAMS

CHAPTER 8

PIVOTING, VECTOR SPACES, MATRICES, AND INVERSES

CHAPTER 9

THE SIMPLEX METHOD USING MULTIPLIERS

CHAPTER 10

FINITENESS OF THE SIMPLEX METHOD UNDER PERTURBATION

CHAPTER 11

VARIANTS OF THE SIMPLEX ALGORITHM

CHAPTER 12

THE PRICE CONCEPT IN LINEAR PROGRAMMING

CHAPTER 13

GAMES AND LINEAR PROGRAMS

CHAPTER 14

THE CLASSICAL TRANSPORTATION PROBLEM

CHAPTER 15

OPTIMAL ASSIGNMENT AND OTHER DISTRIBUTION PROBLEMS

CHAPTER 16

THE TRANSSHIPMENT PROBLEM

CHAPTER 17

NETWORKS AND THE TRANSSHIPMENT PROBLEM

CHAPTER 18

VARIABLES WITH UPPER BOUNDS

CHAPTER 19

MAXIMAL FLOWS IN NETWORKS

CHAPTER 20

THE PRIMAL-DUAL METHOD FOR TRANSPORTATION PROBLEMS

CHAPTER 21

THE WEIGHTED DISTRIBUTION PROBLEM

CHAPTER 22

PROGRAMS WITH VARIABLE COEFFICIENTS

CHAPTER 23

A DECOMPOSITION PRINCIPLE FOR LINEAR PROGRAMS

CHAPTER 24

CONVEX PROGRAMMING

CHAPTER 25

UNCERTAINTY

CHAPTER 26

DISCRETE VARIABLE EXTREMUM PROBLEMS

Chapter 27

STIGLER'S NUTRITION MODEL: AN EXAMPLE OF FORMULATION AND SOLUTION

Chapter 28

THE ALLOCATION OF AIRCRAFT TO ROUTES UNDER UNCERTAIN DEMAND

References to the Bibliography are given in text and at the end of each chapter (see in particular the end of Chapter 2).

LINEAR PROGRAMMING AND
EXTENSIONS

CHAPTER 1

THE LINEAR PROGRAMMING CONCEPT

1-1. INTRODUCTION

In the summer of 1949 at the University of Chicago, a conference was held under the sponsorship of the Cowles Commission for Research in Economics; mathematicians, economists, and statisticians from academic institutions and various government agencies presented research using the linear programming tool. The problems considered ranged from planning crop rotation to planning large-scale military actions, from the routing of ships between harbors to the assessment of the flow of commodities between industries of the economy. What was most surprising was that the research reported had taken place during the preceding two years. See Bibliography, [Koopmans, 1951-1].

During and immediately after World War II, work on these and similar problems had proceeded independently until, in 1947, linear programming unified the seemingly diverse subjects by providing a mathematical framework and a computational method, the simplex algorithm, for formulating such problems explicitly and determining their solutions efficiently. This development coincided with the building of electronic digital computers, which quickly became necessary tools in the application of linear programming to areas where hand computation would not have been feasible.

Our immediate purpose is to define mathematical programming in general and linear programming in particular, citing a few typical problems and the characteristics that make them susceptible to solution through the use of linear programming models. Later in the chapter we shall discuss the relation of linear programming to mathematical programming and the relation of mathematical programming to the age of automation that we are approaching.

1-2. THE PROGRAMMING PROBLEM

Industrial production, the flow of resources in the economy, the exertion of military effort in a war theater—all are complexes of numerous interrelated activities. Differences may exist in the goals to be achieved, the particular processes involved, and the magnitude of effort. Nevertheless, it is possible to abstract the underlying essential similarities in the management of these seemingly disparate systems. To do this entails a look at the structure and

[1]

state of the system, and at the objective to be fulfilled, in order to *construct a statement of the actions to be performed, their timing, and their quantity (called a "program" or "schedule"), which will permit the system to move from a given status toward the defined objective.*

If the system exhibits a structure which can be represented by a mathematical equivalent, called a mathematical model, and if the objective can also be so quantified, then some computational method may be evolved for choosing the best schedule of actions among alternatives. Such use of mathematical models is termed mathematical programming. The observation that a number of military, economic, and industrial problems can be expressed (or reasonably approximated) by mathematical systems of linear inequalities and equations[1] has helped give rise to the development of linear programming.

The following three examples are typical programming problems which can be formulated linearly; they are analogous to the ones which originated research in this area [Wood and Dantzig, 1949-1; Dantzig, 1949-1]. It is well to have them in mind before we discuss the general characteristics of linear programming problems.

The objective of the system in each of the three examples to be considered happens to be the minimization of total costs measured in monetary units. In other applications, however, it could be to minimize direct labor costs or to maximize the number of assembled parts or to maximize the number of trained students with a specified percentage distribution of skills, etc.

1. A cannery example. Suppose that the three canneries of a distributor are located in Portland (Maine), Seattle, and San Diego. The canneries can fill 250, 500, and 750 cases of tins per day, respectively. The distributor operates five warehouses around the country, in New York, Chicago, Kansas City, Dallas, and San Francisco. Each of the warehouses can sell 300 cases per day. The distributor wishes to determine the number of cases to be shipped from the three canneries to the five warehouses so that each warehouse should obtain as many cases as it can sell daily at the minimum total transportation cost.

The problem is characterized by the fifteen possible *activities* of shipping cases from each of the canneries to each of the warehouses (Fig. 1-2-I). There are fifteen *unknown activity levels* (to be determined) which are the *amounts* to be shipped along the fifteen routes. This *shipping schedule* is generally referred to as the *program*. There are a number of constraints that a shipping schedule must satisfy to be feasible: namely, the schedule must show that each warehouse will receive the required number of cases

---

[1] The reader should especially note we have used the word *inequalities*. Systems of linear inequalities are quite general; linear inequality relations such as $x \geq 0$, $x + y \leq 7$ can be used to express a variety of common restrictions, such as quantities purchased, x, must not be negative or the total amount of purchases, $x + y$, must not exceed 7, etc.

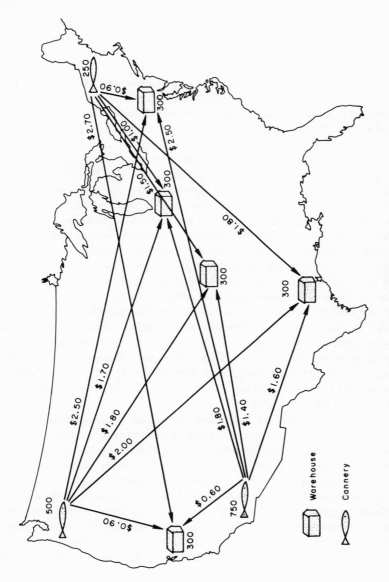

Figure 1-2-I.   The Problem: Find a least cost plan of shipping from canneries to warehouses (the costs per case, availabilities and requirements are as indicated).

and that no cannery will ship more cases than it can produce daily. (Note there is one constraint for each warehouse and one for each cannery.) Several *feasible shipping schedules* may exist which would satisfy these constraints, but some will involve larger shipping costs than others. The problem then is to determine an *optimal shipping schedule*—one that has least costs. *Transportation* problems such as this are formulated in mathematical terms in § 3-3 and their solution properties are studied in Chapters 14 to 20.

2. *The housewife's problem.* A family of five lives on the modest salary of the head of the household. A constant problem is to determine the weekly menu after due consideration of the needs and tastes of the family and the prices of foods. The husband must have 3,000 calories per day, the wife is on a 1,500-calorie reducing diet, and the children require 3,000, 2,700, and 2,500 calories per day, respectively. According to the prescription of the family doctor, these calories must be obtained for each member by eating not more than a certain amount of fats and carbohydrates and not less than a certain amount of proteins. The diet, in fact, places emphasis on proteins. In addition, each member of the household must satisfy his or her daily vitamin needs. The problem is to assemble menus, one for each week, that will minimize costs according to Thursday food prices.

This is a typical linear programming problem: the possible activities are the purchasing of foods of different types; the program is the amounts of different foods to be purchased; the constraints on the problem are the calorie and vitamin requirements of the household, and the upper or lower limits set by the physician on the amounts of carbohydrates, proteins, and fats to be consumed by each person. The number of food combinations which satisfy these constraints is very large. However, some of these feasible programs have higher costs than others. The problem is to find a combination that minimizes the total expense[2] [Stigler, 1945-1]. *Blending* problems such as this are formulated in § 3-4.

3. *On-the-job training.* A manufacturing plant is contracting to make some commodity. Its present work force is considerably smaller than the one needed to produce the commodity within a specified schedule of different amounts to be delivered each week for several weeks hence. Additional workers must, therefore, be hired, trained, and put to work. The present force can either work and produce at some rate of output, or it can train some fixed number of new workers, or it can do both at the same time according to some fixed rate of exchange between output and the number of new workers trained. Even were the crew to spend one entire week training new workers, it would be unable to train the required number.

---

[2] Chapter 27 contains a detailed discussion of a typical nutrition problem. The reader may wonder why this problem is not really five separate problems, one for each member of the family; however, certain foods (such as eggs, milk, meat) can be subdivided into parts of varying fat content and given to different members.

The next week, the old crew *and* the newly trained workers may either work or train new workers, or may both work and train, and so on. The commodity is semi-perishable so that amounts produced before they are needed will have to be stored at a specified cost. The problem is to determine the hiring, production, and storage program that will minimize total costs.

This, too, is a linear programming problem, although with the special property, not shared with the previous two examples, of *scheduling activities through time*. The activities in this problem are the assignment of old workers to either of two jobs, production or training, and the hiring of new workers each week. The quantities of these activities are restricted by the number of workers available at the beginning of each week and by the instructor-student ratio. The cumulative output produced by all workers through the number of weeks in the contractual period has to equal or exceed the required output. A possible production-training program is shown in Fig. 1-2-II. The problem can now be stated more precisely: determine the proper balance between hiring and training of workers, between teaching and production, and between over- and under-production in order to minimize

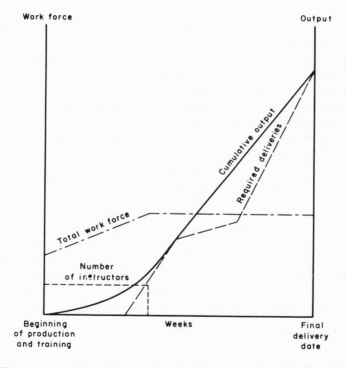

Figure 1-2-II. The Problem: Determine a least-cost hiring, production and storage program to meet required deliveries.

total costs. For mathematical formulation of this problem see § 3-7.

1-3. LINEAR PROGRAMMING DEFINED

Operations research or *management science* is concerned with the science of decision and its application. In this domain the term *model building* refers to the process of putting together of symbols representing objects according to certain rules, to form a structure, *the model*, which corresponds to a system under study in the real world. The symbols may be small-scale replicas of bricks and girders or they may be, as in our application, algebraic symbols.

Linear programming has a certain philosophy or approach to building a model that has application to a broad class of decision problems encountered in government, industry, economics, and engineering. It probably possesses the simplest mathematical structure which can be used to solve the practical scheduling problems associated with these areas. Because it is a method for studying the behavior of systems, it exemplifies the distinguishing feature of management science, or operations research, to wit: "Operations are considered as an entity. The subject matter studied is not the equipment used, nor the morale of the participants, nor the physical properties of the output, it is the combination of these in total as an economic process" [Herrmann and Magee, 1953-1].

Linear programming[3] is concerned with describing the interrelations of the components of a system. As we shall see, the first step consists in regarding a system under design as composed of a number of elementary functions that are called "activities."[4] As a consequence, T. C. Koopmans [1951-1] introduced the term *activity analysis* to describe this approach. The different activities in which a system can engage constitute its technology. These are the representative building blocks of different types that might be recombined in varying amounts to rear a structure that is self-supporting, satisfies certain restrictions, and attains as well as possible a stated objective. Representing this structure in mathematical terms (as we shall see in Chapter 3) often results in a system of linear inequalities and equations; when this is so, it is called a linear programming model. Like architects, people who use linear programming models manipulate "on paper" the symbolic representations of the building blocks (activities) until a satisfactory design is obtained. The theory of linear programming is concerned with scientific procedures for arriving at the best design, given the technology, the required specifications, and the stated objective.

To be a linear programming model, the system must satisfy certain assumptions

[3] The term "linear programming" was suggested to the author by T. C. Koopmans in 1951 as an alternative to the earlier form, "programming in a linear structure" [Dantzig, 1948-1].
[4] The term "activity" in this connection is military in origin. It has been adopted in preference to the term "process," used by von Neumann in "A Model of General Economic Equilibrium," [von Neumann, 1937-1].

of proportionality, nonnegativity, and additivity. How this comes about will be the subject of Chapter 3, where we shall also formulate linear programming models for examples like those already discussed. It is important to realize in trying to construct models of real-life situations, that life seldom, if ever, presents a clearly defined linear programming problem, and that simplification and neglect of certain characteristics of reality are as necessary in the application of linear programming as they are in the use of any scientific tool in problem solving.

The rule is to *neglect the negligible.* In the cannery example, for instance, the number of cases shipped and the number received may well differ because of accidental shipping losses. This difference is not known in advance and may be unimportant. In the optimum diet example the true nutritional value of each type of food differs from unit to unit, from season to season, from one source of food to another. Likewise, production rates and teaching quality will vary from one worker to another and from one hour to another. In some applications it may be necessary to give considerable thought to the differences between reality and its representation as a mathematical model to be sure that the differences are reasonably small and to assure ourselves that the computational results will be operationally useful.

What constitutes the proper simplification, however, is subject to individual judgment and experience. People often disagree on the adequacy of a certain model to describe the situation.

1-4. CLASSIFICATION OF PROGRAMMING PROBLEMS

The programming problems treated in this book, except those of Chapter 25, belong to the *deterministic* class, by which it is meant that if certain actions are taken it can be predicted with *certainty* what will be (a) the requirements to carry out the actions and (b) the outcome of any actions. Few, if any, activities of the real world have this property. Perhaps the activity of burning two parts of hydrogen to one part oxygen to produce water might be cited as a deterministic example. In practice, however, because of contamination, leaks in containers, etc., this assumed relation is an ideal. For many purposes, however, an ideal formula can be used because the deviations from it are so slight that only small adjustments will be necessary from time to time.

A deterministic situation may be created by fiat. For example, the amounts of gas and oil required to carry out certain transportation activities by trucks can never be known with certainty. However, if stocks well above known expected values are used in the plan, it can be assumed that the transportation can be accomplished and any surplus stocks remaining put to good use later. Usually the working time it takes to accomplish a task is a fraction of the time assumed in the plan. For example, consider the fabrication of a part for an airplane: the elapsed time from when it is first cut out of sheet metal until it is ready to be assembled on the airplane may be three months or more; on the other hand, only a few hours may be spent shaping, drilling holes, and mounting. The remainder of the time is accounted for in storage bins whose principal function appears to be that of piling up work orders so that they can be redistributed in such a way that workers can be more effectively employed.

Programs involving *uncertainty* form the other major class which we will call *probabilistic*. Uncertainty can arise in many ways. The outcome of a given action may depend on some chance event such as the weather, traffic delays, government policy, employment levels, or the rise and fall of customer demand. Sometimes the distribution of the chance events is known, sometimes it is unknown or partially known. In some cases uncertainty arises because of the actions of competitors or enemies.

In Fig. 1-4-I the two main classes of programming problems are deterministic and probabilistic. The former is shown subdivided into two main

CLASSIFICATION OF PROGRAMMING PROBLEMS

Discrete or Continuous
Multistage or Non-Multistage
(Dynamic or Non-Dynamic)

Deterministic				Probabilistic			
Linear		Nonlinear		No Opponents		Against Opponents	
General Structures	Special Structures	Convex	Non-Convex	Known Probability Distribution	Unknown Probability Distribution	Two-Person Games	Multi-Person Games

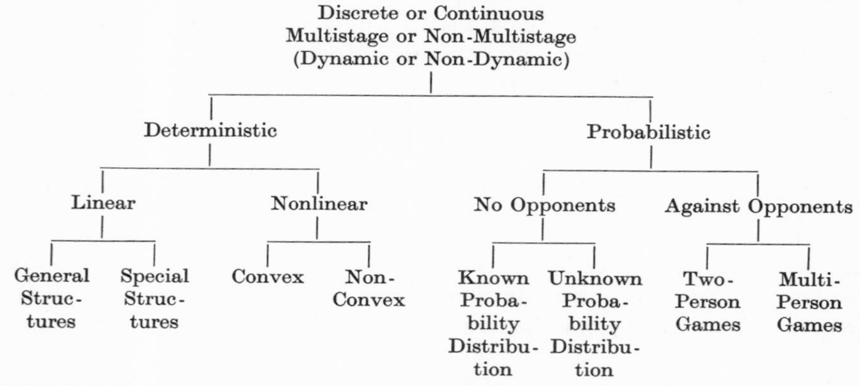

SPECIAL CASES OF THE ABOVE

Linear inequality theory	Dynamic systems, Leontief models, Networks	Decreasing payoff, Chemical equilibrium, Convex programs	Increasing returns to scale, Many local maxima	Inventory control, Markov chains	Sequential decisions	Zero-sum games	Coalition theory

Figure 1-4-I.

mathematical classes that are often studied, linear and nonlinear models; the latter is shown subdivided into two main application classes, those involving an indifferent (or unpredictable) nature, and those against an unfriendly opponent. These are further subdivided and well-known special cases are shown directly below each class.

In this book we will pay particular attention to both general and special linear programming structures, to nonlinear convex programming problems that can be reduced to linear programming problems, and to certain probabilistic problems that can also be reduced to linear programming problems, such as two person-zero sum games, and scheduling problems involving uncertain demand.

One important way to classify programming problems is into multistage and non-multistage groups. *Multistage models* include dynamic models in which the schedule over time is a dominant feature, as in example (3). Examples (1) and (2) are non-multistage problems as are steady-state economic models (whose production rates remain constant over time).

A second important way to classify models is into those in which some of the inputs, outputs, assignments, or production levels to be determined must occur in *discrete* amounts such as 0, 1, 2, . . . (with no intermediate amounts possible), and into those in which these quantities can take on any values over *continuous* ranges. Many combinatorial problems belong to the discrete class, such as problems concerning the assignment of a number of men to an equal number of jobs or the order in which a salesman should visit a number of cities. Strictly speaking, the discrete problems belong to the class of nonlinear programming problems (see Chapter 26).

Dynamic Programming.

Many multistage problems, particularly dynamic problems, exhibit a structure that permits a solution by application of an *inductive principle*. At the beginning of each stage, as in a treasure hunt, directions are given where to proceed next; and the total payoff of future actions, if one continues to follow directions, is indicated. It is assumed (and this is the fundamental assumption on structure) that the optimal direction and payoff depend only on one's *status* at the beginning of a stage, and not on any previous action. At the end of the *last stage* it is usually easy to give the value for all possible final states. This permits one to construct, without too much effort, the direction for maximum payoff from each of the *possible states* at the end of the *next to the last* stage; and from that, to construct the directions for maximum payoff for all possible states at the end of the *second to last* stage, and so forth *inductively backwards in time* until the beginning of the first stage where initial status is assumed known. To proceed backward in this manner it is necessary to know, for every combination of states at the beginning and end of a stage, the gain or loss within a stage. Whether or not the method can be used depends on whether the analysis of the possible combinations is tractable. The inductive principle is as old as the Greeks, but in connection with its early application to decision problems the names of A. Wald [1950-1], P. Massé [1946-1], K. Arrow, T. Harris, and

[9]

J. Marschak [1951-1], A. Dvoretsky, J. Kiefer, and J. Wolfowitz [1952-1] are worthy of mention. Richard Bellman in 1952, however, was the first to see the importance of the inductive principle which he calls the *principle of optimality* to programming applications and has been active in developing its potentialities [Bellman, 1954-1 and 1957-1; Bellman, Glicksberg, and Gross, 1958-1]. The general area of research using this principle is called "Dynamic Programming" because most of its applications happen to be multistage in character.

1-5. MATHEMATICAL PROGRAMMING AND AUTOMATION

The period following World War II has been marked by an accelerated trend toward automation, an advanced form of mechanization. Mechanization's effect is to relieve man of the need to use his human energy for power; automation's effect is to relieve him of certain of his mental tasks and the related necessary physical tasks. Many believe that electronic computers, which are themselves examples of automation, will play an important role in the mechanization of control processes of the routine type.

It is believed by some that "higher level decisions will be made by man primarily because he, through the exercise of his mind, possesses the only means of integrating and interrelating data for which rational formulations are not yet possible or are too expensive" [Boelter, 1955-1]. However, the author believes that even in the realm of higher order controls, particularly the mental tasks which involve choice of selection among alternative courses of action, mechanization is in progress. This applies to mental tasks, known as programming (or scheduling), and their physical realization, known as production control.

These two postwar developments, automation and programming, are often associated because of their use of electronic computers. How closely are they related?

To answer the question, let us inspect some developments in an industry which was one of the first to automatize production and to introduce the programming of the production process. Production in a modern petroleum refinery is a complex of interrelated activities. The number of possible combinations of feed stocks, operating sequences, operating conditions, blending methods, and the choice of final products, is large; as a consequence, mathematical programming methods are used to great advantage in evaluating the economy of an operational scheme. Once the proper production schedule is determined, it is only necessary to set dials and push buttons in the control rooms for the refinery to be able to deliver the products in the preassigned amounts.

This example shows that the two processes, decision-making and production control, could each become completely automated and yet could be linked by human operators who transmit the instructions from one system, the decision-making system, to the other, the production system. It should be emphasized, then, that although programming constitutes a higher order control, it is *not* equivalent to the feedback device which holds the temperature in a boiler constant. It is rather a method for deciding what that temperature should be and for how long, in order that the objective of the production may be attained.

While the mechanization of the higher order decision-making process does not always require the mechanization of the physical links by which the decisions are implemented, it is conceivable that in certain applications it may become economical to combine the two automated processes into one. Such "super-automated" processes are necessary in fast-flying rockets which require tight control and the use of flexible programming techniques. Some industries, such as the aircraft industry, are turning to multipurpose machines which can produce a variety of items depending on the settings of controls. These, in turn, can be changed by an automatic, higher-order control. Ultimately in such systems, machine failures, item rejects, and new orders may make it necessary to reprogram work loads rapidly. Here again, tight methods of production control may have to be linked mechanically to flexible automatic programming techniques.

REFERENCES

Dynamic Programming, Inventory Theory

Arrow, Harris, and Marschak, 1951-1
Arrow, Karlin, and Scarf, 1958-1
Bellman, 1954-1, 1957-1

Bellman, Glicksberg, and Gross, 1958-1
Dvoretzky, Kiefer, and Wolfowitz, 1952-1
Massé, 1946-1

Wald, 1950-1

Automation

Boelter, 1955-1

Dantzig, 1957-1

Linear Programming

Dantzig, 1948-1, 1949-1
Herrmann and Magee, 1953-1
Koopmans, 1951-1

Stigler, 1945-1
von Neumann, 1937-1
Wood and Dantzig, 1949-1

CHAPTER 2

ORIGINS AND INFLUENCES

In the ten years following its conception in 1947 in connection with planning activities of the military, linear programming came into wide use in industry. In academic circles, mathematicians and economists have written books on the subject. The purpose of this chapter is to give a brief account of its origins and of the influences which brought about this rapid development. Table 2-1-I summarizes these, as well as the later growth of linear programming. Arrows indicate the direct influence of one happening on another. Interestingly enough, in spite of its wide applicability to everyday problems, linear programming was unknown before 1947. Fourier may have been aware of its potential in 1823. In the U.S.S.R. in 1939, Kantorovich made proposals that were neglected during the two decades that witnessed the discovery of linear programming and its firm establishment elsewhere.

2-1. WORLD WAR II INFLUENCES

The Nature of Staff Planning.

A nation's military establishment, in wartime or in peace, is a complex of economic and military activities requiring almost unbelievably careful coordination in the implementation of plans produced in its many departments. If one such plan calls for equipment to be designed and produced, then the rate of ordering equipment has to be coordinated with the capabilities of the economy to relinquish men, material, and productive capacity from the civilian to the military sector. These development and support activities should dovetail into the military program itself. To give some idea of the interdependence of various major activities there are hundreds of subtypes within each of its major activities for the case of personnel, and thousands of subtypes for the case of supply. Was it always so complicated? The following statement of M. K. Wood and M. A. Geisler [1951-1, p. 189] is pertinent:

"It was once possible for a Supreme Commander to plan operations personally. As the planning problem expanded in space, time, and general complexity, however, the inherent limitations in the capacity of any one man were encountered. Military histories are filled with instances of commanders who failed because they bogged down in details, not because they could not eventually have mastered the details, but because they could not master all the relevant details in the time available for decision. Gradually, as planning problems became more complex, the Supreme Commander came to be surrounded with a General Staff of specialists, which supplemented the Chief in making decisions. The existence of a General Staff permitted the subdivision of the planning process and the assignment of experts to handle each part. The function of the Chief then became one of selecting objectives, coordinating, planning, and resolving conflicts between staff sections."

TABLE 2-1-I

LINEAR PROGRAMMING TIMETABLE: ORIGINS—INFLUENCES

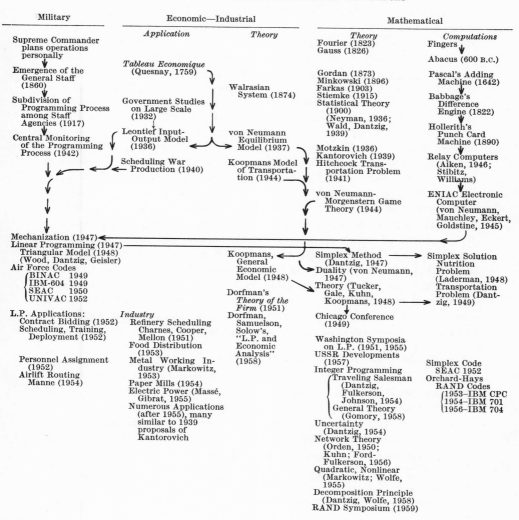

[13]

Large wars have been waged throughout the history of civilization, but the General Staff of the Supreme Commander of military forces emerged only around the middle of the last century (Prussia, 1860) as a consequence of the increased complexity of warfare. The subdivision of the planning of military activities among the staff agencies dates back only to the stalemate and attrition phase of World War I (1917).

World War II Developments.

World War II witnessed the development of staff planning on a gigantic scale in all parts of the U.S. military establishment and in such civilian counterparts as the War Production Board. During this period the U.S. Air Corps grew to a principal arm of the military. Unfettered by tradition, it evolved a number of aids to planning[1] that ultimately led to the consideration of a scientific programming technique in the postwar period.

During the war, the planning process itself became so intricate, lengthy, and multipurposed that a snapshot of the Air Staff at any one time showed it to be working on many different programs—some in early phases of development and based on latest ground rules and status reports, others in later phases but based on earlier ground rules and facts. To cut the time of the planning process, a patchwork of several of these programs was often thrown together based on necessarily inconsistent facts and rules. To coordinate this work better, the Air Staff, around 1943, created the *program monitoring* function under Professor E. P. Learned of Harvard. The entire program was started off with a war plan in which were contained the wartime objectives. From this plan, by successive stages, the wartime program specifying unit deployment to combat theaters, training requirements of flying personnel and technical personnel, supply and maintenance, etc., was computed. To obtain consistent programming the ordering of the steps in the schedule was so arranged that the flow of information from echelon to echelon was only in one direction, and the timing of information availability was such that the portion of the program prepared at each step did not depend on any following step. Even with the most careful scheduling, it took about seven months to complete the process.

Post-World War II Developments.

After the war the U.S. Air Force consolidated the statistical control, program monitoring, and budgeting functions under the staff of the Air Force Comptroller, General E. W. Rawlings, now President of General Mills Corporation. It became clear to members of this organization that efficiently coordinating the energies of whole nations in the event of a total

[1] The most important of these was the development under C. B. Thornton of the Statistical Control System that provided a continuous flow of detailed information on the status of many parts of the Air Force, including personnel, supply, operations, and basic data upon which to base attrition rates, sortie rates, crew rotation rates, maintenance needs, supply rates, etc.

war would require scientific programming techniques. Undoubtedly this need had occurred many times in the past, but this time there were two concurrent developments that had a profound influence: (a) the development of large scale electronic computers, and (b) the development of the inter-industry model. The latter is a method of describing the inter-industry relations of an economy and was originated by Wassily Leontief [1951-1]. This is described in the next section.

Intensive work began in June 1947, in a group that later (October 1948) was given the official title of Project SCOOP (Scientific Computation of Optimum Programs). Principals in this group were Marshall Wood and the author, and soon thereafter John Norton and Murray Geisler.

The potential attraction of the inter-industry model will become apparent in the next section. Its simple structure, particularly its use of linear production functions in the description of industry-wide aggregates of economic activities, had a considerable impact on the thinking of the Air Force research team. Its nondynamic character, however, and the simplifying assumption that each industry had a unique technology which produced only one product, restricted the model's usefulness. Another limitation of the model was that it was not possible to have alternative feasible programs. It was therefore necessary to generalize the inter-industry approach. The result was the development of the linear programming model by July 1947.

The *simplex computational method* for choosing the optimal feasible program was developed by the end of the summer of 1947 (see Chapter 5). Interest in linear programming began to spread quite rapidly. During this period the Air Force sponsored work at the U.S. Bureau of Standards on electronic computers and on mathematical techniques for solving such models. John Curtiss and Albert Cahn of the Bureau played an active role in generating interest in the work among economists and mathematicians.

Contact with Tjalling Koopmans of the Cowles Commission, then at the University of Chicago, now at Yale, and Robert Dorfman, then of the Air Force, now at Harvard, and the interest of such economists as Paul Samuelson of the Massachusetts Institute of Technology, initiated an era of intense re-examination of classical economic theory using results and ideas of linear programming.

Contact with John von Neumann at the Institute for Advanced Study gave fundamental insight into the mathematical theory and sparked the interest of A. W. Tucker of Princeton University and a group of his students, who attacked problems in linear inequality theory and game theory. Since that time his group has been a focal point of work in these related fields.

It was the size of the Air Force programming problem which made the SCOOP personnel recognize, at an early date, that even the best of future computing facilities would not be powerful enough to solve a general detailed Air Force linear programming model. Accordingly, Project SCOOP modified its approach and in the spring of 1948 proposed that there be developed special linear programming models called *triangular models* whose structure and computational solution would parallel the stepwise staff procedure which we described earlier [Wood and Geisler, 1951-1, p. 189].

Since 1948 the Air Staff has been making more and more active use of mechanically computed programs. The triangular models are in constant use for the computation of detailed programs, while the general linear programming models have been applied in certain areas, such as (a) contract bidding, (b) balanced aircraft, crew training, and wing deployment schedules, (c) scheduling of maintenance overhaul cycles, (d) personnel assignment, and (e) airlift routing problems [U.S. Air Force, 1954-1; Jacobs, 1955-1; Natrella, 1955-1].

2-2. ECONOMIC MODELS AND LINEAR PROGRAMMING

The Influence of Theoretical Models.

The current introduction of linear programming in economics appears to be an anachronism; it would seem logical that it should have begun around 1758 when economists first began to describe economic systems in mathematical terms. Indeed, a crude example of a linear programming model can be found in the *Tableau économique* of Quesnay, who attempted to interrelate the roles of the landlord, the peasant, and the artisan [Monroe, 1924-1]. Also, we find that L. Walras proposed in 1874 a sophisticated mathematical model which had as part of its structure fixed technological coefficients. Oddly enough, however, until the 1930's there was little in the way of exploitation of the linear-type model.

For the most part, mathematical economists were occupied with the analysis of theoretical problems associated with the possibility of economic equilibria and its allocative efficiency under competitive or monopolistic conditions. For such studies they found the use of classical convex functions with continuous derivatives more convenient for the demonstration of stability conditions than functions based on linear inequalities. Of particular note, along these lines, is the effort during the 1930's of a group of Austrian and German economists who worked on generalizations of the linear technology of Walras. This work raised some questions that may have stimulated the mathematician von Neumann (1932), in his paper "A Model of General Economic Equilibrium" [von Neumann, 1937-1], to formulate a dynamic linear programming model in which he introduced alternative methods of producing given commodities singly or jointly. Von Neumann assumed (a) a constant rate of expansion of the economy, and (b) a completely self-supporting economy. While the model did not contain any explicit objective, von Neumann showed that market forces would maximize the expansion rate, and proved that at the maximum it was equal to the interest rate on capital invested in production.

As far as influence is concerned, von Neumann's paper, like many other theoretical papers, proved only an interesting mathematical theorem. It is likely that mathematical economists were more interested in getting similar results for a more general model because "To many economists the term linearity is associated with narrowness, restrictiveness, and inflexibility of hypotheses" [Koopmans, 1951-1, p. 6]. In other words, this effort belonged like many others to the qualitative world of the economics of that time, a world in which the purpose of the mathematical model was to describe in a *qualitative* rather than a *quantitative* way the assumed interrelations within a system; the manipulation of equations was a convenient way to make valid logical deductions from the assumptions.

The Influence of Empirical Models.

The inspiration of the general linear programming model was completely independent of these developments and had a different purpose. It arose out of the empirical programming needs of the Air Force and the possibility of generalizing the simple practical structure of the Leontief Model to this end. From a purely formal standpoint the Leontief Model can be considered as a simplification of the Walrasian Model. It is here that the formalism ends.

"One hundred and fifty years ago, when Quesnay first published his famous schema, his contemporaries and disciples acclaimed it as the greatest discovery since Newton's laws. The idea of general interdependence among the various parts of the economic system has become by now the very foundation of economic analysis. Yet, when it comes to the practical application of this theoretical tool, modern economists must rely exactly as Quesnay did upon fictitious numerical examples" [Leontief, 1951-1, p. 9].

Leontief's great contribution, in the opinion of the author, was his construction of a *quantitative model* of the American economy, for the purpose of tracing the impact of government policy and consumer trends upon a large number of industries which were imbedded in a highly complex series of interlocking relationships. To appreciate the difference between a purely formal model and an empirical model, it is well to remember that the acquisition of data for a real model requires an organization working many months, sometimes years. After the model has been put together, another obstacle looms—the solution of a very large system of simultaneous linear equations. In the period 1936–1940, there were no electronic computers; the best that one could hope for in general would be to solve twenty equations in twenty unknowns. Finally, there was the difficulty of "marketing" the results of such studies. Hence, from the onset, the undertaking initiated by Leontief represented a triple gamble.

To appreciate further the significance of this shift from the theoretical to the empirical model it should be remembered that since the 1930's much more information has become available on income, quantities of production, investment, savings, and consumer patterns. Moreover, since 1900, sampling techniques developed by statisticians have come more and more into use as a means of evaluating the interrelationships between observations. Regression analysis began to be used to measure economic phenomena. By 1940 the work of such statisticians as Karl Pearson, R. A. Fisher, and the modern school initiated by J. Neyman had become a science for testing hypotheses and evaluating the parameters in the statistical population.

As a result of the great depression and the advent of the "New Deal" there was a serious attempt on the part of the government to determine, and then support, certain activities which it was hoped would speed recovery. This brought about more intensive collections of statistics on costs of living, wages, national resources, productivity, etc. There was a need to organize and interpret this data by using it to construct a mathematical model to describe the economy in quantitative terms.

From 1936 on, the scope, accuracy, and area of application of Leontief-type models were greatly extended by the Bureau of Labor Statistics (under the direction of Duane Evans, Jerome Cornfield, Marvin Hoffenberg, and others) [Cornfield, Evans, and Hoffenberg, 1947-1]. It was this work that stimulated efforts toward seeking a mathematical generalization suitable for dynamic Air Force applications. Thus the early Air Force interest was in the mathematical structure; it was not until several years later that the military supported work on Leontief inter-industry models to help evaluate the interaction of their programs with the civilian economy.

A few words about the Leontief model itself are in order. The focal point of input-output analysis is an array of coefficients variously called the "input-output" matrix or "tableau économique." A *column* of this matrix represents the input requirements of various commodities for the production of one dollar's worth of a particular commodity. There is exactly one column for each commodity produced in the economy. Thus the *production of a commodity* corresponds to the concept of an *activity* in a linear programming model. If the input factors appearing in a *row* of the matrix are multiplied by the corresponding buying industry's total output, the totals represent the distribution of the dollar value of purchases among the selling industries. Thus, the model makes it possible not only to determine each industry's rate of output to meet specified direct demand by civilians and the military, but also to trace the indirect effect on each industry of government expenditures in, say, military programs.

Postwar Developments.

In 1947, T. C. Koopmans took the lead in bringing to the attention of economists the potentialities of the linear programming models. His rapid development of the economic theory of such models was due to the insight he gained during the war with a special class of linear programming models called *transportation models*. He organized the historic Cowles Commission conference on "linear programming," referred to in Chapter 1. At the conference were such well-known economists as K. Arrow, R. Dorfman, N. Georgescu-Roegen, L. Hurwicz, A. Lerner, J. Marschak, O. Morgenstern, S. Reiter, P. Samuelson, and H. Simon; such mathematicians as G. W. Brown, M. M. Flood, D. Gale, H. W. Kuhn, C. B. Tompkins, A. W. Tucker, and the author, as well as government statisticians, including W. D. Evans, M. A. Geisler, M. Hoffenberg, and M. K. Wood. The papers presented there were later collected into the book *Activity Analysis of Production and Allocation* [Koopmans, 1951-1]. The book reflects the interest awakened among these groups in two short years. The following is an interesting quotation from its introduction, in which Koopmans encourages theoretical economists to set aside some of their traditional beliefs:

"The adjective in 'linear model' relates only to (a) assumption of proportionality of inputs and outputs in each elementary productive activity, and (b) the assumption that the result of simultaneously carrying out two or more activities is the sum of the results of the separate activities. In terms more familiar to the economist, these assumptions imply constant returns to scale in all parts of the technology. They do not imply linearity of the production function. . . . Curvilinear production functions . . . can be obtained from the models here studied by admitting an infinite set of elementary activities. . . .

"Neither should the assumption of constant returns to scale . . . be regarded as essential to the method of approach it illustrates, although new mathematical problems would have to be faced in the attempt to go beyond this assumption. More essential to the present approach is the introduction of . . . the elementary activity, the conceptual atom of technology into the basic postulates of the analysis. The problem of efficient production then becomes one of finding the proper rules for combining these building blocks. The term 'activity analysis' . . . is designed to express this approach" [Koopmans, 1951-1, p. 6].

Koopmans was the first to point out that many theorems of welfare economics, the study of the rules for efficient allocation of resources in the economy, could be restated under the assumption of a linear technology for the "firm." The decisions to be made by his "helmsman" on resource allocation did not conflict with earlier results of traditional economic theory; indeed, they were more general in that the decisions covered joint products and by-products of the firm [Koopmans, 1951-2].

At about the same time, a few other economists had become interested in activity analysis and linear programming. Dorfman (1951) expressed in linear programming terms the economic theory of the firm under competitive and monopolistic conditions, and compared the realm of applicability of this theory with the traditional marginal analysis [Dorfman, 1951-1]. Samuelson (1955) wrote on "Market Mechanisms and Maximization" and stated his Substitution Theorem for a Generalized Leontief Model [Samuelson, 1955-1;

Koopmans, 1951-1]. Various classical economic problems, such as international trade between two countries and the Giffen paradox, could be reformulated as linear programming problems [Beckmann, 1955-1; Dorfman, Samuelson, and Solow, 1958-1; Koopmans, 1951-1].

The number of practical economic applications is continually growing. Linear programming is being used by economists to study in detail the economics of specific industries, such as metalworking [Markowitz, 1954-1], petroleum refining,[2] iron and steel [Fabian, 1958-1], and to yield long-range plans for electricity generation in an entire economy [Massé and Gibrat, 1957-1]. Some of these applications will be presented as examples and exercises in later chapters.

For a fuller appreciation of the economic implications, the reader is referred to *Linear Programming and Economic Analysis* by Dorfman, Samuelson, and Solow [1958-1], and *Economic Theory and Operations Analysis* by W. J. Baumol [1961-1].

2-3. MATHEMATICAL ORIGINS AND DEVELOPMENTS

History Prior to 1947.

The linear programming model, when translated into purely mathematical terms, as will be done in the next chapter, requires a method for finding a solution to a system of simultaneous linear equations and linear inequalities which minimizes a linear form. This central mathematical problem of linear programming was not known to be an important one with many practical applications until the advent of linear programming in 1947. It is this which in part accounts for the lack of active interest among mathematicians in finding efficient solution techniques before that date.

We are all familiar with methods for solving linear equation systems which start with our first course in algebra [Gauss, 1826-1; Jordan, 1904-1]. The literature of mathematics contains thousands of papers concerned with techniques for solving linear equation systems, with the theory of matrix algebra (an allied topic), with linear approximation methods, etc. On the other hand, the study of linear inequality systems excited virtually no interest until the advent of game theory in 1944 and linear programming in 1947. For example T. Motzkin, in his doctoral thesis on linear inequalities in 1936, was able to cite after diligent search only some thirty references for the period 1900–1936, and about forty-two in all [Motzkin, 1936-1]. In the 1930's, four papers dealt with the building of a comprehensive theory of linear inequalities and with an appraisal of earlier works. These were by R. W. Stokes [1931-1], Dines-McCoy [1933-1], H. Weyl [1935-1], and T. Motzkin [1936-1]. As evidence that mathematicians were unaware of the

---

[2] [Charnes, Cooper, and Mellon, 1952-1; Symonds, 1955-1; Manne, 1956-1; Garvin, Crandall, John, and Spellman, 1957-1.]

importance of the problem of seeking a solution to an inequality system that also minimized a linear form, we may note that none of these papers made any mention of such a problem, although there had been earlier instances in the literature.

The famous mathematician, Fourier, while not going into the subject deeply, appears to have been the first to study linear inequalities systematically and to point out their importance to mechanics and probability theory [Fourier, 1826-1]. He was interested in finding the *least maximum deviation* fit to a system of linear equations, which he reduced to the problem of finding the lowest point of a polyhedral set. He suggested a solution by a vertex-to-vertex descent to a minimum, which is the principle behind the simplex method used today. This is probably the earliest known instance of a linear programming problem. Later another famous mathematician, de la Vallée Poussin [1911-1], considered the same problem and proposed a similar solution.

A good part of the early mathematical literature is concerned with finding conditions under which a general homogeneous linear inequality system can be solved. All the results obtained express, in one form or another, a relationship between the original (or *primal*) system and another system (called the *dual*) which uses the columns of the original matrix of coefficients to form new linear equations or inequalities according to certain rules. Typical is the derived theorem of P. Gordan [1873-1] showing that a homogeneous system of equations in nonnegative variables possesses a solution with at least one variable positive if the dual possesses no solution with strict inequalities. Stiemke [1915-1] added a theorem on the existence of a solution with all variables positive. These results are expressed in a sharper form in Motzkin's Transposition Theorem [1936-1] and theorems on Dual Systems by Tucker [1956-1]. Specifically designed for algebraic proof of the Minimax Theorem are the results of Ville [1938-1] and of von Neumann and Morgenstern [1944-1]. Essentially, these theorems state that either the original (primal) system possesses a nontrivial solution or the dual system possesses a strict inequality solution. Because of this "either-or," von Neumann and Morgenstern called their result the Theorem of the Alternative for Matrices (see § 6-4).

The following is a well-known theorem for equations: If every solution to a linear equation system also satisfies a given linear equation, the equation can be formed as a linear combination of the equations of the system. A surprising and important theorem for inequalities due to J. Farkas [1902-1] is as follows: If every solution to a linear homogeneous inequality system also satisfies a given linear inequality (where all inequalities are ≥ 0), the inequality can be formed as a nonnegative linear combination of the inequalities of the system.

Analogous to those for equation systems, other theorems are concerned with building up a general solution of an inequality system by forming a

[21]

linear combination of special solutions. The main result, due to Minkowski [1896-1], states that for a homogeneous system the general solution can be formed as a nonnegative linear combination of a finite number of essential solutions variously called *extreme* solutions, *vertex* solutions, or *basic* solutions (as used in this text).

The Work of Kantorovich.

The Russian mathematician L. V. Kantorovich has for a number of years been interested in the application of mathematics to programming problems. He published an extensive monograph in 1939 entitled *Mathematical Methods in the Organization and Planning of Production* [1939-1].

In his introduction Kantorovich states, "There are two ways of increasing efficiency of the work of a shop, an enterprise, or a whole branch of industry. One way is by various improvements in technology, that is, new attachments for individual machines, changes in technological processes, and the discovery of new, better kinds of raw materials. The other way, thus far much less used, is by improvement in the organization of planning and production. Here are included such questions as the distribution of work among individual machines of the enterprise, or among mechanisms, orders among enterprises, the correct distribution of different kinds of raw materials, fuels, and other factors" [Kantorovich, 1939-1].

Kantorovich should be credited with being the first to recognize that certain important broad classes of production problems had well-defined mathematical structures which, he believed, were amenable to practical numerical evaluation and could be numerically solved.

In the first part of his work Kantorovich is concerned with what we now call the weighted two-index distribution problems. These were generalized first to include a single linear side condition, then a class of problems with processes having several simultaneous outputs (mathematically the latter is equivalent to a general linear program). He outlined a solution approach based on having on hand an initial feasible solution to the dual. (For the particular problems studied, the latter did not present any difficulty.) Although the dual variables were not called "prices," the general idea is that the assigned values of these "resolving multipliers" for resources in short supply can be increased to a point where it pays to shift to resources that are in surplus. Kantorovich showed on simple examples how to make the shifts to surplus resources. In general, however, *how to shift* turns out to be a linear program in itself for which no computational method was given. The report contains an outstanding collection of potential applications.

His 1942 paper "On the Translocation of Masses" [Kantorovich, 1942-1] is the forerunner of his joint paper with M. K. Gavurin on "The Application of Mathematical Methods to Problems of Freight Flow Analysis" [Kantorovich and Gavurin, 1949-1]. Here can be found a very complete theory of the transshipment problem, the relations between the primal and the dual (price) system, the use of the linear graph of the network, and the important extension to capacitated networks. Moreover, it is clear that the authors had developed considerable facility with the adjustment of freight flow patterns from nonoptimal to optimal patterns for elaborate systems of the kind commonly encountered in practice. However, again, an incomplete computational algorithm was given. It is commendable that the paper is written in a nontechnical manner, so as to encourage those responsible for routing freight to use the proposed procedures.

In 1959, twenty years after the publication of his first work, Kantorovich published a second entitled *Economic Computation of the Optimal Utilization of Resources*, a book primarily intended for economists [1959-1].

If Kantorovich's earlier efforts had been appreciated at the time they were first presented, it is possible that linear programming would be more advanced today. However, his early work in this field remained unknown both in the Soviet Union and elsewhere for nearly two decades while linear programming became a highly developed art. According to *The New York Times*, "The scholar, Professor L. V. Kantorovich, said in a debate that, Soviet economists had been inspired by a fear of mathematics that left the Soviet Union far behind the United States in applications of mathematics to economic problems. It could have been a decade ahead" [*New York Times*, 1959-1].

Direct Influences.

With the exception of the game-theoretic results due to von Neumann and to Ville, all the work just cited seems not to have had any influence on the immediate postwar developments in linear programming. Let us now turn to those that are known to have had a direct influence.

In 1936, J. Neyman and E. S. Pearson clarified the basic concepts for validating statistical tests and estimating underlying parameters of a distribution from given observations [Neyman and Pearson, 1936-1]. They used what is now the well-known Neyman-Pearson Lemma for constructing the best test of a simple hypothesis having a single alternative. For a more general class of hypotheses they showed that if a test existed satisfying a generalized form of their lemma, it would be optimal. In 1939 (and as part of his doctoral thesis, 1946), the author first showed that under very general conditions such a test always exists. This work was later published jointly with A. Wald, who independently reached the same result around 1950 [Dantzig and Wald, 1951-1]. This effort constitutes not only an early proof of one form of the important duality theorem of linear programming, but one given for an infinite (denumerable) number of variables or (through the use of integrals) a nondenumerable number of variables. These are referred to by Duffin as *infinite programs* [Duffin, 1956-1]. It is interesting to note that the conditions of the general Neyman-Pearson Lemma are in fact the *conditions that a solution to a bounded variable linear programming problem be optimal*. The author's research on this problem formed a background for his later research on linear programming.

Credit for laying the mathematical foundations of this field goes to John von Neumann more than to any other man (see Kuhn and Tucker, 1958-1). During his lifetime, he was generally regarded as the world's foremost mathematician. He played a leading role in many fields; atomic energy and electronic computer development are two where he had great influence. In 1944 John von Neumann and Oskar Morgenstern published their monumental work on the theory of games, a branch of mathematics that aims to analyze problems of conflict by use of models termed "games" [von Neumann and Morgenstern, 1944-1]. A theory of games was first broached in 1921 by Emile Borel and was first established in 1928 by von Neumann with his famous Minimax Theorem [Ville, 1938-1; Borel, 1953-1]. The significance of this effort for us is that game theory, like linear programming, has its mathematical foundation in linear inequality theory [Kuhn and Tucker, 1958-1].

Postwar Developments (1947-1956).

During the summer of 1947, Leonid Hurwicz, well-known econometrician associated with the Cowles Commission, worked with the author on techniques for solving linear programming problems. This effort and some suggestions of T. C. Koopmans resulted in the "Simplex Method." The obvious idea of moving along edges from one vertex of a convex polyhedron to the next (which underlies the simplex method) was rejected earlier on intuitive grounds as inefficient. In a different geometry it seemed efficient and so, fortunately, it was tested and accepted.

Von Neumann, at the first meeting with the author in October 1947, was able immediately to translate basic theorems in game theory into their equivalent statements for systems of linear inequalities [Goldman and Tucker, 1956-1]. He introduced and stressed the fundamental importance of *duality*[3] and conjectured the equivalence of games and linear programming problems [Dantzig, 1951-1; Gale, Kuhn, and Tucker, 1951-1]. Later he made several proposals for the numerical solution of linear programming and game problems [von Neumann, 1948-1, 1954-1].

A. W. Tucker's interest in game theory and linear programming began in 1948. Since that time Tucker and his former students (notably David Gale and Harold W. Kuhn) have been active in developing and systematizing the underlying mathematical theory of linear inequalities. Their main efforts, like those of a group at The RAND Corporation (notably N. C. Dalkey, M. Dresher, O. Helmer, J. C. C. McKinsey, L. S. Shapley, and

---

[3] D. Ray Fulkerson, in a conversation with S. Karlin, accidentally credited the simplex method to von Neumann when he meant to credit duality to him. This error subsequently appeared in the work of Karlin [1959-1] and then was repeated by Charnes and Cooper [1961-1].

J. D. Williams), have been in the related field of game theory [von Neumann, 1948-1].

The National Bureau of Standards played an important role in the development of linear programming theory. Not only did it arrange through John H. Curtiss and Albert Cahn the important initial contacts between workers in this field, but it provided for the testing of a number of computational proposals in their laboratories. In the fall of 1947, Laderman of the Mathematical Tables Project in New York computed the optimal solution of Stigler's diet problem [Stigler, 1945-1] in a test of the newly proposed simplex method. At the Institute of Numerical Analysis, Professor Theodore Motzkin, whose work on the theory of linear inequalities has been mentioned earlier, proposed several computational schemes for solving linear programming problems such as the "Relaxation Method" [Motzkin and Schoenberg, 1954-1] and the "Double Description Method" [Motzkin, Raiffa, Thompson, and Thrall, 1953-1]. Charles B. Tompkins proposed his projection method [Tompkins, 1955-1]. Alex Orden of the Air Force worked actively with the National Bureau of Standards (N.B.S.) group who prepared codes on the SEAC (National Bureau of Standards Eastern Automatic Computer) for the general simplex method and for the transportation problem. Alan J. Hoffman, with a group at the N.B.S., was instrumental in having experiments run on a number of alternative computational methods [Hoffman, Mannos, Sokolowsky, and Wiegmann, 1953-1]. He was also the first to establish that "cycling" can occur in the simplex algorithm without special provisions for avoiding degeneracy [Hoffman, 1953-1].

In June 1951 the First Symposium in Linear Programming was held in Washington under the joint auspices of the Air Force and the N.B.S. By this time, interest in linear programming was widespread in government and academic circles. A. Charnes and W. W. Cooper had just begun their pioneering work on industrial applications. Aside from this work, which will be discussed in the next section, they published numerous contributions to the theory of linear programming. Their lectures were published in *An Introduction to Linear Programming* [Charnes, Cooper, and Henderson, 1953-1]. A two-volume treatise of the work of Charnes and Cooper was published in 1961.

Computational Developments (1947-1956).

New computational techniques and variations of older techniques are continuously being developed in the United States and abroad. Aside from those mentioned above, there were early proposals by G. W. Brown and T. C. Koopmans [Brown and Koopmans, 1951-1] and a method for solving games by G. W. Brown [Brown, 1951-1]. More recently the well-known econometrician Ragnar Frisch at the University of Oslo has done extensive research work on his "Multiplex Method" [Frisch, 1957-1]. Investigations in Great Britain have been spearheaded by S. Vajda [1958-1]. There are a number of important variants of the simplex method proposed by C. Lemke [1954-1], W. Orchard-Hays [1954-1], E. M. L. Beale [1954-1], and others (see Chapter 11).

Electronic Computer Codes (1947-1956).

The special simplex method developed for the transportation problem [Dantzig, 1951-2] was first coded for the SEAC in 1950 and the general simplex method in 1951 under the general direction of A. Orden of the Air Force and A. J. Hoffman of the Bureau of Standards. In 1952, W. Orchard-Hays of The RAND Corporation worked out a simplex code for the IBM-C.P.C., and for the IBM 701 and 704 in 1954 and 1956, respectively. The latter code was remarkably flexible and solved problems of two hundred equations and a thousand or more variables in five hours or so with great accuracy [Orchard-Hays, 1955-1].

Special routines for solving the Air Force *triangular model* were first developed in 1949. In the spring of 1949, M. Montalbano of the N.B.S. built a preliminary computation system around an IBM 602-A; later a more elaborate system was built for the IBM 604. In early 1950, with C. Diehm, he prepared a simplex code for SEAC which was demonstrated at the dedication of the computer. These computational programs were recoded by the Air Force when they obtained a UNIVAC in 1952.

The use of electronic computers by business and industry has been growing by leaps and bounds. Many of the digital computers which are commercially available have had codes of the simplex technique. In addition, there has been some interest in building *analogue computers* for the sole purpose of solving linear programming problems [Ablow and Brigham, 1955-1; Pyne, 1956-1]. It is possible that such computers may provide an efficient tool for the evaluation of parametric changes in a system represented by a linear programming model and may be useful when quick solutions of linear programming problems are continuously needed, as for example in production scheduling. These computers have worked well on small problems (for example twenty variables and ten equations). Because of distortion of electric signals, it does not seem practical to design analogue computers which can handle the large *general* linear programming problems. However it does appear very worthwhile to try to develop applications of such computers to solving large-scale systems which possess *special structures*.

Extensions of Linear Programming.

If we distinguish, as indeed we must, between those types of generalizations in mathematics that have led to existence proofs and those that have led to constructive solutions of practical problems, then the period following the first decade marks the beginning of several important constructive generalizations of linear programming concepts to allied fields. These are:

(1) *Network Theory.* A remarkable property of a special class of linear programs, the transportation or the equivalent network flow problem, is that their extreme point solutions are integer valued when their constant terms are integers [G. Birkhoff, 1946-1; Dantzig, 1951-2]. This has been a key fact in an elegant theory linking certain combinatorial problems of topology with the continuous processes of network theory. The field has many contributors. Of special mention is the work of Kuhn [1955-1] using an approach of Egerváry on the problem of finding a permutation of ones in a matrix composed of zeros and ones and the related work of Ford and Fulkerson [1954-1] for network flows. For further references, see Chapters 19 and 20, [Hoffman, 1960-1; Berge, 1958-1; Ford and Fulkerson, 1960-1].

(2) *Convex Programming.* A natural extension of linear programming occurs when the linear part of the inequality constraints and the objective are replaced by convex functions. Early work centered about a quadratic objective [Dorfman, 1951-1; Barankin and Dorfman, 1958-1; Markowitz, 1956-1] and culminated in an elegant procedure developed independently by Beale [1959-1], Houthakker [1959-1], and Wolfe [1959-1] who showed how a minor variant of the simplex procedure could be used to solve such problems. Also studied early was the case where the convex objective could be separated into a nonnegative sum of terms, each convex in a single variable [Dantzig, 1956-2; Charnes and Lemke, 1954-1]. The general case has been studied in fundamental papers by Kuhn and Tucker [1950-2], and Arrow, Hurwicz, and Uzawa [1958-1]. See Chapter 24 for further references. In this book we shall attack this problem by using the decomposition principle of linear programs (Chapters 22, 23, 24). Many promising alternative approaches can be found in the literature [Rosen, 1960-1].

(3) *Integer Programming.* Important classes of nonlinear, nonconvex, discrete, combinatorial problems can be shown to be formally reducible to a linear programming type of problem, some or all of whose variables must be integer valued. By the introduction of the concept of cutting planes, linear programming methods were used to construct an optimal tour for a salesman visiting Washington, D.C., and forty-eight state capitals of the United States [Dantzig, Fulkerson, and Johnson, 1954-1]. The theory was incomplete. The foundations for a rigorous theory were first developed by Gomory [1958-1]. See Chapter 26.

(4) *Programming under Uncertainty.* It has been pointed out by Madansky [1960-1] that the area of programming under uncertainty cannot be usefully stated as a single problem. One important class considered in this book is a multistage class where the technological matrix of input-output coefficients is assumed known, the values of the constant terms are uncertain, but the joint probability distribution of their possible values is assumed to be known. Some tools for attacking this class of problems will be found in Chapters 25 and 28. A promising approach based on the decomposition principle has been discussed by Dantzig and Madansky [1960-1].

[27]

2-4. INDUSTRIAL APPLICATIONS OF LINEAR PROGRAMMING

The history of the first years of linear programming would be incomplete without a brief survey of its use in business and industry. These applications began in 1951 but have had such a remarkable growth in the years 1955–1960 that this use is now more important than its military predecessor.

Linear programming has been serving industrial users in several ways. First, it has provided a *novel view of operations*; second, it induced *research in the mathematical analysis of the structure of industrial systems*; and third, it has become an important tool for business and industrial management for *improving the efficiency of their operations*. Thus the application of linear programming to a business or industrial problem has required the mathematical formulation of the problem and an explicit statement of the desired objectives. In many instances such rigorous thinking about business problems has clarified aspects of management decision-making which previously had remained hidden in a haze of verbal arguments. As a partial consequence some industrial firms have started educational programs for their managerial personnel in which the importance of the definition of objectives and constraints on business policies is being emphasized. Moreover, scheduling industrial production traditionally has been, as in the military, based on intuition and experience, a few rules, and the use of visual aids. Linear programming has induced extensive research in developing quantitative models of industrial systems for the purpose of scheduling production. Of course many complicated systems have not as yet been quantified, but sketches of conceptual models have stimulated widespread interest. An example of this is in the scheduling of job-shop production, where M. E. Salveson [1953-1] initiated research work with a linear programming-type tentative model. Research on job-shop scheduling is now being performed by several academic and industrial research groups [Jackson, 1957-1]. Savings by business and industry through the use of linear programming for planning and scheduling operations are occasionally reported [Dantzig, 1957-1].

The first and most fruitful industrial applications of linear programming have been to the scheduling of petroleum refineries. As noted earlier, Charnes, Cooper, and Mellon started their pioneering work in this field in 1951 [Charnes, Cooper, and Mellon, 1952-1]. Two books have been written on the subject, one by Gifford Symonds [Symonds, 1955-1] and another by Alan Manne [Manne, 1956-1]. So intense has been the development that a survey by Garvin, Crandall, John, and Spellman [1957-1] showed that there are applications by the oil industry in exploration and production and distribution as well as in refining. The routing of tanker ships by linear programming methods may soon be added to this list.

The food processing industry is perhaps the second most active user of

[28]

linear programming. In 1953 a major producer first used it to determine shipping of catchup from six plants to seventy warehouses [Henderson and Schlaifer, 1954-1] and a milk producer has considered applying it to a similar problem, except that in this case the number of warehouses is several hundred. A major meat packer determines by means of linear programming the most economical mixture of animal feeds [Fisher and Schruben, 1953-1].

In the iron and steel industry, linear programming has been used for the evaluation of various iron ores and of the pelletization of low-grade ores [Fabian, 1954-1]. Additions to coke ovens and shop loading of rolling mills have provided additional applications [Fabian, 1955-1]; a linear programming model of an integrated steel mill is being developed [Fabian, 1958-1]. It is reported that the British steel industry has used linear programming to decide what products their rolling mills should make in order to maximize profit.

Metalworking industries use linear programming for shop loading [Morin, 1955-1] and for determining the choice between producing and buying a part [Lewis, 1955-1; Maynard, 1955-1]. Paper mills use it to decrease the amount of trim losses [Eisemann, 1957-1; Land and Doig, 1957-1; Paull and Walter, 1955-1; Doig and Belz, 1956-1].

The optimal routing of messages in a communication network [Kalaba and Juncosa, 1956-1], contract award problems [Goldstein, 1952-1; Gainen, 1955-1], and the routing of aircraft and ships [Dantzig and Fulkerson, 1954-1; Ferguson and Dantzig, 1954-1, 1956-1] are problems that have been considered for application of linear programming methods by the military and are under consideration by industry. In France the best program of investment in electric power has been investigated by linear programming methods [Massé and Gibrat, 1957-1].

Since 1957 the number of applications has grown so rapidly that it is not possible to give an adequate treatment here.

REFERENCES

Economic Models

Allen, 1959-1
Arrow, 1951-1
Arrow, Hurwicz, and Uzawa, 1958-1
Arrow, Karlin, and Suppes, 1960-1
Baumol, 1961-1
Beckmann, 1955-1
Cornfield, Evans, and Hoffenberg, 1947-1
Dorfman, 1951-1

Dorfman, Samuelson, and Solow, 1958-1
Gale, 1960-1
Hicks, 1960-1
Koopmans, 1951-1, 1951-2
Leontief, 1951-1
Samuelson, 1955-1
von Neumann, 1937-1
Wald, 1935-1

Walras, 1874-1

Business and Industry

Charnes and Cooper, 1957-1, 1961-1
Charnes, Cooper, and Mellon, 1952-1
Dantzig, 1957-1

Doig and Belz, 1956-1
Eisemann, 1957-1
Fabian, 1954-1, 1955-1, 1958-1

Ferguson and Dantzig, 1954-1, 1956-1
Fisher and Schruben, 1953-1
Gainen, 1955-1
Garvin, Crandall, John, and Spellman, 1957-1
Goldstein, 1952-1
Henderson and Schlaifer, 1954-1
Jackson, 1957-1
Kantorovich, 1939-1
Land and Doig, 1957-1

Lesourne, 1960-1
Lewis, 1955-1
Manne, 1956-1, 2
Markowitz, 1954-1
Massé and Gibrat, 1957-1
Maynard, 1955-1
Morin, 1955-1
Paull and Walter, 1955-1
Salveson, 1953-1
Symonds, 1955-1, 2

Military Applications

Jacobs, 1955-1
Natrella, 1955-1

U.S.A.F., 1954-1
Wood and Geisler, 1951-1

Linear Programming, Activity Analysis, Game Theory

Antosiewicz, 1955-1
Borel, 1953-1
Charnes and Cooper, 1961-1
Charnes, Cooper, and Henderson, 1953-1
Dantzig, 1948-1, 1949-1
Dantzig and Wald, 1951-1
Gale, 1960-1
Garvin, 1960-1
Hadley, 1961-2
Hoffman, 1960-1
Jordan, 1920-1

Karlin, 1959-1
Koopmans, 1951-1
Kuhn and Tucker, 1958-1
Luce and Raiffa, 1957-1
Motzkin, 1936-1
Orden and Goldstein, 1952-1
Stiefel, 1960-1
Tucker, 1950-1, 1955-2
Vajda, 1956-1, 1958-1, 1961-1
Ville, 1938-1
von Neumann and Morgenstern, 1944-1

Wolfe, 1959-2

Infinite Programs

Dantzig and Wald, 1951-1

Duffin, 1956-1

Neyman and Pearson, 1936-1

Operations Research

Bowman and Fetter, 1959-1
Charnes and Cooper, 1959-2
Churchman, Ackoff, Arnoff, *et al.*, 1957-1

Saaty, 1959-1
Sasieni, Yaspan, and Friedman, 1959-1
Vazsonyi, 1958-1

Engineering Design, Physical Chemistry

Charnes and Greenberg, 1951-1
Dorn and Greenberg, 1955-1
Foulkes, 1955-1

Heyman, 1951-1
Kalaba and Juncosa, 1956-1
White, Johnson, and Dantzig, 1958-1

Agriculture

Heady and Candler, 1958-1
Reisch and Eisgruber, 1960-1

Swanson, 1955-1
Tintner, 1955-1

Waugh, 1951-1, 1958-1

Network Theory

Berge, 1962-1
Birkhoff, 1946-1
Dantzig, 1951-2

Ford and Fulkerson, 1954-1, 1960-1
Hoffman, 1960-1
Kuhn, 1955-1

[30]

REFERENCES

Convex Programming

Arrow, Hurwicz, and Uzawa, 1958-1
Barankin and Dorfman, 1958-1
Beale, 1959-1
Charnes and Lemke, 1954-1
Dantzig, 1956-2

Dorfman, 1951-1
Houthakker, 1959-1
Kuhn and Tucker, 1950-2
Markowitz, 1956-1
Rosen, 1960-1

Wolfe, 1959-1

Integer Programming

Dantzig, Fulkerson, and Johnson, 1954-1   Gomory, 1958-1

Programming under Uncertainty

Dantzig and Madansky, 1960-1   Madansky, 1960-1

Mathematical Origins and Developments

Ablow and Brigham, 1955-1
Beale, 1954-1
Brown, 1951-1
Brown and Koopmans, 1951-1
Dantzig, 1951-1, 2
Dantzig and Wald, 1951-1
Dines and McCoy, 1933-1
Duffin, 1956-1
Farkas, 1902-1
Fourier, 1826-1
Frisch, 1957-1
Gale, Kuhn, and Tucker, 1951-1
Gauss, 1826-1
Goldman and Tucker, 1956-1
Gordan, 1873-1
Hoffman, 1953-1
Hoffman, Mannos, Sokolowsky, and
    Wiegmann, 1953-1
Jordan, 1920-1
Kantorovich, 1939-1, 1942-1, 1959-1
Kantorovich and Gavurin, 1949-1

Kuhn and Tucker, 1958-1
Lemke, 1954-1
Minkowski, 1896-1
Motzkin, 1936-1
Motzkin, Raiffa, Thompson, and Thrall,
    1953-1
Motzkin and Schoenberg, 1954-1
Neyman and Pearson, 1936-1
Orchard-Hays, 1954-1, 1955-1
Poussin, 1911-1
Pyne, 1956-1
Stiemke, 1915-1
Stigler, 1945-1
Stokes, 1931-1
Tompkins, 1955-1
Tucker, 1956-1
Vajda, 1958-1
Ville, 1938-1
von Neumann, 1948-1, 1954-1
von Neumann and Morgenstern, 1944-1
Weyl, 1935-1

CHAPTER 3

FORMULATING A LINEAR PROGRAMMING MODEL[1]

3-1. BASIC CONCEPTS

Suppose that the system under study (which may be one actually in existence, or one which we wish to design) is a complex of machines, people, facilities, and supplies. It has certain over-all reasons for its existence. For the military it may be to provide a striking force, or for industry it may be to produce certain types of products.

The linear programming approach is to consider a system as decomposable into a number of elementary functions, the *activities*. An activity is thought of as a kind of "black box"[2] into which flow tangible inputs, such as men, material, and equipment, and out of which may flow the products of manufacture, or the trained crews of the military. What happens to the inputs inside the "box" is the concern of the engineer or of the educator; to the programmer, only the rates of flow into and out of the activity are of interest. The various kinds of flow are called *items*.

The quantity of each activity is called the *activity level*. To change the activity level it is necessary to change the flows into and out of the activity.

Assumption 1: Proportionality.

In the linear programming model the quantities of flow of various items into and out of the activity are always proportional to the activity level. If we wish to double the activity level, we simply double all the corresponding flows for the unit activity level. For instance, in § 1-2, Example 3, if we wish to double the number of workers trained in a period, we would have to double the number of instructors for that period and the number of workers hired. This characteristic of the linear programming model is known as the proportionality assumption.

Assumption 2: Nonnegativity.

While any positive multiple of an activity is possible, negative quantities of activities are not possible. For example, in § 1-2, Example 1, a negative number of cases cannot be shipped. Another example occurs in a well-known classic: the Mad Hatter, you may recall, in *Alice's Adventures in Wonderland*,

---

[1] This chapter, written by Philip Wolfe, is based on earlier drafts by the author.
[2] Black box: Any system whose detailed internal nature one willfully ignores.

was urging Alice to have some more tea, and Alice was objecting that she couldn't see how she could take more when she hadn't had any. "You mean, you don't see how you can take *less* tea," said the Hatter, "it is very easy to take more than nothing." Lewis Carroll's point was probably lost on his pre-linear-programming audience, for why should one emphasize the obvious fact that the activity of "taking tea" cannot be done in negative quantity? Perhaps it was Carroll's way of saying that mathematicians had been so busy for centuries extending the number system from integers, to fractions, to negative, to imaginary numbers, that they had given little thought on how to keep the variables of their problems in their original nonnegative range. This characteristic of the variables of the linear programming model is known as the nonnegativity assumption.

Assumption 3: Additivity.

The next step in building a model is to specify that the system of activities be complete in the sense that a complete accounting by activity can be made of each item. To be precise, for each item it is required that the total amount specified by the system as a whole equals the sum of the amounts flowing into the various activities minus the sum of the amounts flowing out. Thus, each item, in our abstract system, is characterized by a *material balance equation*, the various terms of which represent the flows into or out of the various activities. In the cannery example, the number of cases sent into a warehouse must be completely accounted for by the amounts flowing out of the shipping activities from various canneries including possible storage or disposal of any excess. This characteristic of the linear programming model is known as the additivity assumption.

Assumption 4: Linear Objective Function.

One of the items in our system is regarded as "precious" in the sense that the total quantity of it produced by the system measures the payoff. The precious item could be skilled labor, completed assemblies, an input resource that is in scarce supply like a limited monetary budget. The contribution of each activity to the total payoff is the amount of the precious item that flows into or out of each activity. Thus, if the objective is to maximize profits, activities that require money contribute negatively and those that produce money contribute positively to total profits. The housewife's expenditures for each type of food, in § 1-2, Example 2, is a negative contribution to total "profits" of the household; there are no activities in this example that contribute positively. This characteristic of the linear programming model is known as the linear objective assumption.

The Standard Linear Programming Problem.

The determination of values for the *levels* of activities, which are positive or zero, such that flows of each item (for these activity levels) satisfy the material balance equations and such that the value of the payoff is a maximum is called the standard linear programming problem. The representation of a real system, as in any one of the three examples of § 1-2, as a mathematical system which exhibits the above characteristics, is called a linear programming model. The problem of programming the activities of the real system is thus transformed into the problem of finding the solution of the linear programming model.

3-2. BUILDING THE MODEL

Because model-building is an essential aspect of programming, the separate steps to be taken in building a linear programming model will now be systematized. We then show how the completed model defines the linear programming problem. The simplex method as a means for solving the general problem of linear programming will be dealt with in Chapter 5, but for the present we shall apply a less general method, the graphic, to two typical examples.

The mathematical model of a system is the collection of mathematical relationships which characterize the feasible programs of the system. By *feasible programs* is meant those programs which can be carried out under the system's limitations. Building a mathematical model often provides so much insight into a system and the organization of knowledge about a system that it is considered by many to be more important than the task of mathematical programming which it precedes. The model is often difficult to construct because of the richness, variety, and ambiguity of the real world. Nevertheless, it is possible to state certain principles which distinguish the separate steps in the model-building process.

The outline for this procedure presented below is based on the basic assumptions underlying the linear programming model of (a) proportionality, (b) nonnegativity, (c) additivity, and (d) a linear objective function. It is recommended that the reader review these concepts and identify these characteristics of the model in what follows.

Step 1: Define the Activity Set. Decompose the entire system under study into all of its elementary functions, the *activities,* and choose a unit for each activity in terms of which its quantity, or *level,* can be measured.

Step 2: Define the Item Set. Determine the classes of objects, the *items,* which are consumed or produced by the activities, and choose a unit for measuring each item. Select one item such that the net quantity of it produced by the system as a whole measures the "cost" (or such that its negative measures the "profit") of the entire system.[3]

---

[3] In the examples which follow, the "costs" happen to be money; however, in economic examples, they could be measured in terms of labor or any scarce resource, input which is to be conserved or any item whose total output from the system is to be maximized.

Step 3: Determine the Input-Output Coefficients. Determine the quantity of each item consumed or produced by the operation of each activity at its unit level. These numbers, the *input-output coefficients*, are the factors of proportionality between activity levels and item flows.

Step 4: Determine the Exogenous Flows. Determine the net inputs or outputs of the items between the system, taken as a whole, and the outside.

Step 5: Determine the Material Balance Equations. Assign unknown nonnegative activity levels x_1, x_2, . . ., to all the activities; then, for each item, write the *material balance equation* which asserts that the algebraic sum of the flows of that item into each activity (given as the product of the activity level by the appropriate input-output coefficient) is equal to the exogenous flow of the item.

The result of the model-building is thus the collection of mathematical relationships characterizing all the feasible programs of the system. This collection is the *linear programming model*.

Once the model has been built, the linear programming problem can be posed in mathematical terms and its solution can be interpreted as a *program* for the system—a statement of the time and quantity of actions to be performed by the system so that it may move from its given status toward the defined objective.

The Linear Programming Problem.

Determine levels for all the activities of the system which (a) are non-negative, (b) satisfy the material balance equations, and (c) minimize the total cost.

Devising techniques for solving the linear programming problem constitutes the central mathematical problem of linear programming, to which many of the succeeding chapters are devoted.

In our use of the steps for model-building in the examples below, one feature should be noted: namely, we will not always complete the model in one sequence of steps. It frequently happens that certain activities, commonly those related to the disposal of unused resources or the over-fulfillment of requirements, are overlooked until the formulation of the material balance equations forces their inclusion. Thus a return from Step 5 to Step 1 will sometimes be necessary before the model is complete.

3-3. A TRANSPORTATION PROBLEM

In the cannery example of § 1-2 we required that the shipping schedule for cases minimize the total shipping cost from canneries to warehouses. To simplify that problem we shall suppose that there are two canneries, Cannery I and Cannery II, and three warehouses, labelled A, B, and C. The availability of cases at the canneries and the demands at the warehouses are as follows:

Cases Available	Cases Demanded
350 at Cannery I	300 at Warehouse A
650 at Cannery II	300 at Warehouse B
	300 at Warehouse C
1000 = Total available	900 = Total required

The excess production (100 cases) is to be stored without shipment. The shipping cost per case from either cannery to each warehouse is given in the Shipping Cost Schedule (1). The problem is to determine the number of cases each cannery should ship to each warehouse in order to minimize the total transportation cost.

(1)   Shipping Cost Schedule (dollars per case)

	Warehouses		
Canneries	New York (A)	Chicago (B)	Kansas City (C)
Seattle (I)	2.5	1.7	1.8
San Diego (II)	2.5	1.8	1.4

To formulate the model which describes the interrelations between the availabilities of cases at the canneries and demands at the warehouses, we shall begin by analyzing one of the elementary functions, namely the activity of *shipping from a cannery to a warehouse*. The activity of shipping a case from I to A (i.e., from Seattle to New York) is diagrammed in (2). It requires as *input* two items: one case in Seattle and $2.5 expense. It produces as *output* one item: one case in New York. The basic assumption is that x cases to be shipped from I to A will require as inputs at I, $1 \cdot x$ cases, and $2.5x$ dollars in expenditures; it will produce as output $1 \cdot x$ cases at A.

How this activity is performed, or what is done to a case between its origin and its destination, is not part of the programming problem. In this sense, then, the activity becomes a "black box" into which go certain items and out of which come other items; in this case, the output is a similar item, but at a different location.

(2)   Black Box Diagram of a Transportation Activity

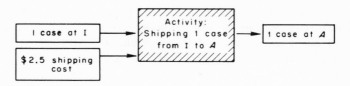

The cannery example contains six such shipping activities, which represent the six possible ways of shipping cases from two canneries to three warehouses. It is also possible to store production at the canneries, which leads to another kind of possible elementary function, the *storage activity*. A storage activity inputs an item and a cost (measured in dollars in this example, see § 3-2, footnote 3) at some time t and outputs the item at some later time $t + 1$.

(3)   Black Box Diagram of a Typical Storage Activity

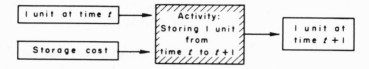

The similarity of the activities depicted in (2) and (3) occurs because the shipping activity is a transfer in *space*, while a storage activity is a transfer in *time*. Because in our particular problem we will not be considering the outputs at later times nor assigning any costs to storage, the two storage activities take on the simplified form (4).

(4)

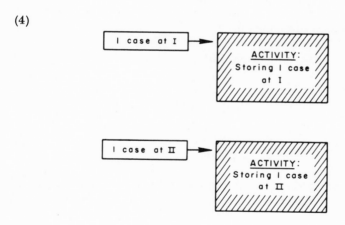

Step 1: Let us now take the first step in formulating the model. We begin by listing in (5) the set of eight possible transportation and storage activities. For convenience the activities are assigned the reference numbers on the left; thus activity "4" is the activity of "Shipping from II to A." For the units to measure the quantity of either the shipping or storage activities, it is natural to choose *one case*; however, one could choose an entirely different kind of unit for each activity. For example, the unit of

[37]

the first activity could be tens of cases shipped and the second could be measured in dollars of transportation charges, etc.

(5)   Activity List

1.   Shipping from I to A
2.   ,,   ,,   I to B
3.   ,,   ,,   I to C
4.   ,,   ,,   II to A
5.   ,,   ,,   II to B
6.   ,,   ,,   II to C
7.   Storing Excess at I
8.   ,,   ,,   at II

Step 2: Except for costs it might be felt that only one other kind of item is available, namely a case. However, economists point out that similar items at different locations[4] or different times[5] are essentially different items. For our present purposes we are ignoring the time dimension and concentrating only on the different locations. Accordingly there will be a list of six items reflecting the two cannery locations, the three warehouse locations, and the cost item (money). The items shown in (6) are assigned the reference numbers on the left; thus item 4 is "Cases at B." The case will be used as the unit of measurement for each item 1–5, and the dollar will be used to measure costs, item 6.

(6)   Item List

1.   Cases at I
2.   ,,   ,,   II
3.   ,,   ,,   A
4.   ,,   ,,   B
5.   ,,   ,,   C
6.   Costs ($)

Step 3: In recording the input-output coefficients of flow for the model, this convention on the algebraic sign of the coefficient will be used: an input will be designated by a positive coefficient, and an output by a negative coefficient. Symbolically:

(7) $+ \longrightarrow$ | Activity | $\longrightarrow -$

We shall not, however, record the values of the coefficients in this form, but construct a coefficient table for them (see Table 3-3-I). There is one

[4] A bird in the hand is worth two in the bush.
[5] A stitch in time saves nine.

TABLE 3-3-I

COEFFICIENT TABLE—TRANSPORTATION MODEL

Activities \ Items	1 I→A	2 I→B	3 I→C	4 II→A	5 II→B	6 II→C	7 Store at I	8 Store at II
1. Cases at I	+1	+1	+1				+1	
2. Cases at II				+1	+1	+1		+1
3. Cases at A	−1			−1				
4. Cases at B		−1			−1			
5. Cases at C			−1			−1		
6. Costs ($)	+2.5	+1.7	+1.8	+2.5	+1.8	+1.4		

vertical *column* in this table for each activity, and one horizontal *row* for each item; at the intersection of each row and each column, we place the *signed* input-output coefficient for the flow of that item required by one unit of the activity.

Thus one unit of activity 4, shipping one case from II to A, has as inputs one case at II (coefficient +1 in row 2, column 4) and $2.5 (coefficient +2.5 in row 6, column 4); it has as output one case at A (coefficient −1 in row 3, column 4). This table is quickly checked by inspecting each row to see whether or not there has been a complete accounting of each item; thus in row 1, item 1 (cases at I) occurs only as an input, and that to activities 1, 2, 3, and 7; and in row 3, item 3 (cases at A) occurs only as output, of activities 1 and 4.

Step 4: Exogenous (outside) flows available to the system and required from the system as a whole are shown in (8) in "black box" form. The inputs

(8)

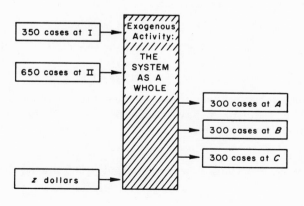

are the availabilities to the system at I and II and the outputs are the required flows from the system. Note that the dollar input has not yet been determined. *It is to be as small as possible.* Until it is determined, it will be denoted by "*z*."

It will be useful to write these exogenous flows in a column, ordered by item, similar to the column for each activity in Table 3-3-I. This is done in (9), where the same convention for the algebraic sign of exogenous flows must be used as for the flows into each activity within the system, because the algebraic sum of flow by activity will be equated to the exogenous flows. Therefore, exogenous inputs will be positive and exogenous outputs negative. Hence:

(9)

Item	Exogenous Flows
1. Cases at I	350⎫
2. Cases at II	650⎭ available inputs into the system
3. Cases at A	−300⎫
4. Cases at B	−300⎬ required outputs from the system
5. Cases at C	−300⎭
6. Costs ($)	z } minimum input into the system

Step 5: With each activity 1, 2, . . ., 8 we associate an unknown quantity to be determined which represents the level of the activity. Customarily we denote the level of activity 1 by x_1, of activity 2 by x_2, . . ., of activity 8 by x_8.

Using the coefficient table generated in Step 3, it is now an easy matter to write the material balance equations for the system, item by item.

For item 1 (cases at I), the activities involved in its flow are 1, 2, 3, and 7 (shipping, storage at I). Because the input-output coefficients relating to item 1 are all +1, the net flow of item 1 is just

$$1 \cdot x_1 + 1 \cdot x_2 + 1 \cdot x_3 + 1 \cdot x_7$$

This flow must equal the exogenous flow of item 1 to the system, which is 350, yielding the first material balance equation,

$$x_1 + x_2 + x_3 + x_7 = 350$$

In precisely the same way, the material balance equation for item 2 (cases at II) is

$$x_4 + x_5 + x_6 + x_8 = 650$$

The equation has a different form for item 3 (cases at A). Here activities 1 and 4, which ship to A, have coefficients −1, and no other activities involve item 3. The net flow is

$$-1 \cdot x_1 - 1 \cdot x_4$$

and because the exogenous flow is the output −300, the equation is

$$-x_1 - x_4 = -300$$

[40]

The remaining equations, corresponding to items 4 and 5, give a similar accounting of cases at B and C respectively:

$$-x_2 - x_5 = -300$$
$$-x_3 - x_6 = -300$$

These equations are summarized in Table 3-3-II, Equations (11).

Finally, the flow of item 6 in the system is evidently given by

$$2.5x_1 + 1.7x_2 + 1.8x_3 + 2.5x_4 + 1.8x_5 + 1.4x_6$$

We place this in a material balance equation by setting it equal to an unspecified dollar input z. Recall that we do not yet know what numerical value z should have:

$$2.5x_1 + 1.7x_2 + 1.8x_3 + 2.5x_4 + 1.8x_5 + 1.4x_6 = z$$

Step 5 is now complete.

The Equation Form.

The set of material balance equations generated here, together with the conditions that all the activity levels $x_1, \ldots, x_8$ be nonnegative, constitutes the linear programming model for this transportation problem. These are summarized in (10) and (11) in what is referred to as the Equation Form of the model.

The Tableau.

The linear programming tableau affords both a compact form for writing the data of the linear programming model and a procedure for generating the material balance equations from these data without going through the detailed reasoning we have in Step 5.

The tableau for this problem is given in Table 3-3-II.

TABLE 3-3-II

LINEAR PROGRAMMING MODEL OF THE TRANSPORTATION PROBLEM

Tableau Form

Activities	I→A x_1	I→B x_2	I→C x_3	II→A x_4	II→B x_5	II→C x_6	Store at I x_7	Store at II x_8	Exogenous Flows
1. Cases at I	1	1	1				1		350
2. Cases at II				1	1	1		1	650
3. Cases at A	−1			−1					−300
4. Cases at B		−1			−1				−300
5. Cases at C			−1			−1			−300
6. Costs ($)	2.5	1.7	1.8	2.5	1.8	1.4			z (Min)

[41]

Equation Form

(10) Nonnega-
    tivity $\quad x_1 \geq 0, \quad x_2 \geq 0, \quad x_3 \geq 0, \quad x_4 \geq 0, \quad x_5 \geq 0, \quad x_6 \geq 0, \quad x_7 \geq 0, \quad x_8 \geq 0$

$$
\begin{cases}
x_1 + x_2 + x_3 & & & +x_7 & & = 350 \\
& x_4 + x_5 + x_6 & & +x_8 & = 650 \\
-x_1 & -x_4 & & & = -300 \\
-x_2 & -x_5 & & & = -300 \\
-x_3 & -x_6 & & & = -300 \\
2.5x_1 + 1.7x_2 + 1.8x_3 + 2.5x_4 + 1.8x_5 + 1.4x_6 & & & & = z \text{ (Min)}
\end{cases}
$$

(11) Material
    Balances

It consists of these parts:

(a) A list of the activities of the system and their unknown levels.
(b) A list of the items of the system.
    The input-output coefficients of the system, arranged in columns by activity and in rows by item, as in the "Coefficient Table" of Table 3-3-I and later in the "Tableau Form" of Table 3-3-II.
(c) The exogenous flows to the system, in a column, as in (9).

The relationship in Table 3-3-II between the Equation Form of the model and the Tableau Form should be carefully noted. The tableau can be obtained from the equations by *detaching the coefficients* of the activity levels $x_1, \ldots, x_8$, that is, by suppressing the variables of the equations. When the model is presented in tableau form, the nonnegativity conditions (10) in Table 3-3-II will be understood to hold; on the other hand, the equations (11) can be immediately reconstructed from the tableau by forming, in each item-row, the products of the input-output coefficients with the appropriate unknown activity levels, summing across, and setting this expression for the net flow equal to the exogenous flow of the item.

The Linear Programming Problem.

Finally, we can state the mathematical problem for our particular example. Determine levels for the activities $x_1, x_2, \ldots, x_8$ which (a) are nonnegative (relations (10), Table 3-3-II), (b) satisfy the material balance equations (11), and (c) minimize z.

3-4. EXAMPLES OF BLENDING

A type of linear programming problem frequently encountered is one involving blending. Typically, different commodities are to be purchased, each having known characteristics and costs. The problem is to give a recipe showing how much of each commodity should be purchased and blended with the rest so that the characteristics of the mixture lie within specified bounds and the total purchase cost is minimized.

In the example we take up here, the characteristics of the blend are precisely specified. As will be seen later, only minor changes in the model are required in the event the blend specifications must lie between certain lower or upper bounds.

Blending Problem I.

A manufacturer wishes to produce an alloy which is 30 per cent lead, 30 per cent zinc, and 40 per cent tin. Suppose there are, on the market, alloys A, B, C, . . . with compositions and prices as given in (1). Per pound of blend produced, how much of each type of alloy should be purchased in order to minimize costs?

(1)   Data for Blending Problem I

Alloy	A	B	C	D	E	F	G	H	I	Desired Blend
% Lead	10	10	40	60	30	30	30	50	20	30
% Zinc	10	30	50	30	30	40	20	40	30	30
% Tin	80	60	10	10	40	30	50	10	50	40
Costs/lb	$4.1	4.3	5.8	6.0	7.6	7.5	7.3	6.9	7.3	Min

Obviously the manufacturer can purchase alloy E alone, but it costs $7.60 per pound. If he buys $\frac{1}{4}$ pound each of alloys A, B, C, and D, he gets one pound of a 30-30-40 mixture at a cost of $5.05; $\frac{1}{4}$ pound of A, $\frac{1}{4}$ pound of B, and $\frac{1}{2}$ pound of H again give one pound of mixture with correct proportions, but costs $5.55. After a few trials of this sort, the manufacturer may well seek a more general approach to his problem.

In formulating the linear programming model for this example, we must first note that the blending problem has not been posed as completely as, say, the transportation problem of the preceding section. The *quantities* of lead, zinc, and tin in the final blend have not been specified, only their proportions have been given, and it is required to minimize the cost per pound of the output. Because we need specific data for the exogenous flows, we shall require that a definite amount of blended metal be produced. It is clear that a recipe giving the most economical purchasing program for one pound of blended metal output can be immediately converted into a recipe giving the most economical purchasing program for n pounds of output by multiplying the levels of all the activities involved by n; and thus we will restrict the *quantity* of *activities to those combinations which produce one pound of blended metal*. This restriction is expressed later, implicitly in the statement of exogenous flows (6), and again explicitly in the material balance equations (8).

This stipulation has the further happy result that the percentage requirements of the original statement of the problem now become concrete: the mixture must contain 0.3 pounds of lead, 0.3 pounds of zinc, and 0.4 pounds of tin. (Often a beginner attempts to formulate the problem without restricting the total amount produced, in which case the material balance equations become difficult to interpret, being expressed in terms of percentages instead of amounts.)

[43]

Step 1: Identifying activities. The only activities we need to consider are those of purchasing each of the nine alloys, because we assume all the metal purchased will be blended. The unit level for each activity will be the purchase of one pound of the alloy.

(2) Activity List

1. Purchasing alloy A; activity level x_1
2.   ,,   ,, B ,,   ,, x_2
3.   ,,   ,, C ,,   ,, x_3
4.   ,,   ,, D ,,   ,, x_4
5.   ,,   ,, E ,,   ,, x_5
6.   ,,   ,, F ,,   ,, x_6
7.   ,,   ,, G ,,   ,, x_7
8.   ,,   ,, H ,,   ,, x_8
9.   ,,   ,, I ,,   ,, x_9

Step 2: Identifying items. The items considered in the system can now be listed:

(3) Item List

1. Metal (*total*) measured in pounds
2. Lead   ,,   ,,   ,,
3. Zinc   ,,   ,,   ,,
4. Tin   ,,   ,,   ,,
5. Cost   ,,   ,, dollars

Step 3: Input-output coefficients. We shall adopt the first of the three points of view discussed in the footnote[6] in what follows. A typical activity —say activity 1, purchasing alloy A—has the appearance

(4)

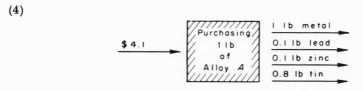

using the data of (1). Each of the nine activities has likewise one input and four outputs. Each activity has, of course, one pound of metal as one

---

[6] There are three points of view that one can take in formulating this model: (1) the viewpoint of the alloy purchaser is that he receives dollars and outputs contributions to pounds of finished blend and to the lead, tin, zinc characteristics; (2) the viewpoint of the blender is that he inputs contributions to lead, tin, zinc characteristics and outputs dollars and pounds of finished blend; (3) the viewpoint of the receiver of the finished blend is that he receives finished metal and contributions to lead, tin, zinc characteristics and outputs money.

output; the remaining entries in Table 3-4-I, of input-output coefficients are extracted directly from the data in (1).

TABLE 3-4-I

COEFFICIENT TABLE: BLENDING PROBLEM I

Activities / Items	1 A	2 B	3 C	4 D	5 E	6 F	7 G	8 H	9 I
1. Metal	−1	−1	−1	−1	−1	−1	−1	−1	−1
2. Lead	−0.1	−0.1	−0.4	−0.6	−0.3	−0.3	−0.3	−0.5	−0.2
3. Zinc	−0.1	−0.3	−0.5	−0.3	−0.3	−0.4	−0.2	−0.4	−0.3
4. Tin	−0.8	−0.6	−0.1	−0.1	−0.4	−0.3	−0.5	−0.1	−0.5
5. Costs ($)	4.1	4.3	5.8	6.0	7.6	7.5	7.3	6.9	7.3

Step 4: Exogenous flows. These are shown in "black box" form in (5), and as a list in (6):

(5)   Exogenous Flows—Blending Problem I

z dollars → System as a whole → 1 lb metal, 0.3 lb lead, 0.3 lb zinc, 0.4 lb tin

(6)

Item	Exogenous Flows
1. Metal	−1.0
2. Lead	−0.3
3. Zinc	−0.3
4. Tin	−0.4
5. Costs ($)	z (Min)

Step 5: Material balance equations. As noted in § 3-3, the Equation Form for the model can be assembled directly from the results of Steps 3 and 4. Combining the coefficient table (Table 3-4-I) and the exogenous flow list (6), we arrive at the Tableau Form of our model shown in Table 3-4-II.

Linear Programming Problem for Blending Model I. Determine levels for the activities $x_1, x_2, \ldots, x_9$ which (a) are nonnegative (relations (7), Table 3-4-II), (b) satisfy the material balance equations (8), and (c) minimize z.

TABLE 3-4-II

LINEAR PROGRAMMING MODEL OF BLENDING PROBLEM I

Tableau Form

Activities	A	B	C	D	E	F	G	H	I	Exog- enous Flow
Buy at level Items	x_1	x_2	x_3	x_4	x_5	x_6	x_7	x_8	x_9	
1. Metal (total)	-1	-1	-1	-1	-1	-1	-1	-1	-1	-1
2. Lead	$-.1$	$-.1$	$-.4$	$-.6$	$-.3$	$-.3$	$-.3$	$-.5$	$-.2$	$-.$
3. Zinc	$-.1$	$-.3$	$-.5$	$-.3$	$-.3$	$-.4$	$-.2$	$-.4$	$-.3$	$-.$
4. Tin	$-.8$	$-.6$	$-.1$	$-.1$	$-.4$	$-.3$	$-.5$	$-.1$	$-.5$	$-.4$
5. Costs ($)	4.1	4.3	5.8	6.0	7.6	7.5	7.3	6.9	7.3	z (Min)

Equation Form

(7) Non-
negativity $\quad x_1 \geq 0,\ x_2 \geq 0,\ x_3 \geq 0,\ x_4 \geq 0,\ x_5 \geq 0,\ x_6 \geq 0,\ x_7 \geq 0,\ x_8 \geq 0,\ x_9 \geq 0$

(8) Material
Balances
$$
\begin{cases}
-x_1 & -x_2 & -x_3 & -x_4 & -x_5 & -x_6 & -x_7 & -x_8 & -x_9 = -1 \\
-.1x_1 & -.1x_2 & -.4x_3 & -.6x_4 & -.3x_5 & -.3x_6 & -.3x_7 & -.5x_8 & -.2x_9 = -. \\
-.1x_1 & -.3x_2 & -.5x_3 & -.3x_4 & -.3x_5 & -.4x_6 & -.2x_7 & -.4x_8 & -.3x_9 = -. \\
-.8x_1 & -.6x_2 & -.1x_3 & -.1x_4 & -.4x_5 & -.3x_6 & -.5x_7 & -.1x_8 & -.5x_9 = -. \\
4.1x_1 & +4.3x_2 & +5.8x_3 & +6.0x_4 & +7.6x_5 & +7.5x_6 & +7.3x_7 & +6.9x_8 & +7.3x_9 = z\ \text{(Mi}
\end{cases}
$$

Blending Problem II.

The particular linear programming problem considered above is a little too large for us to solve conveniently until the techniques of Chapter 5 have been developed. (It is given as the Illustrative Example 2 of that chapter.) Its solution is found to be $x_1 = 0$, $x_2 = \frac{3}{5}$, $x_4 = \frac{2}{5}$, and all the remaining activities at zero level. The minimum cost for one pound of metal is $4.98. As an alternative we shall consider an easier and different problem.

To simplify the blending problem so that it can be solved here graphically, let us try to find the cheapest blend of alloys that will have .4 lb. of tin per pound of metal (the remaining .6 lb. of metal may have lead and zinc in any ratio). This is, of course, not the problem we formulated earlier, but it will not be necessary to go through the whole model-building process again in order to formulate it. All we have done is to drop here the requirements laid down in (6) for items 2 (lead) and 3 (zinc); the other requirements, the activities and the input-output coefficients, need not be changed in building this simpler model. Thus, we can obtain the equation form of the simplified model by merely deleting the second and third equations of (8), which relate to lead and zinc. We are left with the first, fourth, and fifth equations of (8).

The discussion will be made still easier if we change the signs of all the terms in the "Metal" and "Tin" equations.

Linear Programming Problem for Blending Model II. Determine levels for the activities $x_1, x_2, \ldots, x_9$ which (a) are nonnegative, (b) satisfy the equations

$$(9) \quad x_1 + x_2 + x_3 + x_4 + x_5 + x_6 + x_7 + x_8 + x_9 = 1$$
$$(10) \quad .8x_1 + .6x_2 + .1x_3 + .1x_4 + .4x_5 + .3x_6 + .5x_7 + .1x_8 + .5x_9 = .4$$
$$(11) \quad 4.1x_1 + 4.3x_2 + 5.8x_3 + 6.0x_4 + 7.6x_5 + 7.5x_6 + 7.3x_7 + 6.9x_8 + 7.3x_9 = z$$

and (c) minimize z.

Graphical Representation. The data of the blending problem have now been reduced sufficiently to permit their graphical representation in Fig. 3-4-I. For each of the nine activities we take its two coefficients from equations (10) and (11), and represent the activity by a point having these two numbers as coordinates. Thus the point A, representing alloy A, has coordinates (.8, 4.1), which are the amount of tin and the cost per pound of alloy A; similarly, the point B has coordinates (.6, 4.3), the amount of tin and cost per pound of alloy B; etc. Let (u, v) be the coordinates of a general point.

The fact which makes this graphical representation valuable is that not only can the input-output coefficients of any activity be represented by a point, but the net exogenous flow to the system as a whole can be represented also as a point for any program involving nonnegative levels $x_1, \ldots, x_9$, which *sum to unity*. Consider, for example, the program $x_1 = x_2 = \frac{1}{2}$, $x_3 = x_4 = \ldots = 0$, which consists of using one-half pound each of alloys A and B. It yields $.8(\frac{1}{2}) + .6(\frac{1}{2}) = 0.7$ pound of tin and costs $4.1(\frac{1}{2}) + 4.3(\frac{1}{2}) = 4.2$, and can thus be represented in Fig. 3-4-I by the point p_1, half-way between A and B. Another program, $x_1 = \frac{1}{2}$, $x_2 = x_9 = \frac{1}{4}$, using one-half pound of A and one-quarter each of B and I, has coordinates $.8(\frac{1}{2}) + .6(\frac{1}{4}) + .5(\frac{1}{4}) = 0.675$ for tin and $4.1(\frac{1}{2}) + 4.3(\frac{1}{4}) + 7.3(\frac{1}{4}) = 4.95$ for cost, and can be represented by p_2.

In each case, the coordinates of the point representing the mixture are a *weighted average* of the corresponding coordinates of the points representing the pure alloys; thus, we say that the point p_1 is the weighted average of the points A and B with weights $\frac{1}{2}$ and $\frac{1}{2}$, respectively, and that p_2 is the weighted average of the points A, B, and I with weights $\frac{1}{2}$, $\frac{1}{4}$, and $\frac{1}{4}$, respectively. (In physics, p_1 is said to be the *center of gravity* of the system consisting of a weight of $\frac{1}{2}$ unit at A and $\frac{1}{2}$ unit at B; likewise, p_2 is the center of gravity of the system consisting of weights $\frac{1}{2}$, $\frac{1}{4}$, and $\frac{1}{4}$ at A, B, and I, respectively.)

It should now be clear that all the nonnegative programs satisfying just relation (9) are represented by the shaded region of Fig. 3-4-I, the collection of all possible weighted averages of the nine points A, $\ldots$, I. The *feasible programs*, however, are those which yield exactly 0.4 pound of tin; they are represented by the points of the shaded region which lie on the vertical line having abscissa 0.4. The point E is such a program, as well as the point R = (0.4, 5.55), which is the weighted average of A, B, and H with weights $\frac{1}{4}$, $\frac{1}{4}$, and $\frac{1}{2}$, respectively. Evidently neither of these points represents the least-z solution of the problem; the point which does, is the lowest point on the vertical line which is in the shaded region. Thus, the linear programming problem can be interpreted graphically as one of assigning nonnegative weights to the vertices of the figure in such a way that the weighted average of the vertices lies on the vertical line whose abscissa is 0.4 and has as

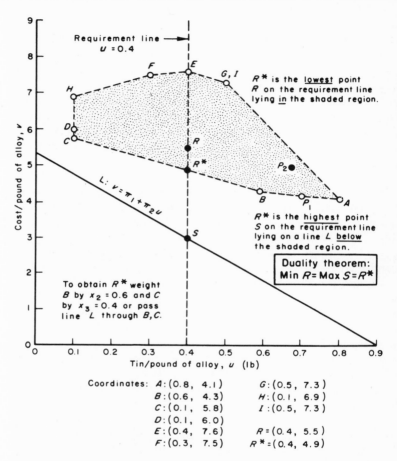

Figure 3-4-I.   Duality theorem illustrated on blending model II.

small an ordinate z as possible. From the graph we can see that the desired weighted average, R*, lies on the line BC; i.e., it is the average obtained by giving certain weights, x_2 and x_3, to B and C, and weights of zero to all the others. To determine x_2 and x_3, set all $x_j = 0$ except x_2 and x_3 in (9) and (10), i.e., consider mixtures consisting only of B and C; then we must have

$$x_2 + x_3 = 1$$
$$.6x_2 + .1x_3 = .4$$

which yields
$$x_2 = .6, \; x_3 = .4$$
and
$$\text{Min } z = 4.3x_2 + 5.8x_3 = 4.9$$

We conclude that it is best to blend in the proportions of .6 pound of alloy B to .4 pound of alloy C to produce the cheapest alloy containing 40 per cent tin. The blend will cost \$4.9 per pound.

Algebraic Check—the Dual Linear Program. We can check algebraically whether our choice of B, C in Fig. 3-4-I is correct by first determining the line joining B to C and then testing to see if each of the points of the shaded region has an ordinate value v greater than that of the point on the line with the same abscissa u. If the latter is true we say the shaded region lies "above" the extended line joining B to C.

Now the equation of a *general line* in the (u, v) plane is

$$v = \pi_1 + \pi_2 u$$

where π_1 is the *intercept* and π_2 the *slope*. In order that the shaded region lie above this line, each of the points A, B, C, . . ., G, I (which generated the shaded region) must lie on or above the line. Substituting the $u = .8$ coordinate of A into the equation, the value $v = \pi_1 + \pi_2(.8)$ must be *less than or equal to* the v coordinate of A. Thus our test for A is $\pi_1 + \pi_2(.8) \leq 4.1$ and for the entire set A, B, C, . . . we must have

(12)
$$\pi_1 + \pi_2(.8) \leq 4.1$$
$$\pi_1 + \pi_2(.6) \leq 4.3$$
$$\pi_1 + \pi_2(.1) \leq 5.8$$
$$\pi_1 + \pi_2(.1) \leq 6.0$$
$$\pi_1 + \pi_2(.4) \leq 7.6$$
$$\pi_1 + \pi_2(.3) \leq 7.5$$
$$\pi_1 + \pi_2(.5) \leq 7.3$$
$$\pi_1 + \pi_2(.1) \leq 6.9$$
$$\pi_1 + \pi_2(.5) \leq 7.3$$

Let $S = (.4, \bar{v})$ be the intersection of the vertical line $u = .4$ with $v = \pi_1 + \pi_2 u$; then the line we are looking for (and which we hope will be the one joining B to C) is the one below the shaded region whose $v = \bar{v}$ coordinate of S is *maximum*, i.e.,

(13)
$$\pi_1 + \pi_2(.4) = \bar{v} \; (\text{Max})$$

The problem of finding π_1, π_2 and Max $\bar{v}$ satisfying (12) and (13) is known as the *dual* of our original (*primal*) problem (9), (10), and (11). The fact that Max $\bar{v} = $ Min z for these two problems is a particular case of the Duality Theorem for Linear Programs (see Chapter 6).

[49]

If we conjecture that some pair like B, C (obtained by visual inspection of the graph or otherwise) is an optimal choice, it is an easy matter to verify this choice by checking whether (i) the intersection S lies *between* the selected two points and (ii) all points A, B, C, . . . lie *on or above* the extended line joining the selected two points. To check the first, we solve

$$(14) \qquad \begin{aligned} x_2 + x_3 &= 1 \\ .6x_2 + .1x_3 &= .4 \end{aligned}$$

obtaining $x_2 = .6$, $x_3 = .4$ which are positive, so that S lies between B and C. Thus these values with remaining $x_i = 0$ satisfy the primal system (9), (10), and (11). To check the second we determine the equation of the line by stating the conditions that the line pass through B and C,

$$(15) \qquad \begin{aligned} \pi_1 + \pi_2(.6) &= 4.3 \\ \pi_1 + \pi_2(.1) &= 5.8 \end{aligned}$$

This yields $\pi_1 = 6.1$, $\pi_2 = -3$, which satisfy the dual system (12).

3-5. A PRODUCT MIX PROBLEM

A furniture company manufactures four models of desks. Each desk is first constructed in the carpentry shop and is next sent to the finishing shop, where it is varnished, waxed, and polished. The number of man hours of labor required in each shop is as follows:

		Desk 1	Desk 2	Desk 3	Desk 4
(1)	Carpentry Shop	4	9	7	10
	Finishing Shop	1	1	3	40

Because of limitations in capacity of the plant, no more than 6,000 man hours can be expected in the carpentry shop and 4,000 in the finishing shop in the next six months.

The profit (revenue minus labor costs) from the sale of each item is as follows:

	Desk	1	2	3	4
(2)	Profit	$12	$20	$18	$40

Assuming that raw materials and supplies are available in adequate supply and all desks produced can be sold, the desk company wants to determine the optimal product mix, i.e., the quantities to make of each type product which will maximize profit.

Step 1: Activities. The four manufacturing activities are

1.   Manufacturing desk 1 (measured in desks produced)
2.   ,,   ,, 2 (,,   ,,   ,,   ,,   )
3.   ,,   ,, 3 (,,   ,,   ,,   ,,   )
4.   ,,   ,, 4 (,,   ,,   ,,   ,,   )

Step 2: Items.

1.   Capacity in Carpentry Shop (measured in man hours)
2.   Capacity in Finishing Shop (measured in man hours)
3.   Costs (measured in dollars)

Step 3: Coefficients. Manufacturing activity 1, for example, can be diagrammed as follows:

(3)

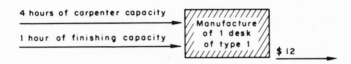

The table of input-output coefficients constructed from (1) and (2) is shown in Table 3-5-I.

TABLE 3-5-I

COEFFICIENT TABLE: PRODUCT MIX PROBLEM

Activities Items	Manufacturing Desks			
	(1)	(2)	(3)	(4)
1. Carpentry capacity (hours)	4	9	7	10
2. Finishing capacity (hours)	1	1	3	40
3. Cost ($)	-12	-20	-18	-40

Step 4: Exogenous flows. Since capacities, in carpentry and finishing, are inputs to each of these activities, they must be inputs to the system as a whole. At this point, however, we must face the fact that a feasible program need not use up all of this capacity. The total inputs must not be more than 6,000 carpentry hours and 4,000 finishing hours, but they can be less, and so cannot be specified precisely in material balance equations.

Step 5: Material balances. If we went ahead with the formulation anyway, using these figures for the exogenous flows, then in order to retain reality in the mathematical formulation, we should have to write material balance inequalities instead of equations, expressing, for example, the carpentry capacity limitation as

$$4x_1 + 9x_2 + 7x_3 + 10x_4 \leq 6000$$

instead of as an equation, which is not according to our rules.

We see that the model cannot be completed with the lists of activities and items given above, and we have here the case mentioned in the first section in which a second pass at the initial building of the model is necessary.

In this instance all we need to do is add activities to the model which will account for the carpentry and finishing capacity not used by the remainder of the program. If we specify "not using capacity" as an activity, we have the two additional activities to add to those listed in Step 1:

5. Not using Carpentry Shop capacity (measured in man hours)
6. Not using Finishing Shop capacity (measured in man hours)

Activity 5 can be abstracted as

(4)

The full tableau of inputs and outputs of the activities and the exogenous availabilities to the system as a whole is shown in Table 3-5-II.

TABLE 3-5-II

LINEAR PROGRAMMING PROBLEM FOR A PRODUCT MIX MODEL

Activities / Items	Manufacturing Desks				Not Using Capacity Carp. Fin.		Exogenous Flows Input (+) Output (−)
	(1) x_1	(2) x_2	(3) x_3	(4) x_4	(5) x_5	(6) x_6	
1. Carpentry capacity (hours)	4	9	7	10	1		6000
2. Finishing capacity (hours)	1	1	3	40		1	4000
3. Costs ($)	−12	−20	−18	−40			z (Min)

Thus the programming problem is to determine numbers

(5) $x_1 \geq 0,\ x_2 \geq 0,\ x_3 \geq 0,\ x_4 \geq 0,\ x_5 \geq 0,\ x_6 \geq 0$

and minimum z satisfying

$$
\begin{align}
(6) \qquad 4x_1 + 9x_2 + 7x_3 + 10x_4 + x_5 \qquad &= 6000, \\
x_1 + x_2 + 3x_3 + 40x_4 \qquad + x_6 &= 4000, \\
-12x_1 - 20x_2 - 18x_3 - 40x_4 \qquad &= z
\end{align}
$$

Note that the same values of the x's which minimize the cost function will also maximize its negative, namely the profit function p given by

$$+12x_1 + 20x_2 + 18x_3 + 40x_4 = p$$

Thus, a profit maximization problem can be stated as an equivalent to a cost minimization problem.

Graphical Solution. To apply the method of solution of the last section to the product mix model, it is necessary to change the definitions of items and activity levels so that the activity levels sum to unity. This is simply done by introducing as an item, *total capacity*, which is the sum of the carpentry capacity and the finishing capacity, and *changing units* for measuring activity levels so that 1 new unit of each activity requires the full $6000 + 4000 = 10,000$ hours of total capacity. To change units note that one unit of the first activity in Table 3-5-II requires 5 hours of total capacity; thus, 2,000 units of the first activity would require 10,000 hours of capacity and is equivalent to *one new unit* of the first activity. In general, if y_1 is the number of new units of the first activity, then $2000y_1 = x_1$. The relationships between the old and new activity levels after such a change in units for each activity is

$$
\begin{align}
2000y_1 = x_1, \quad 1000y_2 = x_2, \quad 1000y_3 = x_3, \\
200y_4 = x_4, \quad 10,000y_5 = x_5, \quad 10,000y_6 = x_6.
\end{align}
$$

It is also convenient to change the units for measuring capacity and costs. Let 10,000 hours $= 1$ new capacity unit; \$10,000 $= 1$ new cost unit. Then it is easy to see (and this is left as an exercise) that the Product Mix Model Table 3-5-II will become Table 3-5-III after the changes in the units for

TABLE 3-5-III

A PRODUCT MIX MODEL (after change in units)

Activities / Items	Manufacturing Desks (1 = 10,000 hours)				Not Using Capacity Carp. Fin.		Exogenous Flows
	(1) y_1	(2) y_2	(3) y_3	(4) y_4	(5) y_5	(6) y_6	
0. Total capacity (1 = 10,000 hours)	1.0	1.0	1.0	1.0	1.0	1.0	1.0
1. Carpentry capacity	.8	.9	.7	.2	1.0		.6
2. Finishing capacity	.2	.1	.3	.8		1.0	.4
3. Costs (1 = \$10,000)	−2.4	−2.0	−1.8	− .8			z' (Min)

activities and items given above, the replacing of z by $10,000z' = z$ in the cost equation, and the adding of the two equations to form a total capacity equation.

We are now ready to find the graphical solution. Because the unknowns $y_j \geq 0$ sum to unity, we shall interpret this as assigning nonnegative weights to points A_1, A_2, . . ., A_6 in Fig. 3-5-I. As in the blending problem of the

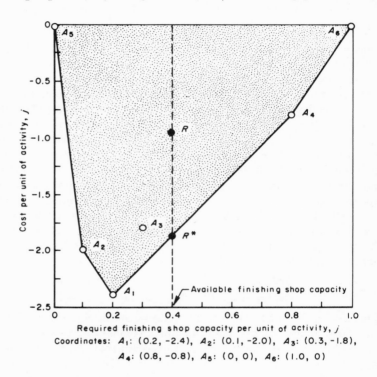

Coordinates: A_1: (0.2, -2.4), A_2: (0.1, -2.0), A_3: (0.3, -1.8), A_4: (0.8, -0.8), A_5: (0, 0), A_6: (1.0, 0)

Figure 3-5-I. Graphical solution of the product mix problem.

preceding section, we shall ignore one of the material balance equations, namely that for item 1, carpentry capacity; however, here we will find that ignoring it does not affect the minimal solution because the equation is redundant.

In Fig. 3-5-I each point A_j corresponds to a column, or activity, of Table 3-5-III; its coordinates are the coefficients for the *finishing* capacity and cost of the activity. Thus the coordinates of A_1 are (.2, −2.4); of A_2 are (.1, −2.0), . . .; of A_5 are (0, 0); and of A_6 are (1.0, 0).

We seek an assignment of nonnegative weights y_j for each of the six points which sum to unity, so that their weighted average has coordinates (.4, z') and z' is minimal. This, clearly, is the point R* found by assigning zero weights to all points, except A_1 and A_4, and appropriately weighting the latter so that the center of gravity of A_1 and A_4 has abscissa 0.4. To determine y_1 and y_4, set all $y_j = 0$ except y_1 and y_4 in Table 3-5-III, yielding

$$.2y_1 + .8y_4 = .4$$
$$y_1 + y_4 = 1$$
$$-2.4y_1 - .8y_4 = z'$$

whence

$$y_1 = 2/3, \ y_4 = 1/3, \ z' = -5.6/3$$

Thus the optimal solution is to manufacture $x_1 = \frac{2}{3}(2000)$ desks of Type 1, $x_4 = \frac{1}{3}(200)$ desks of Type 4, which will use the full capacity of the plant and will cost $z = \$10,000 \ (-5.6/3)$, or yield \$18,666.66 profit.

The carpentry capacity is completely accounted for by this solution, despite the fact that its material balance equation was omitted in the above calculation. As noted earlier, this is because adding the *total capacity* equation to the system enables us to drop either of the remaining equations and still have a model which accounts for all the capacities; the carpentry capacity equation becomes redundant, and can be dropped.

3-6. A SIMPLE WAREHOUSE PROBLEM

Consider the problem of stocking a warehouse with a commodity for sale at a later date. The warehouse can stock only 100 units of the commodity. The storage costs are \$1.00 per quarter for each unit. In each quarter the purchase price equals the selling price. This price varies from quarter to quarter according to (1):

(1)

Quarter (t)	Price per unit (dollars)
1	10
2	12
3	8
4	9

This implies that a profit can be realized by buying when the price is low and selling when the price is high. The problem is to determine the optimal selling, storing, and buying program for a one-year period by quarters, assuming that the warehouse has an initial stock of 50 units.

In each period (quarter), t, we distinguish four types of activities:

		Quantity
1.	Selling stock	x_{t1}
2.	Storing stock	x_{t2}
3.	Buying stock	x_{t3}
4.	Not using capacity (slack)	x_{t4}

and three types of items:

    1. Stock
    2. Storage Capacity
    3. Costs

These activities have the input-output characteristics sketched in (2).

    With four time periods each item and activity is repeated four times, which leads to Table 3-6-I, the tableau for the warehouse problem. The problem here is to find the values of $x_{ti} \geq 0$ which satisfy the equations implied by the tableau and which minimize the total cost.

(2)

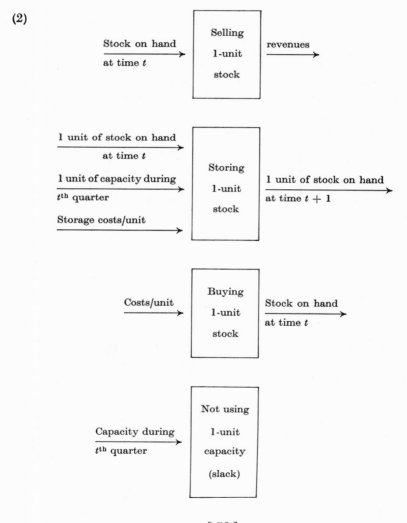

TABLE 3-6-I

A SIMPLE WAREHOUSE MODEL

Activities / Items	1st Quarter Sell x_{11}	Store x_{12}	Buy x_{13}	Slack x_{14}	2nd Quarter Sell x_{21}	Store x_{22}	Buy x_{23}	Slack x_{24}	3rd Quarter Sell x_{31}	Store x_{32}	Buy x_{33}	Slack x_{34}	4th Quarter Sell x_{41}	Store x_{42}	Buy x_{43}	Slack x_{44}	Exogenous Flows
$t=0$ Stock	1	1	−1														50
Capac.		1		1													100
$t=1$ Stock		−1			1	1	−1										0
Capac.						1		1									100
$t=2$ Stock						−1			1	1	−1						0
Capac.										1		1					100
$t=3$ Stock										−1			1	1	−1		0
Capac.														1		1	100
Costs	−10	1	10		−12	1	12		−8	1	8		−9	1	9		z (Min)

3-7. ON-THE-JOB TRAINING

The purpose of this example is to illustrate the ability of the linear programming model to cover the many and varied conditions that are so characteristic of practical applications.

The problem. A manufacturing plant has a contract to produce 1200 units of some commodity, C, with the required delivery schedule r_t as in (1).

(1)

End of week	1	2	3	4	5
No. of units	$r_1 = 100$	$r_2 = 200$	$r_3 = 300$	$r_4 = 400$	$r_5 = 200$

What hiring, firing, producing, and storing schedule should the manufacturer adopt to minimize the costs of his contract under the following conditions?

(a) Each unit of production not delivered on schedule involves a penalty of $p = \$30$ per week until delivery is effected.

(b) Any production ahead of schedule requires storage at $s = \$10$/unit/week.

(c) All required deliveries must be met by the end of the fifth week.

(d) Initially there are $g = 20$ workers and $h = 10$ units of C on hand.

(e) Each worker used in production during a week can turn out $k = 8$ units of C.

(f) Each worker used for training recruits during a week can train $l - 1 = 5$ new workers (i.e., produce l trained workers including himself).

(g) Wages of a worker are $m = \$100$/week when used in production or when idle.

(h) Wages of a worker plus $l - 1$ recruits used in training for one week are $n = \$600$.

(i) The cost to fire one worker is $f = \$100$.

We shall choose for our unit of time a period of one week. At the beginning of each week we shall assign the necessary number of workers and units of C to carry out an activity that takes place during the week. Accordingly, at each of the six times $t = 0, 1, 2, \ldots, 5$, material balance equations for two items will be set up:

	Symbol for item
Workers	W_t
Commodity	C_t

In addition to these equations there will be a cost equation for the *cost item*. In each of five weekly periods six activities will be set up as in (2).

(2)

		Symbol for Activity
1.	Training	T_t
2.	Producing	P_t
3.	Idling	I_t
4.	Firing	F_t
5.	Storing	S_t
6.	Penalizing (for Deficit)	D_t

The input-output characteristics of each of the activities, except perhaps the penalizing activity, are straightforward. Each failure to deliver a unit makes it necessary to decrease by one unit the present demand for the commodity and to increase the demand one unit in the next time period at a cost of p dollars. Another rationalization of this activity is to imagine that the deficit is temporarily satisfied by renting on the open market one unit of the commodity which must be returned the following week at a cost of p dollars.

(3)

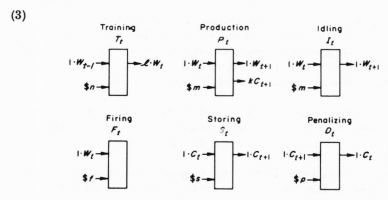

These activities are shown in conventional tableau form in Table 3-7-I. In the fifth week the penalizing activity is omitted because condition (c) states that all deliveries must be met by the end of the fifth week. In the sixth week a firing activity F_6 has been introduced to get rid of all workers and to terminate the program. (Why is this necessary?)

[58]

TABLE 3-7-I

THE JOB TRAINING MODEL

Item	1st Week						2nd Week						3rd Week						4th Week						5th Week						Exogenous Flows
	T_1 x_{11}	P_1 x_{12}	I_1 x_{13}	F_1 x_{14}	S_1 x_{15}	D_1 x_{16}	T_2 x_{21}	P_2 x_{22}	I_2 x_{23}	F_2 x_{24}	S_2 x_{25}	D_2 x_{26}	T_3 x_{31}	P_3 x_{32}	I_3 x_{33}	F_3 x_{34}	S_3 x_{35}	D_3 x_{36}	T_4 x_{41}	P_4 x_{42}	I_4 x_{43}	F_4 x_{44}	S_4 x_{45}	D_4 x_{46}	T_5 x_{51}	P_5 x_{52}	I_5 x_{53}	F_5 x_{54}	S_5 x_{55}	F_6 x_{64}	
W_0	1	1	1	1																											g
C_0					1	-1																									h
W_1	$-\ell$	-1	-1				1	1	1	1																					0
C_1	$-k$				-1	1					1	-1																			$-r_1$
W_2							$-\ell$	-1	-1				1	1	1	1															0
C_2							$-k$				-1	1					1	-1													$-r_2$
W_3													$-\ell$	-1	-1				1	1	1	1									0
C_3													$-k$				-1	1					1	-1							$-r_3$
W_4																			$-\ell$	-1	-1				1	1	1	1			0
C_4																			$-k$				-1	1					1		$-r_4$
W_5																									$-\ell$	-1	-1			1	0
C_5																									$-k$				-1		$-r_5$
Cost	n	m	m	f	s	p	n	m	m	f	s	p	n	m	m	f	s	p	n	m	m	f	s	p	n	m	m	f	s	f	z (Min)

3-8. THE CENTRAL MATHEMATICAL PROBLEM

In the preceding sections, linear programming models were constructed for several examples. In each of these the problem was to find the solution of a system of linear equations or inequalities which minimized or maximized a linear form. This optimizing of a linear form, subject to linear restraints, is called the central mathematical problem of linear programming.

Whenever the restraints were stated as inequalities in the examples, it was possible to change each inequality to an equation by the addition of a *slack variable*. Furthermore, a problem in which a linear function was to be maximized could be converted to a problem of minimizing the negative of this form.

Thus, it is possible to formulate all linear programming problems in the same general manner; namely, to find the solution of a system of linear equations in nonnegative variables which minimizes a linear form. Since this algebraic statement of the problem arises naturally in many applications, it is called the "standard form" of the linear programming problem. In this section the formulation of the standard form of the central mathematical problem of linear programming will be reviewed and formalized.

If the subscript $j = 1, 2, \ldots, N$ denotes the jth type of activity and x_j its quantity (or activity level), then usually $x_j \geq 0$. If, for example, x_j represents the quantity of a stockpile allocated for the jth use, it does not, as a rule, make sense to allocate a negative quantity. In certain cases, however, one may wish to interpret a negative quantity as meaning taking stock from the jth use. Here some care must be exercised; for example, there may be costs, such as transportation charges, which are positive regardless of the direction of flow of the stock. One must also be careful not to overdraw the stock of the using activity. For these reasons it is better in formulating models to distinguish two activities, each with a nonnegative range, for their respective x_j, rather than to try incorporating them into a single range.

The interdependencies between various activities arise because all practical programming problems are circumscribed by commodity limitations of one kind or another. The limited commodity may be raw materials, manpower, facilities, or funds; these are referred to by the general term *item*. In chemical equilibrium problems, where molecules of different types play the roles of activities, the different kinds of atoms in the mixture are the items. The various items are denoted by a subscript i ($i = 1, 2, \ldots, M$).

In linear programming work, the quantity of an item required by an activity is assumed to be *proportional* to the quantity of activity level; if the item is not required, but produced, it is again assumed to be proportional to the quantity (or level) of the activity. The coefficient of proportionality is denoted by a_{ij}. The sign of a_{ij} depends on whether the item is required or produced by the activity. As we have already seen in § 3-3-(7), the sign

[60]

convention used will be $(+)$ if required and $(-)$ if produced. Finally, b_i denotes the quantity of the ith item made available to the program from outside (or exogenous) sources, if it is positive; it denotes the quantity to be produced by the program, if it is negative. The interdependencies between the x_j are expressed as a set of M linear equations such that the ith equation gives a complete account of the ith item. In general, this set of M linear equations is represented by

(1)
$$a_{11}x_1 + a_{12}x_2 + \ldots + a_{1N}x_N = b_1$$
$$a_{21}x_1 + a_{22}x_2 + \ldots + a_{2N}x_N = b_2$$
$$\cdots\cdots\cdots\cdots\cdots\cdots\cdots\cdots$$
$$a_{M1}x_1 + a_{M2}x_2 + \ldots + a_{MN}x_N = b_M$$

where

(2)
$$x_j \geq 0 \qquad j = (1, 2, \ldots, N)$$

We shall use capital M and N whenever we wish to refer to the *standard form* and use m and n for a *general* $m \times n$ system of linear equations. Any set of values x_j satisfying (1) and (2) is called a *feasible solution* because the corresponding schedule is possible or feasible.

The objective of a program, in practice, is often the most difficult part to express in mathematical terms. There are many historical reasons for this which go beyond the scope of this text. In many problems, however, the objective is simply one of carrying out the requirements (expressed by those b_i which are negative) in such a manner *that total costs are minimum*. Costs may be measured in dollars, in the number of people involved, or in a quantity of a scarce commodity used. In linear programming the total costs, denoted by z, are assumed to be a *linear function of the activity levels*:

(3)
$$c_1x_1 + c_2x_2 + \ldots + c_Nx_N = z$$

DEFINITION: The linear form z is called the *objective function* (or form).

For purposes of solution we shall, as a rule, rewrite (3) as just another equation (4), where z is a *variable* whose value is to be minimized

(4)
$$(-z) + c_1x_1 + c_2x_2 + \ldots + c_Nx_N = 0$$

In some problems the linear objective form is to be *maximized* rather than minimized. For example, the problem may be to produce the maximum dollar value of products under a fixed budget, fixed machine capacity, and fixed labor supply. Suppose the linear form expressing total profits to be maximized is

$$p_1x_1 + p_2x_2 + \ldots + p_Nx_N$$

This is obviously mathematically equivalent to minimizing

$$-p_1x_1 - p_2x_2 - \ldots - p_Nx_N = c_1x_1 + c_2x_2 + \ldots + c_Nx_N = z$$

where $c_1 = -p_1, c_2 = -p_2, \ldots, c_N = -p_N$.

[61]

Thus, the standard form of the linear programming problem is taken as the determination of a solution, called *an optimal feasible solution*, of a system of linear equations in nonnegative variables which minimizes a linear form. The minimum is called the *value of the linear program*.

The Dual Linear Program. Associated with a linear program (called the *primal*) is another called the *dual*. The objective of the primal is to minimize, while that of the dual is to maximize. We have already seen in § 3-4 how the dual problem arises quite naturally as an algebraic check of a conjectured optimal solution to the primal problem. It will be noted that the array of coefficients and constants of the dual are obtained by transposing those of the primal. The variables π_i of the dual correspond to the equation i of the primal and are, however, unrestricted in sign. The variables x_j of the primal, restricted in sign to greater than or equal to zero, correspond to an inequality relation of "less than or equal" relations in the dual. For the general primal problem in standard form, the dual is to find values $\pi_1, \pi_2, \ldots, \pi_M$ and Max v satisfying

$$a_{11}\pi_1 + a_{21}\pi_2 + \ldots + a_{M1}\pi_M \leq c_1$$
$$a_{12}\pi_1 + a_{22}\pi_2 + \ldots + a_{M2}\pi_M \leq c_2$$
$$\cdots\cdots\cdots\cdots\cdots\cdots\cdots\cdots\cdots\cdots\cdots\cdots\cdots$$
$$a_{1N}\pi_1 + a_{2N}\pi_2 + \ldots + a_{MN}\pi_M \leq c_N$$
$$b_1\pi_1 + b_2\pi_2 + \ldots + b_M\pi_M = v \text{ (Max)}$$

In Chapter 4, a method is given for transforming the dual into a standard linear program. When a feasible solution to the primal is optimal the method for checking optimality gives rise automatically to an optimal solution for the dual problem. Since the dual of the dual problem is the primal problem, it is a matter of convenience whether one selects to solve the primal problem or the dual.

3-9. PROBLEMS

General.

1. (a) What is meant by the objective function; the central problem of linear programming; a feasible solution?
   (b) In many applications the variables and the equations each have a typical interpretation. What is it? Where do the inequality relations come in; the objective function?
   (c) Assuming that firing is the opposite of hiring, give reasons why it is better to treat these as two nonnegative activities rather than as a single activity with positive and negative activity levels.
2. If an activity such as steel production needs capital such as bricks and cement to build blast furnaces, what would the negative of these activities imply if they were used as admissible activities?
3. If the difference between production and requirements is interpreted as surplus or deficit (depending on sign), illustrate how surplus can be

interpreted as a storage activity and deficit as a purchasing activity in which all coefficients of the associated variables can be quite different.

Transportation Problem. (Refer to § 3-3. See § 3-4 for duality explanation.)

4. Two warehouses have canned tomatoes on hand and three stores require more in stock.

Ware-house	Cases on Hand	Store	Cases Required
I	100	A	75
II	200	B	125
		C	100

The cost (in cents) of shipping between warehouses and stores per case is given in the following table:

	A	B	C
I	10	14	30
II	12	20	17

(a) Set up the model describing the shipping of tomatoes from warehouses to stores, where the objective is to minimize the total shipping cost.

(b) Reformulate this problem assuming the cases required at B are only 60, and introducing a disposal activity at the warehouses at a loss of 5 cents per case disposed.

(c) Show that the optimal solution to problem (a) is the same if the cost per case from Warehouse I is increased by 3 cents; by 10 cents.

(d) Reformulate problem (a) assuming the cases available at Warehouse I are 90. Introduce a purchase activity from outside sources at a cost of 20 cents per case over the costs at Warehouses I and II.

(e) How would you formulate a model to include both the possibility of outside purchases at the destinations and disposal at the warehouses?

(f) State the dual of problems (b) and (d). How is the dual for (c) related to that for (a)?

5. Generalize problem 4 (a) for m warehouses and n destinations. Assume that the availability at the i source is a_i and requirement at the jth destination is b_j. For part (a) assume $\sum_1^m a_i = \sum_1^n b_j$. Make the necessary modifications for parts (b), (c), and (d). The cost of transportation from source i to destination j is c_{ij}. Show in (a) there is one redundant equation. How does the deletion of one redundant equation affect the dual?

Blending Problem. (Refer to § 3-4.)

6. A housewife asks a butcher to grind up several cuts of beef to form a blend of equal parts of proteins and fats. The butcher, being conscientious,

wishes to do this at the least cost per pound of meat purchased exclusive of water content.

	Chuck	Flank	Porter-house	Rib Roast	Round	Rump	Sirloin
% Protein	19	20	16	17	19	16	17
% Fat	16	18	25	23	11	28	20
Cost/lb	69	98	1.39	1.29	1.19	1.50	1.65

(a) What amounts of each type of meat should he use and how much should he charge?

(b) Usually he has extra fat available free per pound. How does this alter the solution?

(c) Solve the problem graphically.

(d) Find the dual.

7. (Thrall.)

(a) Suppose steaks contain per unit 1 unit of carbohydrates, 3 units of vitamins, 3 units of proteins and cost 50 units of cash. Suppose potatoes per unit contain 3, 4, 1, and cost 25 units of these items respectively. Letting x_1 be the quantity of steaks and x_2 the quantity of potatoes, express the mathematical relations that must be satisfied to meet the minimum requirements of 8 units of carbohydrates, 19 units of vitamins, and 7 units of protein. If x_1 and x_2 are to be chosen so that the cost of diet is a minimum, what is the objective function?

(b) Reduce the inequality system of (a) to an equality system in non-negative variables.

8. (a) Formulate the housewife problem of § 1-2.

(b) Is there any difference between the activity of inserting food i into the father's diet and the activity of inserting the same food into the children's diet?

(c) Could the housewife conceivably end up with the task of cooking five different dinners on the same day, one for each member of the family?

Product Mix Problem. (Refer to § 3-5.)

9. Solve the duals of the three primal problems within the product mix problem. How are the duals interrelated?

10. (a) Suppose contracts with various retailers have already been signed for the following quantities of desks:

Desk	1	2	3	4
Number sold	60	30	10	50

How does this affect the model?

(b) How does one interpret an optimal solution, if a fractional number of desks is obtained? One possible interpretation is that these are rates for a six-month period. Suppose the fractional solution is rounded to the nearest integer, find out how much change is required in the productivity coefficients or in the shop capacities for the adjusted solution to be optimal. Are the coefficients and constant terms really known accurately in any real situation?

11. A subcontractor has made arrangements to supply a company with 150 assemblies in January and 225 in February. Using an eight-hour shift the subcontractor can produce only 160 assemblies each month. By working the regular shift for two hours overtime, an additional 30 assemblies can be made, each with an overtime penalty of $20. Assemblies can be stored at a cost of $3 per month. Set up a model for finding the production program which minimizes costs.

12. A mass production house builder plans to build homes on 100 lots in a new subdivision. He has decided on 5 basic styles of homes: Ranch, Split-level, Colonial, Cape Cod, and Modern. To build the homes, the builder has two major contractors: masons for foundation work, and carpenters for the rest of the construction. The number of days required for the work is as follows:

	Ranch	Split-level	Colonial	Cape Cod	Modern
Foundation	1	2	2	1	1
Framework	4	7	6	5	3
Profit	2,000	3,000	2,500	1,700	2,000

The builder borrowed money at a very low interest rate for three years. Because it normally takes two months to sell a house, the builder wanted all homes to be completed in 34 months, or approximately 610 working days.

(a) How many of each style home should be built to maximize profit?

(b) If the builder wanted to build at least 10 of each style, what should be his building program to insure maximum profit?

(c) Solve by the method used for the product mix problem, § 3-5.

13. A machine problem of Kantorovich [1939-1].

Formulate, but do not solve. An assembled item consists of two metal parts. The milling work can be done on different machines, milling machines, turret lathes, or on automatic turret lathes. The basic data are available in the table at the top of p. 66. From this:

(a) Divide the work time of each machine to obtain the maximum number of completed items per hour.

(b) Prove that an optimal solution has the property that there will be no slack time on any of the machines; that equal numbers of each part will be made.

(c) State the dual of the primal problem.

[65]

Productivity of the Machines for Two Parts

Type of Machine	Number of Machines	Maximum Output* per Machine per Hour	
		First Part	Second Part
Milling machines	3	10	20
Turret lathes	3	20	30
Automatic turret lathes	1	30	80

* If devoted exclusively to making one of the parts.

14. (a) Generalize problem 13 to n machines, m parts, where the objective is to produce the largest number of completed assemblies.

(b) Show, in general, if each machine is capable of making each part, and there is no value to the excess capacity of the machines or unmatched parts, any optimal solution will have only matched parts and will use all the machine capacity. What can happen if some machines are incapable of producing certain parts?

(c) State the dual of the primal problem.

15. Suppose there are two types of assemblies instead of one and a "value" can be attached to each. Maximize the weighted output.

16. Extend the formulation of problems 14 and 15 to cover the following:

(a) Suppose there is a limit on electricity used which depends on the task-machine combination.

(b) Suppose it is possible, by the ith mode of production, to produce $c_{i,k,l}$ units of the kth part on the lth machine.

(c) Suppose it is possible to put values on surplus parts; on unused machine capacity.

17. Three parts can each be produced on two machines. Assume that there is no set-up time and that this is a continuous type production, that is, a part is first inserted in Machine 1 and then is immediately put in Machine 2 with practically no time elapsing between operations. The unit time per part in each machine and profit on each finished part is given by:

Machine	Part		
	A	B	C
1	.02	.03	.05
2	.05	.02	.04
Profit	.05	.04	.03

(a) Formulate a model for the optimal product mix. Express this in terms of a linear inequality model, given that there are available only 40 hours on each machine. Transform the system into an equality system.

(b) Generalize to n different kinds of parts and m machines.

(c) State the dual of problems (a) and (b).

Simple Warehouse Problem. (Refer to § 3-6.)

18. (a) Reformulate the simple warehouse problem, § 3-6, if it is desired to have the quantities of selling, storing, and buying to be the same for the corresponding quarter each year. Formulate the yearly least-cost model assuming that the initial stock level is the same as the stock held in storage at the end of the year.

(b) Discuss the special properties of the coefficient matrix in a dynamic problem of this type.

On-the-Job Training Problem. (Refer to § 3-7.)

19. Reformulate the on-the-job training problem, § 3-7, assuming the cost of increasing the level of production above last week's level is $q = 4$ per unit of increase. There is no cost to decrease. All production is stored at a cost of $s = 1$ per unit per week until the last week. If the initial production level is $P_0 = 5$ and the final required inventory position is $g_5 = 200$ workers, what is an optimal production program?

20. A farmer may sell part of his crop and plant the remainder where his yield will be λ bushels per bushel planted. He expects to get p_1 dollars profit per bushel for the crop he has planted, p_2 and p_3 dollars per bushel for the two following crops. His first crop will be A bushels.

Problem: Set up the basic equations and the linear form which represents his total profits for the three periods. Show that it always pays to sell the third crop. Show that it pays to plant his entire first and second crop if $\lambda^2 p_3 > p_1$, $\lambda p_3 > p_2$. Show that it pays to sell the entire first crop if $p_1 - \lambda p_2 > 0$, $p_2 - \lambda p_3 > 0$. When does it pay to sell the entire second crop?

21. (Kemeny) The Chicken and Egg Problem.

Formulate: Suppose it takes a hen two weeks to lay 12 eggs for sale or to hatch 4. What is the best laying and hatching program if at the end of the fourth period all hens and chicks accumulated during the period are sold at 60 cents apiece and eggs at 10 cents apiece. Assume

(a) An initial inventory of 100 hens and 100 eggs,

(b) 100 hens and zero eggs,

(c) 100 hens and zero eggs and also a final inventory of 100 hens and zero eggs.

22. (Orchard-Hays.) A factory buys item A and produces item B. Each B requires one A and the factory has a production capacity of 3,000 B's per quarter year. However, A's are available in different amounts and B's are required in different amounts each quarter. Furthermore,

storing B's is expensive and the carryover of this item from one quarter to the next is to be minimized. At the beginning of the year, 3,000 A items are on hand and at least this many must be left over at the end of the year. The availability of A items and the requirement of B items by quarters is as follows:

1st quarter:	5,000 A's available,	1,000 B's required
2nd ,,	3,000 ,,	4,000 ,,
3rd ,,	1,000 ,,	3,000 ,,
4th ,,	2,000 ,,	1,500 ,,

There is storage room available for 10,000 A's or 2,000 B's or any combination in this ratio. Assume that, for each quarter q, the equation

$$s_q\colon\ A_q + 5B_q + S_q = 10{,}000 \qquad (q = 1, 2, 3, 4)$$

is sufficient to express the storage constraint (this ignores bottlenecks during a quarter). The variables are defined below.

Set up a linear programming model to minimize the carryover of item B each quarter subject to the stated restraints. For each quarter, use the following 7 variables:

M_q: amount of B items manufactured in quarter q.

p_q: amount of A items purchased in quarter q for use in quarter q (or later).

A_q: amount of A items unused at end of quarter q.

B_q: amount of B items on hand (over requirements) at end of quarter q.

C_q: excess production capacity during quarter q.

S_q: excess storage capacity during quarter q.

U_q: excess availability of A items during quarter q.

This gives 28 variables; one special one, for the end-of-year requirement on A's, is

v: excess inventory of A at end of year.

These 29 variables will have coefficients in 21 restraint equations as follows:

a_q: Balance equation in A items for quarter q.

b_q: Balance equation in B items produced in quarter q.

c_q: Production capacity restraint equation for quarter q.

p_q: Restraint equation for availability of A items in quarter q.

s_q: Balance equation for storage capacity in quarter q (see above).

v: Requirement equation for carryover of A items at end of year.

Find any feasible solution. Is your solution optimal? If the availability of A items is changed to 3,000 per quarter, what happens? Can you see how other changes in availability and requirement constants would make the problem harder? Impossible? Redundant? Inconsistent?

CHAPTER 4

LINEAR EQUATION AND INEQUALITY SYSTEMS

4-1. SYSTEMS OF EQUATIONS WITH THE SAME SOLUTION SET

Consistent Equations and Linear Combinations.

Because methods used for solving the linear programming problem depend on familiar methods for solving a system of linear equations, it is well at this point to review some elementary concepts. To facilitate the discussion, we consider the following example of two equations in three variables:

$$(1) \qquad \begin{aligned} x_1 - x_2 + x_3 &= 2 \qquad &(\mathrm{E}_1) \\ 2x_1 + x_2 - x_3 &= 7 \qquad &(\mathrm{E}_2) \end{aligned}$$

The ordered set of values $x_1 = 3$, $x_2 = 2$, $x_3 = 1$ is said to be a *solution* of E_1 because substitution of these values for x_1, x_2, x_3 in the first equation produces the identity, $2 = 2$. The solution $(3, 2, 1)$ is said to *satisfy* equation E_1.

In general, suppose we have a system of m equations in n variables,

$$(2) \qquad \begin{cases} a_{11}x_1 + a_{12}x_2 + \ldots + a_{1n}x_n = b_1 \\ a_{21}x_1 + a_{22}x_2 + \ldots + a_{2n}x_n = b_2 \\ \ldots\ldots\ldots\ldots\ldots\ldots\ldots\ldots\ldots\ldots\ldots\ldots \\ a_{m1}x_1 + a_{m2}x_2 + \ldots + a_{mn}x_n = b_m \end{cases}$$

(This is an *arbitrary* $m \times n$ system of linear equations. We shall use capital M, N when we wish to designate the system of linear equations in the *standard* linear program arrived at in § 3-8-(1).) A *solution* of the ith equation is an ordered set of numbers $(x_1', x_2', \ldots, x_n')$ such that

$$a_{i1}x_1' + a_{i2}x_2' + \ldots + a_{in}x_n' = b_i$$

An ordered set of numbers is said to be a *solution of a system* of equations provided it is a solution of each equation of the system. For example, because substituting $(3, 2, 1)$ for the variables in equation E_2 yields $7 = 7$, an identity, we have $(3, 2, 1)$ as a solution of both E_1 and E_2 and therefore of the system.

We usually speak of "a" solution rather than "the" solution to avoid questions of uniqueness. It is certainly evident that a system of equations need not possess a unique solution nor, indeed, any solution at all. Besides $(3, 2, 1)$ for example, the system above is satisfied by any set of numbers of the form $(3, x_3' + 1, x_3')$ where x_3' may be chosen arbitrarily. A system which has solutions, unique or not, is called *consistent* or *solvable*. Otherwise, we refer to it as *inconsistent* or *unsolvable*.

The aggregate of solutions of a system is called its *solution set*. If the system is inconsistent its solution set is said to be *empty*.

Given a system such as (1) it is easy to construct new equations from it that have the property that every solution of (1) is also a solution of the new equation. In (3) the new equation is shown below the line; it is formed by multiplying the first equation by 2 and the second by -3, shown on the left, and summing.

$$(3) \qquad \begin{array}{rl} 2: & x_1 - x_2 + x_3 = 2 \\ -3: & 2x_1 + x_2 - x_3 = 7 \\ \hline & -4x_1 - 5x_2 + 5x_3 = -17 \end{array}$$

It will be noted that the solution, $(3, 2, 1)$, of the system (1) is also a solution of the new equation.

A scheme for generating new equations, whose solution set includes all the solutions of a general linear system (2), is shown in (4). For each equation i an arbitrary number, k_i, is chosen,[1] shown on the left; the new equation below the line is formed by multiplying the ith equation by k_i and summing:

$$(4) \quad \left\{ \begin{array}{rl} k_1: & a_{11}x_1 + a_{12}x_2 + \ldots + a_{1n}x_n = b_1 \\ k_2: & a_{21}x_1 + a_{22}x_2 + \ldots + a_{2n}x_n = b_2 \\ & \cdots\cdots\cdots\cdots\cdots\cdots\cdots\cdots\cdots\cdots\cdots \\ k_m: & a_{m1}x_1 + a_{m2}x_2 + \ldots + a_{mn}x_n = b_m \end{array} \right.$$

$$(5) \qquad\qquad \begin{array}{l} \hline d_1x_1 + d_2x_2 + \ldots + d_nx_n = d \end{array}$$

The coefficients of the sum are easily read off; they are

$$(6) \quad \left\{ \begin{array}{l} d_1 = k_1a_{11} + k_2a_{21} + \ldots + k_ma_{m1} \\ d_2 = k_1a_{12} + k_2a_{22} + \ldots + k_ma_{m2} \\ \cdots\cdots\cdots\cdots\cdots\cdots\cdots\cdots\cdots \\ d_n = k_1a_{1n} + k_2a_{2n} + \ldots + k_ma_{mn} \\ d = k_1b_1 + k_2b_2 + \ldots + k_mb_m \end{array} \right.$$

An equation such as (5) formed in this manner is called a *linear combination* of the original equations. The numbers k_i are called *multipliers* or *weights* of the linear combination.

---

[1] The constants k_i may be zero.

Writing (4) and (5) in *detached coefficient form* (7) and (8) we see that the operation of forming a linear combination of the equations corresponds to forming a linear combination of the *rows* of (7). By this we mean that we can form each element of row (8) by summing the products of k_i by the corresponding element in row i of (7).

Multiplier

$$(7) \qquad \begin{bmatrix} a_{11} & a_{12} & \ldots & a_{1n} & b_1 \\ a_{21} & a_{22} & \ldots & a_{2n} & b_2 \\ \ldots & \ldots & \ldots & \ldots & \ldots \\ a_{m1} & a_{m2} & \ldots & a_{mn} & b_m \end{bmatrix} \qquad \begin{matrix} :k_1 \\ :k_2 \\ \\ :k_m \end{matrix}$$

$$(8) \qquad \begin{bmatrix} d_1 & d_2 & \ldots & d_n & d \end{bmatrix}$$

EXERCISE: Suppose a linear combination of the *columns* of (7) equals some other column. Show that this is true if the row in (8) is adjoined to those of (7).

Whenever a set of numbers $(x_1, x_2, \ldots, x_n)$ constitutes a solution of (4), equation (5) becomes, upon substitution, a weighted sum of identities and hence an identity itself. Therefore, *every solution of a linear system is also a solution of any linear combination of the equations of the system.* Such an equation may therefore be inserted into a system of equations without affecting the solution set.

DEFINITIONS: If in a system of equations, an equation is a linear combination of the others, it is said to be *dependent* upon them; the dependent equation is called *redundant.* A *vacuous equation,* i.e., an equation of the form

$$0x_1 + 0x_2 + \ldots + 0x_n = 0$$

is also called redundant when it occurs in a *single* equation system. A system containing no redundancy is called *independent.*

A linear system is clearly unsolvable or inconsistent if it is possible to exhibit a linear combination of the equations of the system of the form

$$(9) \qquad 0x_1 + 0x_2 + \ldots + 0x_n = d \qquad \text{with } d \neq 0;$$

for any solution of the system would have to satisfy (9), but this is impossible no matter what values are assigned to the variables. We shall refer to (9) as an *inconsistent equation.* (See exercise below.) For example, the system

$$\begin{array}{rl} 1: & x_1 + x_2 + x_3 = 5 \\ -1: & x_1 + x_2 + x_3 = 4 \\ \hline & 0x_1 + 0x_2 + 0x_3 = 1 \end{array}$$

is unsolvable because the first equation states that a sum of three numbers is 5, while the second states that this same sum is 4. However, if we had proceeded to apply multipliers $k_1 = 1$, $k_2 = -1$, by way of eliminating, say, x_1, we would arrive automatically at the contradiction displayed below the equations. In general, the process of elimination applied to an inconsistent system will lead in due course to an inconsistent equation, as we shall show in the next section.

EXERCISE: Show that the only single-equation inconsistent linear system is of form (9).

EXERCISE: Show that if a system contains a vacuous equation, it is dependent.

How Systems Are Solved.

The usual "elimination" procedure for finding a solution of a system of equations is to *augment* the system by generating new equations by taking linear combinations in such a way that certain coefficients are zero. (This may be followed by the deletion of certain redundant equations.)

For example in (10) below, the equation E_1 is multiplied by $k_1 = -2$ and E_2 by $k_2 = 1$ so that upon summing the coefficient of x_1 vanishes. This yields equation E_3. These operations may be written symbolically, $E_3 = (-2)E_1 + (1)E_2$. Similarly we can form equation E_4 by multiplying E_3 by $\frac{1}{3}$ and we can form E_5 by adding E_4 to E_1. The *augmented system* $\{E_1, E_2, \ldots, E_5\}$ has the same solution set as the original system (1) because all equations such as E_4 and E_5 can be re-expressed as direct linear combinations of E_1 and E_2.

$$
\begin{aligned}
x_1 - x_2 + x_3 &= 2 & (E_1) \\
2x_1 + x_2 - x_3 &= 7 & (E_2) \\
3x_2 - 3x_3 &= 3 & (E_3 = -2E_1 + E_2) \\
x_2 - x_3 &= 1 & (E_4 = \tfrac{1}{3}E_3) \\
x_1 \phantom{{}- x_2 + x_3} &= 3 & (E_5 = E_1 + E_4)
\end{aligned}
$$

(10)

It is interesting to note that the subsystem $\{E_4, E_5\}$ can be used to easily detect whether any equation is linearly dependent on it. Note that x_2 appears in E_4 with a unit coefficient and zero coefficient in E_5 and the opposite is true for x_1. This makes it easy to eliminate x_1 and x_2 from any other equation. For example, it is clear that if E_1 is to be a linear combination of E_4 and E_5 the multiplier of E_5 must be 1 and of E_4 must be -1. It is easily verified that $E_1 = E_5 - E_4$, $E_2 = 2E_5 + E_4$, $E_3 = 3E_4$. Thus all solutions of $\{E_4, E_5\}$ are also solutions of $\{E_1, E_2\}$, and as noted earlier, all solutions of $\{E_1, E_2\}$ are solutions of $\{E_4, E_5\}$; therefore *the solutions of the two subsystems are the same.*

A second advantage of $\{E_4, E_5\}$ is that it is easy to state the set of all possible solutions. Indeed, choose any arbitrary value for $x_3 = x_3^0$ and evaluate x_2 and x_1 in terms of x_3. In this case, $(x_1 = 3, x_2 = 1 + x_3^0, x_3 = x_3^0)$ describes the set of all solutions. For example, $x_3 = 0$ yields the *particular* solution $(x_1 = 3, x_2 = 1, x_3 = 0)$.

In general, the method of solving a system (we shall describe this in detail in § 4-2) is one of augmentation by linear combinations until in the enlarged system there is a subsystem whose solution set is easy to describe and such that each equation of the full system is linearly dependent upon it except possibly for the constant term. The subsystem arrived at belongs to a class called canonical.

DEFINITION: A *canonical* system with an ordered subset of variables, called *basic*, is a system such that for each i, the ith basic variable has a unit coefficient in the ith equation and has zero coefficients elsewhere.

For example, $\{E_4, E_5\}$ in (10) is canonical with x_2 associated with E_4 and x_1 with E_5. System (11) below is canonical because for each i, x_i has a unit coefficient in the ith equation and zero elsewhere.

$$
\begin{aligned}
x_1 & \qquad + \bar{a}_{1,r+1}x_{r+1} + \ldots + \bar{a}_{1,n}x_n = \bar{b}_1 \\
& x_2 \qquad + \bar{a}_{2,r+1}x_{r+1} + \ldots + \bar{a}_{2,n}x_n = \bar{b}_2 \\
& \qquad\qquad\qquad \vdots \\
& x_r + \bar{a}_{r,r+1}x_{r+1} + \ldots + \bar{a}_{r,n}x_n = \bar{b}_r
\end{aligned}
$$

(11)

EXERCISE: Show how by arbitrarily choosing values for $x_{r+1}, \ldots, x_n$ the class of all solutions can be generated. How can (11) be used to check easily whether or not another equation is dependent upon it?

Deletion of an equation that is a linear combination of the others is another operation that does not affect the solution set. If after an augmentation, one of the original equations in the system is found to be a linear combination of the others, it may be deleted. In effect the new equation becomes a "substitute" for one of the original equations. Where electronic computers are used, their limited capacity to store information makes this ability to throw away equations particularly important.

DEFINITION:[2] Two systems are called *equivalent* if one system may be derived from the other by inserting or by deleting a redundant equation or if one system may be derived from the other through a chain of systems each linked to its predecessor by such an insertion or deletion.

THEOREM 1: *Equivalent systems have the same solution set.*

Elementary Operations.

There are two simple but important types of linear combinations which may be used to obtain equivalent systems.

1. Replacing any equation, E_t, by the equation $[kE_t]$ with $k \neq 0$.
2. Replacing any equation, E_t, by the equation $[E_t + kE_i]$ where E_i is any other equation of the system.

To prove an elementary operation of the first type results in an equivalent

---

[2] This definition of equivalence is due to A. W. Tucker (verbal communication).

system, insert $k\mathrm{E}_t$ as a new equation after E_t, then delete E_t. Note that E_t is a redundant equation for it can be formed from $k\mathrm{E}_t$ by $1/k[k\mathrm{E}_t]$ if $k \neq 0$. Similarly, for the second type, insert $\mathrm{E}_t + k\mathrm{E}_i$ after E_t and then delete E_t. Note that E_t is a redundant equation, for it is given by $[\mathrm{E}_t + k\mathrm{E}_i] - k\mathrm{E}_i$.

One way to transform our example (1) into the equivalent system (10) by a sequence of elementary operations is given below:

Elementary Operation

$$x_1 - x_2 + x_3 = 2 \qquad (\mathrm{E}_1)$$
$$2x_1 + x_2 - x_3 = 7 \qquad (\mathrm{E}_2)$$

Replace E_2 by $\mathrm{E}_2' = \mathrm{E}_2 + \mathrm{E}_1$

$$x_1 - x_2 + x_3 = 2 \qquad (\mathrm{E}_1)$$
$$3x_1 = 9 \qquad (\mathrm{E}_2')$$

Replace E_1 by $\mathrm{E}_1' = \mathrm{E}_1 - \tfrac{1}{3}\mathrm{E}_2'$

$$-x_2 + x_3 = -1 \qquad (\mathrm{E}_1')$$
$$3x_1 = 9 \qquad (\mathrm{E}_2')$$

Replace E_1' by $\mathrm{E}_1'' = -\mathrm{E}_1'$

$$x_2 - x_3 = 1 \qquad (\mathrm{E}_1'')$$
$$3x_1 = 9 \qquad (\mathrm{E}_2')$$

In general, corresponding to each elementary operation there is an *inverse* operation which is also elementary and of the same type. For example, starting with the last pair of equations, we can obtain the next to last pair by replacing E_1'' by $\mathrm{E}_1' = -\mathrm{E}_1''$; then we can obtain the second pair from it in turn by replacing E_1' by $\mathrm{E}_1 = \mathrm{E}_1' + \tfrac{1}{3}\mathrm{E}_2'$ and then the first pair by replacing E_2' by $\mathrm{E}_2 = \mathrm{E}_2' - \mathrm{E}_1$.

THEOREM 2: *Corresponding to a sequence of elementary operations is an inverse sequence of elementary operations by which a given system can be obtained from the derived system.*

We can also see that if a system can be derived from a given system by a sequence of elementary operations it implies that it is possible to obtain each row of the derived system in detached coefficient form directly by a linear combination of the rows of the given system. Conversely, by Theorem 2, each row of the given system is some linear combination of the rows of the derived system.

THEOREM 3: *The rows of two equivalent systems in detached coefficient form can be obtained one from the other by linear combinations.*

THEOREM 4: *If the tth equation of a given system is replaced by a linear combination with multipliers k_i where $k_t \neq 0$, an equivalent system is obtained.*

EXERCISE: Prove Theorems 2, 3, 4.

The most important property of systems derived by elementary operations is, by Theorem 1, that they have the *same solution set*.

An interesting question now arises. Are all linear equation systems with the same solution set obtainable by a sequence of inserting and deleting of redundant equations? We shall show (and this is the substance of § 4-2, Theorem 1 and § 8-1, Theorem 4) that if two systems have the same solution set and are solvable, then they are equivalent. On the other hand, if the systems are not solvable, this is not necessarily the case. Indeed, consider the two systems

$$\{0x = 1\} \quad \text{and} \quad \begin{cases} 0x = 1 \\ 1x = 1 \end{cases};$$

both have empty, hence identical, solution sets. It is obvious that if these two systems were equivalent some multiple (linear combination) of the equation $0x = 1$ of the first system would yield the equation $1x = 1$ of the second. This is clearly impossible.

4-2. CANONICAL SYSTEMS

Solving Square Systems.

The systems of linear equations dealt with in high school algebra courses commonly have exactly as many equations as variables; in the general system (2) of the preceding section this would be the case when $m = n$. Such a system of equations is called a square system.

Assuming a square system of m equations in m unknowns possesses a unique solution, the usual process of solving such a system consists in eliminating one unknown, setting aside one equation, and working with a reduced system having one less equation and one less unknown. The process is repeated a total of $m - 1$ times, resulting in a single equation with one variable. Its value is then substituted in the preceding equation to determine the value of another variable. This process, called "back solution," is repeated until all the variables are evaluated [Gauss, 1826-1]. Our immediate purpose is to review this procedure in detail to show that it is in fact nothing more than a sequence of elementary operations that replaces the original system by an equivalent system in simple *diagonal form* (1). Here the solution set is evident.

(1)
$$\begin{aligned} x_1 \phantom{{}+x_2} &= b_1 \\ x_2 \phantom{{}+x_2} &= b_2 \\ &\ \ \vdots \\ x_m &= b_m \end{aligned}$$

Consider a system of 3 equations in 3 unknowns:

(2)
$$\begin{aligned} a_{11}x_1 + a_{12}x_2 + a_{13}x_3 &= b_1 \\ a_{21}x_1 + a_{22}x_2 + a_{23}x_3 &= b_2 \\ a_{31}x_1 + a_{32}x_2 + a_{33}x_3 &= b_3 \end{aligned}$$

[75]

If $a_{11} \neq 0$, then the first equation can be used to eliminate x_1 from the second equation by the elementary operation $E_2' = E_2 - (a_{21}/a_{11})E_1$, and to eliminate x_1 from the third equation by the elementary operation on the resulting system $E_3' = E_3 - (a_{31}/a_{11})E_1$. Thus we obtain an equivalent system

$$(3) \qquad \begin{aligned} a_{11}x_1 + a_{12}x_2 + a_{13}x_3 &= b_1 \\ a_{22}'x_2 + a_{23}'x_3 &= b_2' \\ a_{32}'x_2 + a_{33}'x_3 &= b_3' \end{aligned} \qquad (a_{11} \neq 0)$$

The top equation is normally set aside and the process repeated with the reduced system. If $a_{22}' \neq 0$ then the second equation can be used to eliminate x_2 from the third equation, resulting in the equivalent *triangular system:*

$$(4) \qquad \begin{aligned} a_{11}x_1 + a_{12}x_2 + a_{13}x_3 &= b_1 \\ a_{22}'x_2 + a_{23}'x_3 &= b_2' \\ a_{33}''x_3 &= b_3'' \end{aligned} \qquad (a_{11} \neq 0,\ a_{22}' \neq 0)$$

If $a_{33}' \neq 0$, the back solution begins by solving for x_3 in the last equation. Then one substitutes x_3 into the second equation to evaluate x_2. Finally, both values are substituted into the first equation. These two substitutions amount to exactly the same thing as using the third equation to eliminate x_3 from the second and first equations by the successive elementary operations $E_2' = E_2' - (a_{23}'/a_{33}'')E_3''$ and $E_1' = E_1 - (a_{13}/a_{33}'')E_3''$, resulting in

$$(5) \qquad \begin{aligned} a_{11}x_1 + a_{12}x_2 \qquad\quad &= b_1' \\ + a_{22}'x_2 \qquad\quad &= b_2'' \\ + a_{33}''x_3 &= b_3'' \end{aligned} \qquad (a_{11} \neq 0,\ a_{22}' \neq 0,\ a_{33}'' \neq 0)$$

Substituting the value of x_2 obtained from the second equation into the first to evaluate x_1 has the same effect as the elementary operation $E_1'' = E_1 - (a_{12}/a_{22}')E_2''$ and yields

$$(6) \qquad \begin{aligned} a_{11}x_1 \qquad\qquad &= b_1'' \\ a_{22}'x_2 \qquad\quad &= b_2'' \\ a_{33}''x_3 &= b_3'' \end{aligned} \qquad (a_{11} \neq 0,\ a_{22}' \neq 0,\ a_{33}'' \neq 0)$$

Finally, division by the diagonal coefficients, which is a sequence of three successive elementary operations, yields a diagonal system of the form (1).

If the system possesses a *unique* solution it will always be possible to carry out this process, but not always in the order indicated. Thus, if $a_{1s} = 0$, for example, one may pass to any other term whose coefficient is non-zero, say $a_{ts}x_s$, called the *pivot*, for the elimination of x_s.

In this case the tth equation may be used to eliminate x_s from the other equations by a sequence of elementary operations, replacing the ith equation by the sum of the ith equation, and the tth equation multiplied by $-a_{is}/a_{ts}$. If this process is repeated on each reduced system obtained by setting aside the equation used for the elimination, this will result finally in a system corresponding to (1) and (4) which can be put into diagonal and triangular forms by suitable rearrangement of the order of the equations.

In general a square system will be said to be *triangular* if upon suitable rearrangement of its rows and its variables, all coefficients below the diagonal are zero and all coefficients on the diagonal are non-zero; if, in addition, only the diagonal coefficients are non-zero, it is called *diagonal*.

As an example of reduction to triangular and diagonal forms, consider the 3×3 system

$$\begin{aligned} \text{I}_0: \quad & x_1 + x_2 + x_3 = 1 \\ \text{II}_0: \quad & x_1 - x_2 + x_3 = 3 \\ \text{III}_0: \quad & x_1 + 2x_2 - x_3 = 4 \end{aligned}$$

It can be reduced to triangular form as follows:

Operation

$$\begin{array}{lll} \text{I}_1: & x_1 + x_2 + x_3 = 1 & \text{I}_1 = \text{I}_0 \\ \text{II}_1: & - 2x_2 = 2 & \text{II}_1 = \text{II}_0 - \text{I}_0 \\ \text{III}_1: & x_2 - 2x_3 = 3 & \text{III}_1 = \text{III}_0 - \text{I}_0 \end{array}$$

Operation

$$\begin{array}{lll} \text{I}_2: & x_1 + x_2 + x_3 = 1 & \text{I}_2 = \text{I}_1 \\ \text{II}_2: & x_2 = -1 & \text{II}_2 = -\tfrac{1}{2}\text{II}_1 \\ \text{III}_2: & x_3 = -2 & \text{III}_2 = -\tfrac{1}{2}(\text{III}_1 + \tfrac{1}{2}\text{II}_1) \end{array}$$

This last system, $(\text{I}_2, \text{II}_2, \text{III}_2)$, is triangular and can readily be reduced to the diagonal form,

Operation

$$\begin{array}{lll} \text{I}_3: & x_1 = +4 & \text{I}_3 = \text{I}_2 - \text{II}_2 - \text{III}_2 \\ \text{II}_3: & x_2 = -1 & \text{II}_3 = \text{II}_2 \\ \text{III}_3: & x_3 = -2 & \text{III}_3 = \text{III}_2 \end{array}$$

in which the solution is explicit.

A Pivotal Reduction of a General System.

Instead of a square system suppose, more generally, we have a system of m equations in n variables, with $m \leq n$,

(7)
$$a_{11}x_1 + a_{12}x_2 + \ldots + a_{1n}x_n = b_1$$
$$a_{21}x_1 + a_{22}x_2 + \ldots + a_{2n}x_n = b_2$$
$$\ldots\ldots\ldots\ldots\ldots\ldots\ldots\ldots\ldots\ldots$$
$$a_{m1}x_1 + a_{m2}x_2 + \ldots + a_{mn}x_n = b_m$$

We are interested in ways of replacing this system, if possible, by an equivalent *canonical* system (see § 4-1 for definition). In this form the solution set is evident and it is easy to detect whether or not any other system is equivalent to it.

(8)

Canonical system with basic variables $x_1, x_2, \ldots, x_m$		
x_1 $\qquad + \bar{a}_{1,m+1}x_{m+1} \ldots + \bar{a}_{1j}x_j + \ldots + \bar{a}_{1n}x_n = \bar{b}_1$		
$\qquad x_2 \quad + \bar{a}_{2,m+1}x_{m+1} \ldots + \bar{a}_{2j}x_j + \ldots + \bar{a}_{2n}x_n = \bar{b}_2$		
$x_m + \bar{a}_{m,m+1}x_{m+1} \ldots + \bar{a}_{mj}x_j + \ldots + \bar{a}_{mn}x_n = \bar{b}_m$		
Basic Variables	Non-basic (or Independent) Variables	Constants

The diagonal system (1) for square systems is clearly a special case of the canonical system (8) with $m = n$. The standard procedure for reducing (if possible) a general system (7) to equivalent canonical form will now be discussed.

The principles are best illustrated with an example and then generalized. Consider the 2×4 system,

$$+ \quad x_2 + x_3 + x_4 = 5$$
$$x_1 - 2x_2 - x_3 + x_4 = 2$$

Choose as "pivot element" any term with non-zero coefficient such as the *boldfaced* term in the first equation, and eliminate the corresponding variable, x_2, from the other equations by means of elementary operations.

$$x_2 + x_3 + \quad x_4 = 5$$
$$+ x_1 \quad + x_3 + 3x_4 = 12$$

Next choose as pivot any term in the remaining equations such as the bold-faced term in the second equation above. Eliminate the corresponding variable, in this case x_1, from all the other equations. (Because x_1 happens to have a zero coefficient in the first equation, no further eliminations are in fact required.) Hence, rearranging the equations gives the system

$$x_1 \quad + x_3 + 3x_4 = 12$$
$$x_2 + x_3 + \quad x_4 = 5$$

From this canonical system with basic variables x_1, x_2 it is evident, by setting $x_3 = x_4 = 0$, that one solution is $x_1 = 12$, $x_2 = 5$, $x_3 = x_4 = 0$.

[78]

Pivoting.

DEFINITION: A *pivot operation* consists of m elementary operations which replace a system by an equivalent system in which a specified variable has a coefficient of unity in one equation and zero elsewhere. The detailed steps are as follows:

(a) Select a term $a_{rs}x_s$ in system (7) such that $a_{rs} \neq 0$, called the *pivot term*.

(b) Replace the rth equation by the rth equation multiplied by $(1/a_{rs})$.

(c) For each $i = 1, 2, \ldots, m$ except $i = r$, replace the ith equation by the sum of the ith equation and the replaced rth equation multiplied by $(-a_{is})$.

In general the reduction to some canonical form can be accomplished by a sequence of pivot operations. For the first pivot term select any term $a_{rs}x_s$ such that $a_{rs} \neq 0$. After the first pivoting, the second pivot term is selected using a non-zero term from any equation except r, say equation r'. After pivoting, the third pivot term is selected in the resulting m-equation system from any equation except r and r', say equation r''. In general, repeat the pivoting operation, always choosing the pivot term from equations that do not correspond to equations previously selected. Continue in this manner, terminating either when m pivots have been used or when, after selecting r variables, it is not possible to find a non-zero term in any equation except those corresponding to previously selected pivot terms.

For example, if the successive pivoting was done on variables x_1, x_2, $\ldots, x_r$ in the corresponding equations $i = 1, 2, \ldots, r$, then the original system (7) would be reduced to an equivalent system of form (9), which we will refer to as the *reduced system* with pivotal variables $x_1, x_2, \ldots, x_r$. We shall also refer to a system as reduced relative to r pivotal variables if, by changing the order of the variables and equations, it can be put into form (9).

(9)

$$
\begin{array}{|l|}
\hline
\text{Reduced system with pivotal variables } x_1, x_2, \ldots, x_r \\
\hline
\end{array}
$$

$$
\begin{aligned}
x_1 \quad\quad &+ \bar{a}_{1,r+1}x_{r+1} + \bar{a}_{1,r+2}x_{r+2} + \ldots + \bar{a}_{1n}x_n = \bar{b}_1 \\
x_2 \quad &+ \bar{a}_{2,r+1}x_{r+1} + \bar{a}_{2,r+2}x_{r+2} + \ldots + \bar{a}_{2n}x_n = \bar{b}_2 \\
&\quad\quad\quad\quad\vdots \\
x_r &+ \bar{a}_{r,r+1}x_{r+1} + \bar{a}_{r,r+2}x_{r+2} + \ldots + \bar{a}_{rn}x_n = \bar{b}_r \\
\hline
&0 \cdot x_{r+1} + \ldots\ldots\ldots\ldots + 0 \cdot x_n = \bar{b}_{r+1} \\
&\quad\quad\quad\quad\vdots \\
&0 \cdot x_{r+1} + \ldots\ldots\ldots\ldots + 0 \cdot x_n = \bar{b}_m
\end{aligned}
$$

Since (9) was obtained from (7) by a sequence of pivoting operations each of which consists of m elementary operations, it follows that the reduced system is (a) formed from *linear combinations* of the original system, and (b) *equivalent* to the original system.

The original system (7) is solvable if and only if its reduced system (9) is solvable, and (9) is solvable if and only if

(10) $$\bar{b}_{r+1} = \bar{b}_{r+2} = \ldots = \bar{b}_m = 0$$

If (10) holds, the solution set is immediately evident because any values of the (independent) variables $x_{r+1}, \ldots, x_n$ determine corresponding values for the (dependent) variables $x_1, \ldots, x_r$. On the other hand if $\bar{b}_{r+i} \neq 0$ for some i, the solution set is *empty* because the $(r + i)^{\text{th}}$ equation is inconsistent for it states that $0 = \bar{b}_{r+i}$. In this case the original system (7) and the reduced system (9) are both inconsistent (unsolvable).

Canonical System.

If the original system is consistent, the system formed by dropping the vacuous equations from the reduced system is called its *canonical equivalent* with the pivotal variables as basic.

(11)

Canonical system with basic variables $x_1, x_2, \ldots, x_r$		
x_1 $\quad$ $+ \bar{a}_{1,r+1}x_{r+1} + \bar{a}_{1,r+2}x_{r+2} + \ldots + \bar{a}_{1n}x_n = \bar{b}_1$		
$\quad x_2$ $\quad + \bar{a}_{2,r+1}x_{r+1} + \bar{a}_{2,r+2}x_{r+2} + \ldots + \bar{a}_{2n}x_n = \bar{b}_2$		
$x_r + \bar{a}_{r,r+1}x_{r+1} + \bar{a}_{r,r+2}x_{r+2} + \ldots + \bar{a}_{rn}x_n = \bar{b}_r$		
Dependent (basic) Variables	Independent Variables	Con- stants

Uniqueness of a Canonical Equivalent.

The fundamental property of a canonical system resulting from the reduction process is that for any other system with the same solution set a reduction can be effected using the same pivotal variables and the resulting canonical system will be *identical* if the equations are reordered so that their correspondence with the basic variables is the same in both systems.

THEOREM 1: *There is at most one equivalent canonical system with a fixed set of basic variables.*

PROOF: Let there be two equivalent canonical systems relative to $x_1, x_2, \ldots, x_r$. Substituting $x_{r+1} = x_{r+2} = \ldots = x_n = 0$ into the first system, we get $x_1 = \bar{b}_1, x_2 = \bar{b}_2, \ldots, x_r = \bar{b}_r$. Because of equivalence, substitution into the second system should yield the same values; this will only be true if their respective constant terms are the same. Similarly, substituting the values for independent variables of $x_{r+1} = x_{r+2} = \ldots$ $= x_n = 0$, except $x_s = 1$, will show (after equating constant terms) that their corresponding coefficients of x_s are the same for any $s = r + 1, r + 2, \ldots, n$.

The above theorem can also be established by applying

LEMMA 1: *Any equation can either be generated by a unique linear combination of the equations of a canonical system (the weights being the coefficients of the basic variables in the equation) or no linear combination exists.*

EXERCISE: Apply the lemma to test whether a system is equivalent to a canonical system.

Basic Solutions.

The special solution obtained by setting the independent variables equal to zero and solving for the dependent variables is called a basic solution. Thus if (8) is the canonical system of (7) with basic variables $x_1, x_2, \ldots, x_m$, the corresponding basic solution is

$$(12) \quad x_1 = \bar{b}_1, x_2 = \bar{b}_2, \ldots, x_m = \bar{b}_m; x_{m+1} = x_{m+2} = \ldots = x_n = 0$$

Degenerate Solutions.

A basic solution is degenerate if the values of one or more of the dependent (basic) variables are zero. In particular, the basic solution (12) is degenerate if $\bar{b}_i = 0$ for at least one i.

Basis.

In accordance with the special usage in linear programming, the term *basis* refers to the *ordered set* of columns of the original *independent* system (in detached coefficient form) corresponding to the ordered set of basic variables of a canonical equivalent. The columns of the basis will be called *basic columns* (or *basic activities*).

In the example following (8) the basis associated with the canonical system with basic variables x_2, x_1 is $\begin{bmatrix} 1 & 0 \\ -2 & 1 \end{bmatrix}$.

The reader is referred to § 8-1, "Pivot Theory," which extends the results of this section. A proof is given there that solvable systems with identical solution sets are equivalent.

4-3. LINEAR INEQUALITIES

In the remaining sections of this chapter we shall turn our attention to linear inequality systems which also play an important role in the solution of linear programs.

Just as in the special case of solving linear equations, it is possible that there exist no solutions to a system of linear inequalities, or there may exist many. To see this geometrically, let us take the linear programming restraints in the form of a system of linear inequalities instead of standard form. Consider the system

(1)
$$x_1 + x_2 \geq 2$$
$$x_1 \geq 0$$
$$x_2 \geq 0$$
$$x_1 - x_2 \geq 3$$

Let (x_1, x_2) represent the cartesian coordinates of a point in a plane. All points (x_1, x_2) that satisfy $x_1 + x_2 \geq 2$ lie on one side of the line $x_1 + x_2 = 2$. The correct side can be determined by substituting the coordinates of some fixed point (such as the origin) into the linear inequality. If the linear inequality is satisfied, all such points are on the same side as the fixed point; otherwise, on the opposite side. To indicate the side of the line represented by the inequality, we shall use a little arrow in Fig. 4-3-I.

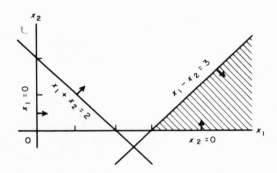

Figure 4-3-I.

The shaded area is the region of points satisfying all four inequalities simultaneously. In this case the region is *unbounded*. If the restraint

(2)
$$x_1 + 2x_2 \leq 6$$

is added to the system, the common region will become bounded (see Fig. 4-3-III omitting the z-equation). If now the restraint

(3)
$$4x_2 - x_1 \geq 0$$

is added, the region is reduced to a unique point $(4, 1)$ as in Fig. 4-3-II. Finally, if the condition

(4)
$$-2x_1 + x_2 \geq 2$$

is added to the system, no points satisfy all restraints simultaneously and no solutions exist.

If it is required to find a solution that minimizes the form

(5) $$-5x_1 - x_2 = z$$

where the point (x_1, x_2) lies in the shaded region of Fig. 4-3-III, the line $5x_1 + x_2 = constant$ is moved parallel to itself until it just touches the

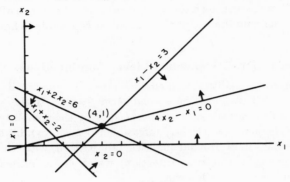

Figure 4-3-II.

shaded area at the extreme right point (6,0). The (unique) optimal solution is given by $x_1 = 6$, $x_2 = 0$, and $z = -5(6) - (0) = -30$. On the other hand, if the problem were to minimize this same form in, say Fig. 4-3-I, it would

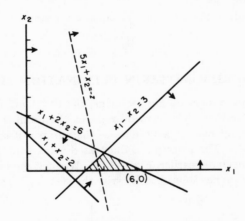

Figure 4-3-III.

be possible to move the line $5x_1 + x_2 = -z$ indefinitely to the right and still cut the unbounded region of solutions. In the latter case, it would be possible to construct solutions such that z can be made smaller than any preassigned value.

It will be noted that for each linear cost form for z, the minimizing

[83]

solution is unique in Figs. 4-3-I and 4-3-III, respectively. On the other hand, if the line $z = constant$ is parallel to one of the sides of the shaded area, it is possible to have non-unique solutions. In general for linear inequality systems involving many variables, the optimal solution is unique except, when the hyperplane represented by the objective form $= z$ (where the value of z is the unknown constant term) is *parallel* to one of the boundary hyperplanes defining the region of solutions, it is possible to have non-unique solutions.

Feasible Inequality Systems and Linear Combinations.

A system of inequalities with one or more solutions is called *consistent* or *solvable*. We shall also use the special term *feasible*. If the solution set is empty it is called *inconsistent* or *unsolvable*, or by the special term *infeasible*. A system of inequalities is clearly infeasible if we can exhibit a nonnegative linear combination of the inequalities (all written with their inequality symbols pointing in the same direction) which is an *infeasible inequality*, namely an inequality of the form

$$(6) \qquad 0x_1 + 0x_2 + \ldots + 0x_n \leq d \quad \text{with } d < 0$$

An important theorem we shall prove later tells us that if an inequality system is infeasible we shall always be able to exhibit a nonnegative linear combination that is an infeasible inequality (§ 6-3, Theorem 3(b)). See also the exercise at the end of § 4-5.

EXERCISE: State the analogue for equation systems.

4-4. FOURIER-MOTZKIN ELIMINATION METHOD[3]

For small linear programming problems, the Elimination Method can be used to obtain solutions. The method reduces the number of variables by one in each cycle but may greatly increase the number of inequalities in the remaining variables. The principle is illustrated using example (1a) which is similar to one considered earlier, Fig. 4-3-III. We seek the smallest value of z for which the system has solutions. Rewrite the system (1a) as shown in (1b)

$$(1a) \left\{ \begin{array}{rcl} x_1 & \geq & 0 \\ x_1 + 2x_2 & \leq & 6 \\ x_1 + x_2 & \geq & 2 \\ x_1 - x_2 & \geq & 3 \\ x_2 & \geq & 0 \\ -2x_1 - x_2 & \leq & z \end{array} \right. \quad \text{or (1b)} \left\{ \begin{array}{rcl} 0 & \leq & x_1 \\ & & x_1 \leq 6 - 2x_2 \\ 2 - x_2 & \leq & x_1 \\ 3 + x_2 & \leq & x_1 \\ -\tfrac{1}{2}z - \tfrac{1}{2}x_2 & \leq & x_1 \\ \multicolumn{3}{c}{\dotfill} \\ & & \text{and } x_2 \geq 0 \end{array} \right.$$

[3] Fourier first proposed this method [Fourier, 1826-1]. It was reintroduced by T. Motzkin and is often referred to as the Motzkin Elimination Method [Motzkin, 1936-1].

The six inequalities with respect to x_1 (the first variable to be eliminated) can be divided into three classes, those (four in this example) in which x_1 can be expressed as greater than certain linear forms and those (one in this example) in which x_1 is less than other linear forms, and the remaining inequalities in which x_1 does not appear.

This implies that every form of the first class is less than or equal to every form of the second class, i.e.,

$$\text{(2a)} \quad \left\{ \begin{array}{c} 0 \leq 6 - 2x_2 \\ 2 - x_2 \leq 6 - 2x_2 \\ 3 + x_2 \leq 6 - 2x_2 \\ -\tfrac{1}{2}z - \tfrac{1}{2}x_2 \leq 6 - 2x_2 \\ \text{and} \\ x_2 \geq 0 \end{array} \right. \quad \text{or (2b)} \quad \left\{ \begin{array}{c} x_2 \leq 3 \\ x_2 \leq 4 \\ x_2 \leq 1 \\ x_2 \leq 4 + \tfrac{1}{3}z \\ \\ 0 \leq x_2 \end{array} \right.$$

where we have included $x_2 \geq 0$ from the third class. Conversely, any x_2 satisfying these five inequalities can be used to find an x_1 satisfying (1a) or (1b). If values of x_2 and z can be found satisfying (2a), then the largest expression on the left of the first five inequalities of (2a) is less than or equal to the smallest expression on the right; hence a value of x_1 can be arbitrarily chosen between these two values and will, together with the assigned x_2, z, constitute a solution to (1a) and (1b).

The next step is to repeat the process with (2b) by eliminating x_2. There is one inequality where x_2 is greater than or equal to a constant (zero) and four inequalities in which x_2 is less than or equal to a constant or a linear form in z (of which two are implied by the others and may be dropped). This implies that every form of the first class is less than or equal to every form of the second class. Three of the resulting relations are $0 \leq 3$, $0 \leq 4$, $0 \leq 1$, leaving $0 \leq 4 + \tfrac{1}{3}z$ or $z \geq -12$. Hence, $z = -12$ is the *smallest z* for which the system has solutions. Setting $z = -12$ in (2b), any value of x_2 in the range $0 \leq x_2 \leq 0$ may be chosen, or (in this case) $x_2 = 0$. Substituting $z = -12$ and $x_2 = 0$ in (1b) yields the range $6 \leq x_1 \leq 6$ or $x_1 = 6$.

Thus, the solution that $x_1 = 6$ and $x_2 = 0$ was found rather easily for this relatively small problem. For larger problems more formal methods are needed. In general, if half of the m coefficients of x_1 appear with opposite sign, then the elimination would cause the number of inequalities to grow from m to $(m/2)^2$. Thus it is possible after a few eliminations, that the number of remaining inequalities might become too numerous.

4-5. LINEAR PROGRAMS IN INEQUALITY FORM

We shall now show that the linear programming problem in standard form, as formulated in § 3-8, is equivalent to the problem of finding a solution to a linear inequality system. For this reason, the central problem is often alternatively stated as that of *minimizing a linear form subject to a system of linear inequalities.*

Reduction of Linear Inequality Systems to Standard Form.

By a linear inequality is meant a relation of the form

$$(1) \qquad a_1 x_1 + a_2 x_2 + \ldots + a_n x_n \leq b$$

rather than a *strict* linear inequality

$$(2) \qquad a_1 x_1 + a_2 x_2 + \ldots + a_n x_n < b$$

It should be noted that if a system includes strict inequalities, it is not always possible to find values for the variables which satisfy the inequalities and at the same time minimize a linear form. For example, there is no value of $x_1 > 1$ which minimizes the form $z = x_1$.

Any problem involving a system of linear inequalities can be transformed into another system in standard form, i.e., into a system of equations in nonnegative variables by one of several devices. Steps (A) and (B) below constitute one method; Steps (A) and (B') below constitute a second method. In Chapter 6 the dual is developed for a system of linear inequalities; it will be noted that the dual system is in standard form. This constitutes a third way. The first method and perhaps the easiest is:

Step (A). Change any linear inequality restraint, such as (1), to an equation by adding a slack variable $x_{n+1} \geq 0$, thus

$$(3) \qquad a_1 x_1 + a_2 x_2 + \ldots + a_n x_n + x_{n+1} = b$$

Step (B). Noting that any number can be written as the difference of two positive numbers, replace any variable x_j not restricted in sign by the difference of two nonnegative variables

$$(4) \qquad x_j = x'_j - x''_j \qquad\qquad (x'_j \geq 0, \, x''_j \geq 0)$$

EXERCISE: (Tucker) Prove in place of (4) that each x_j unrestricted in sign can be replaced by $x'_j - x_0$ where $x'_j \geq 0$ and where $x_0 \geq 0$ is the same for all such j.

Step (B'). As an alternative to Step (B), let x_j be any variable not restricted in sign that appears in the kth equation with a non-zero coefficient. Solve the equation for x_j and substitute its value in the remaining equations if any and in the objective form z. Setting the equation aside, the remaining modified equations (if any) constitute a reduced system of constraints. The procedure is repeated with the new linear programming problem until either: (i) a reduced system of constraints is obtained in which all remaining variables are nonnegative, or (ii) no equations remain in the reduced system.

Once a solution to the reduced problem is obtained, a solution to the original problem is obtained by successive substitutions, in reverse order, in the eliminated equations.

To justify the procedure, note first that the minimum for the reduced system is less than or equal to that of the full system, because it involves only part of the conditions of the problem. On the other hand, the solution obtained for the full system (by the reverse substitution) has the same value for z and is, therefore, minimum.

EXAMPLE 1: Transform the system into standard form.

(5)
$$x_1 + x_2 \geq 6$$
$$x_1 + 2x_2 = z$$

Step (A). Introduce slack variable x_3.

(6)
$$x_1 + x_2 - x_3 = 6 \qquad (x_3 \geq 0)$$
$$x_1 + 2x_2 \qquad = z$$

Step (B). Substitute $x_1 = x_1' - x_1''$, $x_2 = x_2' - x_2''$, obtaining

(7)
$$(x_1' - x_1'') + (x_2' - x_2'') - x_3 = 6 \quad (x_3 \geq 0, x_j' \geq 0, x_j'' \geq 0)$$
$$(x_1' - x_1'') + 2(x_2' - x_2'') \qquad = z$$

Step (B'). Solve the equation $x_1 + x_2 - x_3 = 6$ for x_1, which is unrestricted in sign, obtaining

(8)
$$x_1 = 6 - x_2 + x_3 \qquad (x_3 \geq 0)$$

and substitute in the objective form z to get

(9)
$$x_2 + x_3 + 6 = z \qquad (x_3 \geq 0)$$

We now solve for x_2, but no equations remain for substitution; this is case (ii). A general solution to the original system (5) can be obtained by choosing any value for $x_3 \geq 0$, any value for z, and substituting these values in (9) and then in (8) to determine x_2 and x_1. Notice that no finite lower bound for z exists since z may be chosen arbitrarily.

EXAMPLE 2: Transform the system

(10)
$$-x_1 - x_2 \leq -6$$
$$-x_1 + x_2 \geq 5$$
$$x_1 + 2x_2 = z$$

into standard form.

Step (A). Introduce slack variables x_3 and x_4

(11)
$$-x_1 - x_2 + x_3 \qquad = -6 \qquad (x_3 \geq 0, x_4 \geq 0)$$
$$-x_1 + x_2 \qquad - x_4 = 5$$
$$x_1 + 2x_2 \qquad = z$$

Step (B). Substitute $x_1' - x_1''$, $x_2' - x_2''$ for x_1, x_2 where $x_j' \geq 0$, $x_j'' \geq 0$; or

Step (B'). Solve the first equation for x_1 and substitute in the second equation and the z-form. Next, solve the modified second equation for x_2 and substitute in the modified z-form. This eliminates the constraint equations and we are left with a reduced system consisting of only one constraint in nonnegative variables x_3, x_4:

$$(12) \qquad z = (23 + 3x_3 + x_4)/2 \qquad (x_3, x_4 \geq 0)$$

and the eliminated equations

$$(13) \qquad \begin{aligned} x_1 &= 6 - x_2 + x_3 \\ x_2 &= (11 + x_3 + x_4)/2 \end{aligned}$$

A general solution to the original system of constraints is obtained by selecting any $x_3 \geq 0$, $x_4 \geq 0$, and determining x_2 and x_1 from (13). If the objective is to minimize z, then, from (12), the optimum solution is found by setting $x_3 = 0$, $x_4 = 0$, obtaining $z = \frac{23}{2}$, $x_2 = \frac{11}{2}$, $x_1 = \frac{1}{2}$.

In general, suppose we have n inequalities in $k \leq n$ variables $(u_1, u_2, \ldots, u_k)$ which are unrestricted in sign, and a form z in these variables to be minimized:

$$\begin{aligned} \alpha_{j1}u_1 + \alpha_{j2}u_2 + \ldots + \alpha_{jk}u_k - \alpha_{j0} &\geq 0 \qquad (j = 1, 2, \ldots, n) \\ \gamma_1 u_1 + \gamma_2 u_2 + \ldots + \gamma_k u_k &= z \end{aligned}$$

where α_{ji} and γ_i are constants. If we set

$$x_j = \alpha_{j1}u_1 + \alpha_{j2}u_2 + \ldots + \alpha_{jk}u_k - \alpha_{j0} \qquad (j = 1, 2, \ldots, n)$$

then clearly

$$x_j \geq 0 \qquad (j = 1, 2, \ldots, n)$$

If we assume that it is possible to solve at least one set of k of the equations for $u_1, u_2, \ldots, u_k$ in terms of the x_j, then the substitution of these values of u_i in the remaining equations and the z-form yields $n - k$ equations and a z-form in nonnegative variables. Thus under this assumption, *n inequalities in $k \leq n$ variables is equivalent to $m = n - k$ equations in n nonnegative variables.*

Reduction of an Equation System to an Inequality System.

Conversely, any problem involving equations can be replaced by an equivalent system involving only linear inequality restraints. One way is to replace each equation

$$(14) \qquad a_1x_1 + a_2x_2 + \ldots + a_nx_n = b$$

by the two inequalities,

$$(15) \qquad \begin{aligned} a_1x_1 + a_2x_2 + \ldots + a_nx_n &\geq b \\ a_1x_1 + a_2x_2 + \ldots + a_nx_n &\leq b \end{aligned}$$

Another way is to change each equation into an inequality ($\geq$) and to change the sum of the equations into the opposite inequality. Thus, we may replace the equation system § 4-1-(2) by

$$(16) \quad \begin{cases} a_{11}x_1 + a_{12}x_2 + \ldots + a_{1n}x_n \geq b_1 \\ a_{21}x_1 + a_{22}x_2 + \ldots + a_{2n}x_n \geq b_2 \\ \ldots\ldots\ldots\ldots\ldots\ldots\ldots\ldots\ldots\ldots\ldots \\ a_{m1}x_1 + a_{m2}x_2 + \ldots + a_{mn}x_n \geq b_m \end{cases}$$

$$(\textstyle\sum a_{i1})x_1 + \ldots + (\textstyle\sum a_{in})x_n \leq \textstyle\sum b_i$$

An equation in nonnegative variables of the form

$$d_1x_1 + d_2x_2 + \ldots + d_nx_n = -d_0, \quad d_0 > 0, \quad d_i \geq 0$$

is called an *infeasible equation*.

EXERCISE: Write the above as an inequality system (with inequality symbols all pointing in the same direction) and prove there exists a linear combination that is an infeasible inequality.

4-6. PROBLEMS

Systems of Equations with the Same Solution Set. (Refer to § 4-1.)

1. *Review.* What are the elementary operations? Why do they lead to an equivalent system of equations?

2. In a transportation problem without slack variables, show that the system of equations in § 3-3 is redundant. Show any equation is redundant. Is redundancy possible with slack variables? Write out the equations in Tableau Form for both cases.

3. Reduce the system:

$$3x_1 + 2x_2 + x_3 = 4, \quad x_1 + x_2 + x_3 = 3$$

to the system: $\quad 2x_1 + x_2 = 1, \quad x_1 - x_3 = -2$

by elementary operations. What solution is evident from the reduced system? Check this solution by substituting in the original system.

4. Prove that it is not possible to transform systems § 4-1-(1) by elementary operations to equivalent form $\{E_4, E_5\}$ of § 4-1-(10) without using at least one elementary operation of the first type.

Canonical Systems. (Refer to § 4-2.)

5. Prove that (except possibly for sign) the product of the pivots equals the determinant of the basis.

6. *Review.* What is the canonical form? Can every system of equations be reduced to canonical form?

7. *Review.* What constitutes a basic set of variables? What is the basic solution associated with the basic set? What is a degenerate basic solution?

8. What are the independent or non-basic variables?
9. Need a basic solution be feasible, i.e., are the values of variables associated with a basic solution necessarily nonnegative?
10. What elementary operations can be used to transform

$$\begin{cases} 2x_1 + x_2 + x_3 = 6 \\ x_1 + x_2 + x_3 = 4 \\ 2x_1 + 3x_2 + x_3 = 8 \end{cases} \text{ into } \begin{cases} x_1 \qquad\qquad = 2 \\ \qquad x_2 \qquad = 1 \\ x_1 + 3x_2 + x_3 = 6 \end{cases}$$

Can you find a solution to this system? Now reduce this system to canonical form.
11. Put the following system in canonical form with x_1 and x_4 as basic variables.

$$\begin{aligned} x_1 - 2x_2 + x_3 \qquad &= 1 \\ x_1 + x_2 \qquad + x_4 &= 4 \end{aligned}$$

12. Reduce the system

$$\begin{aligned} 5x_1 - 4x_2 + 13x_3 - 2x_4 + x_5 &= 20 \\ x_1 - x_2 + 5x_3 - x_4 + x_5 &= 8 \end{aligned}$$

to canonical form using variables x_2 and x_4 as basic variables.
13. Reduce the system below to canonical form with respect to variables x_2 and x_4 if possible and find the associated basic solution.

$$\begin{aligned} 2x_1 + 3x_2 + 4x_3 + 5x_4 &= -1 \\ 2x_1 - 3x_2 - x_3 - x_4 &= -7 \end{aligned}$$

14. Consider the system

$$\begin{aligned} 3x_1 + 2x_2 + 11x_3 + 5x_4 - 3x_5 &= 5 \\ x_1 + x_2 + 4x_3 + 3x_4 + x_5 &= 2 \end{aligned}$$

(a) Reduce this system to canonical form using x_1 and x_2 as basic variables. What solution is suggested by this canonical form when variables x_3, x_4, x_5 are all zero?
(b) Reduce the original system to canonical form with x_1 and x_3 as basic variables. What solution is suggested by this canonical form?
(c) Now, using the results of (a), find the canonical form of (b) without referring to the original system of equations.
15. Consider the system

$$\begin{aligned} 2x_1 + 3x_2 - 2x_3 - 7x_4 &= 1 \\ x_1 + x_2 + x_3 + 3x_4 &= 6 \\ x_1 - x_2 + x_3 + 5x_4 &= 4 \end{aligned}$$

(a) Reduce this to a canonical system with x_1, x_2, and x_3 as basic variables. What solution is suggested by this canonical form? Check by substitution into the original system.

(b) From the canonical form of (a) find another canonical form with x_1, x_2, and x_4 as basic variables. What is the solution when $x_3 = 0$?

(c) From the canonical form of (b) find the canonical form with x_1, x_3, and x_4 as basic variables. What is the solution when $x_2 = 0$?

(d) From the canonical form of (c) find the canonical form with x_2, x_3, and x_4 as basic variables. What is the solution when $x_1 = 0$?

16. In the system below the variables y_1, y_2, y_3 are expressed in terms of x_1, x_2, x_3. Re-express the values of x_1, x_2, x_3 in terms of y_1, y_2, y_3 and show that the resulting system is equivalent to the original system. Show that the original system is essentially in canonical form with respect to y_1, y_2, y_3 while the resulting system is in canonical form with respect to x_1, x_2, x_3.

$$2x_1 + 3x_2 + 4x_3 = y_1$$
$$x_1 - x_2 + x_3 = y_2$$
$$4x_1 + 3x_2 + 2x_3 = y_3$$

17. The system expressing y_1, y_2, y_3 in terms of x_1, x_2, x_3 is called the *inverse system*. Why is the inverse unique? Show, in general, that if there are m equations that express y_1, y_2, . . ., y_m in terms of x_1, x_2, . . ., x_m, the inverse system expressing x_1, x_2, . . ., x_m in terms of y_1, y_2, . . ., y_m exists if x_1, x_2, . . ., x_m is a basic set of variables.

18. *Review.* Why are two equivalent canonical systems with respect to the same basic variables identical?

19. Why is it not possible to have two or more different basic solutions relative to a given set of basic variables?

Linear Inequalities. (Refer to § 4-3.)

20. Reduce each of the inequality systems (a), (b), and (c) to an equivalent system of equations with nonnegative variables by two different methods.

(a) $x_1 + 2x_2 \geq 3$ (b) $x_1 + x_2 \geq 2$ (c) $x_1 + x_2 \geq 2$
$x_1 - 2x_2 \geq -4$ $x_1 - x_2 \leq 4$ $x_1 - x_2 \leq 4$
$x_1 + 7x_2 \leq 6$ $x_1 + x_2 \leq 7$ $x_1 + x_2 + x_3 \leq 7$

Show that systems (b) and (c) correspond to cases (i) and (ii) of the alternate (B'). Show how to construct the class of all solutions for (c).

21. Transform the system of equations in nonnegative variables into a system of inequalities:

$$2x_1 + 3x_2 + 4x_3 = 5 \qquad (x_1 \geq 0, \, x_2 \geq 0, \, x_3 \geq 0)$$
$$4x_1 - 7x_2 + 3x_3 = 4$$

22. Show that no lower bound for z exists

(a) for the system $x_1 \geq 0$, $-x_1 = z$;

(b) for the system

$$x_1 - x_2 = 1 \qquad\qquad (x_1 \geq 0, \, x_2 \geq 0)$$
$$-x_1 - x_2 = z$$

(c) Show that a lower bound for z exists for the system $x_1 > 0$, $x_1 = z$, but while there are *feasible* solutions, there exists no *optimal* feasible solution.

23. Suppose (a_{ij}, b_i, c_j) denote the coefficients and constants before reduction to canonical form with respect to $x_1, x_2, \ldots, x_m$, and $(\bar{a}_{ij}, \bar{b}_i, \bar{c}_j)$ denote the coefficients and constants after reduction. In the dual of the original system,

$$\sum_{1}^{m} a_{ij}\pi_i \leq c_j \qquad\qquad (j = 1, 2, \ldots, n)$$

$$\sum_{1}^{m} b_i\pi_i = v \text{ (Max)}$$

introduce slack variables $y_j \geq 0$ and eliminate the unrestricted variables π_i by using pivots in the first m of the n equations. Show that the result is the standard linear program in n nonnegative variables and $n - m$ equations, and results in

$$\begin{cases} \displaystyle\sum_{1}^{m} \bar{a}_{ij}y_i + y_j = \bar{c}_j & (j = m+1, \ldots, n) \\[2ex] \displaystyle\sum_{1}^{m} \bar{b}_i y_i = v - \sum_{1}^{m} \bar{b}_i c_i \end{cases}$$

24. Use the "center of gravity method" of Chapter 3 to find $x_j \geq 0$ and Min z satisfying

$$z = 1x_1 + 2x_2 + 3x_3 + 4x_4$$
$$4 = x_1 + x_2 + x_3 + x_4$$
$$-2 = 1x_1 - 2x_2 + 3x_3 - 4x_4$$

25. Reduce the system

$$x_1 + x_2 + x_3 = 5 \qquad\qquad (x_1 \geq 0, \, x_3 \geq 0)$$
$$x_1 - x_2 + x_3 = 7$$
$$x_1 + 2x_2 + 4x_3 = 2$$

to an equivalent inequality system.

26. Solve graphically the system in nonnegative variables:

$$x_1 + x_2 \leq 1$$
$$4x_1 + 8x_2 \leq 32$$
$$x_1 + x_2 \leq 4$$
$$x_1 - 2x_2 \geq 2$$

What inequalities are implied by others?

Fourier-Motzkin Elimination Method. (Refer to § 4-4.)

27. Using the Fourier-Motzkin Elimination Method, find values of x_1, x_2, and z satisfying Problem 29, Case (c), and yielding Min $z = x_2$.

28. Use the Elimination Method to solve for nonnegative x_i and Min z satisfying the system

$$x_1 + x_2 \geq 1$$
$$x_1 + x_2 \leq 2$$
$$x_1 - x_2 \leq 1$$
$$x_1 - x_2 \geq -1$$
$$-x_2 = z$$

Graph and show the convex set of feasible solutions. Modify the z form in four different ways, so that the solution is not unique.

Linear Programs in Inequality Form. (Refer to § 4-5.)

29. Discuss, by graphing, whether there exists zero, one, or many solutions to a system of inequalities in the following cases:

Case (a)	Case (b)	Case (c)	Case (d)
$x_1 \geq 0$	$x_1 \geq 0$	$x_1 \geq 0$	$x_1 \geq 0$
$x_2 \geq 0$	$x_2 \geq 0$	$x_2 \geq 0$	$x_2 \geq 0$
$x_1 + x_2 \geq 2$	$x_1 + x_2 \geq 2$	$x_1 + x_2 \geq 2$	$x_1 + x_2 \geq 2$
	$x_1 + 2x_2 \leq 6$	$x_1 + 2x_2 \leq 6$	$x_1 + 2x_2 \leq 6$
	$-x_1 + 4x_2 \geq 0$	$-x_1 + 4x_2 \geq 0$	$-x_1 + 4x_2 \geq 0$
		$-x_1 + x_2 \geq 2$	$-x_1 + x_2 \geq 2$
			$-x_1 + x_2 \geq 3$

REFERENCES

General Background

Hadley, 1961-2

Kemeny, Snell, and Thompson, 1957-1

Stiefel, 1960-1

Equality Systems

Forsythe, 1953-1
Fox, 1954-1
Gale, 1960-1

Gauss, 1826-1
Jordan, 1920-1
Kuhn, 1956-1

Tucker, 1950-1, 1960-2

Inequality Systems

Fourier, 1826-1
Gale, 1960-1

Kuhn, 1956-1
Motzkin, 1936-1

CHAPTER 5

THE SIMPLEX METHOD

Outline: The standard form for the central problem of linear programming, as developed in § 3-8-(1), consists in finding values for a set of nonnegative variables that satisfies a system of linear equations and minimizes a linear form z.

We distinguish between the *simplex method* which starts with a linear program in standard form and the *simplex algorithm* which starts with a canonical form, consists of a sequence of pivot operations, and forms the main *subroutine* of the simplex method.

The first step of the simplex method is the introduction into the standard form of certain *artificial variables*. The resulting auxiliary problem is in canonical form. At this point the simplex algorithm is employed. It consists of a sequence of pivot operations referred to as Phase I that produces a succession of different canonical forms. The objective is to find a feasible solution if one exists. If the final canonical form yields such a solution, the simplex algorithm is again applied in a second succession of pivot operations referred to as Phase II. The objective is to find an optimal feasible solution if one exists.

In § 5-1 that follows the simplex algorithm will be described; its use, as part of the simplex method, will be developed in § 5-2.

5-1. SIMPLEX ALGORITHM

The simplex algorithm is always initiated with a program whose equations are in canonical form; for example, let us suppose we have canonical system (1), (2) with basic variables x_1, x_2, . . ., x_m, $(-z)$.[1] The relation of this m-equation n-variable canonical system to the M-equation, N-variable system of the standard form will become clear in § 5-2.

Problem: Find values of $x_1 \geq 0$, $x_2 \geq 0$, . . ., $x_n \geq 0$ and Min z satisfying

$$(1) \quad x_1 \qquad\qquad + \bar{a}_{1,m+1} x_{m+1} + \ldots + \bar{a}_{1j} x_j + \ldots + \bar{a}_{1n} x_n = \bar{b}_1$$

$$x_2 \qquad\qquad + \bar{a}_{2,m+1} x_{m+1} + \ldots + \bar{a}_{2j} x_j + \ldots + \bar{a}_{2n} x_n = \bar{b}_2$$

$$x_m \qquad + \bar{a}_{m,m+1} x_{m+1} + \ldots + \bar{a}_{mj} x_j + \ldots + \bar{a}_{mn} x_n = \bar{b}_m$$

$$(2) \qquad\qquad (-z) + \quad \bar{c}_{m+1} x_{m+1} + \ldots + \bar{c}_j x_j + \ldots + \bar{c}_n x_n = -\bar{z}_0$$

[1] That is to say $-z$ is treated as a basic variable. In the literature the reader may find this variable labeled x_0 and equation (2) arranged ahead of those of (1).

where $\bar{a}_{ij}$, $\bar{c}_j$, $\bar{b}_i$, and $\bar{z}_0$ are constants. In this canonical form the basic solution is

(3) $\quad z = \bar{z}_0; \; x_1 = \bar{b}_1; \; x_2 = \bar{b}_2, \ldots, x_m = \bar{b}_m; \; x_{m+1} = x_{m+2} = \ldots = x_n = 0$

Since it is *assumed* that this basic solution is also *feasible*, the values of the x_j in (3) are nonnegative, so that

(4) $\qquad\qquad\qquad\qquad \bar{b}_1 \geq 0, \, \bar{b}_2 \geq 0, \ldots, \bar{b}_m \geq 0$

DEFINITION: If (4) holds, we say that the linear program is presented in *feasible canonical form*.

Test for Optimality.

We have seen that the canonical form can provide an immediate evaluation of the associated basic solution. It may also be used to determine whether the basic solution (if feasible) is minimal, through an examination of the coefficients of the "modified" objective equation (2).

DEFINITION: The coefficients, $\bar{c}_j$, in the cost or objective form of the canonical system (2), are called *relative cost factors*—"relative" because their values will depend on the choice of the basic set of variables.

THEOREM 1: *A basic feasible solution is a minimal feasible solution with total cost $\bar{z}_0$ if all relative cost factors are nonnegative:*

$$\bar{c}_j \geq 0 \qquad\qquad\qquad (j = 1, 2, \ldots, n)$$

PROOF: Referring to the canonical form, it is obvious that if the coefficients of the modified cost form are all positive or zero, the smallest value of the sum $\Sigma \bar{c}_j x_j$ is zero for *any choice* of nonnegative x_j. Thus, the smallest value of $z - \bar{z}_0$ is zero and Min $z \geq \bar{z}_0$. In the particular case of the basic feasible solution, we have $z = \bar{z}_0$; hence Min $z = \bar{z}_0$ and the solution is optimal. It is also clear that

THEOREM 2: *Given a minimal basic feasible solution with relative cost factors $\bar{c}_j \geq 0$, then any other feasible solution (not necessarily basic) with the property that $x_j = 0$ for all $\bar{c}_j > 0$ is also a minimal solution; moreover, a solution with the property that $x_j > 0$ and $\bar{c}_j > 0$ for some j cannot be a minimal solution.*

COROLLARY: *A basic feasible solution is the unique minimal feasible solution if $\bar{c}_j > 0$ for all non-basic variables.*

Improving a Non-optimal Basic Feasible Solution: An Example.

To illustrate, consider the problem of minimizing z where

(5) $\qquad\qquad \begin{aligned} 5x_1 - 4x_2 + 13x_3 - 2x_4 + x_5 &= 20 \\ x_1 - x_2 + 5x_3 - x_4 + x_5 &= 8 \\ x_1 + 6x_2 - 7x_3 + x_4 + 5x_5 &= z \end{aligned} \qquad\qquad (x_j \geq 0)$

Let us assume we know that x_1, x_5, and $(-z)$ can be used as basic variables and that the basic solution will be feasible. Accordingly, we can reduce system (5) to equivalent canonical form relative to x_5, x_1, $(-z)$:

$$
\begin{aligned}
-\tfrac{1}{4}x_2 + 3x_3 - \tfrac{3}{4}x_4 + x_5 &= 5 \\
x_1 - \tfrac{3}{4}x_2 + 2x_3 - \tfrac{1}{4}x_4 &= 3 \\
8x_2 - 24x_3 + 5x_4 \qquad -z &= -28
\end{aligned}
\tag{6}
$$

except that we have not bothered to rearrange the order of the variables and equations. The meaning of the boldfaced term will be discussed later. The basic feasible solution to (6) is immediately,

$$
x_1 = 3,\ x_5 = 5,\ x_2 = x_3 = x_4 = 0,\ z = 28
\tag{7}
$$

Note that an arbitrary pair of variables will not necessarily yield a basic solution to (5) which is feasible. For example, had the variables x_1 and x_2 been chosen as basic variables, the basic solution would have been

$$
x_1 = -12,\ x_2 = -20,\ x_3 = x_4 = x_5 = 0,\ z = -132
$$

which is not feasible since x_1 and x_2 are negative.

For the numerical example (5), one relative cost factor of its canonical form, (6), is negative, namely -24, the coefficient of x_3. The optimality test of Theorem 1 thus fails. If x_3 is increased to any positive value (the other non-basic variables remaining zero), it is evident that the value of z would be reduced because the corresponding value of z is given by

$$
z = 28 - 24x_3
\tag{8}
$$

It seems reasonable, therefore, to try to make x_3 as large as possible, since the larger the value of x_3, the smaller will be the value of z. Now the value of x_3 cannot be increased indefinitely while the other non-basic variables remain zero, because the corresponding values of the basic variables satisfying (6) are

$$
\begin{aligned}
x_5 &= 5 - 3x_3 \\
x_1 &= 3 - 2x_3
\end{aligned}
\tag{9}
$$

and we see that if x_3 increases beyond $\tfrac{3}{2}$, then x_1 becomes negative, and that if x_3 increases beyond $\tfrac{5}{3}$, x_5 also becomes negative. Obviously, the largest permissible value of x_3 is the smaller of these, namely $x_3 = \tfrac{3}{2}$, which yields upon substitution in (8) and (9) a new feasible solution with lower cost:

$$
x_3 = \tfrac{3}{2},\ x_5 = \tfrac{1}{2},\ x_1 = x_2 = x_4 = 0,\ z = -8
\tag{10}
$$

This solution reduces z from 28 to -8; our immediate objective is to discover whether or not it is a minimal solution. This time a short cut is possible. A new canonical form with new basic variables, x_3 and x_5, can be obtained directly from the old canonical form with x_1 and x_5 basic. Choose as *pivot term* that x_3 term which limited the maximum amount that the basic variables, x_1 and x_5, could be adjusted without becoming negative, namely the boldfaced term, $2x_3$. Eliminating with respect to x_3, the new canonical form relative to x_5, x_3 and $(-z)$ becomes

(11)
$$-\tfrac{3}{2}x_1 + \tfrac{7}{8}x_2 \quad\quad - \tfrac{3}{8}x_4 + x_5 \quad = \tfrac{1}{2}$$
$$\tfrac{1}{2}x_1 - \tfrac{3}{8}x_2 + x_3 - \tfrac{1}{8}x_4 \quad\quad = \tfrac{3}{2}$$
$$12x_1 - \ x_2 \quad\quad + 2x_4 \quad\quad - z = 8$$

This gives the basic feasible solution, (10). Although the value of z has been reduced, the coefficient $\bar{c}_2 = -1$ indicates that the solution still is not minimal and that a better solution can be obtained by increasing the value of x_2, keeping the other non-basic variables, $x_1 = x_4 = 0$, and solving for new values for x_5, x_3, and z in terms of x_2:

(12)
$$x_5 = \tfrac{1}{2} - \tfrac{7}{8}x_2$$
$$x_3 = \tfrac{3}{2} + \tfrac{3}{8}x_2$$
$$z = -8 - x_2$$

Note that the second equation places no bound on the increase of x_2, but that the first equation restricts x_2 to a maximum of $(1/2) \div (7/8)$ which reduces x_5 to zero. Therefore, the *pivot term*, $\tfrac{7}{8}x_2$ in the first equation of (11), is used for the next elimination. The new set of basic variables is x_2 and x_3. Reducing system (11) to canonical form relative to x_2, x_3, $(-z)$ gives

(13)
$$-\tfrac{12}{7}x_1 + x_2 \quad\quad - \tfrac{3}{7}x_4 + \tfrac{8}{7}x_5 \quad = \tfrac{4}{7}$$
$$-\tfrac{1}{7}x_1 \quad\quad + x_3 - \tfrac{2}{7}x_4 + \tfrac{3}{7}x_5 \quad = \tfrac{12}{7}$$
$$\tfrac{72}{7}x_1 \quad\quad + \tfrac{11}{7}x_4 + \tfrac{8}{7}x_5 - z = \tfrac{60}{7}$$

and the basic feasible solution

(14)
$$x_2 = \tfrac{4}{7}, \ x_3 = \tfrac{12}{7}, \ x_1 = x_4 = x_5 = 0, \ z = -\tfrac{60}{7}$$

Since all relative cost factors for the non-basic variables are positive, this solution is the unique minimal solution by the corollary of Theorem 2. This optimal solution was found from our initial basic solution (7) in two iterations.

Improving a Non-optimal Basic Feasible Solution in General.

As we have seen in the numerical example, the canonical form provides an immediate criterion for testing the optimality of a basic feasible solution. Furthermore, if the criterion is not satisfied, another solution is generated which reduces the value of the cost or objective function (except for certain degenerate cases).

Let us now formalize this procedure of improving a non-optimal basic feasible solution. If at least one relative cost factor, $\bar{c}_j$, in the canonical form (2) is negative, it is possible, assuming non-degeneracy (all $b_i > 0$), to construct a new basic feasible solution with a total cost lower than $z = \bar{z}_0$. The lower cost solution can be obtained by increasing the value of one of the non-basic variables, x_s, and adjusting the values of the basic variables accordingly, where x_s is any variable whose relative cost factor $\bar{c}_s$ is negative. In particular, the index s can be chosen such that

(15) $$\bar{c}_s = \text{Min } \bar{c}_j < 0$$

This is the rule for choice of s followed in practical computational work because it is convenient and because it has been found that it usually leads to fewer iterations of the algorithm than just choosing for s any j such that $\bar{c}_j < 0$.

Using the canonical form (1) and (2), we construct a solution in which x_s takes on some positive value, the values of all other non-basic variables are still zero, and the values of the basic variables, including z, are adjusted to take care of the increase in x_s:

(16) $$\begin{aligned} x_1 &= \bar{b}_1 - \bar{a}_{1s}x_s \\ x_2 &= \bar{b}_2 - \bar{a}_{2s}x_s \\ &\cdots\cdots\cdots \\ x_m &= \bar{b}_m - \bar{a}_{ms}x_s \end{aligned}$$

(17) $$z = \bar{z}_0 + \bar{c}_sx_s \qquad (\bar{c}_s < 0)$$

Since $\bar{c}_s$ has been chosen negative, it is clear that the value of x_s should be made as large as possible in order to make the value of z as small as possible. The only thing that prevents our setting x_s infinitely large is the possibility that the value of one of the basic variables in (16) will become negative. However, if all $\bar{a}_{is} \leq 0$, then x_s can be made arbitrarily large, establishing:

THEOREM 3: *If in the canonical system, for some s, all coefficients $\bar{a}_{is}$ are nonpositive and $\bar{c}_s$ is negative, then a class of feasible solutions can be constructed where the set of z values has no lower bound.*

On the other hand, if at least one $\bar{a}_{is}$ is positive, it will not be possible to increase the value of x_s indefinitely, because, whenever $x_s > \bar{b}_i/\bar{a}_{is}$, the value of x_i must be negative. If $\bar{a}_{is}$ is positive for more than one value of i, then the smallest of such ratios, whose row subscript will be denoted by r, will determine the largest value of x_s possible under the nonnegativity assumption. The greatest value for x_s permissible under the assumption will be

(18) $$x_s^* = \frac{\bar{b}_r}{\bar{a}_{rs}} = \underset{\bar{a}_{is}>0}{\text{Min}} \frac{\bar{b}_i}{\bar{a}_{is}} \geq 0 \qquad (\bar{a}_{rs} > 0)$$

where it should be particularly noted that *only* those i and r are considered for which $\bar{a}_{is} > 0$, $\bar{a}_{rs} > 0$. The choice of r in case of a tie is arbitrary unless among those tied, $\bar{b}_i = 0$; in the latter (degenerate) case r may be chosen at random (with equal probability) from among them. For example, if

$\bar{a}_{1s} > 0$ and $\bar{a}_{2s} > 0$ but $\bar{b}_1 = \bar{b}_2 = 0$, then one may flip a coin to decide whether $r = 1$ or $r = 2$.[2]

The basic solution is degenerate if the values of one or more of the basic variables are zero (see § 4-2). In this case it is clear by (16) that, if for some $\bar{a}_{is} > 0$, it happens that the corresponding value $\bar{b}_i$ of the basic variable is zero, then no increase in x_s is possible that will maintain nonnegative values of the basic variables and therefore z will not decrease. However, if the basic solution is *nondegenerate* we have:

THEOREM 4: *If in the canonical system for some s the relative cost factor $\bar{c}_s$ is negative and at least one other coefficient $\bar{a}_{is}$ is positive, then from a nondegenerate basic feasible solution a new basic feasible solution can be constructed with lower total cost z.*

Specifically, we shall show that the replacing of x_r by x_s in the set of basic variables $x_1, x_2, \ldots, x_m$, results in a new set that is basic, and a corresponding basic solution that is feasible. We shall show feasibility first. Substituting the value of $x_s^* \geq 0$ determined by (18) into (16) and (17) gives a feasible solution,

$$(19) \qquad \begin{aligned} x_i &= \bar{b}_i - \bar{a}_{is} x_s^* \geq 0 & (i = 1, 2, \ldots, m\,;\, i \neq r) \\ x_s &= x_s^* & \text{where} \quad x_s^* = \bar{b}_r / \bar{a}_{rs} \geq 0 \\ x_j &= 0 & (j = r, m+1, \ldots, n\,;\, j \neq s) \end{aligned}$$

with total cost

$$(20) \qquad z = \bar{z}_0 + \bar{c}_s x_s^* \leq \bar{z}_0 \qquad\qquad (\bar{c}_s < 0)$$

This feasible solution is different from the previous one since $\bar{b}_r \neq 0$ by assumption; $x_s^* > 0$ and $z < \bar{z}_0$.

It remains to be shown that the new feasible solution is basic. It is clear, from the definition in (18) of the index r, that

$$(21) \qquad x_r = \bar{b}_r - \bar{a}_{rs} x_s^* = 0$$

We are trying to show that x_s and $x_1, x_2, \ldots, x_m$ (excluding x_r) constitute a new basic set of variables. To see this, we simply observe that since $\bar{a}_{rs} > 0$, we may use the rth equation of (1) and $\bar{a}_{rs}$ as pivot element to eliminate the variable, x_s, from the other equations and the minimizing form. Only this one elimination is needed to reduce the system to canonical form relative to the new set of variables. This fact constitutes the key to the computational efficiency of the simplex method. The new basic solution is unique by § 4-2, Theorem 1; hence its values are given by (19).

---

[2] The choice of r in case of a tie has been the subject of much investigation because of the theoretical possibility that a poor choice could lead to a repetition of the same basic solution after a number of iterations. For practical work an arbitrary choice may be used—W. Orchard-Hays [1956-1] who has experimented with various procedures, reports fewer iterations often result in practical problems using $i = r$ with maximum denominator $\bar{a}_{is}$ among those tied. (See § 6-1 and Chapter 10.)

[99]

Iterative Procedure.

The new basic feasible solution can be tested again for optimality by $\bar{c}_s = \text{Min } \bar{c}_j \geq 0$. If it is not optimal, then one may choose by criterion (15) a new variable, x_s, to increase and proceed to construct either: (a) a class of solutions in which there is no lower bound for z (if all $\bar{a}_{is} \leq 0$), or (b) a new basic feasible solution in which the cost z is lower than the previous one (provided the values of the basic variables for the latter are strictly positive; otherwise the new value of z may be equal to the previous value).

The simplex algorithm consists of repeating this cycle again and again, terminating only when there has been constructed either

(a) a class of feasible solutions for which $z \rightarrow -\infty$ or

(b) an optimal basic feasible solution (all $\bar{c}_j \geq 0$).

THEOREM 5: *Assuming nondegeneracy at each iteration, the simplex algorithm will terminate in a finite number of iterations.*

PROOF: There is only a finite number of ways to choose a set of m basic variables out of n variables. If the algorithm were to continue indefinitely, it could only do so by repeating the same basic set of variables—hence, the same canonical system and the same value of z. (See Uniqueness Theorem, § 4-2, Theorem 1.) This repetition cannot occur since the value of z decreases with each iteration.

When degenerate solutions occur, we can no longer argue that the procedure will necessarily terminate in a finite number of iterations, because under degeneracy it is possible for $\bar{b}_r = 0$ in (19), in which case the value of z decreases a *zero* amount in (20) and it is conceivable that the same basic set of variables may recur. If one were to continue, with the same selection of s and r for each iteration as before, the same basic set would recur after, say, k iterations, and again after $2k$ iterations, etc., indefinitely. There is therefore the possibility of circling (cycling)[3] in the simplex algorithm. In fact, examples have been constructed to show that this can happen; see Chapter 10.

We have shown the convergence of the simplex method to an optimal solution in a finite number of iterations only for the case of nondegenerate basic solutions. In § 6-1 we will justify the random choice rule, and in Chapter 10 we will show a simple way to change (perturb) the constant terms slightly, so as to assure nondegeneracy. We will prove that the procedure given there is valid even under degeneracy.

5-2. THE TWO PHASES OF THE SIMPLEX METHOD

The Problem.

The standard form, developed in Chapter 3, for the central mathematical problem of linear programming consists of finding values for $x_1, x_2, \ldots, x_N$ satisfying the simultaneous system of equations,

---

[3] In the literature the term "cycling" is used [Hoffman, 1951-1; Beale, 1952-1]. To avoid possible confusion with the term "cycle," which we use synonymously with "iteration," we have adopted "circling."

(1)
$$a_{11}x_1 + a_{12}x_2 + \ldots + a_{1N}x_N = b_1$$
$$a_{21}x_1 + a_{22}x_2 + \ldots + a_{2N}x_N = b_2$$
$$\ldots\ldots\ldots\ldots\ldots\ldots\ldots\ldots\ldots\ldots\ldots$$
$$a_{M1}x_1 + a_{M2}x_2 + \ldots + a_{MN}x_N = b_M$$

and minimizing the objective form

(2)
$$c_1x_1 + c_2x_2 + \ldots + c_Nx_N = z$$

where the x_j are restricted to be nonnegative:

(3)
$$x_j \geq 0 \qquad\qquad (j = 1, 2, \ldots, N)$$

The simplex method is in general use for solving this problem. The method employs the simplex algorithm presented in § 5-1 in two phases which will be described in this section.

Many problems encountered in practice often have a starting feasible canonical form readily at hand. For example, one can immediately construct a great variety of starting basic feasible solutions for the important class called "transportation" problems; see Chapter 14. Economic models often contain storage and slack activities, permitting an obvious starting solution in which nothing but these activities takes place. Such a solution may be a long way from the optimum solution, but at least it is an easy start. Usually little or no effort is required in these cases to reduce the problem to canonical form. When this is the case, the Phase I procedure referred to above will not be necessary.

Other problems encountered in practice do not provide an obvious starting feasible canonical form. This is true when the model does not have slack variables for some equations, or when the slack variables have negative coefficients. Nothing may be known (mathematically speaking) about the problem. It may have

(a) *Redundancies:* This could occur, for example, if an equation balancing money flow had been obtained from the equations balancing material flows by multiplying price by quantity and summing. The classic transportation problem provides a second example (see § 3-3; see also the blending problem, § 3-4, for a third case).

(b) *Inconsistencies:* This could be caused by outright clerical errors, the use of inconsistent data, or by the specification of requirements which cannot be filled from the available resources. For example, one may pose a problem in which resources are known to be in short supply, and the main question is whether or not a feasible solution exists.

It is clear that a general mathematical technique must be developed to solve linear programming problems free of any prior knowledge or assumptions about the systems being solved. In fact, if there are inconsistencies or redundancies, these are important facts to be uncovered.

The Phase I procedure uses the simplex algorithm itself to provide a starting feasible canonical form (if it exists) for Phase II. It has several important features.

(a) No assumptions are made regarding the original system; it may be redundant, inconsistent, or not solvable in nonnegative numbers.

(b) No eliminations are required to obtain an initial solution in canonical form for Phase I.

(c) The end product of Phase I is a basic feasible solution (if it exists) in canonical form ready to initiate Phase II.

Outline of the Procedure.

A. Arrange the original system of equations so that all constant terms b_i are positive or zero by changing, where necessary, the signs on both sides of any of the equations.

B. Augment the system to include a basic set of *artificial* or *error variables* $x_{N+1} \geq 0$, $x_{N+2} \geq 0, \ldots, x_{N+M} \geq 0$, so that it becomes

(4)

$$
\begin{aligned}
a_{11}x_1 + a_{12}x_2 + \ldots + a_{1N}x_N + x_{N+1} &= b_1 \\
a_{21}x_1 + a_{22}x_2 + \ldots + a_{2N}x_N \quad\quad + x_{N+2} &= b_2 \; (b_i \geq 0) \\
\vdots \\
a_{M1}x_1 + a_{M2}x_2 + \ldots + a_{MN}x_N \quad\quad\quad\quad + x_{N+M} &= b_M \\
c_1x_1 + c_2x_2 + \ldots + c_Nx_N \quad\quad\quad\quad\quad + (-z) &= 0
\end{aligned}
$$

and

(5) $$x_j \geq 0 \quad (j = 1, 2, \ldots, N, N+1, \ldots, N+M)$$

C. (Phase I): Use the simplex algorithm (with no sign restriction on z) to find a solution to (4) and (5) which minimizes the sum of the artificial variables, denoted by w:

(6) $$x_{N+1} + x_{N+2} + \ldots + x_{N+M} = w$$

Equation (6) is called the *infeasibility form*. The initial feasible canonical system for Phase I is obtained by selecting as basic variables $x_{N+1}, x_{N+2}, \ldots, x_{N+M}, (-z), (-w)$ and eliminating these variables (except w) from the w form by subtracting the sum of the first M equations of (4) from (6), yielding

(7)

Admissible Variables	Artificial Variables		
$a_{11}x_1 + a_{12}x_2 + \ldots + a_{1N}x_N$	$+x_{N+1}$		$= b_1$
$a_{21}x_1 + a_{22}x_2 + \ldots + a_{2N}x_N$	$+x_{N+2}$		$= b_2$
$\vdots$			$\vdots$
$a_{M1}x_1 + a_{M2}x_2 + \ldots + a_{MN}x_N$		$+ x_{N+M}$	$= b_M$
$c_1x_1 + c_2x_2 + \ldots + c_Nx_N$		$-z$	$= 0$
$d_1x_1 + d_2x_2 + \ldots + d_Nx_N$		$-w$	$= -w_0$

where $b_i \geq 0$ and

(8)
$$d_j = -(a_{1j} + a_{2j} + \ldots + a_{Mj}) \quad (j = 1, 2, \ldots, N)$$
$$-w_0 = -(b_1 + b_2 + \ldots + b_M)$$

Writing (7) in detached coefficient form constitutes the *initial tableau* for Phase I (see Table 5-2-I).

D. If Min $w > 0$, then no feasible solution exists and the procedure is terminated. On the other hand, if Min $w = 0$, initiate Phase II of the simplex algorithm by (i) dropping from further consideration all non-basic variables x_j whose corresponding coefficients d_j are positive (not zero) in the final modified w-equation; (ii) replacing the linear form w (as modified by various eliminations) by the linear form z, after first eliminating from the z-form all basic variables. (In practical computational work the elimination of the basic variables from the z-form is usually done on each iteration of Phase I; see Tables 5-2-I, 5-2-II, and 5-2-III. If this is the case, then the modified z-form may be used immediately to initiate Phase II.)

E. (Phase II): Apply the simplex algorithm to the adjusted feasible canonical form at end of Phase I to obtain a solution which minimizes the value of z or a class of solutions such that $z \rightarrow -\infty$.

The above procedure for Phase I deserves some discussion. It is clear that if there exists a feasible solution to the original system (1) then this same solution also satisfies (4) and (5) with the artificial variables set equal to zero; thus, $w = 0$ in this case. From (6), the smallest possible value for w is zero since w is the sum of nonnegative variables. Hence, if feasible solutions exist, the minimum value of w will be $w = 0$; conversely, if a solution is obtained for (4) and (5) with $w = 0$, it is clear that all $x_{N+i} = 0$ and the values of x_j for $j \leq N$ constitute a feasible solution to (1). It also follows that if Min $w > 0$, then no feasible solutions to (1) exist.

Whenever the original system contains redundancies and often when degenerate solutions occur, artificial variables will remain as part of the basic set of variables in Phase II. Thus, it is necessary that their values in Phase II never exceed zero. This is accomplished in D above where all non-basic variables are dropped whose relative cost factors for w are positive. To see this we note that the w form at the end of Phase I satisfies

(9)
$$d_1 x_1 + d_2 x_2 + \ldots + d_{M+N} x_{M+N} = w - \bar{w}_0$$

where $d_j \geq 0$ and $\bar{w}_0 = 0$, if feasible solutions exist. For feasibility, w must be zero, which means that every x_j corresponding to $d_j > 0$ must be zero; hence, all such x_j may be set equal to zero and dropped from further consideration in Phase II. If we drop them, our attention is confined only to variables whose corresponding $d_j = 0$. By (9) solutions involving only these variables now have $w = 0$, and consequently are feasible for the original problem. Thus,

THEOREM 6: *If artificial variables form part of the basic sets of variables in the various cycles of Phase II, their values will never exceed zero.*

As one alternative to dropping variables x_j corresponding to $d_j > 0$ at the end of Phase I, we can also maintain the basic artificial variables at zero values during Phase II by first eliminating (if possible) all artificial variables still in the basic set. This is done by choosing a pivot in a row r corresponding to such an artificial variable and in any columns s such that $\bar{a}_{rs} \neq 0$. If all coefficients in such a row for $j = 1, \ldots, N$ are zero, the row is deleted because the corresponding equation in the original system is redundant (see § 8-1).

As a second alternative, keep the w-equation during Phase II, and treat the $(-w)$ variable as just another variable which is restricted to nonnegative values. The system is then augmented by introducing the z-equation after eliminating the basic variables from it. Since $w \geq 0$ is always true, the added condition $(-w) \geq 0$ implies $w = 0$ during Phase II.

The computational procedures of Phase I with artificial variables and the transition to Phase II are summarized in the flow diagram, Fig. 5-2-I.

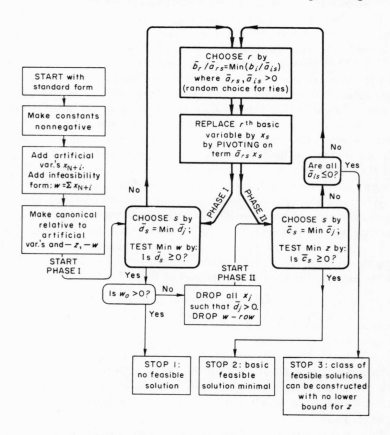

Figure 5-2-I. Flow diagram of the simplex method.

Detailed Iterative Procedure.

The *tableau* of the simplex method is given at various stages in Tables 5-2-I, II, and III. At the beginning of some cycle k all entries in a tableau associated with a cycle are known (see Table 5-2-II). Below each column corresponding to a basic variable, which includes $(-z)$ and $(-w)$, a ● symbol or ○ symbol is placed. Since the system is in canonical form (except that the original order of the variables has been preserved) all entries in the columns marked ● or ○ will be zero except one whose value is unity. If unity appears in the ith row (except the last two), we will refer to the basic variable as the ith basic variable and give it the symbol, x_{j_i}. For example, if unity occurs in the first, second, and third rows for basic variables x_3, x_5, and x_2, respectively, then $x_{j_1} = x_3$, $x_{j_2} = x_5$, and $x_{j_3} = x_2$ are the symbols entered in the left-hand margin of the tableau; their respective values in the corresponding basic solution are $\bar{b}_1, \ldots, \bar{b}_M$, which are shown in the last column, as are the values of the basic variables $(-z)$ and $(-w)$, which are the last two entries denoted by the symbols $-\bar{z}_0$ and $-\bar{w}_0$. The column of a variable entering the basic set on the next iteration is indicated by a ★; it replaces the basic variable indicated by a ○.

The following rules apply to all cycles but differ slightly depending on whether the computations are in Phase I or Phase II.

Step I:

(i) If all entries $\bar{d}_j \geq 0$ (in Phase I) or $\bar{c}_j \geq 0$ (in Phase II), then for

   (a) Phase I with $\bar{w}_0 > 0$: *terminate*—no feasible solution exists.

   (b) Phase I with $\bar{w}_0 = 0$: *initiate* Phase II by

      (1) dropping all variables x_j with $\bar{d}_j > 0$,[4]
      (2) dropping the w row of tableau, and
      (3) restarting cycle (Step I) using Phase II rules.

   (c) Phase II: *terminate*—an optimal solution is $x_{j_i} = \bar{b}_i$, $x_j = 0$, $z = \bar{z}_0$ ($j \neq j_i$, $i = 1, 2, \ldots, $ M).

(ii) If some entry $\bar{d}_j < 0$ (Phase I) or $\bar{c}_j < 0$ (Phase II), choose x_s as the variable to enter the basic set in the next cycle in place of the rth basic variable (r to be determined in Step II), such that

$$\text{Phase I:} \quad \bar{d}_s = \text{Min } \bar{d}_j < 0$$

$$\text{Phase II:} \quad \bar{c}_s = \text{Min } \bar{c}_j < 0$$

---

[4] As an alternative, this step may be omitted and Step II-(ii) modified during Phase II as follows: If corresponding to an artificial basic variable x_{N+i} there is an $\bar{a}_{is} \neq 0$ for $s \leq N$, then drop the first such $i = r$ after pivoting on $\bar{a}_{rs}$; if none, perform Step II-(ii) as given.

TABLE 5-2-I

TABLEAU OF THE SIMPLEX METHOD

Initial Tableau, Cycle 0

Basic Variables	Admissible Variables			Artificial Variables			Objective Variables		Con-stants
	$x_1 \cdots x_s \cdots x_N$			x_{N+1}	$x_{N+2} \cdots x_{N+M}$		$-z$	$-w$	
x_{N+1}	$a_{11} \cdots a_{1s} \cdots a_{1N}$		1						b_1
x_{N+2}	$a_{21} \cdots a_{2s} \cdots a_{2N}$			1					b_2
.	. . . .				.				.
.	. . . .					.			.
x_{N+M}	$a_{M1} \cdots a_{Ms} \cdots a_{MN}$					1			b_M
$-z$	$c_1 \cdots c_s \cdots c_N$						1		0
$-w$	$-\Sigma a_{i1}\ldots -\Sigma a_{is}\ldots -\Sigma a_{iN}$							1	$-\Sigma b_i$
Basic Variables[1]	★			●	●		●	●	●

← (these columns may be omitted)[2] →

TABLE 5-2-II

Tableau Start of Some Cycle k

Basic Variables									Constants
x_{j_1}	$\bar{a}_{11}$	$\bar{a}_{1s}$	$\bar{a}_{1N}$	1					$\bar{b}_1$
x_{j_2}	$\bar{a}_{21}$	$\bar{a}_{2s}$	$\bar{a}_{2N}$		1				$\bar{b}_2$
.	.	.	.						.
.	.	.	.						.
x_{j_r}	$\bar{a}_{r1}$	$\bar{a}_{rs}$[3] 1	$\bar{a}_{rN}$						$\bar{b}_r$
.	.	.	.						.
.	.	.	.						.
x_{j_M}	$\bar{a}_{M1}$ 1	$\bar{a}_{Ms}$	$\bar{a}_{MN}$						$\bar{b}_M$
$-z$	$\bar{c}_1$	$\bar{c}_s$	$\bar{c}_N$				1		$-\bar{z}_0$
$-w$	d_1	d_s	d_N					1	$-\bar{w}_0$
Basic Variables	● ★ ○			●	●	(drop)	●	●	

[1] The ● or ○ indicates a column corresponding to a basic variable. All values in these columns are zero except one whose value is unity. The ★ indicates the position of most negative $d_j < 0$, Phase I (or $\bar{c}_j < 0$, Phase II); i.e., the column of the variable entering the basic set on the next iteration by replacing the one indicated by ○.

[2] It is customary to omit the $-z$ and $-w$ columns because these remain the same through all tableaux and to omit the artificial variable columns because these, once dropped from the basic set, can be dropped from further consideration. Contrariwise, in the *simplex method using multipliers* (Chapter 9) the only entries recorded are those corresponding to the artificial variable columns.

[3] The bold-faced entry indicates position of pivot term for elimination for the next cycle; see Table 5-2-III.

TABLE 5-2-III

Tableau Beginning of Next Cycle, $k + 1$

Basic Variables	Admissible Variables			Artificial Variables			Objective Variables		Constants
	$x_1 \ldots x_s \ldots x_N$			x_{N+1}	$x_{N+2} \ldots x_{N+M}$		$-z$	$-w$	
x_{j_1}	$\bar{a}_{11} - \bar{a}_{1s}a_{r1}^*$		$\bar{a}_{1N} - \bar{a}_{1s}a_{rN}^*$ 1						$\bar{b}_1 - \bar{a}_{1s}b_r^*$
x_{j_2}	$\bar{a}_{21} - \bar{a}_{2s}a_{r1}^*$		$\bar{a}_{2N} - \bar{a}_{2s}a_{rN}^*$	1					$\bar{b}_2 - \bar{a}_{2s}b_r^*$
$\cdot$	$\cdot$		$\cdot$						$\cdot$
$\cdot$	$\cdot$		$\cdot$						$\cdot$
x_s	a_{r1}^*	1	a_{rN}^*						b_r^*
$\cdot$	$\cdot$		$\cdot$						$\cdot$
$\cdot$	$\cdot$		$\cdot$						$\cdot$
x_{j_M}	$\bar{a}_{M1} - \bar{a}_{Ms}a_{r1}^* \, 1$		$\bar{a}_{MN} - \bar{a}_{Ms}a_{rN}^*$						$\bar{b}_M - \bar{a}_{Ms}b_r^*$
$-z$	$\bar{c}_1 - \bar{c}_s a_{r1}^*$		$\bar{c}_N - \bar{c}_s a_{rN}^*$				1		$-\bar{z}_0 - \bar{c}_s b_r^*$
$-w$	$d_1 - d_s a_{r1}^*$		$d_N - d_s a_{rN}^*$					1	$-\bar{w}_0 - d_s b_r^*$
Basic Variables	● ●			●	● (drop)				

where $\quad (a_{r1}^* = \bar{a}_{r1}/\bar{a}_{rs}), \ldots, (a_{rN}^* = \bar{a}_{rN}/\bar{a}_{rs})$ $\qquad (b_r^* = \bar{b}_r/\bar{a}_{rs})$

Step II:

(i) If all entries $\bar{a}_{is} \leq 0$ *terminate*;[5] the class of solutions

$$x_s \geq 0 \text{ arbitrary}$$
$$x_{j_i} = \bar{b}_i - \bar{a}_{is}x_s \qquad (x_{j_i} \text{ basic variables})$$
$$x_j = 0 \qquad (x_j \text{ non-basic variables}; j \neq s)$$

satisfies the original system and has the property

$$z = \bar{z}_0 + \bar{c}_s x_s \to -\infty \text{ as } x_s \to +\infty$$

(ii) If some $\bar{a}_{is} > 0$, choose the rth basic variable to drop in the next cycle, where

$$\bar{b}_r/\bar{a}_{rs} = \text{Min } \bar{b}_i/\bar{a}_{is}$$

and i and r are restricted to those i such that $\bar{a}_{is} > 0$. In case of ties[6] choose r at random (with equal probability) from those i which are tied.

Step III:

To obtain entries in the tableau for the next cycle from the current cycle, multiply each entry in the selected row r by the reciprocal of the pivot term $\bar{a}_{rs}$ and record the products in row r of the next cycle; see the starred entries in row r, Table 5-2-III. Enter the rth basic

[5] In Phase I, this case cannot occur, for it would imply that w has no finite lower bound.

[6] See discussion on degeneracy, Chapter 10; see also § 6-1.

variable as x_s in place of x_{j_r} of the current cycle. To obtain the row i, column j entry of the next cycle, subtract from the corresponding entry of the current cycle the product of the entry in row i, column s of the current cycle and the entry in row r, column j of the next cycle.

Illustrative Example 1.

We shall now carry out the steps of the simplex method on our simple numerical example.

$$5x_1 - 4x_2 + 13x_3 - 2x_4 + x_5 = 20$$
$$x_1 - x_2 + 5x_3 - x_4 + x_5 = 8$$
$$x_1 + 6x_2 - 7x_3 + x_4 + 5x_5 = z$$

Since the constant terms are nonnegative, we initiate Phase I of the simplex method with the augmented system

Admissible Variables	Artificial Variables		
$5x_1 - 4x_2 + 13x_3 - 2x_4 + x_5$	$+ x_6$		$= 20$
$x_1 - x_2 + 5x_3 - x_4 + x_5$	$+ x_7$		$= 8$
$x_1 + 6x_2 - 7x_3 + x_4 + 5x_5$		$-z$	$= 0$
	$x_6 + x_7$	$-w$	$= 0$

This is reduced to canonical form by subtracting the sum of the first two equations from the last. This then becomes the starting tableau for initiating Phase I. In order to show the relation between the ordinary elimination of a system of equations and the simplex algorithm, the computations are carried out in parallel in equation form in (10) and in tableau or detached coefficient form in Table 5-2-IV.

The steps for the minimization of w in Phase I are similar to those for minimizing z. The reader is referred to § 5-1, (4) through (14), for a detailed explanation for this example. On the first cycle the value of w is reduced from 28 to $\frac{4}{13}$, on the second cycle to zero, and a basic feasible solution $x_3 = \frac{3}{2}$, $x_5 = \frac{1}{2}$, $z = -8$ is obtained for the original unaugmented system. Variables x_6 and x_7 have positive relative cost factors for w and hence must be dropped for Phase II. On the third cycle the value of z dropped from $z_0 = -8$ (cycle 2) to $z_0 = -\frac{60}{7}$ which is minimum. The optimal solution is $x_2 = \frac{4}{7}$, $x_3 = \frac{12}{7}$, all other $x_j = 0$, $z = -\frac{60}{7}$.

(10)   Simplex Method: Equation Form

Cycle 0 (Phase I)

$$5x_1 - 4x_2 + \mathbf{13x_3} - 2x_4 + x_5 + x_6 = 20$$
$$x_1 - x_2 + 5x_3 - x_4 + x_5 + x_7 = 8$$
$$x_1 + 6x_2 - 7x_3 + x_4 + 5x_5 - z = 0$$
$$-\mathbf{6x_1} + 5x_2 - 18x_3 + 3x_4 - 2x_5 - w = -28$$

$\bigstar$ $\circ$ $\bullet$ $\bullet$ $\bullet$

TABLE 5-2-IV
SIMPLEX METHOD: TABLEAU FORM

Cycle 0 (Phase I)

Basic Variables	Admissible Variables					Artificial Variables		$-z$	$-w$	Constants
	x_1	x_2	x_3	x_4	x_5	x_6	x_7			
x_6	5	-4	**13**	-2	$+1$	1				20
x_7	1	-1	$+5$	-1	$+1$		1			8
$-z$	1	6	-7	1	5			1		0
$-w$	-6	$+5$	-18	$+3$	-2				1	-28
			★			O	●	●	●	

Cycle 1 (Phase I)

	x_1	x_2	x_3	x_4	x_5	x_6	x_7	$-z$	$-w$	
x_3	$\frac{5}{13}$	$-\frac{4}{13}$	1	$-\frac{2}{13}$	$\frac{1}{13}$	$\frac{1}{13}$				$\frac{20}{13}$
x_7	$-\frac{12}{13}$	$+\frac{7}{13}$		$-\frac{3}{13}$	$\frac{8}{13}$	$-\frac{5}{13}$	1			$\frac{4}{13}$
$-z$	$\frac{48}{13}$	$\frac{50}{13}$		$-\frac{1}{13}$	$\frac{72}{13}$	$\frac{7}{13}$		1		$\frac{140}{13}$
$-w$	$+\frac{12}{13}$	$-\frac{7}{13}$		$+\frac{3}{13}$	$-\frac{8}{13}$	$\frac{18}{13}$			1	$-\frac{4}{13}$
		●		★	drop	O		●	●	

Cycle 2 (Phase I–II)

	x_1	x_2	x_3	x_4	x_5	x_6	x_7	$-z$	$-w$	
x_3	$\frac{1}{2}$	$-\frac{3}{8}$	1	$-\frac{1}{8}$		$+\frac{1}{8}$	$-\frac{1}{8}$			$\frac{3}{2}$
x_5	$-\frac{12}{8}$	$\frac{7}{8}$		$-\frac{3}{8}$	1	$-\frac{5}{8}$	$\frac{13}{8}$			$\frac{4}{8}$
$-z$	12	-1		2		4	-9	1		8
$-w$						1	1		1	0
	★	●		O	drop	drop	●	●		

Cycle 3 (Phase II–Optimal)

	x_1	x_2	x_3	x_4	x_5	x_6	x_7	$-z$		
x_3	$-\frac{1}{7}$		1	$-\frac{2}{7}$	$\frac{3}{7}$	$-\frac{1}{7}$	$+\frac{4}{7}$			$\frac{12}{7}$
x_2	$-\frac{12}{7}$	1		$-\frac{3}{7}$	$\frac{8}{7}$	$-\frac{5}{7}$	$\frac{13}{7}$			$\frac{4}{7}$
$-z$	$\frac{72}{7}$			$\frac{11}{7}$	$\frac{8}{7}$	$\frac{23}{7}$	$-\frac{50}{7}$	1		$\frac{60}{7}$
	●	●				drop	drop	●		

(11)   Cycle 1 (Phase I)

$$\frac{5}{13}x_1 - \frac{4}{13}x_2 + x_3 - \frac{2}{13}x_4 + \frac{1}{13}x_5 + \frac{1}{13}x_6 \qquad\qquad = \frac{20}{13}$$
$$-\frac{12}{13}x_1 + \frac{7}{13}x_2 \qquad - \frac{3}{13}x_4 + \frac{8}{13}x_5 - \frac{5}{13}x_6 + x_7 \qquad = \frac{4}{13}$$
$$\frac{48}{13}x_1 + \frac{50}{13}x_2 \qquad - \frac{1}{13}x_4 + \frac{72}{13}x_5 + \frac{7}{13}x_6 \qquad - z \;= \frac{140}{13}$$
$$\frac{12}{13}x_1 - \frac{7}{13}x_2 \qquad + \frac{3}{13}x_4 - \frac{8}{13}x_5 + \frac{18}{13}x_6 \qquad\qquad - w = -\frac{4}{13}$$

● ★ (drop) ○ ● ●

(12)   Cycle 2 (Phase I–II)

$$\frac{1}{2}x_1 - \frac{3}{8}x_2 + x_3 - \frac{1}{8}x_4 \qquad + \frac{1}{8}x_6 - \frac{1}{8}x_7 \qquad = \frac{3}{2}$$
$$-\frac{12}{8}x_1 + \frac{7}{8}x_2 \qquad - \frac{3}{8}x_4 + x_5 - \frac{5}{8}x_6 + \frac{13}{8}x_7 \qquad = \frac{4}{8}$$
$$12x_1 - \; x_2 \qquad + 2x_4 \qquad + 4x_6 - \; 9x_7 - z \qquad = 8$$
$$\qquad\qquad\qquad\qquad\qquad\qquad x_6 + \; x_7 \quad - w = 0$$

★ ● ○ (drop) (drop) ● ●

(13)   Cycle 3 (Phase II—Optimal)

$$-\frac{1}{7}x_1 \qquad + x_3 - \frac{2}{7}x_4 + \frac{3}{7}x_5 - \frac{1}{7}x_6 + \frac{4}{7}x_7 \qquad = \frac{12}{7}$$
$$-\frac{12}{7}x_1 + x_2 \qquad - \frac{3}{7}x_4 + \frac{8}{7}x_5 - \frac{5}{7}x_6 + \frac{13}{7}x_7 \qquad = \frac{4}{7}$$
$$\frac{72}{7}x_1 \qquad\qquad + \frac{11}{7}x_4 + \frac{8}{7}x_5 + \frac{23}{7}x_6 - \frac{50}{7}x_7 - z = \frac{60}{7}$$

● ● (drop) (drop) ●

Optimal Solution: $x_3 = \frac{12}{7}$, $x_2 = \frac{4}{7}$, all other $x_j = 0$, $z = -\frac{60}{7}$.

Illustrative Example 2.

TABLE 5-2-V

Simplex Method in Tableau Form for the Blending Problem, § 3-4

Cycle 0 (Phase I)

Basic Variables	Admissible Variables									Artificial Variables						
	x_1	x_2	x_3	x_4	x_5	x_6	x_7	x_8	x_9	x_{10}	x_{11}	x_{12}	x_{13}	$-z$	$-w$	s
x_{10}	1	1	1	1	1	1	1	1	1	1						
x_{11}	.1	.1	.4	.6	.3	.3	.3	.5	.2		1					
x_{12}	.1	.3	.5	.3	.3	.4	.2	.4	.3			1				
x_{13}	+ .8	.6	.1	.1	.4	.3	.5	.1	.5				1			
$-z$	4.1	4.3	5.8	6.0	7.6	7.5	7.3	6.9	7.3					1		
$-w$	-2.0	-2.0	-2.0	-2.0	-2.0	-2.0	-2.0	-2.0	-2.0						1	
	★									●	●	●	○	●	●

Cycle 1 (Phase I)

Basic Variables	Admissible Variables									Artificial Variables						
	x_1	x_2	x_3	x_4	x_5	x_6	x_7	x_8	x_9	x_{10}	x_{11}	x_{12}	x_{13}	$-z$	$-w$	s
x_{10}		.250	.875	.875	.500	.625	.375	.875	.375	1						
x_{11}		.025	.388	.588	.250	.262	.238	.488	.138		1					
x_{12}		.225 +	.488	.288	.250	.362	.138	.388	.238			1				
x_1	1	.750	.125	.125	.500	.375	.625	.125	.625							
$-z$		1.22	5.29	5.49	5.55	5.96	4.74	6.39	4.74					1		
$-w$		- .50	-1.75	-1.75	-1.00	-1.25	- .75	-1.75	- .75						1	
	●		★							●	●	○	drop	●	●

[110]

Cycle 2 (Phase I)

	x_1	x_2	x_3	x_4	x_5	x_6	x_7	x_8	x_9	x_{10}	x_{11}	x_{12}	x_{13}	$-z$	$-w$	Con-stants
				Admissible Variables						Artificial Variables						
		−.154		.359	.051	−.026	.128	.179	−.051	1						.05
		−.154		+.359	.051	−.026	.128	.179	−.051		1					.05
		.462	1	.590	.513	.744	.282	.795	.487							.51
	1	.692		.051	.436	.282	.590	.026	.564							.44
		−1.22		2.37	2.84	2.03	3.25	2.18	2.16					1		−4.76
		.31		−.72	−.10	.05	−.26	−.36	.10						1	−.10
	●		●	★						●	○	drop	drop	●	●	

Cycle 3 (Phase I–II)

	x_1	x_2	x_3	x_4	x_5	x_6	x_7	x_8	x_9	x_{10}	x_{11}	x_{12}	x_{13}	$-z$	$-w$	Con-stants
				Admissible Variables						Artificial Variables						
		−.428		1	.142	−.071	.357	.500	−.143	1						0
		+.714	1		.428	.786	.071	.500	.571							.14
	1	.714			.428	.286	.571	0	.571							.43
																.43
		−.20			2.50	2.20	2.40	1.00	2.50					1		−5.10
															1	0
	●	★	○	●						●	drop	drop	drop	●	●	

Drop w-equation after dropping all variables with $\bar{d}_j > 0$ (in this case w only).

Cycle 4 (Phase II—Optimal)

	x_1	x_2	x_3	x_4	x_5	x_6	x_7	x_8	x_9	x_{10}	x_{11}	x_{12}	x_{13}	$-z$	$-w$	Con-stants
				Admissible Variables						Artificial Variables						
			.6	1	.4	.4	.4	.8	.2	1						0
		1	1.4		.6	1.1	.1	.7	.8							.4
	1		−1.0			−.5	.5	−.5								.6
																0
			.28		2.62	2.42	2.42	1.14	2.66					1		−4.98
	●	●		●						●	drop	drop	drop	●	drop	

5-3. PROBLEMS

1. What condition must be satisfied for a set of variables to be a basic set of variables? What is the difference between a feasible solution, a basic solution, a basic feasible solution, an optimal solution, and an optimal basic solution? Why is the term "an" optimal solution used instead of "the" optimal solution?

The Simplex Algorithm. (Refer to § 5-1 and § 5-2.)

2. Describe briefly in words the simplex algorithm. Make a "flow diagram" of the sequence of steps, cycles, etc. What is degeneracy?

3. Show for the redundant system

$$x_1 + a_{12}x_2 + a_{13}x_3 = b_1$$
$$a_{22}x_2 + a_{33}x_3 = 0$$
$$-a_{22}x_2 - a_{33}x_3 = 0$$

with $0 < a_{12} < 1$, $0 < a_{13} < 1$, $b_1 > 0$ that augmentation by artificial variables plus the usual Phase I procedure of the simplex method terminates with two artificial variables, and that the two equations associated with the artificial variables in the canonical form have one redundancy when the artificial variables are dropped but neither equation vanishes.

4. Show in general that if the original system is of rank r, i.e., has $m - r$ redundant equations, then there are at least $m' \geq m - r$ artificial variables left at the end of Phase I. If these artificial variables are dropped, then the subsystem of equations associated with these artificial variables is of rank $m' - (m - r)$, i.e., has also $m - r$ redundant equations. If $m' = m - r$, these equations are vacuous.

5. Discuss weaknesses and possible ways to improve the final solution to Phase I of the simplex method so as to have less Phase II cycles.

6. Show, by changing units of any activity k whose $\bar{c}_k < 0$, that it can be chosen by the rule of $\bar{c}_s = \text{Min } \bar{c}_j$ to be the candidate to enter the next basic set. Can you suggest another selection rule which might be better; does it involve more work?

7. What is a sufficient condition that an optimum solution be unique? If the condition is not satisfied, how can one go about constructing a different optimal solution if it exists?

8. Show that if $(x_1, x_2, \ldots, x_m)$ are basic variables, x_s can replace x_r as a basic variable only if the coefficient of $\bar{a}_{rs} \neq 0$ in canonical form.

9. Prove, using the method of artificial variables of Phase I of the simplex method, that if any feasible solution to a system in m linear equations in nonnegative variables exists, then one exists in which no more than m variables are positive.

10. (T. Robacker): In some applications it often happens that many variables initially in the basic set for some starting canonical form remain until the final canonical form, so that their corresponding rows in the successive tableaux of the simplex method, though continuously modified, have never been used for pivoting. Devise a technique for generating rows only as needed for pivoting and thereby avoiding needless work.

11. Suppose that in the canonical form at the end of Phase I with $w = 0$ an artificial variable remains in the basic set with its unit coefficient in row k. Show that any admissible variable x_j can replace the artificial one, providing $\bar{a}_{kj} \neq 0$. If all $\bar{a}_{kj} = 0$ for admissible j, the kth row may be dropped from further consideration and this means that the kth equation was redundant in the original system.

12. *Prove:* If there are no degenerate solutions after removal of the redundant equations, then the number of artificial variables at the end of Phase I, *without removal of these equations*, equals the number of redundant equations; and the equations, associated with the artificial variables in the canonical form (after dropping the artificial variables), are vacuous.

13. Identify the redundant equation if no artificial variable is allowed to re-enter when once dropped from a basic set. When can a class of solutions each having m variables with positive values (m = number of equations) have a lower bound of minus infinity?

14. Show that if the rank (see Problem 4) of a system of equations is the same as the number of equations and if feasible solutions exist, then basic feasible solutions exist; moreover if z has a finite lower bound a minimal basic feasible solution exists.

15. Discuss how the simplex method can be used to distinguish between a consistent system which is not solvable in nonnegative numbers and an inconsistent system.

16. How is redundancy identified in the simplex method?

17. Given a basic nonfeasible solution (i.e., at least one $\bar{b}_i < 0$) with all relative cost factors $\bar{c}_j \geq 0$, prove that $\bar{z}_0$ is a lower bound for possible values of z in § 5-1-(2).

18. Show that uniqueness of the canonical form means that there is one and only one linear form which can express a basic variable in terms of the non-basic variables. Use this to prove for the infeasibility form that the relative cost factors $d_j = 0$ for non-artificial variables x_j, and $d_j = 1$ for artificial variables, if the basic set of variables contains no artificial variables.

19. Show that the condition $\bar{c}_j \geq 0$ for all j is necessary for a nondegenerate basic feasible solution to be minimal.

20. Show that a degenerate basic feasible solution may be minimal without satisfying the condition $\bar{c}_j \geq 0$ for all j.

21. Show that no lower bound for z exists for the system

$$x_1 - x_2 = 1 \qquad\qquad (x_1 \geq 0,\ x_2 \geq 0)$$
$$-x_1 - x_2 = z$$

and thus can be made to satisfy the conditions of § 5-1, Theorem 3.

22. In the following system one solution is $x_1 = 3$, $x_2 = 1$, $x_3 = 2$, $x_4 = 2$.

$$\begin{aligned}
x_1 + x_2 - 2x_3 + x_4 &= 2 \qquad\qquad (x_j \geq 0) \\
x_1 - 2x_2 - x_3 + 2x_4 &= 3 \\
x_1 \qquad\qquad + 3x_4 &= 9
\end{aligned}$$

(a) Reduce to canonical form with respect to x_1, x_2, x_3; treat x_4 as an independent variable; and show how to reduce x_4 from its value $x_4 = 2$ toward zero and, at the same time adjust the values of the basic variables to obtain a solution with at most 3 variables positive.

(b) Find all solutions with at most 3 positive variables.

23. (a) Using the approach outlined in Problem 22 above, develop a variant of the simplex algorithm to reduce the number of positive variables

[113]

by at least one if the rank (see Problem 4) of their subsystem is less than their number. Under what circumstances can there be a change of more than one variable from a positive value to zero?

(b) Along the same lines as above, develop a variant of the simplex algorithm which begins with any feasible solution (basic or not) and by adjusting the values of non-basic variables up or down (if not at zero value), successively improves the solution towards optimality.

(c) Prove, using the above variant of the simplex algorithm, that (i) if feasible solutions exist then a basic feasible solution exists, (ii) if an optimal feasible solution exists then a basic feasible solution exists which is optimal, and (iii) if feasible solutions exist and the values of z associated with the solution set have a finite lower bound, then a basic feasible solution exists which is optimal.

24. If there is a feasible solution involving k variables, and if the rank (see Problem 4) of the subsystem formed by dropping the remaining variables is r, show that there is a feasible solution involving at most r variables where $r \leq k$.

25. If a system of m equations in n nonnegative variables has a feasible solution, then a solution exists in which k variables are positive and $n - k$ are zero, where $k \leq \text{Min}(m, n)$.

26. Show that in a nutrition problem with slacks where there is one food F that contains a little of each nutrient, there is a starting basic feasible solution involving $m - 1$ excess variables and the variable associated with F. Which excess variable is omitted?

The Two Phases of the Simplex Method. (Refer to § 5-2.)

27. Use the simplex method to solve the system

$$x_1 + x_2 \geq 1$$
$$x_1 + x_2 \leq 2$$
$$x_1 - x_2 \leq 1$$
$$x_1 - x_2 \geq -1$$
$$- x_2 = z$$

for nonnegative x_j and Min z. Plot the inequalities using x_1 and x_2 as coordinates, follow the solution steps graphically, and interpret the shift from one solution to the next on the graph. See Fig. 7-2-I.

28. [Waugh, 1951-1]: Dairy cows require a certain minimum combination of nutrients for maintenance and for milk production. Part of these requirements must be purchased. Given the following data, how much of each feed should the dairyman buy in order to supply all needed nutrients at the least possible cost? (Hint: Find proportions of requirements supplied by $1 worth of each feed.)

A. Wholesale Prices and Nutritive Content of Feeds					
	Wholesale Price, Kansas City, $/100 lbs.	Nutritive Content of Feeds (Pounds of each element in 100 pounds of feed)			
Feed		Total Digestible Nutrients	Digestible Protein	Calcium	Phosphorus
Corn	2.40	78.6	6.5	0.02	0.27
Oats	2.52	70.1	9.4	0.09	0.34
Milo maize	2.18	80.1	8.8	0.03	0.30
Bran	2.14	67.2	13.7	0.14	1.29
Flour middlings	2.44	78.9	16.1	0.09	0.71
Linseed meal	3.82	77.0	30.4	0.41	0.86
Cottonseed meal	3.55	70.6	32.8	0.20	1.22
Soybean meal	3.70	78.5	37.1	0.26	0.59
Gluten feed	2.60	76.3	21.3	0.48	0.82
Hominy feed	2.54	84.5	8.0	0.22	0.71
B. Requirements for 24% total protein		74.2	19.9	0.21	0.67

29. Show that the feasible solution $x_1 = 1$, $x_2 = 0$, $x_3 = 1$, $z = 6$ to the system

$$x_1 + x_2 + x_3 = 2 \qquad\qquad (x_j \geq 0)$$
$$x_1 - x_2 + x_3 = 2$$
$$2x_1 + 3x_2 + 4x_3 = z \text{ (Min)}$$

is not basic.

30. In the system below, the z form has all positive coefficients and $x_1 = x_2 = x_3 = x_4 = x_5 = 1$; $z = 5$ is a feasible solution. Without doing any calculations prove an optimal basic feasible solution must exist. Using Phase I and II of the simplex method construct an optimal solution.

$$z = x_1 + x_2 + x_3 + x_4 + x_5 \qquad (x_j \geq 0, \text{ Min } z)$$
$$2 = 2x_1 + x_2 - x_3 + x_4 - x_5$$
$$2 = -x_1 + x_2 + 3x_3 - 2x_4 + x_5$$

31. Consider the system

$$2x_1 - x_2 + x_3 = 2 \qquad (x_1 \geq 0, x_2 \geq 0, x_3 \geq 0)$$
$$4x_1 + x_2 + x_3 = 6$$
$$x_1 + x_2 + x_3 = z$$

(a) What is the maximum number of solutions with at most two positive variables?

(b) Find all solutions with at most two positive variables. Which solution gives the smallest value of z?

(c) Reduce the problem to canonical form relative to x_1 and x_2. Is this solution optimal? If not, use the iterative procedure of the simplex algorithm to find the optimal solution. How does this agree with the result of (b)?

32. Find $x_j \geq 0$ and Min z for each of the following systems for the optimal solution:

(a)
$$2x_1 - 3x_2 + x_3 + 3x_4 - x_5 = 3$$
$$x_1 + x_2 - 2x_3 + 9x_4 = 4$$
$$2x_1 - 3x_2 + 6x_3 + x_4 - 2x_5 = z$$

(b)
$$3x_1 + x_2 + 2x_3 + x_4 + x_5 = 2$$
$$2x_1 - x_2 + x_3 + x_4 + 4x_5 = 3$$
$$x_1 - x_2 + 3x_3 - 2x_4 + x_5 = z$$

(c)
$$x_1 + 2x_2 + 3x_3 + 2x_4 - x_5 = 6$$
$$2x_2 + 4x_3 - 4x_4 + 2x_5 = 6$$
$$x_2 + x_3 + x_4 + x_5 = 5$$
$$-x_1 + 2x_2 + x_3 + 3x_4 - x_5 = z$$

33. Solve the Product Mix Problem of § 3-5 by the simplex method. Note that the model with the slack variables added is already in canonical form.

34. Using the simplex method, solve Problem 12, Chapter 3.

35. Solve the following problems by the simplex method. Verify your answers graphically (except c). Find $x_j \geq 0$, Min z satisfying

(a)
$$x_1 + x_2 - x_3 = 2$$
$$x_1 + x_2 + x_4 = 4$$
$$-2x_1 - x_2 = z$$

(b)
$$x_1 + x_2 + x_3 = 2$$
$$x_1 - 3x_2 - x_4 = 3$$
$$-2x_1 - x_2 = z$$

(c)
$$2x_1 + x_2 - x_3 + x_4 = 2$$
$$2x_1 - x_2 + 5x_3 + x_5 = 6$$
$$4x_1 + x_2 + x_3 + x_6 = 6$$
$$-x_1 - 2x_2 - x_3 = z$$

(d)
$$-4x_1 + x_2 + x_3 = 4$$
$$2x_1 - 3x_2 + x_4 = 6$$
$$-x_1 - 2x_2 = z$$

36. Is the solution of the Illustrative Example 1, § 5-2, unique? Give a rule for determining whether or not a solution is unique.

[116]

37. Solve for the optimal solution of each part of Problem 32, using artificial variables.

38. The problem of minimizing $4x_1 + 8x_2 + 3x_3$, subject to the five constraints

$$x_1 + x_2 \geq 2$$
$$2x_2 + x_3 \geq 5$$
$$x_j \geq 0 \qquad\qquad (j = 1, 2, 3)$$

may be converted into the following form, for immediate application of the simplex procedure:

Minimize $4x_1 + 8x_2 + 3x_3 + Wx_6 + Wx_7$, subject to the nine constraints:

$$x_1 + x_2 \qquad - x_4 \qquad + x_6 \qquad\quad = 2$$
$$2x_2 + x_3 \qquad - x_5 \qquad + x_7 = 5$$
$$x_j \geq 0 \qquad\qquad (j = 1, 2, \ldots, 7)$$

where W is an arbitrarily large positive quantity.

(a) Explain the roles played by x_4 and x_5.

(b) Explain the roles played by x_6 and x_7.

(c) Why is it necessary to introduce x_6 and x_7, if x_4 and x_5 have already been introduced?

(d) What is the role played by W? Show that if W is large enough the sequence of steps is identical with the Phase I, Phase II procedure.

(e) Solve using the simplex method.

39. Minimize $-2y_1 - 5y_2$

subject to
$$y_1 \qquad + y_3 \qquad\qquad = 4$$
$$y_1 + 2y_2 \qquad + y_4 \qquad = 8$$
$$y_2 \qquad\qquad + y_5 = 3$$
and
$$y_j \geq 0$$

40. State and give the solution to the problem that is *dual* to the following problem.

Maximize $\qquad u_1 + u_2 + v_1 + v_2$

subject to $\qquad u_i + v_j = ij$ (the *product* of i and j; $i, j = 1, 2$)

A Nutrition Problem.

41. Formulate as a linear programming problem: Suppose six foods listed below have calories, amounts of protein, calcium, vitamin A, and costs per pound purchased as shown. In what amounts should these foods be purchased in order to meet exactly the daily equivalent per person shown in the last column at minimum cost? How is the model

modified if the daily requirements may be exceeded; if the requirements except for calories may be exceeded?

	Contents and Costs Per Pound Purchased						Daily Requirement
	Bread	Meat	Potatoes	Cabbage	Milk	Gelatin	
Calories	1254	1457	318	46	309	1725	3000
Protein	39	73	8	4	16	43	70 (grams)
Calcium	418	41	42	141	536	—	800 (mg.)
Vitamin A	—	—	70	860	720	—	500 (I.U.)
Cost	$0.30	$1.00	$0.05	$0.08	$0.23	$0.48	Minimum

(a) Reformulate the model with exact requirements if the unit of each activity is changed from a per pound purchased to a per 3,000 calories of bread, of meat, etc. purchased. Obtain graphically an optimal solution for a simplified problem in which the material balance equations for calories, proteins, and costs only are considered (i.e., those for calcium and vitamin A are dropped). Solve the full problem using the simplex method.

42. [Greene, Chatto, Hicks, and Cox, 1959-1]: Find the optimum plan for a meat packing plant that wishes to know what proportion of hams, bellies, and picnic hams should be processed for sale as smoked product, and what proportion should be sold fresh, or "green."

Maximum flow in the processing operation before overtime work is necessary on any given day is smoked ham = 106 (per 100 weight), total bellies and picnics = 315.

Total Amount of Fresh Product Available for Processing

Hams	Bellies	Picnics
480	400	230

Processing Costs in Dollars for Final Product

	Hams	Bellies	Picnics
Smoked product (Reg. time)	$5.18	$4.76	$5.62
Smoked product (Overtime)	$6.58	$5.54	$6.92
Green product	$ .50	$ .48	$ .51

Smoked products sell higher than green products: the difference between the selling prices for smoked and green hams = $6.00; between smoked and green bellies = $5.00; between smoked and green picnics = $6.00.

REFERENCES

Simplex Method

Beale, 1954-1
Dantzig, 1951-3
Garvin, 1960-1
Gass, 1964-1
Hadley, 1961-2
Hadley and Simonnard, 1959-1

Hoffman, 1953-1
Lehman, 1954-1
Orchard-Hays, 1956-1
Orchard-Hays, Cutler, and Judd, 1956-1
Vajda, 1956-1, 1958-1, 1961-1
Vazsonyi, 1958-1

Solving Linear Programs by Methods Other than the Simplex Method

Ablow and Brigham, 1955-1
Agmon, 1954-1
Bélakrekó, 1964-1
Brown and Koopmans, 1951-1
Frisch, 1957-1
Hoffman, Mannos, Sokolowsky, and
  Wiegmann, 1953-1

Kantorovich, 1939-1
Motzkin, Raiffa, Thompson, and Thrall,
  1953-1
Motzkin and Schoenberg, 1954-1
Pyne, 1956-1
Rosen, 1960-1
Stiefel, 1960-1

Tompkins, 1955-1, 1957-1

CHAPTER 6

PROOF OF THE SIMPLEX ALGORITHM AND THE DUALITY THEOREM

6-1. INDUCTIVE PROOF OF THE SIMPLEX ALGORITHM

The proof given in § 5-1 of the simplex algorithm assumed all basic solutions generated by the iterative process to be nondegenerate. To cover the *degenerate* case there are two types of proofs available. The first, based on *induction*, has the advantage that at an early stage it yields a rigorous elementary proof of the fundamental duality theorem [Dantzig, 1959-1]. For a constructive procedure using this approach see [Wolfe, 1963-1].

From a constructive viewpoint, the second proof, based on *perturbation* or *lexicographic* modification of the constant terms, has the advantage that it yields an easy rule for deciding which basic variable to drop when there is ambiguity [Dantzig, Orden, and Wolfe, 1954-1]. The proof requires, however, more background knowledge and is therefore postponed until Chapter 10. Either proof can be used to establish the simple *random choice rule* which requires the least work and guarantees with "probability one" that the simplex algorithm will terminate in a finite number of steps. Proof of the latter will be found at the end of this section. Our immediate objective is to show

THEOREM 1: *Given a linear program presented in feasible canonical form, there exists a finite sequence of pivot operations each yielding a basic feasible solution such that the final canonical form yields an optimal basic feasible solution, or an infinite class of feasible solutions for which the values of z have no lower bound.*

Discussion: For a linear program to be presented in feasible canonical form with the basic variables $x_1, \ldots, x_r, \ldots, x_m$, say, we must have

$$
\begin{array}{llll}
x_1 & + \bar{a}_{1,m+1} x_{m+1} + \ldots + \bar{a}_{1s} x_s + \ldots + \bar{a}_{1n} x_n = & \bar{b}_1 \\
& \cdots\cdots\cdots\cdots\cdots\cdots\cdots\cdots\cdots\cdots\cdots\cdots\cdots\cdots \\
(1) \quad x_r & + \bar{a}_{r,m+1} x_{m+1} + \ldots + \bar{a}_{rs} x_s + \ldots + \bar{a}_{rn} x_n = & \bar{b}_r \\
& \cdots\cdots\cdots\cdots\cdots\cdots\cdots\cdots\cdots\cdots\cdots\cdots\cdots\cdots \\
x_m & + \bar{a}_{m,m+1} x_{m+1} + \ldots + \bar{a}_{ms} x_s + \ldots + \bar{a}_{mn} x_n = & \bar{b}_m \\
(-z) & + \bar{c}_{m+1} x_{m+1} + \ldots + \bar{c}_s x_s + \ldots + \bar{c}_n x_n = & -\bar{z}_0
\end{array}
$$

where $\bar{z}_0$, $\bar{a}_{ij}$, and the $\bar{b}_i \geq 0$ are constants. (See § 5-1.) The basic feasible solution is obtained by assigning each of the non-basic variables the value zero and solving for the values of the basic variables, including z.

The simplex algorithm described in Chapter 5 may be outlined as follows: each iteration begins with a feasible canonical form with some set of basic variables. The associated basic solution is also *feasible*, i.e., the constants $\bar{b}_i$ (as modified) are nonnegative. The procedure terminates when a canonical form is achieved for which either $\bar{c}_j \geq 0$ for all j (in which case the basic feasible solution is optimal), *or* in some column with $\bar{c}_s < 0$, the coefficients are all nonpositive, $\bar{a}_{is} \leq 0$ (in which case a class of feasible solutions exists for which $z \rightarrow -\infty$). In all other cases a *pivot term* is selected in a column, s, and row, r, such that $\bar{c}_s = \text{Min } \bar{c}_j < 0$ and $\bar{b}_r/\bar{a}_{rs} = \text{Min } (\bar{b}_i/\bar{a}_{is})$ for $\bar{a}_{rs}$ and $\bar{a}_{is}$ positive. The variable x_s becomes a new basic variable replacing one in the basic set—namely, by using the equation with the pivot term to eliminate x_s from the other equations. When the coefficient of the pivot term is adjusted to be unity, the modified system is in canonical form, and a new basic feasible solution is available in which the value of $z = \bar{z}_0$ is decreased by a positive amount, if $\bar{b}_r > 0$. In the nondegenerate case, we have all $\bar{b}_i$'s positive. If this remains true from iteration to iteration, then a termination must be reached in a finite number of steps, because: (1) each canonical form is uniquely determined by choice of the m basic variables; (2) the decrease in value of $\bar{z}_0$ implies that all the basic sets are strictly different; (3) the number of basic sets is finite; indeed, not greater than the number of combinations of n things taken m at a time, $\binom{n}{m}$.

In the degenerate case it is possible that $\bar{b}_r = 0$; this results in $\bar{z}_0$ having the *same* value before and after pivoting. It has been shown by Hoffman and Beale (see § 10-1) that the procedure can repeat a canonical form and hence circle indefinitely. This phenomenon occurs, as can be inferred from what follows, when there is ambiguity in the choice of the pivot term by the above rules. A proper choice among them will always get around the difficulty. To show this we establish first the convenient lemma:

LEMMA 1: *If Theorem 1 holds for a system with at least one non-zero constant term, it holds for the system formed by replacing all constants by zero.*

PROOF: Suppose a system in canonical form has all constant terms zero. Change one or more $\bar{b}_i = 0$ to $\bar{b}_i' = 1$ (or any other positive value). Then, by hypothesis, there exists a sequence of basic feasible solutions obtained by pivoting, such that the final canonical form has the requisite properties. If exactly the same sequence of pivot choices are used for the totally degenerate problem, each basic solution remains feasible—namely zero. Since the desired property of the final canonical form depends only on the choice of basic variables, and not on the right-hand side, the lemma is demonstrated.

[121]

PROOF OF THEOREM 1 : To establish the main theorem for the degenerate as well as the nondegenerate case we make the following:

INDUCTIVE ASSUMPTION: *Assume for* 1, 2, . . ., $m - 1$ *equations that only a finite number of feasible basic set changes are required to obtain a canonical form, such that the z-equation has all nonnegative coefficients* ($\bar{c}_j \geq 0$) *or some column s has* $\bar{c}_s < 0$ *and all nonpositive coefficients* ($\bar{a}_{is} \leq 0$).

We first verify the truth of the inductive assumption for one equation. If the initial basic solution is nondegenerate ($\bar{b}_1 > 0$), then we note that each subsequent basic solution must be nondegenerate (this remark holds only for the case of a single equation system). It follows that the finiteness proof of the simplex algorithm outlined above is valid, so that a final canonical form will be obtained that satisfies our inductive assumption. The degenerate case $\bar{b}_1 = 0$ is established by Lemma 1.

To establish the inductive step, suppose our inductive assumption holds for 1, 2, . . ., $m - 1$ equations and that $\bar{b}_i \neq 0$ for at least one i in the m-equation system (1). If we are not at the point of termination, then the iterative process is applied until on some iteration a further decrease in the value of $\bar{z}_0$ is not possible, because of degeneracy. By rearrangement of equations, let $\bar{b}_1 = \bar{b}_2 = \ldots = \bar{b}_r = 0$ and $\bar{b}_i \neq 0$ for $i = r + 1, \ldots, m$. Note that for *any* iteration, $r < m$ holds, because it is not possible to have *total* degeneracy on a subsequent cycle, if it is assumed that at least one of the $\bar{b}_i \neq 0$ initially. Let us set aside momentarily equations $r + 1, \ldots, m$. According to our inductive assumption there exists a finite series of basic set changes, *using pivots from the first r equations*, that results in a subsystem satisfying all $\bar{c}_j \geq 0$, *or* for some s, all $\bar{a}_{is} \leq 0$, $1 \leq i \leq r$ and $\bar{c}_s < 0$. Let us perform these *same* pivots, but this time with the full system. *Since the constant terms for the first r 'equations are all zero, their values will all remain zero throughout the sequence of pivot term choices for the subsystem; this means we can apply the same sequence of choices for the entire system of m equations, without replacing* $x_{r+1}, \ldots, x_m$ *as basic variables or changing their values in the basic solutions.*

It follows then, that if the final basis for the subsystem has all $\bar{c}_j \geq 0$ then the same property holds for the system as a whole. If it has the property that for some s, $\bar{c}_s < 0$ and $\bar{a}_{is} \leq 0$ for $i = 1, 2, \ldots, r$, then either $\bar{a}_{is} \leq 0$ for all the remaining $i = r + 1, \ldots, m$ (in which case the inductive property holds for m equations) or $\bar{a}_{is} > 0$ for at least one $i > r$, in which case the variable x_s can be introduced into the basic set for the system as a whole, producing a *positive decrease* in $\bar{z}_0$, since $\bar{b}_i > 0$ for $i = r + 1, \ldots, m$. We have seen earlier that this value of z can decrease only a finite number of times. Hence, the iterative process must terminate, but the only way it can is when the inductive property holds for the m-equation system.

This completes the proof for m-equations, except for the completely degenerate case where $\bar{b}_i = 0$ for all $i = 1, 2, \ldots, m$. The latter proof, however, now follows directly from the lemma. Q.E.D.

An efficient, constructive procedure for avoiding cycling (based on this inductive approach) has been developed by Wolfe (1963-2).

As a corollary to Theorem 1 we have the following theorem.

THEOREM 2: *If there is only one choice of variable to drop under degeneracy, the simplex algorithm will terminate in a finite number of steps.*

Proof of the Random Choice Rule: This rule selects the variable to drop from the basic set with *equal probability* among those r, satisfying

$$(2) \qquad \bar{b}_r/\bar{a}_{rs} = \text{Min } \bar{b}_i/\bar{a}_{is} \qquad (\bar{a}_{rs} > 0, \ \bar{a}_{is} > 0)$$

Starting with any basic feasible set, T, we know by Theorem 1, there exists a finite number of iterations leading to a final canonical form. Let k_T be the smallest number of iterations starting with T. Since there is only a finite number of starting basic sets, there exists a $k = \text{Max } k_T$, which is the *longest* of these shortest chains of steps.

LEMMA 2: *The random choice rule will terminate in k iterations with probability*

$$(3) \qquad P \geq (1/m)^k$$

where m is the number of equations and k the longest of the shortest chain of steps leading to an optimal canonical form.

PROOF: There are m or less selections on each iteration. Thus, in k iterations, there are at most m^k sequences ("paths") of which at least one leads to an optimum; the probability of making a selection along such a path on each step is at least $(1/m)$, since we choose with equal probability. Hence for k steps (3) holds. Moreover, the probability of failing to reach an optimum before k iterations is less than $[1 - (1/m)^k]$. It follows that the probability of failing to reach an optimum by $2k$ iterations is less than $[1 - (1/m)^k]^2$ and failing to reach an optimum by $N = tk$ iterations is less than

$$(4) \qquad [1 - (1/m)^k]^t$$

This expression, however, tends to zero as $t \to \infty$; therefore

THEOREM 3: *Given a random choice rule of which basic variable to drop from the basic set in case of a tie, the probability of failing to reach an optimum in N iterations tends to zero as $N \to \infty$.*

6-2. EQUIVALENT DUAL FORMS

As noted in § 3-8, associated with every linear programming problem is another linear programming problem called the *dual*. This fundamental notion was introduced by John von Neumann (in conversations with the author in October 1947) and appears implicitly in a working paper he wrote a few weeks later [von Neumann, 1947-1]. Subsequently Gale, Kuhn, and Tucker [1951-1] formulated an explicit Duality Theorem which they proved by means of the classical lemma of Farkas [1902-1]. Farkas's Lemma is described in § 6-4, Theorem 6. A systematic presentation of theoretical properties of dual linear programs will be found in Goldman and Tucker [1956-1], and Gale [1956-1]. A review of von Neumann's contributions can be found in Kuhn and Tucker [1958-1].

The original problem in its relation to the dual is called the *primal*. Feasible solutions to the primal and to the dual may appear to have little relation to one another; however, their optimum basic feasible solutions are such that it is possible to use one to obtain the other readily. It is often more convenient to use the dual to solve a linear programming problem than the primal. In this connection, it should be remarked that no advantage can be derived by solving the dual of the dual problem, because the latter turns out to be equivalent to the primal problem.

The Dual Problem.

A nearly symmetric relation between a primal problem and its dual problem results if the following system of linear inequalities (rather than equations) in nonnegative variables is considered.

Primal Problem: Find $x_j \geq 0$ and Min z, satisfying

$$
\begin{aligned}
a_{11}x_1 + a_{12}x_2 + \ldots + a_{1n}x_n &\geq b_1 \\
a_{21}x_1 + a_{22}x_2 + \ldots + a_{2n}x_n &\geq b_2 \\
&\cdots\cdots\cdots \\
a_{m1}x_1 + a_{m2}x_2 + \ldots + a_{mn}x_n &\geq b_m \\
c_1x_1 + c_2x_2 + \ldots + c_nx_n &= z \text{ (Min)}[1]
\end{aligned}
$$

(1)

In this form the dual problem is obtained by transposing the coefficient matrix, interchanging the role of the constant terms and the coefficients of the objective form, changing the direction of inequality, and maximizing instead of minimizing.

Dual Problem: Find $y_i \geq 0$ and Max v, satisfying

$$
\begin{aligned}
a_{11}y_1 + a_{21}y_2 + \ldots + a_{m1}y_m &\leq c_1 \\
a_{12}y_1 + a_{22}y_2 + \ldots + a_{m2}y_m &\leq c_2 \\
&\cdots\cdots\cdots \\
a_{1n}y_1 + a_{2n}y_2 + \ldots + a_{mn}y_m &\leq c_n \\
b_1y_1 + b_2y_2 + \ldots + b_my_m &= v \text{ (Max)}
\end{aligned}
$$

(2)

This form of the dual problem, due to von Neumann, has the particular merit that it is easy to see that the dual of the dual is the primal (see Problem 5).

To see more clearly the connection between the primal and dual problems we shall use A. W. Tucker's detached coefficient array, Table 6-2-I. The primal problem reads across, the dual problem down. A simple way to remember the direction of inequality is to write the primal inequalities $\geq$

---

[1] "z (Min)" means z is to be minimized; not to be confused with Min z, which is the minimum value of z.

to correspond to the z-form, being always $\geq$ Min z, and to write the dual inequalities $\leq$ to correspond to the v-form, being always $\leq$ Max v.

TABLE 6-2-I

TUCKER DIAGRAM

		Primal				Relation	Constants
	Variables	$x_1 \geq 0$	$x_2 \geq 0$	$\ldots$	$x_n \geq 0$	Relation	Constants
Dual	$y_1 \geq 0$ $y_2 \geq 0$ . . . $y_m \geq 0$	a_{11} a_{21} . . . a_{m1}	a_{12} a_{22} . . . a_{m2}	$\ldots$ $\ldots$ $\ldots$	a_{1n} a_{2n} . . . a_{mn}	$\geq$ $\geq$ $\geq$	b_1 b_2 . . . b_m
	Relation	$\leq$	$\leq$		$\leq$		$\leq$ Max v
	Constants	c_1	c_2	$\ldots$	c_n	$\geq$ Min z	

The Duality Theorem is a statement about the range of possible z values for the primal versus the range of possible v values for the dual. This is depicted graphically in (3), for the case where the primal and dual are both feasible.

(3)   *Dual*   *Primal*

$-\infty$ ——— v range ———→	←——— z range ——— $+\infty$
or finite Max $v \rightarrow$	$\leftarrow$ Min z or finite

DUALITY THEOREM. *If solutions to the primal and dual system exist, the value z of the objective form corresponding to any feasible solution of the primal is greater than or equal to the value v of the objective form corresponding to any feasible solution to the dual; moreover, optimal feasible solutions exist for both systems and* Max $v = $ Min z.

The Dual of a Mixed System.

It is always possible to obtain the dual of a system consisting of a mixture of equations, inequalities (in either direction), nonnegative variables, or variables unrestricted in sign by reducing the system to an equivalent inequality system (1). In fact, this approach can be used to establish that the dual of a linear program in the standard form, as given in § 3-8, is the same as the one given here. Both the primal and dual systems can be viewed as consisting of a set of variables with their sign restrictions and a set of linear equations and inequalities, such that the variables of the primal are in one-to-one correspondence with the equations and inequalities of the dual, and the equations and inequalities of the primal are in one-to-one correspondence with the variables of the dual. When the primal relation is

[125]

a linear inequality ($\geq$), the corresponding variable of the dual is nonnegative; if the relation is an equation, the corresponding variable will be unrestricted in sign. The following correspondence rules apply:

Primal	*Dual*
Objective Form ($\geq$ Min z)	Constant Terms
Constant Terms	Objective Form ($\leq$ Max v)
Coefficient Matrix	Transpose Coefficient Matrix
Relation:	Variable:
(i^{th}) Inequality: $\geq$	$y_i \geq 0$
(i^{th}) Equation: $=$	y_i unrestricted in sign
Variable:	Relation:
$x_j \geq 0$	(j^{th}) Inequality: $\leq$
x_j unrestricted in sign	(j^{th}) Equation: $=$

To illustrate, suppose we have the mixed primal system

(4)
$$x_1 - 3x_2 + 4x_3 = 5 \qquad (x_1 \geq 0, \, x_2 \geq 0)$$
$$x_1 - 2x_2 \qquad \leq 3 \qquad (x_3 \text{ unrestricted in sign})$$
$$2x_2 - \quad x_3 \geq 4$$
$$x_1 + \quad x_2 + \quad x_3 = z \text{ (Min)}$$

Applying the rules, we have the primal system in detached coefficient form by reading across and the dual system reading down (Table 6-2-II).

TABLE 6-2-II

		Primal				
	Variables	$x_1 \geq 0$	$x_2 \geq 0$	x_3	Relation	Constants
	y_1	1	-3	4	$=$	5
Dual	$-y_2 \geq 0$	1	-2		$\leq$	3
	$y_3 \geq 0$		2	-1	$\geq$	4
	Relation	$\leq$	$\leq$	$=$		$\leq$ Max v
	Constants	1	1	1	$\geq$ Min z	

To see why this is the case, suppose we rewrite system (4) in equivalent inequality form (see § 4-5).

(5)
$$x_1 - 3x_2 + 4(x_3' - x_3'') \geq 5, \qquad (x_1 \geq 0, \, x_2 \geq 0, \, x_3' \geq 0, \, x_3'' \geq 0)$$
$$-[x_1 - 3x_2 + 4(x_3' - x_3'')] \geq -5$$
$$-(x_1 - 2x_2) \qquad \geq -3$$
$$2x_2 - \quad (x_3' - x_3'') \geq 4$$
$$x_1 + \quad x_2 + \quad (x_3' - x_3'') \geq \text{Min } z$$

Here we have written $x_3 = x_3' - x_3''$ as *the difference of two nonnegative*

[126]

variables and we have written the first equation of (4) as *equivalent to two inequalities*, $x_1 - 3x_2 + 4x_3 \geq 5$ and $x_1 - 3x_2 + 4x_3 \leq 5$. The relationship between the primal and dual by (1) and (2) is shown in Table 6-2-III.

TABLE 6-2-III

		Primal					
	Variables	$x_1 \geq 0$	$x_2 \geq 0$	$x_3' \geq 0$	$x_3'' \geq 0$	Relation	Constants
Dual	$y_1' \geq 0$ $y_1'' \geq 0$	1 -1	-3 $+3$	4 -4	-4 $+4$	$\geq$ $\geq$	5 -5
	$y_2 \geq 0$ $y_3 \geq 0$	-1 	$+2$ 2	 -1	 $+1$	$\geq$ $\geq$	-3 4
	Relation	$\leq$	$\leq$	$\leq$	$\leq$		$\leq$ Max v
	Constants	1	1	1	-1	$\geq$ Min z	

Here it is convenient to let $y_1' \geq 0$ and $y_1'' \geq 0$ be the dual variables corresponding to the first two inequalities. Since coefficients of y_1' and y_1'' differ only in sign in every inequality, we may set $y_1' - y_1'' = y_1$, where y_1 can have either sign. Note next that the coefficients in the inequalities of the dual corresponding to x_3' and x_3'' differ only in sign, which implies the equation

$$4(y_1' - y_1'') - y_3 = 1 \quad \text{or} \quad 4y_1 - y_3 = 1$$

From these observations it is clear that Table 6-2-II is the same as Table 6-2-III.

The Dual of the Standard Form.

We may apply the rules above to obtain the dual of the standard form; see Table 6-2-IV. It will be convenient to denote the dual variables (which in this case are unrestricted in sign) by $+\pi_i$ (instead of y_i in (2), which were restricted in sign).

TABLE 6-2-IV

		Primal					
	Variables	$x_1 \geq 0$	$x_2 \geq 0$	$\ldots$	$x_N \geq 0$	Relations	Constants
Dual	$+\pi_1$ $+\pi_2$ . . . $+\pi_M$	a_{11} a_{21} a_{M1}	a_{12} a_{22} $\ldots\ldots$ a_{M2}	$\cdots$ $\cdots$ $\cdots$	a_{1N} a_{2N} a_{MN}	$=$ $=$ . . . $=$	b_1 b_2 (Dual · obj.) . . b_M
	Relations	$\leq$	$\leq$	$\cdots$	$\leq$		$\leq$ Max v
	Constants	c_1	c_2 (Primal objective)	$\cdots$	c_N	$\geq$ Min z	

6-3. PROOF OF THE DUALITY THEOREM

The primal problem for the standard linear program given in Table 6-2-IV is to choose variables $x_j \geq 0$ and Min z, satisfying

$$(1) \qquad a_{11}\, x_1 + a_{12}\, x_2 + \ldots + a_{1\mathrm{N}}\, x_\mathrm{N} = b_1$$
$$a_{21}\, x_1 + a_{22}\, x_2 + \ldots + a_{2\mathrm{N}}\, x_\mathrm{N} = b_2$$
$$\cdots\cdots\cdots\cdots\cdots\cdots\cdots\cdots\cdots\cdots$$
$$a_{\mathrm{M}1} x_1 + a_{\mathrm{M}2} x_2 + \ldots + a_{\mathrm{MN}} x_\mathrm{N} = b_\mathrm{M}$$
$$c_1 x_1 + \quad c_2 x_2 + \ldots + \quad c_\mathrm{N} x_\mathrm{N} = z\ (\mathrm{Min})$$

The dual problem for the standard linear program is to choose variables $\pi_1, \pi_2, \ldots, \pi_\mathrm{M}$ and Max v, satisfying

$$(2) \qquad a_{11}\, \pi_1 + a_{21}\, \pi_2 + \ldots + a_{\mathrm{M}1}\, \pi_\mathrm{M} \leq c_1$$
$$a_{12}\, \pi_1 + a_{22}\, \pi_2 + \ldots + a_{\mathrm{M}2}\, \pi_\mathrm{M} \leq c_2$$
$$\cdots\cdots\cdots\cdots\cdots\cdots\cdots\cdots\cdots\cdots$$
$$a_{1\mathrm{N}} \pi_1 + a_{2\mathrm{N}} \pi_2 + \ldots + a_{\mathrm{MN}} \pi_\mathrm{M} \leq c_\mathrm{N}$$
$$b_1 \pi_1 + \quad b_2 \pi_2 + \ldots + \quad b_\mathrm{M} \pi_\mathrm{M} = v\ (\mathrm{Max})$$

where π_i is unrestricted in sign.

All four combinations of feasibility and infeasibility of the primal and dual systems are possible. The four cases may be summarized as follows:

	Primal has feasible solution(s)	Primal has no feasible solution
Dual has feasible solution(s)	Min z = Max v	Max $v \to +\infty$
Dual has no feasible solution	Min $z \to -\infty$	Possible

The following examples show that each case is possible.

	Primal $\qquad$ Dual
(a) Primal feasible, Dual feasible	$x_1 \geq 0$ $x_1 = 5 \qquad\qquad\qquad \pi_1 \leq 1$ $x_1 = z\ (\mathrm{Min}) \qquad\quad 5\pi_1 = v\ (\mathrm{Max})$ $\qquad$ [Min z = Max v = 5]
(b) Primal feasible, Dual infeasible	$x_1 \geq 0,\ x_2 \geq 0 \qquad \pi_1 \leq -1$ $x_1 - x_2 = 5 \qquad\quad -\pi_1 \leq -1$ $-x_1 - x_2 = z\ (\mathrm{Min}) \quad 5\pi_1 = v\ (\mathrm{Max})$ $\qquad\quad [z \to -\infty]$
(c) Primal infeasible, Dual feasible	$x_1 \geq 0$ $x_1 = -5 \qquad\qquad\quad \pi_1 \leq 1$ $x_1 = z\ (\mathrm{Min}) \qquad -5\pi_1 = v\ (\mathrm{Max})$ $\qquad\quad [v \to +\infty]$
(d) Primal infeasible, Dual infeasible	$x_1 \geq 0,\ x_2 \geq 0$ $x_1 - x_2 = +5 \qquad\quad \pi_1 + \pi_2 \leq -1$ $x_1 - x_2 = -5 \qquad\quad -\pi_1 - \pi_2 \leq -1$ $-x_1 - x_2 = z\ (\mathrm{Min}) \quad 5\pi_1 - 5\pi_2 = +v\ (\mathrm{Max})$

Proof of Duality Theorem and Related Theorems.

We shall use the simplex method to establish a group of fundamental theorems concerned with duality.

THEOREM 1: *Duality Theorem. If feasible solutions to both the primal and dual systems exist, there exists an optimum solution to both systems and*

$$\text{Min } z = \text{Max } v$$

THEOREM 2: *Unboundedness Theorem.*

(a) *If a feasible solution to the primal system exists, but not to the dual, there exists a class of solutions to the primal, such that* $z \to -\infty$.

(b) *If a feasible solution to the dual system exists, but not to the primal, there exists a class of solutions to the dual, such that* $v \to +\infty$.

THEOREM 3: *Infeasibility Theorem.*

(a) *If a system of linear equations in nonnegative variables is infeasible, there exists a linear combination of the equations which is an infeasible equation.*

(b) *If a system of linear inequalities is infeasible, there exists a nonnegative linear combination of the inequalities which is an infeasible inequality.*

Since a system of equations in nonnegative variables is equivalent to a linear inequality system, and conversely, Theorem 3(b) is a restatement of Theorem 3(a) in the equivalent system. Since the dual of a dual system is equivalent to the primal system, as we have just seen, Theorem 2(b) is a restatement of Theorem 2(a) for the dual system.

We shall, however, give direct proofs of all parts of these theorems by applying the simplex method. Before doing so, let us make a few preliminary observations that are related to the proof of the duality theorem.

When feasible solutions exist for both the primal and the dual problems, an important relation exists between the values of v and those of z, namely, the values of v are always less than (or equal to) the values of z. This was depicted in § 6-2-(3). To prove this, let $(x_1, x_2, \ldots, x_N, \text{ and } z)$ be any solution to the primal system (1), and let $(\pi_1, \pi_2, \ldots, \pi_M, \text{ and } v)$ be any solution to the dual system (2). Let us denote by $\bar{c}_j \geq 0$ the differences between the right and left members of (2), thus

$$(3) \qquad c_j - \sum_{i=1}^{M} a_{ij}\pi_i = \bar{c}_j \qquad (j = 1, 2, \ldots, N)$$

If we multiply the first equation of the primal system (1) by π_1, the second by $\pi_2, \ldots$, and subtract the sum of the resulting equations from the z-equation, we obtain immediately

$$(4) \qquad \bar{c}_1 x_1 + \bar{c}_2 x_2 + \ldots + \bar{c}_N x_N = z - v$$

The fact that $\bar{c}_j \geq 0$, $x_j \geq 0$ implies that all terms which appear on the left are nonnegative; hence, for any solution of the dual, $0 \leq z - v$ or,

$$(5) \qquad z \geq v$$

[129]

Thus, when solutions to both the primal and dual systems exist, the value of z for any primal solution forms an *upper bound* for values of v, and the value of v of any dual solution forms a *lower bound* for values of z; therefore, it is not possible in this case for either $z \to -\infty$ or $v \to +\infty$. Thus it is clear, *if optimum solutions exist*[2] to the primal and dual problems, then for such solutions

$$(6) \qquad \qquad \text{Min } z \geq \text{Max } v$$

This is known as the *weak form* of the Duality Theorem.

To establish Theorem 1, we consider an auxiliary problem formed from (1) by first changing the signs of the terms of each equation i (if necessary), so that $b_i \geq 0$, and then introducing an "error" or "artificial" variable $x_{N+i} \geq 0$. Let us define variables $w \geq 0$ and $w' \geq 0$ by

$$(7) \qquad \qquad w = \sum_1^M x_{N+i}; \qquad w + w' = W$$

where w measures the total sum of errors x_{N+i}. W is some known upper bound on the total error, and $w' \geq 0$ measures the slack between w and W. For example, an upper bound which could be used for w is $W = \sum_1^M b_i$, which corresponds to the initial basic solution of Phase I (see § 5-2).

Auxiliary Problem. Find $x_j \geq 0$, w', z such that $z = \text{Min } z$, given that $w' = \text{Max } w'$, which satisfy

$$(8) \quad \begin{aligned} a_{11} x_1 + \ldots + a_{1N} x_N + x_{N+1} & & = b_1 \\ & & \\ \cdots\cdots\cdots\cdots\cdots\cdots\cdots\cdots & & \\ a_{M1} x_1 + \ldots + a_{MN} x_N & \quad x_{N+M} & = b_M \\ x_{N+1} + \ldots + x_{N+M} + (w') & \Rightarrow W \\ c_1 x_1 + \ldots + c_N x_N & (-z) = 0 \end{aligned}$$

It will be noted that (8) is just the standard form for Phase I of the simplex method, if w' is replaced by $W - w$. It will be in canonical form with respect to $x_{N+1}, \ldots, x_{N+M}$, w', $-z$ after elimination of these variables from the w'-form. We can now proceed to maximize w', which means we are minimizing $w = W - w'$. Since a lower bound to w exists (namely 0), there exists by Theorem 1 of § 6-1 an optimal canonical form at termination of this Phase I, such that all the coefficients and the constant in the w'-equation (9) are nonnegative.

$$(9) \qquad \sum_{j=1}^{N+M} \bar{d}_j x_j + w' = +\bar{w}_0' \qquad \qquad (\bar{d}_j \geq 0, \ \bar{w}_0' \geq 0)$$

[2] Notice that at this point we do not know that a minimizing solution to the primal or a maximizing solution to the dual exists.

On the other hand, this equation was generated from the auxiliary system (8) by a sequence of pivot operations; this implies that there exists some linear combination of the equations $i = 1, 2, \ldots, M$ of (8) with weights $\sigma_1^o, \sigma_2^o, \ldots, \sigma_M^o$, which, added to the w'-equation of (8), yields (9). The weights $\sigma_i = \sigma_i^o$ therefore satisfy

$$\sum_{i=1}^{M} \sigma_i^o a_{ij} = \bar{d}_j \geq 0, \qquad \text{for } j = 1, 2, \ldots, N,$$

(10)
$$\sigma_i^o + 1 = \bar{d}_{N+i} \geq 0, \qquad \text{for } i = 1, 2, \ldots, M,$$

$$\sum_{i=1}^{M} \sigma_i^o b_i + W = \bar{w}_0' \geq 0$$

Taking this *same* linear combination of equations of the primal system (1), and setting $\bar{w}_0 = W - \bar{w}_0'$, yields

(11)
$$\sum_{j=1}^{N} \bar{d}_j x_j = -\bar{w}_0 \qquad\qquad (\bar{d}_j \geq 0, \; \bar{w}_0 \geq 0)$$

In particular, if feasible solutions to (1) exist, Min $w = \bar{w}_0 = 0$. On the other hand, if no feasible solution to the primal exists, so that $\bar{w}_0 > 0$, then (11) becomes an infeasible equation in nonnegative variables x_j; this establishes Theorem 3(a).

Let us now assume a solution $(\pi_1 = \pi_1^o, \ldots, \pi_M = \pi_M^o)$ to the dual exists, so that

(12)
$$\sum_{i=1}^{M} \pi_i^o a_{ij} \leq c_j \qquad\qquad (j = 1, 2, \ldots, N)$$

$$\sum_{i=1}^{M} \pi_i^o b_i = v^o$$

then the dual relations (12) are also satisfied by the class of solutions $\pi_1 = (\pi_1^o - \theta\sigma_1^o), \ldots, \pi_M = (\pi_M^o - \theta\sigma_M^o), \; v = v^o + \theta\bar{w}_0$, for any $\theta > 0$ because, by (12) and (10),

(13)
$$\sum_{i=1}^{M} (\pi_i^o - \theta\sigma_i^o) a_{ij} = \sum_{i=1}^{M} \pi_i^o a_{ij} - \theta\bar{d}_j \leq c_j$$

$$\sum_{i=1}^{M} (\pi_i^o - \theta\sigma_i^o) b_i = v^o + \theta\bar{w}_0 = v$$

Let us assume, in addition, that the primal problem is infeasible, so that Min $w = \bar{w}_0 > 0$. Then this class of solutions to the dual has the property that $v = v^o + \theta\bar{w}_0 \to \infty$ as $\theta \to +\infty$, establishing Theorem 2(b).

Our objective now is to seek a solution to our system (8), that *minimizes*

[131]

z for some specified value of W, starting with the last achieved canonical form (end of Phase I). The value of W that we choose at this stage may be the one we used initially or any other $W \geq Min\ w$. For example, we might redefine W to be Min w, as is customary in the usual Phase II procedure, in which case the value of the constant $\bar{w}_0'$ in the canonical form at the end of Phase I becomes $\bar{w}_0' = 0$. Whatever the choice of $W \geq Min\ w$, we shall refer to this as *the Phase II problem*.

According to Theorem 1 of § 6-1, if we begin with this adjusted canonical form, there exists a final canonical form, after a sequence of pivot operations, that yields either a solution that minimizes z or a class of solutions for which $z \rightarrow -\infty$. Let us consider the latter first.

The case $z \rightarrow -\infty$, for the auxiliary problem can arise only if some column, $j = s$, in the final canonical form (obtained at the end of Phase II), consists of all $\bar{a}_{is} \leq 0$ and $\bar{c}_s < 0$. We now observe that if an artificial variable, x_{N+i}, is in the final basic set, the corresponding row coefficient $\bar{a}_{is} = 0$, because otherwise an increase of the variable $x_s \rightarrow +\infty$ would generate an allowable class of solutions, with values of $x_{N+i} \rightarrow +\infty$, contradicting our hypothesis that $w = \sum x_{N+i} \leq W$. For the same reason x_s cannot correspond to any artificial variable x_{N+k}; hence, $1 \leq s \leq N$. In the final canonical form, we now note that we can obviously form the coefficients in column s as a linear combination of the coefficients[3] in columns corresponding to the basic variables $x_{j_1}, x_{j_2}, \ldots, x_{j_M}; -w, -z$ with weights $+\bar{a}_{1s}, +\bar{a}_{2s}, \ldots, +\bar{a}_{Ms}; \bar{d}_s, \bar{c}_s$ (because the matrix of coefficients of these columns is all zero, except for ones down the diagonal). This same linear combination must hold not only for the corresponding columns of the auxiliary system (8) but also for those of the primal system (1) because the weights $\bar{a}_{is}$ corresponding to augmented columns of (8), if any, have all zero values.[4] This is displayed in (14) in conventional matrix notation as discussed later in Chapter 8.

$$(14) \quad \begin{bmatrix} a_{1j_1} & a_{1j_2} & \cdots & a_{1j_M} & 0 & 0 \\ a_{2j_1} & a_{2j_2} & \cdots & a_{2j_M} & 0 & 0 \\ \cdot & \cdot & & \cdot & \cdot & \cdot \\ \cdot & \cdot & & \cdot & \cdot & \cdot \\ \cdot & \cdot & & \cdot & \cdot & \cdot \\ a_{Mj_1} & a_{Mj_2} & \cdots & a_{Mj_M} & 0 & 0 \\ 0 & 0 & \cdots & 0 & +1 & 0 \\ c_{j_1} & c_{j_2} & \cdots & c_{j_M} & 0 & +1 \end{bmatrix} \begin{bmatrix} \bar{a}_{1s} \\ \bar{a}_{2s} \\ \cdot \\ \cdot \\ \cdot \\ \bar{a}_{Ms} \\ \bar{d}_s \\ \bar{c}_s \end{bmatrix} = \begin{bmatrix} a_{1s} \\ a_{2s} \\ \cdot \\ \cdot \\ \cdot \\ a_{Ms} \\ 0 \\ c_s \end{bmatrix}$$

[3] By a linear combination of columns we mean a column of numbers formed by multiplying the corresponding entries in each column by weights associated with the column and summing the products. See Chapter 8 where such operations on column "vectors" are discussed.

[4] *Exercise:* Show that if a certain linear combination of the columns of a linear system vanishes before pivoting, it will vanish after pivoting, and conversely.

Exercise: When is it valid to form linear combinations of inequalities to form a new inequality?

As applied to the coefficients in the z-equation, this yields, in particular, the relation $+c_{j_1}\bar{a}_{1s} + c_{j_2}\bar{a}_{2s} + \ldots + c_{j_M}\bar{a}_{Ms} + \bar{c}_s = c_s$. Since the *columns* of the primal are in one-to-one correspondence with the *linear inequalities* of the dual system, this and the other relations state that if we multiply inequality j_1 of the dual system (2) by $-\bar{a}_{1s} \geq 0$, inequality j_2 by $-\bar{a}_{2s} \geq 0$, . . ., inequality j_M by $-\bar{a}_{Ms} \geq 0$, and inequality $j = s$ by $+1$, and then sum, we will form the infeasible inequality

$$(15) \qquad\qquad 0 \cdot \pi_1 + 0 \cdot \pi_2 + \ldots + 0 \cdot \pi_M \leq \bar{c}_s \qquad (\bar{c}_s < 0)$$

This proves that *the dual system is infeasible if* $z \rightarrow -\infty$ *for the auxiliary problem.*

The case of z having a finite lower bound for the auxiliary problem arises only if a canonical form is obtained for (8) at the end of Phase II, such that the coefficients are nonnegative in the z-equation,

$$(16) \qquad\qquad \sum_{j=1}^{N+M} \bar{c}_j^* x_j + \pi_w^* w' = z - \bar{z}_0 \qquad (\bar{c}_j^* \geq 0, \bar{z}_0 = \text{Min } z)$$

On the other hand, this equation can be formed directly from (8) by taking some linear combination of equations $i = 1, 2, \ldots, M$ with weights $-\pi_i^*$, the w-equation with weight $+\pi_w^*$, and the z-equation with weight 1. Since coefficients of x_j for $j = 1, 2, \ldots, N$ are all zero in the w-equation, we have constructed a feasible solution to dual $\pi_i = \pi_i^*$,

$$(17) \qquad \begin{aligned} \sum_{i=1}^{M} \pi_i^* a_{ij} &\leq c_j \qquad\qquad (j = 1, 2, \ldots, N) \\[2mm] \sum_{i=1}^{M} \pi_i^* b_i &= \bar{z}_0 + \pi_w^* W = v^* \end{aligned}$$

This proves that *the dual system is feasible if* z *has a finite lower bound for any auxiliary problem whatever be the choice of* $W \geq 0$. Thus feasibility of the primal depends on the outcome of Phase I and feasibility of the dual on the outcome of Phase II (independent of the outcome of Phase I).

Assuming infeasibility of the dual system of inequalities, so that $z \rightarrow -\infty$ for any $W \geq 0$, then we have constructed the infeasible inequality (15). Theorem 3(b) is thus established. If the primal problem is also feasible and W was replaced at the beginning of Phase II by $W = 0$, then a class of primal *feasible* solutions has been constructed at the end of Phase II such that the values of z tend to $-\infty$. This establishes Theorem 2(a).

Assuming a feasible solution to the primal exists and W replaced by $W = 0$ for Phase II and assuming a feasible solution to the dual exists so that Phase II has a finite lower bound, then setting $W = 0$ in (17), we have shown the existence of feasible solutions to both systems such that

Min $z = z_0 = v^*$. But any z associated with a primal feasible solution is an upper bound for v, hence

(18) $$\text{Max } v = \text{Min } z$$

establishing the Duality Theorem (Theorem 1).

6-4. BASIC THEOREMS ON DUALITY

Consider a system in standard form—we now state and prove the following related and important theorems.

THEOREM 1: *If $(x_1^*, \ldots, x_N^*, z^*)$ is a feasible solution to the primal and $(\pi_1^*, \ldots, \pi_M^*, v^*)$ is a feasible solution to the dual, satisfying for $j = 1, 2, \ldots, N$,*

(1) $$\bar{c}_j^* = c_j - \sum_{i=1}^{M} \pi_i^* a_{ij} \geq 0, \quad \sum_{1}^{M} \pi_i^* b_i = v^*$$

a necessary and sufficient condition for optimality of both solutions is

(2) $$\bar{c}_j^* = 0 \quad for \quad x_j^* > 0$$

THEOREM 2: *If a feasible solution exists for the primal, and z has a finite lower bound, an optimal feasible solution exists.*

THEOREM 3: *If an optimal feasible solution exists for the primal, there exists an optimal feasible solution to the dual.*

PROOF OF THEOREM 1: Let $x_j \geq 0$ be any feasible solution satisfying § 6-3-(1), and π_i be any multipliers, such that $\bar{c}_j \geq 0$ (see § 6-3-(3)). If the first equation of § 6-3-(1) is multiplied by π_1, the second by $\pi_2, \ldots,$ etc., and the weighted sum of the first M equations is subtracted from the z-equation, there results

(3) $$\bar{c}_1 x_1 + \bar{c}_2 x_2 + \ldots + \bar{c}_N x_N = z - v$$

Since $\bar{c}_j \geq 0$ and $x_j \geq 0$ by hypothesis, the left-hand side is nonnegative term by term, hence always

(4) $$v = \sum_{i=1}^{M} \pi_i b_i \leq z$$

and v is a lower bound for values of z. By the hypothesis of Theorem 1, there is a particular feasible solution $x_j = x_j^* \geq 0$, $z = z^*$, and particular multipliers, $\pi_i = \pi_i^*$ and $\bar{c}_j^*$, such that $\bar{c}_j^* = 0$, if $x_j^* > 0$. Substituting these values in (3), the left-hand side vanishes term by term and $v^* = z^*$, and we conclude, by § 6-3-(6), that Max $v = v^* = z^* = $ Min z.

To show the necessity part of Theorem 1, we assume $v^* = z^*$. Substituting into (3) *all terms on the left must vanish*, which means $\bar{c}_j^* = 0$ for $x_j^* > 0$.

[134]

PROOF OF THEOREM 2: A proof of this theorem was given in § 6-2 and is an immediate consequence of applying the simplex algorithm to the auxiliary problem specified there. We have shown that in a finite number of cycles the process will terminate because (a) no feasible solution exists, (b) a class of feasible solutions has been constructed for which $z \to -\infty$, or (c) a basic optimal feasible solution $x_j = x_j^*$ has been obtained. Since cases (a) and (b) are ruled out by hypothesis, the theorem follows.

PROOF OF THEOREM 3: Referring again to the auxiliary problem of § 6-3-(8), the hypothesis of Theorem 3 satisfies the case of a feasible primal and finite minimum z. Hence there exist optimal multipliers for the dual, namely π_i^*, v^* specified in § 6-3-(17), (18).

Complementary Slackness in the Primal and Dual Systems.

When the primal and dual systems are expressed as systems of inequalities, Theorem 1 takes on a more symmetric form.

Let $x_j \geq 0$ be any feasible solution satisfying § 6-2-(1) and $y_i \geq 0$ be any feasible solution satisfying § 6-2-(2). We write the former in standard-equality form: Find $x_j \geq 0$, Min z, satisfying

$$
(5) \quad
\begin{aligned}
a_{11}x_1 + a_{12}x_2 + \ldots + a_{1n}x_n - x_{n+1} \qquad\qquad\qquad &= b_1 \\
a_{21}x_1 + a_{22}x_2 + \ldots + a_{2n}x_n \qquad - x_{n+2} \qquad\qquad &= b_2 \\
\ldots\ldots\ldots\ldots\ldots\ldots\ldots\ldots\ldots\ldots\ldots\ldots\ldots\ldots\ldots\ldots & \\
a_{m1}x_1 + a_{m2}x_2 + \ldots + a_{mn}x_n \qquad\qquad - x_{n+m} &= b_m \\
c_1x_1 + c_2x_2 + \ldots + c_nx_n \qquad\qquad\qquad\qquad &= z \ (\text{Min})
\end{aligned}
$$

where $x_{n+i} \geq 0$ are variables that measure the extent of inequality, or *negative slack*, between the left- and right-hand sides of the ith inequality.

It will be convenient also to let y_{m+j} measure the *positive slack* in the jth inequality, $j = 1, 2, \ldots, n$, of the dual system. Thus § 6-2-(2) in standard-equality form becomes: find $y_i \geq 0$, Max v satisfying

$$
(6) \quad
\begin{aligned}
a_{11}y_1 + a_{21}y_2 + \ldots + a_{m1}y_m + y_{m+1} \qquad\qquad\qquad &= c_1 \\
a_{12}y_1 + a_{22}y_2 + \ldots + a_{m2}y_{in} \qquad + y_{m+2} \qquad\qquad &= c_2 \\
\ldots\ldots\ldots\ldots\ldots\ldots\ldots\ldots\ldots\ldots\ldots\ldots\ldots\ldots\ldots\ldots & \\
a_{1n}y_1 + a_{2n}y_2 + \ldots + a_{mn}y_m \qquad\qquad + y_{m+n} &= c_n \\
b_1y_1 + b_2y_2 + \ldots + b_my_m \qquad\qquad\qquad\qquad &= v \ (\text{Max})
\end{aligned}
$$

Multiplying the ith equation of (5) by y_i, $i = 1, 2, \ldots, m$, and subtracting their sum from the z-form yields

$$
(7) \quad (c_1 - \sum_{i=1}^{m} a_{i1}y_i)x_1 + (c_2 - \sum_{i=1}^{m} a_{i2}y_i)x_2 + \ldots + (c_n - \sum_{i=1}^{m} a_{in}y_i)x_n
$$

$$
+ y_1 x_{n+1} + y_2 x_{n+2} + \ldots + y_m x_{n+m} = z - \sum_{i=1}^{m} y_i b_i
$$

or, from the definitions of y_{m+j} and v given in (6) we have,

(8) $(y_{m+1}x_1 + y_{m+2}x_2 + \ldots + y_{m+n}x_n)$
$$+ (y_1x_{n+1} + y_2x_{n+2} + \ldots + y_nx_{n+m}) = z - v$$

The left-hand side of (8) is nonnegative term by term, hence $0 \le z - v$ or $v \le z$.

Since we are assuming that primal and dual solutions exist, the hypothesis of the Duality Theorem is satisfied and there exist optimal feasible solutions to both systems. We shall now prove

THEOREM 4: *For optimal feasible solutions of the primal and dual systems, whenever slack occurs in the kth relation of either system, the kth variable of its dual vanishes; if the kth variable is positive in either system, the kth relation of its dual is equality.*

PROOF: Let $x_j = x_j^* \ge 0$ $(j = 1, 2, \ldots, n)$, $z = z^*$ and $y_i = y_i^* \ge 0$ $(i = 1, 2, \ldots, m)$, $v = v^*$ be the values associated with an optimal solution to the primal and the dual, and let $x_{n+i}^* \ge 0$ and $y_{m+j}^* \ge 0$ be the corresponding values of the slack variables obtained by substitution in (5) and (6); then $z^* - v^* = \text{Min } z - \text{Max } v = 0$ by the fundamental theorem, so that the right-hand side of (8) vanishes. However, as noted in the sequel to (8), each term on the left is nonnegative and hence must vanish term by term; i.e., $y_{m+j}^*x_j^* = 0$ and $y_i^*x_{n+i}^* = 0$. However, the term $y_{m+j}^*x_j^* = 0$ is the product of the slack in the jth relation of the dual and its corresponding variable in the primal; the term $y_i^*x_{n+i}^*$ is the product of slack in the ith relation of the primal and its corresponding dual variable. Hence, if $y_{m+j}^* > 0$, then $x_j^* = 0$; similarly, if $x_{n+i}^* > 0$, then $y_i^* = 0$. This is a restatement of Theorem 1 on the correspondence between an optimal solution of the primal system and the corresponding slack relations of an optimal solution of the dual system.

Homogeneous Systems.

There are several important duality-type theorems that predated the linear programming era [Tucker, 1956-1]. The earliest known result on feasibility is one concerning *homogeneous systems* (systems with constant terms all zero).

THEOREM 5: [Gordan, 1873-1] *Either a linear homogeneous system of equations possesses a nontrivial solution in nonnegative variables or there exists an equation, formed by taking some linear combination, that has all positive coefficients.*

PROOF: Let the homogeneous system for $i = 1, 2, \ldots, m - 1$ be

$$(9) \qquad \sum_{j=1}^{n} a_{ij}x_j = 0 \qquad (x_j \ge 0)$$

If such a system possesses a nontrivial solution (not all $x_j = 0$), a solution exists that also satisfies

$$(10) \qquad \sum_{j=1}^{n} x_j = 1$$

We shall treat (10) as the mth equation of the system. According to the Infeasibility Theorem, §6-3, Theorem 3(a), *either* there exists a feasible solution *or* there exist multipliers $(\pi_1, \pi_2, \ldots, \pi_{m-1}; \pi_m)$, such that the resulting linear combination is an infeasible equation in nonnegative variables;

$$(11) \qquad \sum_{j=1}^{n} d_j x_j = -\bar{w}_0 \qquad \text{where } d_j \geq 0, \bar{w}_0 > 0$$

It follows under the second alternative that $\pi_m = -\bar{w}_0 < 0$ and

$$(12) \qquad \sum_{i=1}^{m-1} a_{ij} \pi_i = d_j - \pi_m > 0 \qquad (j = 1, 2, \ldots, n)$$

Hence, if multipliers $(\pi_1, \pi_2, \ldots, \pi_m)$ are used to form the linear combination of the equations (9), the coefficients of the resulting equation are given by (12) and are all positive.

EXERCISE: Show the converse of Gordan's Theorem, namely, if there exists a linear combination whose coefficients are all positive, the homogeneous system in nonnegative variables possesses only a trivial solution.

THEOREM 6. [Farkas' Lemma, 1902-1] *If a linear homogeneous inequality,*

$$(13) \qquad \sum_{i=1}^{m} \pi_i b_i \leq 0$$

holds for all sets of values of π_i satisfying a system of homogeneous inequalities

$$(14) \qquad \sum_{i=1}^{m} a_{ij} \pi_i \leq 0 \qquad (j = 1, 2, \ldots, n)$$

then the inequality is a nonnegative linear combination of the inequalities of the system.

PROOF: Assume there exists no nonnegative linear combination of (14) that yields (13). Then there exists no feasible solution to the system

$$(15) \qquad \sum_{j=1}^{n} a_{ij} x_j = b_i \qquad (x_j \geq 0)$$

By Theorem 3(a) of §6-3, there exist multipliers $\pi_i = \pi_i^o$, which, when applied to (15), yield an infeasible equation; the coefficients of this equation are

$$(16) \qquad \sum_{i=1}^{m} a_{ij} \pi_i^o \leq 0 \qquad (j = 1, 2, \ldots, n)$$

$$\sum_{i=1}^{m} b_i \pi_i^o = \bar{w}_0 > 0$$

which contradicts (13).

EXERCISE: What is the analogue of this theorem for linear equation systems?

THEOREM 7: [Stiemke, 1915-1] *Either a linear homogeneous system possesses a solution with all variables positive, or there exists a linear combination that has all nonnegative coefficients, one or more of which are positive.*

PROOF: If the homogeneous system possesses a strictly positive solution, there exists a solution to the system

$$(17) \qquad \sum_{j=1}^{n} a_{ij}x_j = 0 \qquad\qquad (i = 1, 2, \ldots, m)$$

$$x_j \geq 1 \qquad\qquad (j = 1, 2, \ldots, n)$$

Replacing $x_j \geq 1$ by $x_j = x'_j + 1$, where $x'_j \geq 0$, results in the system

$$(18) \qquad \sum_{j=1}^{n} a_{ij}x'_j = - \sum_{j=1}^{n} a_{ij} \qquad\qquad (x'_j \geq 0)$$

By Theorem 3(a) of § 6-3, *either* this system possesses a feasible solution (which is the first alternative), *or* there exist multipliers $\pi_1, \pi_2, \ldots, \pi_m$, such that the resulting linear combination

$$(19) \qquad \sum_{j=1}^{n} d_j x_j = -\bar{w}_0 \qquad\qquad (d_j \geq 0, +\bar{w}_0 \geq 0).$$

is an infeasible equation in nonnegative variables. In the latter case $\bar{w}_0 > 0$) It is also easy to see that $\sum_1^n d_j = \bar{w}_0$, because the negative sum of the coefficients of each equation (18), from which it was derived, equals the corresponding constant term. It follows that at least one coefficient d_j of this equation must be positive (which is the second alternative).

Motzkin's Transposition Theorem [1936-1].

Consider the dual linear programs satisfying the Tucker Diagram (20).

			Primal				
		Variables	$x_1 \geq 0, \ldots, x_k \geq 0$		$x_{k+1} \geq 0, \ldots, x_n \geq 0$		Constants
(20)	Dual	u_1 u_2 $\cdot$ $\cdot$ $\cdot$ u_m	a_{11} $\cdots$ a_{1k} a_{21} $\cdots$ a_{2k} $\ldots\ldots\ldots$ a_{m1} $\cdots$ a_{mk}		a_{1k+1} $\cdots$ a_{1n} a_{2k+1} $\cdots$ a_{2n} $\ldots\ldots\ldots$ a_{mk+1} $\cdots$ a_{mn}		$= 0$ $= 0$ $\cdot$ $\cdot$ $\cdot$ $= 0$
		Relations	$\leq$	$\leq$	$\leq$	$\leq$	
		Constants	0	0	0	0	

We assume all columns are non-vacuous. Consider *any arbitrary subset* of k columns; for example the first k columns shown in (20) to the left of the vertical dashed line.

THEOREM 8: *Either there exists a solution to the dual system, such that all inequalities corresponding to the subset hold strictly, or the primal system has a solution, such that at least one corresponding variable has positive value.*

PROOF: If there exists a solution to the primal system with the requisite property, then one exists such that

$$(21) \qquad x_1 + x_2 + \ldots + x_k = 1$$

where $j = 1, 2, \ldots, k$ is the assumed subset. The remainder of the proof parallels that of Theorem 5.

Theorem of Alternatives for Matrices [Ville, 1938-1].

Consider the dual homogeneous programs with vacuous objective forms,

$$(22) \qquad \sum_{j=1}^{n} a_{ij}x_j \geq 0, \qquad x_j \geq 0 \qquad (i = 1, 2, \ldots, m)$$

and

$$(23) \qquad \sum_{i=1}^{m} a_{ij}y_i \leq 0, \qquad y_i \geq 0 \qquad (j = 1, 2, \ldots, n)$$

and let either system be the primal and the other the dual.

THEOREM 9: *Either there exists a solution to the primal where all inequalities hold strictly or there exists a nontrivial solution to the dual.*

EXERCISE: Show that this theorem is a special case of the Transposition Theorem by introducing slack variables into the primal system.

EXERCISE: Given two solutions to a homogeneous system (22), show that the sum of their corresponding values is also a solution.

EXERCISE: Suppose there exists a solution to a homogeneous system of inequalities all satisfied with strict equalities. Show that there exists a solution if the zero constants are all replaced by ones.

Tucker's Complementary Slackness Theorem [1956-1].

A sharper form of the Theorem of Alternatives can be obtained by judicious application of the Transposition Theorem.

THEOREM 10: *There exist solutions to the homogeneous dual programs (22) and (23) such that every variable and its complementary slack have one positive and one zero value.*

PROOF: Augment the systems with slack variables as in (5) and (6). Partition the primal system so that the subset consists of the one slack variable, x_{n+p}. By Theorem 8, a solution can be obtained such that either $x_{n+p} > 0$ for the primal system or $y_p > 0$ for the dual. If a solution to the primal exists with $x_{n+p} > 0$, let $x_j = x_j^p$ for $j = 1, 2, \ldots, n, \ldots, n + m$

be this solution, and let $y_i = y_i^p = 0$ for $i = 1, 2, \ldots, m, \ldots, m + n$ be an associated (trivial) solution to the dual. On the other hand, if a solution to the dual exists with $y_p > 0$, let the values of y_i for this solution be $y_i = y_i^p$ and let $x_j = x_j^p = 0$ be the values of x_j for an associated (trivial) solution to the primal. If now we *add* the corresponding values x_j^p and y_j^p for different p, we will obtain a pair of "composite" solutions to the primal and dual systems with the property that every slack variable of the primal or its corresponding dual variable has a positive value.

If we interchange the role of the primal and dual systems, we can generate another pair of composite solutions with the property that every variable of the (original) primal or its corresponding dual slack has positive value. Let us now add these two pairs of composite solutions. This will yield solutions to the primal and dual systems with the property that at least one member of each complementary pair is positive. The proof of Theorem 10 is completed by proving the following:

EXERCISE: Referring to (8), show for the homogeneous case (all $b_i = 0$, $c_j = 0$) every solution to the primal and dual systems is optimal and the products of all complementary pairs vanish.

6-5. LAGRANGE MULTIPLIERS

There is another way in which the dual system might arise. In the calculus if we wish to minimize a function z of two variables

$$(1) \qquad F(x_1, x_2) = z$$

subject to the relation

$$(2) \qquad G(x_1, x_2) = 0$$

between x_1 and x_2, the standard procedure is to find the *unrestricted* minimum of the function Z given by

$$(3) \qquad Z = F(x_1, x_2) - \pi G(x_1, x_2)$$

where π is a parameter, called the Lagrange multiplier, whose value will be specified later. If the unrestricted minimum of Z for some fixed value $\pi = \pi^o$ happens to be at values $x_1 = x_1^o$, $x_2 = x_2^o$ that satisfy (2), then these clearly are the values that minimize (1) subject to (2), since $Z = z$ for all (x_1, x_2) satisfying (2). We assume that a value of π can be found for which this is the case, and that at an unrestricted minimum the partial derivatives of Z with respect to x_1 and x_2 exist and vanish. This yields two equations in two unknowns, x_1 and x_2, which can be solved for x_1 and x_2 in terms of π. The value of π is obtained by substituting the expressions of x_1 and x_2 into (2); in other words, the value of π is then adjusted so that the unrestricted minimizing solution satisfies (2).

For example, let us find the point (x_1, x_2) on the unit circle the sum of whose coordinates, z, is a minimum:

(4)
$$x_1^2 + x_2^2 = 1$$
$$x_1 + x_2 = z$$

We consider the unrestricted minimum of the expression

(5)
$$Z = (x_1 + x_2) - \pi(x_1^2 + x_2^2 - 1)$$

At an unrestricted minimum the partials of Z with respect to x_1 and x_2 vanish:

(6)
$$\frac{\partial Z}{\partial x_1} = 0: \quad 1 - 2x_1\pi = 0$$

$$\frac{\partial Z}{\partial x_2} = 0: \quad 1 - 2x_2\pi = 0$$

Whence the minimizing solution is $x_1 = x_2 = 1/(2\pi)$. We now determine π, so that the solution satisfies the equation of the circle; substituting,

(7)
$$\left(\frac{1}{2\pi}\right)^2 + \left(\frac{1}{2\pi}\right)^2 = 1$$

or $\pi = \pm\sqrt{2}/2$, whence $(x_1 = 1/\sqrt{2}, \ x_2 = 1/\sqrt{2})$ or $(x_1 = -1/\sqrt{2}, x_2 = -1/\sqrt{2})$. The first solution *maximizes* the sum of the coordinates, and the second (the solution sought) *minimizes*.

The same procedure is followed in general if the problem is to find values that minimize $F(x_1, x_2, \ldots, x_n) = z$, subject to the k restrictions

(8)
$$G_1(x_1, x_2, \ldots, x_n) = 0$$
$$G_2(x_1, x_2, \ldots, x_n) = 0$$
$$\cdots\cdots\cdots\cdots\cdots\cdots$$
$$G_k(x_1, x_2, \ldots, x_n) = 0$$

In this case the unrestricted minimum of the function

(9)
$$Z = F(x_1, x_2, \ldots, x_n) - [\pi_1 G_1(x_1, x_2, \ldots, x_n) + \pi_2 G_2(x_1, x_2, \ldots, x_n)$$
$$+ \ldots + \pi_k G_k(x_1, x_2, \ldots, x_n)]$$

is found, where the π_i, Lagrange multipliers, are unspecified constants to be determined later. It is assumed that values of π_i can be found so that the unrestricted minimum solution satisfies the restrictions. The n equations resulting from the vanishing of the n partial derivatives of this expression at a minimum are solved for $x_1, x_2, \ldots, x_n$ in terms of $\pi_1, \pi_2, \ldots, \pi_k$. These values are substituted into the k expressions $G_i(x_1, x_2, \ldots, x_n) = 0$, and the resulting k equations in $\pi_1, \pi_2, \ldots, \pi_k$ are solved for $\pi_1, \pi_2, \ldots, \pi_k$.

For example, consider the *linear programming problem*

(10)
$$x_1 + 2x_2 + 3x_3 = 6 \qquad (x_1 \geq 0, x_2 \geq 0, x_3 \geq 0)$$
$$x_1 + \ \ x_2 + \ \ x_3 = z \ (\text{Min})$$

This is equivalent to the system in (real) variables x_1, x_2, x_3 and the squares of real variables u_1, u_2, u_3:

Lagrange multipliers:

$$(11) \qquad
\begin{aligned}
x_1 - u_1^2 && &= 0 && : \bar{c}_1 \\
& x_2 - u_2^2 & &= 0 && : \bar{c}_2 \\
&& x_3 - u_3^2 &= 0 && : \bar{c}_3 \\
x_1 &+ 2x_2 &+ 3x_3 &= 6 && : \pi \\
x_1 &+ x_2 &+ x_3 &= z \ (\text{Min})
\end{aligned}$$

where the first three equations replace the nonnegative restrictions. We now find the unrestricted minimum of the expression

$$(12) \quad Z = (x_1 + x_2 + x_3) - \bar{c}_1(x_1 - u_1^2) - \bar{c}_2(x_2 - u_2^2)$$
$$- \bar{c}_3(x_3 - u_3^2) - \pi(x_1 + 2x_2 + 3x_3 - 6)$$

or

$$(13) \quad Z = 6\pi + (1 - \pi - \bar{c}_1)x_1 + (1 - 2\pi - \bar{c}_2)x_2 + (1 - 3\pi - \bar{c}_3)x_3$$
$$+ \bar{c}_1 u_1^2 + \bar{c}_2 u_2^2 + \bar{c}_3 u_3^2$$

The vanishing of the six partial derivatives yields, on slight rearrangement,

$$(14) \qquad
\begin{cases}
\bar{c}_1 = 1 - \pi, & \bar{c}_1 u_1 = 0, \\
\bar{c}_2 = 1 - 2\pi, & \bar{c}_2 u_2 = 0, \\
\bar{c}_3 = 1 - 3\pi, & \bar{c}_3 u_3 = 0.
\end{cases}$$

To these relations we may further add, if we like, conditions that guarantee the existence of a minimum,

$$(15) \qquad\qquad \bar{c}_1 \geq 0,\ \bar{c}_2 \geq 0,\ \bar{c}_3 \geq 0$$

for the function Z obviously does not possess an unrestricted minimum, if the coefficient $\bar{c}_j$ of u_j^2 is negative in (13).

In this case, if we try to solve explicitly (14) and (15) for x_j and u_j in terms of Lagrange multipliers, a distressing thing happens—there are no x_j terms; moreover, for each j there are two possibilities—either $\bar{c}_j = 0$ or $u_j = 0$. Noting that $x_j = u_j^2$, we may replace the condition $\bar{c}_j u_j = 0$ by $\bar{c}_j x_j = 0$, so that either $\bar{c}_j = 0$ or $x_j = 0$. Since $j = 1, 2, 3$, there is a total of 2^3 different cases to be considered; in the general linear programming problem as we shall see, there are 2^n cases to be considered. In view of (15) we may rewrite the Lagrange multiplier conditions for a minimum, as finding x_i and $\bar{i}_j$, $\bar{c}_i = 1, 2, 3$ such that

(16) (a) $\qquad x_1 \geq 0,\ \ x_2 \geq 0, \qquad x_3 \geq 0$ satisfying $x_1 + 2x_2 + 3x_3 = 6,$

(b) $\qquad \bar{c}_1 \geq 0,\ \ \bar{c}_2 \geq 0, \qquad \bar{c}_3 \geq 0,\ \pi$ satisfying $\begin{cases} \bar{c}_1 = 1 - \pi \\ \bar{c}_2 = 1 - 2\pi \\ \bar{c}_3 = 1 - 3\pi \end{cases}$

(c) $\qquad \bar{c}_1 x_1 = 0,\ \ \bar{c}_2 x_2 = 0, \qquad \bar{c}_3 x_3 = 0.$

For the *general* linear programming problem, to determine $x_j \geq 0$ and Min z satisfying

$$(17) \qquad \begin{aligned} a_{11} x_1 + a_{12} x_2 + \ldots + a_{1n} x_n &= b_1 \\ a_{21} x_1 + a_{22} x_2 + \ldots + a_{2n} x_n &= b_2 \\ &\cdots\cdots\cdots\cdots\cdots\cdots\cdots\cdots\cdots\cdots \\ a_{m1} x_1 + a_{m2} x_2 + \ldots + a_{mn} x_n &= b_m \\ c_1 x_1 + c_2 x_2 + \ldots + c_n x_n &= z \end{aligned}$$

we replace the nonnegative relations by

$$(18) \qquad\qquad x_j - u_j^2 = 0 \qquad\qquad (j = 1, 2, \ldots, n)$$

and seek an unrestricted minimum of the form

$$(19) \; Z = \sum_{j=1}^{n} c_j x_j - \left[\pi_1 \left(\sum_{j=1}^{n} a_{1j} x_j - b_1 \right) + \ldots + \pi_m \left(\sum_{j=1}^{n} a_{mj} x_j - b_m \right) \right]$$
$$- [\bar{c}_1(x_1 - u_1^2) + \ldots + \bar{c}_n(x_n - u_n^2)]$$

or

$$(20) \; Z = \left(\sum_{i=1}^{m} \pi_i b_i \right) + \left(c_1 - \sum_{i=1}^{m} \pi_i a_{i1} - \bar{c}_1 \right) x_1$$
$$+ \ldots + \left(c_n - \sum_{i=1}^{m} \pi_i a_{in} - \bar{c}_n \right) x_n$$
$$+ \bar{c}_1 u_1^2 + \bar{c}_2 u_2^2 + \ldots + \bar{c}_n u_n^2$$

The function Z does not possess an unrestricted minimum unless (a) the coefficients of x_j vanish and (b) the coefficients of u_j^2 are nonnegative; hence we can further require, if we like, that the multipliers π_i and $\bar{c}_j$ satisfy for $j = 1, 2, \ldots, n$,

$$(21) \qquad \bar{c}_j = c_j - [\pi_1 a_{1j} + \pi_2 a_{2j} + \ldots + \pi_m a_{mj}] \geq 0$$

Moreover, at the unrestricted minimum the partial derivative with respect to u_j must also vanish, yielding

$$(22) \qquad\qquad \bar{c}_j u_j = 0 \quad \text{or} \quad \bar{c}_j x_j = 0 \qquad (j = 1, 2, \ldots, n)$$

If for *fixed* $\pi_j = \pi_j^*$, there exists $\bar{c}_j$ satisfying (21) and u_j or $x_j = u_j^2$ satisfying (22), this will clearly yield $\sum_1^m \pi_i^* b_i$, in (20), hence the true (global) minimum of Z (ruling out the possibility of a local minimum; see Fig. 7-1-VII). Since $Z = z$ for any $x_j = u_j^2$ and z satisfying (17), we conclude

THEOREM 1: *If there exist multipliers $(\pi_i = \pi_i^*)$ and $(\bar{c}_j = \bar{c}_j^*)$ satisfying* (21), *and variables $(x_j = x_j^* \geq 0$, and $z = z^*)$ satisfying* (17), *such that all products $\bar{c}_j^* x_j^* = 0$, then $(x_1^*, \ldots, x_n^*, z^*)$ is a minimizing solution.*

Conclusion.

If the linear programming problem is attacked by the method of Lagrange multipliers, we find that the multipliers, if they exist, must satisfy a "dual" system—namely, the linear inequality system (21), and maximize $v = \sum \pi_i b_i$ when conditions (22) pertain (see § 6-4, Theorem 1). Also the multipliers $\bar{c}_j$ (or relative cost factors) have the property that $\bar{c}_j x_j = 0$ for $j = 1, 2, \ldots, n$. The latter leads to 2^n possible cases of either $\bar{c}_j = 0$ or $x_j = 0$. It is here that the Lagrange multipliers approach breaks down, for it is not practical to consider all the 2^n cases for large n.

In a certain sense the simplex method can be viewed as a systematic way to eliminate most of the cases and to consider only a few. Indeed, it immediately restricts the number of cases by considering only those with $n - m$ of the $x_j = 0$ at one time and such that the determinant of the coefficients of the remaining m variables is non-zero and the unique value of these variables is positive (under nondegeneracy). The conditions $\bar{c}_j x_j = 0$ tell us that $\bar{c}_j = 0$ for $x_j > 0$, and this determines uniquely π_i and the remaining $\bar{c}_j$. If not all $\bar{c}_j \geq 0$, the case is dropped and a special new one is examined on the next iteration, and so on.

6-6. PROBLEMS

1. Prove that the optimal dual solution is never unique if the optimal primal basic solution is degenerate and the optimal dual is not.
2. Show that if no artificial variables remain at the end of Phase I, $\sigma_i^0 = 0$ for $i = 1, 2, \ldots,$ M. See § 6-3-(10).
3. Prove: If there exists one nondegenerate optimal basic feasible solution the optimal dual multipliers π_i are unique. (See § 6-3.)
4. Prove: All $d_j = 0$ at end of Phase I if there are no artificial variables in the basic solution except w'. (See § 6-3-(11).)
5. Show that the dual of the dual is the primal by reversing first all signs in § 6-2-(2), to have it in standard inequality form for finding the dual.
6. Let the "dual" be alternatively defined by transposing and changing the sign of the coefficient matrix, including the interchange of (and change of sign of) the constant terms and coefficients of the objective form, maintaining the same direction of inequality, and minimizing. Show in this form that the proof of "the dual of the dual is the primal" is immediate and that this definition of the dual is equivalent to the one of § 6-2.
7. Show that neither the primal nor the dual of the system

$$x_1 - x_2 \geq 2 \qquad\qquad (x_1 \geq 0, x_2 \geq 0)$$
$$-x_1 + x_2 \geq -1$$
$$x_1 - 2x_2 = z \text{ (Min)}$$

has a feasible solution.
8. Construct other examples to illustrate all four cases of primal and dual feasibility and infeasibility.
9. Is it possible for the primal and dual problems § 6-3-(1), (2) to have solutions if the restrictions $x_j \geq 0$, $y_i \geq 0$ are removed, but no solutions if the restrictions are included?

10. Prove in general that an equation in the primal corresponds to an unrestricted variable in the dual and a variable unrestricted in sign corresponds to an equation.

11. Suppose z^o; $x_1^o > 0$, $x_2^o > 0$, . . ., $x_k^o > 0$ and $x_{k+1}^o = \ldots = x_n^o = 0$ constitute a feasible solution to a linear program. Show that, if the canonical form for the subsystem formed by dropping $x_{k+1}, \ldots, x_n$ has less than k equations, a new solution can be formed involving fewer variables with positive values and a value of z not greater than z^o. Show that this process can be repeated until a subsystem is formed with an equal number of variables with positive values, as in its canonical form. Show that this solution is unique if all other variables are zero.

12. Apply the results of Problem 11 to give a direct proof that if a feasible solution to a linear program exists, and if the values of z have a finite lower bound, then an optimal feasible solution also exists.

13. Assuming Farkas' Lemma is true, derive the Duality Theorem.

14. (a) Consider the following "game" problem; find $y_j \geq 0$, Min M satisfying

$$\sum_{j=1}^{n} y_j = 1 \qquad (i = 1, 2, \ldots, m)$$

$$\sum_{j=1}^{n} a_{ij} y_j \leq M$$

Show that the dual is to find $x_i \geq 0$ and Max N satisfying

$$\sum_{i=1}^{m} x_i = 1$$

$$\sum_{i=1}^{m} x_i a_{ij} \geq N$$

(b) Prove $N \leq \sum_{i=1}^{m} \sum_{j=1}^{n} x_i a_{ij} y_j \leq M$ and Max N = Min M.

(c) Prove that feasible solutions to primal and dual systems always exist.

(d) Why is Max N = Min M positive, if all $a_{ij} > 0$? See Chapter 13 for application of this type of system.

15. Find the dual of a *bounded variable* linear program:

$$\alpha_j \leq x_j \leq \beta_j \qquad (j = 1, 2, \ldots, n)$$

$$\sum_{j=1}^{n} a_{ij} x_j = b_i \qquad (i = 1, 2, \ldots, m)$$

$$\sum_{j=1}^{n} c_j x_j = z \text{ (Min)}$$

16. The Fourier-Motzkin elimination method permits one to drop a variable by increasing the number of inequalities. Dualize the procedure and

find a method for decreasing the number of inequalities by increasing the number of variables.

17. Suppose that an optimal solution with respect to a given objective form z is not unique and that it is desired to introduce an alternative objective z^* and to minimize z^*, given that z is minimum. Show that if an optimal solution exists, then one exists which is basic in the restraint system, excluding the z and z^* forms. Prove that this solution can be obtained by first dropping all variables x_j, such that $\bar{c}_j > 0$ at the end of Phase II, and then replacing the z-form by the z^* form.

18. Generalize the usual Phase I, Phase II procedure to find a solution that is as "feasible as possible" (Min w) and given that it is and is not unique, find the one which minimizes z, given that $w = $ Min w.

19. Show that it is not possible for $z \to -\infty$, if no positive combination of activities vanishes. Discuss what this means in a practical situation if a positive combination vanishes except for a positive cost, a negative cost, a zero cost. Show that if $z \to -\infty$, there exists a homogeneous feasible solution to the system. Show that it is possible to have $z \to +\infty$ and $z \to -\infty$ in the same system.

20. Generalize the Phase I procedure to allow an artificial variable to have either sign. Allow the variable entering to increase as long as the sum of the absolute values of the artificial variables decreases.

21. Prove that if an optimal solution $x_j^o \geq 0$, $z = z^o = $ Min z exists, then the system of equations formed by dropping all x_j, such that $x_j^o = 0$ and setting $z = z^o$, is redundant.

22. Does a column with all negative entries in the original tableau imply that (if feasible solutions exist) a class of solutions exists such that $z \to -\infty$?

REFERENCES

Proof of Simplex Method

Dantzig, 1959-1   Dantzig, Orden, and Wolfe, 1955-1

Proof of Duality Theorem, Duality Type Theorems

Dantzig and Orden, 1953-1
Dantzig and Wald, 1950-1
Farkas, 1902-1
Gale, 1960-1
Gale, Kuhn, and Tucker, 1951-1
Goldman, 1956-1
Goldman and Tucker, 1956-1, 2
Gordon, 1873-1

Karlin, 1959-1
Kuhn and Tucker, 1958-1
Minkowski, 1910-1
Motzkin, 1936-1
Stiefel, 1960-1
Stiemke, 1915-1
Tucker, 1950-1, 1956-1, 1957-1
Vajda, 1961-1

von Neumann, 1947-1

Lagrange Multipliers

Courant and Hilbert, 1953-1
Dorn, 1963-1
Everett, 1963-1
Forsythe, 1955-1

John, 1948-1
Kuhn and Tucker, 1950-2, 1956-1
Phipps, 1952-1
Slater, 1950-1

Tucker, 1957-1

CHAPTER 7

THE GEOMETRY OF LINEAR PROGRAMS

7-1. CONVEX REGIONS

Convex Two-Dimensional Regions.

The set of points (x_1, x_2) satisfying the relation

(1) $$x_1 + x_2 \geq 2$$

consists of a region in two-dimensional space on one side of the line (see Fig. 7-1-Ia)

(2) $$x_1 + x_2 = 2$$

This is an example of a convex region, or, what is the same thing, a convex set of points. The region defined by the angle between two lines, Fig. 7-1-Ib, is also a convex set.

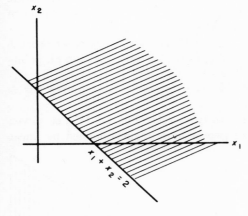

Figure 7-1-Ia.

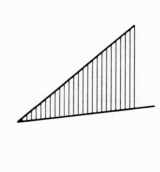

Figure 7-1-Ib.

Other examples in two dimensions are the region inside the rectangle, Fig. 7-1-IIa; the circle, Fig. 7-1-IIb; or the polygon, Fig. 7-1-IIc.

In three dimensions the volumes inside a cube and inside a sphere are also convex sets. The region defined may include or exclude the boundary. It may be bounded in extent or unbounded.

[147]

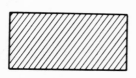

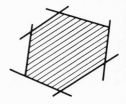

Figure 7-1-IIa.   Figure 7-1-IIb.   Figure 7-1-IIc.

On the other hand the sets depicted by the shaded region in Figs. 7-1-IIIa, IIIb, IIIc are not convex.

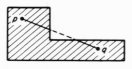

Figure 7-1-IIIa.   Figure 7-1-IIIb.   Figure 7-1-IIIc.

DEFINITION: A set of points is called a *convex* set if all points on the straight line segment joining any two points in the set belong to the set.

DEFINITION: A *closed* convex set is one which includes its boundaries. (For example, a circle and its interior is a closed convex set; the interior of a circle is a convex set, but is not closed.)

Thus the "L" shaped region of Fig. 7-1-IIIa is not a convex set because it is possible to find two points, p and q, in the set such that not all points on the line joining them belong to the set.

THEOREM 1: *The set of points common to two or more convex sets is convex.*

For example, the region common to two circles, Fig. 7-1-IVa, is convex or the points in the intersection of two or more regions defined by linear

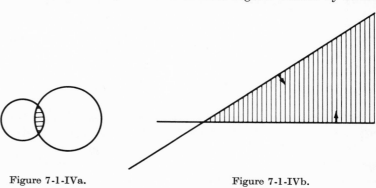

Figure 7-1-IVa.   Figure 7-1-IVb.

inequalities form a convex region, Figs. 7-1-IVb, IVc and Figs. 7-1-Ib, IIc. In § 4-3, a succession of convex regions of feasible solutions was formed by successively adding restrictions (§ 4-3-(1), Fig. 4-3-I, and sequel).

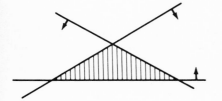

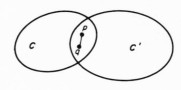

Figure 7-1-IVc.   Figure 7-1-V.

PROOF: Let C and C' be two convex sets and R the set of points common to C and C' (see Fig. 7-1-V). Let p and q be any two points in R. Since p and q are also in C and since C is convex, then the line segment joining p to q must be in C; for a similar reason the segment must be in C'. Hence the segment lying in both C and C' is in R.

EXERCISE: Extend the proof to more than two convex regions.

General Convex Regions.

Since in linear programming we will be dealing with linear inequalities involving many variables, it will not be possible to visualize the solution as a point in many dimensions. Accordingly we must be able to demonstrate algebraically whether or not certain sets are convex. The definition of a convex set requires that all points on a straight line segment joining any two points in the set belong to the set. It will be necessary to define in general what is meant by a "point" and a "straight line segment."

DEFINITION: By a *point* x in n dimensions is meant an ordered set of n values or coordinates $(x_1, x_2, \ldots, x_n)$. The coordinates of x are also referred to as the *components* of x.

DEFINITION: The *line segment* joining two points, p and q, with coordinates $(p_1, p_2, \ldots, p_n)$ and $(q_1, q_2, \ldots, q_n)$, respectively, in n-dimensional space is all points x whose coordinates are

$$(3) \qquad \begin{cases} x_1 = \lambda p_1 + (1 - \lambda)q_1 \\ x_2 = \lambda p_2 + (1 - \lambda)q_2 \\ \cdots\cdots\cdots\cdots\cdots \\ x_n = \lambda p_n + (1 - \lambda)q_n \end{cases}$$

where λ is a parameter such that $0 \leq \lambda \leq 1$. For example, consider the two points in two-dimensional space: $p = (6, 2)$ and $q = (1, 4)$. These are represented geometrically in Fig. 7-1-VI.

[149]

Consider now the point x, with coordinates (x_1, x_2). By definition if x is to be on the line segment joining p and q, then

(4)
$$\begin{cases} x_1 = \lambda p_1 + (1 - \lambda)q_1 = 6\lambda + 1(1 - \lambda) = 5\lambda + 1 \\ x_2 = \lambda p_2 + (1 - \lambda)q_2 = 2\lambda + 4(1 - \lambda) = -2\lambda + 4 \end{cases}$$

For example, let $\lambda = 1$, then $x_1 = 6$ and $x_2 = 2$ and the point x is point p. Likewise let $\lambda = 0$, then $x = q$. For other λ values $(0 < \lambda < 1)$ we get all

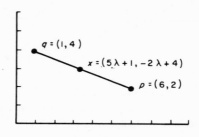

Figure 7-1-VI.

points between p and q. For example, when $\lambda = \frac{1}{2}$, the coordinates of x become $x_1 = \frac{7}{2}$, $x_2 = 3$ which is the point midway between p and q.

EXERCISE: Obtain the straight line relationship between x_1 and x_2 by eliminating λ in (4).

With this definition of a line segment, it is possible to determine whether a given set is convex. For example, consider the region R defined by all points whose coordinates satisfy

(5)

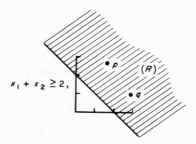

To prove that this region is convex, let $p = (p_1, p_2)$ and $q = (q_1, q_2)$ be any two points in R. For p and q to be in R their respective coordinates must satisfy (5), whence

(6)
$$p_1 + p_2 \geq 2$$
$$q_1 + q_2 \geq 2$$

Then the coordinates (x_1, x_2) of an arbitrary point, x, on the segment joining p to q, are found by forming a weighted combination of the coordinates of the two points as in (7) and (8).

$$
\begin{aligned}
&\bullet \ \ p = (p_1, p_2) \\
(7) \qquad &\bullet \ \ x = [\lambda p_1 + (1 - \lambda)q_1, \ \lambda p_2 + (1 - \lambda)q_2] \\
&\bullet \ \ q = (q_1, q_2)
\end{aligned}
$$

where λ is the ratio of the distance xq to pq. Using vector notation (this will be discussed more fully in § 8-2), the identical weighting of the corresponding coordinates of p and q may be written compactly $x = \lambda p + (1 - \lambda)q$, which means

$$
(8) \qquad\qquad
\begin{aligned}
x_1 &= \lambda p_1 + (1 - \lambda)q_1 \\
x_2 &= \lambda p_2 + (1 - \lambda)q_2
\end{aligned}
\qquad\qquad (0 \le \lambda \le 1)
$$

To prove convexity for (5) we wish to show that x lies in R, which means its coordinates should satisfy $x_1 + x_2 \ge 2$ or to show that

$$
(9) \qquad\qquad \lambda p_1 + (1 - \lambda)q_1 + \lambda p_2 + (1 - \lambda)q_2 \ge 2
$$

To prove this we multiply the first inequality of (6) by $\lambda \ge 0$ and the second, by $1 - \lambda \ge 0$ to obtain

$$
(10) \qquad\qquad
\begin{aligned}
\lambda p_1 + \lambda p_2 &\ge 2\lambda \\
(1 - \lambda)q_1 + (1 - \lambda)q_2 &\ge 2(1 - \lambda)
\end{aligned}
$$

These two inequalities, when added together, result in (9), which establishes the convexity of R.

Convexity of Regions Defined by Linear Inequalities and Equations.

In n dimensions, the set of points whose coordinates satisfy a linear equation

$$
(11) \qquad\qquad a_1 x_1 + a_2 x_2 + \ldots + a_n x_n = b
$$

is called a *hyperplane*, and the set of points whose coordinates satisfy a linear inequality such as

$$
(12) \qquad\qquad a_1 x_1 + a_2 x_2 + \ldots + a_n x_n \le b
$$

is called a *half-space* or to be precise, a *closed half-space* because we include the boundary. (In two dimensions it is called a *half-plane*.)

To prove the half-space defined by a linear inequality is convex, let p and q be any two points in the set, so that

$$
(13a) \qquad\qquad a_1 p_1 + a_2 p_2 + \ldots + a_n p_n \le b
$$

$$
(13b) \qquad\qquad a_1 q_1 + a_2 q_2 + \ldots + a_n q_n \le b
$$

Let $0 \le \lambda \le 1$ be the value of the parameter associated with an arbitrary point x on the line segment joining p to q. Multiplying (13a) by $\lambda \geq 0$ and (13b) by $(1 - \lambda) \geq 0$ and adding, one obtains

(14) $a_1[\lambda p_1 + (1 - \lambda)q_1] + a_2[\lambda p_2 + (1 - \lambda)q_2] + \ldots$
$$+ a_n[\lambda p_n + (1 - \lambda)q_n] \leq b$$

whence, substituting $x_i = \lambda p_i + (1 - \lambda)q_i$ by (3),

(15) $a_1 x_1 + a_2 x_2 + \ldots + a_n x_n \leq b$

Hence, an arbitrary point x on the line segment joining any two points lies in the half-space, establishing convexity.

To prove that a hyperplane is convex, let (11) be written as

(16) $a_1 x_1 + a_2 x_2 + \ldots + a_n x_n \leq b$
$$a_1 x_1 + a_2 x_2 + \ldots + a_n x_n \geq b$$

Each of these inequalities defines a half-space and their intersection defines a hyperplane. Since a half-space is a convex set, then, by Theorem 1, a hyperplane is also a convex set. An n-dimensional space may contain many such convex sets. By Theorem 1, their common intersection is a convex set.

DEFINITION: A *convex polyhedron* is the set common to one or more half-spaces. In particular, a *convex polygon* is the intersection of one or more half-planes.

Convexity of the Set of Feasible and Optimal Feasible Solutions.

Consider now a general linear programming problem given by

(17) $\begin{aligned} a_{11} x_1 + a_{12} x_2 + \ldots + a_{1n} x_n &= b_1 \\ a_{21} x_1 + a_{22} x_2 + \ldots + a_{2n} x_n &= b_2 \end{aligned}$ $(x_j \geq 0)$

$$\cdots\cdots\cdots\cdots\cdots\cdots\cdots\cdots\cdots$$
$$a_{m1} x_1 + a_{m2} x_2 + \ldots + a_{mn} x_n = b_m$$

(18) $c_1 x_1 + c_2 x_2 + \ldots + c_n x_n - z = 0$

where z is to be minimized. We have just established

THEOREM 2:   *The set of points corresponding to feasible (or optimal feasible) solutions of the general linear programming problem constitutes a convex set.*

Thus, if $p = (p_1, p_2, \ldots, p_n, z_p)$ is a feasible solution and $q = (q_1, q_2, \ldots, q_n, z_q)$ is another, the weighted linear combination of these two feasible solutions,

(19) $[\lambda p_1 + (1 - \lambda)q_1, \ldots, \lambda p_n + (1 - \lambda)q_n; \lambda z_p + (1 - \lambda)z_q]$

where λ is a constant, $0 \leq \lambda \leq 1$, is also a feasible solution. (This may be written compactly $x = \lambda p + (1 - \lambda)q$.) Moreover, assigning a fixed value for z, say $z = z_0$, the set of points satisfying (17), (18), and $z = z_0$ is also a convex set. In particular, setting $z_0 = \text{Min } z$, it is clear that the set of minimal feasible solutions is also a convex set.

A Local Minimum Solution Is Global.

In the calculus, the minimum (or maximum) of a function $f(x)$ with a continuous derivative is attained at a value x whose derivative is zero. This can result in a point like $x = x_1$ in Fig. 7-1-VII where $f(x)$ is minimum in the

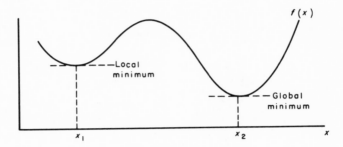

Figure 7-1-VII.

neighborhood of x_1; this is called a *local* minimum. However, it will also be noted there is another local minimum at $x = x_2$ where $f(x)$ attains its lowest value; this is called the *global* minimum. Any solution that is a local minimum solution is also a true (or global) minimum solution for the linear programming problem. To see this, let $p = (p_1, p_2, \ldots, p_n, z_p)$ be a local minimum solution and assume that it is not a true minimum solution, so that there is another solution $q = (q_1, q_2, \ldots, q_n, z_q)$ with $z_p > z_q$. Then any point $x = (x_1, x_2, \ldots, x_n, z)$ on a line segment joining these two points is a feasible solution and its $z = \lambda z_p + (1 - \lambda)z_q$. In this case the value of z decreases uniformly from z_p to z_q and thus all points on the line segment between p and q (including those in the neighborhood of p) have z values less than z_p and correspond to feasible solutions. Therefore, it is not possible to have a local minimum at p and at the same time another point q such that $z_p > z_q$. This means for all q, $z_p \leq z_q$, so that z_p is the true (global) minimum value.

DEFINITION: A function $f(x_1, x_2, \ldots, x_n)$ is a *convex function* if (1) it is defined over a set of points $p = (x_1, x_2, \ldots, x_n)$ which lie in a convex set C and if (2) the set of points in the one higher dimensional space $\bar{p} = (x_1, x_2, \ldots, x_n; z)$, where $z \geq f(x_1, x_2, \ldots, x_n)$, is a convex set $\bar{C}$.

For example, the function $f(x) = x^2$ is convex because the set of points (x, z) where $z \geq x^2$ is a convex set (see Fig. 7-1-VIII).

A *Property of Convex Functions:* If we let $x' = (x_1', x_2', \ldots, x_n')$ and $x'' = (x_1'', x_2'', \ldots, x_n'')$ be any two points in the convex set C over which the convex function $f(x) = f(x_1, x_2, \ldots, x_n)$ is defined and x^* be any point on

[153]

the segment joining x' to x'', so that $x^* = \lambda x' + (1 - \lambda)x''$ where $0 \leq \lambda \leq 1$, then

(20) $$\lambda f(x') + (1 - \lambda) f(x'') \geq f(x^*)$$

For consider the two points $\bar{p}' = (x_1', x_2', \ldots, x_n'; z')$ and $\bar{p}'' = (x_1'', x_2'', \ldots, x_n''; z'')$ where $z' = f(x'), z'' = f(x'')$. The point $\bar{p}^* = (x_1^*, x_2^*, \ldots, x_n^*; z^*)$ where $z^* = \lambda z' + (1 - \lambda)z''$ lies in the convex set $\bar{C}$, and $z^* \geq f(x^*)$ because all points in the convex set $\bar{C}$ whose first n coordinates $x = x^*$ have a z coordinate greater or equal to $f(x^*)$ by definition. Geometrically (20) states that the z coordinate of $\bar{q} = [x_1^*, x_2^*, \ldots, x_n^*; f(x^*)]$ will never be higher than $\bar{p}^*$ if $f(x^*)$ is a convex function (see Fig. 7-1-VIII).

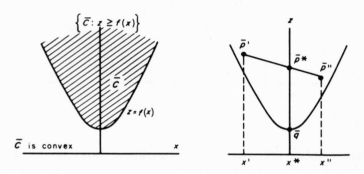

Figure 7-1-VIII. The curve $z = f(x)$ is called convex if $z \geq f(x)$ defines a convex set $\bar{C}$.

EXERCISE: Show that if the function $f(x)$ is not convex then (20) does not hold for at least two points x' and x'' in C.

DEFINITION: Any point x in a convex set C which is not a midpoint of the line segment joining two other points in C is by definition an *extreme point* or *vertex* of the convex set. (Referring to Fig. 7-1-IX, the corners of

Figure 7-1-IX.

the square and every point on the circumference of a circle are extreme points. The points where three or more facets of a diamond come together are extreme points.)

THEOREM 3: *A basic feasible solution corresponds to an extreme point in the convex set of feasible solutions.*

It is easy to show that a basic feasible solution corresponds to an extreme point. For example, suppose $x^o = (\bar{b}_1, \bar{b}_2, \ldots, \bar{b}_m, 0, \ldots, 0)$ is a basic feasible solution for (17) with basic variables $x_1, x_2, \ldots, x_m$ and suppose it is the average of two other feasible solutions $p = (p_1, p_2, \ldots, p_m, \ldots, p_n)$ and $q = (q_1, q_2, \ldots, q_m, \ldots, q_n)$. Then

$$\tfrac{1}{2}(p_j + q_j) = 0$$

for all j corresponding to independent variables. But $p_j \geq 0$ and $q_j \geq 0$ because p and q are feasible solutions to (17). This is possible only if $p_j = q_j = 0$ for $j = m + 1, \ldots, n$. Thus p, q, and x^o have the same values (namely zero) for their independent variables. But the values of the basic variables are uniquely determined by the values of the independent variables and hence must be the same also. This shows $p = q = x^o$ and proves that x^o cannot be the average of two solutions p and q different from x^o.

DEFINITION: An *edge* of a convex polyhedron C is the straight line segment joining two extreme points such that no point on the segment is the midpoint of two other points in C not on the segment; in this case the two extreme points are said to be *neighbors* or *adjacent* to each other.

THEOREM 4: *The class of feasible solutions generated by increasing the value of a non-basic variable and adjusting the values of the basic variables in the change from one basic solution to the next corresponds to a movement along an edge of the convex set.*

PROOF: Suppose $p = (\bar{b}_1, \bar{b}_2, \ldots, \bar{b}_m; 0, 0, \ldots, 0)$ is one basic feasible solution and $q = (0; \bar{b}_2^*, \ldots, \bar{b}_m^*, \bar{b}_{m+1}^*; 0, 0, \ldots, 0)$ is a basic feasible solution found by replacing x_1 in the basic set by, say, x_{m+1}. It is clear that any point $u = \lambda p + (1 - \lambda)q$ on the segment joining p to q has $u_{m+2} = u_{m+3} = \ldots = u_n = 0$. Hence, if u is to be the midpoint of two points p' and q' which are in the convex of feasible solutions, these components of p' and q' must also vanish. This permits one to express each of the first m components of p' and q' as a linear function of the value of the $(m + 1)$st component of p' and q', respectively. In fact, for any point x in the convex C whose components $x_{m+2} = x_{m+3} = \ldots = x_n = 0$ and x_{m+1} is arbitrary, we have

$$x_i = \bar{b}_i - \bar{a}_{im+1}x_{m+1} \qquad (i = 1, 2, \ldots, m); \tag{21}$$

in particular, we have for $q = (0; \bar{b}_2^*, \bar{b}_3^*, \ldots, \bar{b}_m^*, \bar{b}_{m+1}^*; 0, \ldots, 0)$ that

$$\bar{b}_i^* = \bar{b}_i - \bar{a}_{im+1}\bar{b}_{m+1}^* \qquad (i = 1, 2, \ldots, m) \tag{22}$$

Multiplying (22) by $\lambda = x_{m+1}/\bar{b}_{m+1}^*$ and subtracting from (21) yields

$$\begin{aligned}
x_i &= \lambda \bar{b}_i^* &&+ (1 - \lambda)\bar{b}_i &\qquad (i = 1, 2, \ldots, m) \\
x_{m+1} &= \lambda \bar{b}_{m+1}^* &&+ (1 - \lambda)0 \\
x_j &= \lambda 0 &&+ (1 - \lambda)0 &\qquad (j = m + 2, \ldots, n)
\end{aligned} \tag{23}$$

This proves that any two points, p' and q' in C, whose midpoint is u on the line segment joining p and q, are also on the line joining p and q. The assumption that p and q are extreme points implies $0 \leq \lambda \leq 1$, so that p' and q' are on the line segment joining p to q, which proves the line segment joining p and q forms an edge.

[Tucker, 1955-1] is recommended as collateral reading for this section.

7-2. THE SIMPLEX METHOD VIEWED AS THE STEEPEST DESCENT ALONG EDGES

Using a Set of Independent Variables as Coordinates of a Point in n — m Dimensions.

Consider a linear programming problem with $n = m + 2$ that has a basic feasible solution with respect to some m basic variables, say $x_3, x_4, \ldots, x_{m+2}$. The canonical form with respect to these variables is

$$(1) \qquad \begin{aligned} \bar{a}_{11} x_1 + \bar{a}_{12} x_2 + x_3 \qquad\qquad &= \bar{b}_1 \qquad\qquad (\bar{b}_i \geq 0) \\ \bar{a}_{21} x_1 + \bar{a}_{22} x_2 \qquad + x_4 \qquad &= \bar{b}_2 \\ \cdots\cdots\cdots\cdots\cdots\cdots\cdots\cdots\cdots& \\ \bar{a}_{m1} x_1 + \bar{a}_{m2} x_2 \qquad\quad + x_{m+2} &= \bar{b}_m \\ \bar{c}_1 x_1 + \quad \bar{c}_2 x_2 \qquad\qquad\quad &= z - \bar{z}_0 \end{aligned}$$

where the problem is to find $x_j \geq 0$ and Min z satisfying (1). This is equivalent to finding values of x_1 and x_2 and the smallest constant $\bar{c}_0 = z - \bar{z}_0$ satisfying the system of linear inequalities

$$(2) \qquad \begin{aligned} x_1 \qquad\qquad &\geq 0 \\ x_2 &\geq 0 \\ \bar{a}_{11} x_1 + \bar{a}_{12} x_2 &\leq \bar{b}_1 \\ \bar{a}_{21} x_1 + \bar{a}_{22} x_2 &\leq \bar{b}_2 \\ \cdots\cdots\cdots\cdots& \\ \bar{a}_{m1} x_1 + \bar{a}_{m2} x_2 &\leq \bar{b}_m \\ \bar{c}_1 x_1 + \quad \bar{c}_2 x_2 &= \bar{c}_0 \end{aligned}$$

We may graph these $m + 2$ relations in the two-dimensional space of the non-basic or independent variables x_1 and x_2 as illustrated in Fig. 7-2-I.

The convex region K formed by the half-spaces (in this case half-planes) $\bar{a}_{i1} x_1 + \bar{a}_{i2} x_2 \leq \bar{b}_i$ is shown by the solid lines in Fig. 7-2-I. The optimum solution is found by moving the dotted line $\bar{c}_1 x_1 + \bar{c}_2 x_2 = \bar{c}_0$ parallel to itself until the line just touches the convex and $\bar{c}_0$ is minimum. (If $\bar{c}_1$ and $\bar{c}_2$ are both less than zero this would be in the direction away from the origin.) Associated with every point P in K is a unique feasible solution to (1). In fact such a point P must satisfy all the inequalities (2) and the nonnegative difference between the values on the left hand side of (2) and the right hand side are the unique values of the basic variables in (1) when the non-basic variables x_1 and x_2 have the specified values (x_1^o, x_2^o). The value $x_{i+2} = x_{i+2}^o$ of the ith basic variable is proportional to the distance of the point $P = (x_1^o, x_2^o)$ from the boundary of the ith constraint because, from analytic

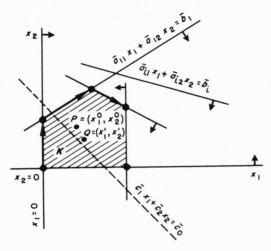

Figure 7-2-I. Geometrically the simplex algorithm
moves along edges of the convex.

geometry, the *distance* of P from $\bar{a}_{i1}x_1 + \bar{a}_{i2}x_2 = \bar{b}_i$ is given by (3) for $i = 1, 2, \ldots, m$,

$$(3) \qquad \text{distance} = \frac{\bar{b}_i - \bar{a}_{i1}x_1^o - \bar{a}_{i2}x_2^o}{[\bar{a}_{i1}^2 + \bar{a}_{i2}^2]^{\frac{1}{2}}} = k_i x_{i+2}^o$$

If the point (x_1^o, x_2^o) satisfies the inequality, then the geometric picture is

(4)

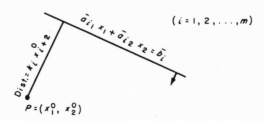

where $k_i = (\bar{a}_{i1}^2 + \bar{a}_{i2}^2)^{-\frac{1}{2}}$.

If the variables are replaced by $y_i = k_i x_{i+2}$ for $i = 1, 2, \ldots, m$, and the coordinates of a point P are the values of the independent variables, then

[157]

the value of the ith basic variable is just the distance from the point P to the corresponding ith constraint.

Every basic solution to (1) has at least two $x_j = 0$, hence the corresponding P is at the same time a point in K and is at zero distance to two distinct boundary lines of K. It is intuitively evident (and we show this rigorously below) that such a P is a vertex of K. In particular, the basic feasible solution with respect to the canonical form (1) is associated with the point $(x_1^o = 0, x_2^o = 0)$ in Fig. 7-2-I, hence the origin is always in the convex K.

We now show in a little more rigorous manner that *associated with every extreme point in the convex set of feasible solutions to (1) is an extreme point of K and conversely.* To this end, let $P = (x_1^o, x_2^o)$ and $Q = (x_1', x_2')$ be any two points in K, and let the corresponding feasible solutions satisfying (1) be $p = (x_1^o, x_2^o, \ldots, x_n^o)$ and $q = (x_1', x_2', \ldots, x_n')$ which as we have seen in Theorem 2 of § 7-1 lie in a convex set C. It is easy to see that any point $\lambda P + (1 - \lambda)Q$ on the line joining P to Q corresponds to a point $\lambda p + (1 - \lambda)q$ that satisfies (1), and conversely. Hence line segments in the convex C of solutions satisfying (1) correspond to line segments in K, and in particular the midpoint of a segment in C corresponds to the midpoint in K and conversely. It follows that non-extreme points must correspond to each other and it must logically follow that extreme points (basic feasible solutions) to (1) correspond to extreme points of K and conversely.

Moreover, *the movement along the edge* corresponding to the class of feasible solutions generated by increasing a non-basic variable and adjusting the values of the basic variables in the shift from one basic solution to the next, must correspond to a movement around the boundary of K from one vertex to the next. To see this, let p and q be successive distinct extreme points corresponding to basic feasible solutions obtained by the simplex method under non-degeneracy, so that the line segment joining p to q is an edge in C. If now the corresponding vertices P and Q in K were not neighbors, there would be a point X on the segment joining P to Q that would be the midpoint of two points P' and Q' in K, but not on the segment. We shall show, however, that P' and Q' must lie on the line joining P to Q. We have shown that x, corresponding to X must be the midpoint of p' and q' corresponding to P' and Q'. However, x must also be on the line joining p to q since X was on the line joining P to Q. It follows since the segment pq is an *edge* (§ 7-1, Theorem 4), p' and q' must both be on this edge and hence their corresponding points P' and Q' must lie on the line joining P to Q. This shows that edges in the convex of feasible solutions to (1), correspond to edges in Fig. 7-2-I.

Thus the simplex method proceeds from one vertex to the next in the space of a fixed set of non-basic variables. Starting with the vertex at the origin and moving successively from one neighboring vertex to another, each step decreases the value of $\bar{c}_0$ until a minimum value for $\bar{c}_0$ is obtained as shown by the arrows in Fig. 7-2-I.

The General Case.

While our remarks have been restricted to the case of $n = m + 2$ for simplicity, they hold equally well for the general case of $n = m + k$. In this case, the values of $k = n - m$ of any set of non-basic variables become the coordinates of a point in k dimensions. In this geometry the convex K of feasible solutions is defined by a set of m inequalities formed by dropping the basic variables in the canonical form and adding the k inequalities $x_j \geq 0$ where x_j are the non-basic variables. Each basic feasible solution corresponds to a vertex of K. In the general (non-degenerate) situation, there are $n - m$ edges from each vertex leading to $n - m$ neighboring vertices; these correspond to the $n - m$ basic solutions obtained by introducing one of the $n - m$ non-basic variables in place of one of the basic variables. *The simplex criterion of choosing $\bar{c}_s = \text{Min } \bar{c}_j < 0$ followed by an increase in x_s corresponds to a movement along that edge of the convex which induces the greatest decrease in z per unit change in the variable introduced.*

(5)

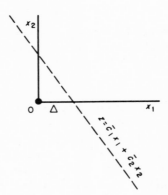

For example, for $n = m + 2$, see (5), if $\bar{c}_1 < \bar{c}_2$, then any movement for a distance Δ along the x_1-axis produces a greater decrease in z than an equal movement along the x_2-axis.

It can be shown in general that the simplex method is a steepest descent "gradient" technique in which the "gradient direction" is defined in the space of non-basic variables, say $x_{m+1}, x_{m+2}, \ldots, x_n$. Translating the origin to some trial solution point, the *usual* steepest gradient direction is defined by finding the limiting direction as $\Delta \to 0$ from this origin to a point on the *spherical* surface

(6)
$$x_{m+1}^2 + x_{m+2}^2 + \ldots + x_n^2 = \Delta^2 \qquad (x_j \geq 0)$$

where the function z is minimized. In contradistinction, the simplex

[159]

algorithm's steepest gradient direction is found using a *planar* surface instead of a spherical surface

$$(7) \qquad x_{m+1} + x_{m+2} + \ldots + x_n = \Delta \qquad (x_j \geq 0)$$

In other words, in defining the gradient, the usual (Euclidean) distance (6) from the origin (located at some trial solution point) is replaced by one based on the sum of the absolute values of the coordinates (7).

EXERCISE: Consider the problem of minimizing $\bar{c}_{m+1}x_{m+1} + \bar{c}_{m+2}x_{m+2} + \ldots + \bar{c}_n x_n$ subject to (7) for fixed Δ where $x_j \geq 0$. Show that the solution is to choose $x_s = \Delta$ and all other $x_j = 0$ where $\bar{c}_s = \text{Min } \bar{c}_j$. What is the steepest gradient direction as $\Delta \to 0$?

EXERCISE: Consider the problem of minimizing $\bar{c}_{m+1}x_{m+1} + \bar{c}_{m+2}x_{m+2} + \ldots + \bar{c}_n x_n$ subject to (6) for fixed Δ where x_j is unrestricted in sign. Show that the solution is to choose $x_j = -\bar{c}_j\theta$ where $\theta = \Delta^2/\Sigma\bar{c}_j^2$. What is the steepest gradient direction as $\Delta \to 0$?

7-3. THE SIMPLEX INTERPRETATION OF THE SIMPLEX METHOD

While the simplex method appears a natural one to try in the n-dimensional space of the variables, it might be expected, *a priori*, to be inefficient as there could be considerable wandering on the outside edges of the convex of solutions before an optimal extreme point is reached. This certainly appears to be true when $n - m = k$ is small, such as in Fig. 7-2-I where $k = 2$. However, empirical experience with thousands of practical problems indicates that the number of iterations is usually close to the number of basic variables in the final set which were not present in the initial set. For an m-equation problem with m different variables in the final basic set, the number of iterations may run anywhere from m as a minimum, to $2m$ and rarely to $3m$. The number is usually less than $3m/2$ when there aré less than 50 equations and 200 variables (to judge from informal empirical observations). Some believe that for a randomly chosen problem with fixed m, the number of iterations grows in proportion to n.

It has been conjectured that, by proper choice of variables to enter the basic set, it is possible to pass from any basic feasible solution to any other in m or less pivot steps, where each basic solution generated along the way must be feasible. For the cases $m \leq 4$ the conjecture is known to be true. [W. M. Hirsch, 1957, verbal communication.]

Moreover, when the simplex method is viewed in the m-dimensional space associated with the columns of coefficients of the variables, as will be done in this section, the method appears to be quite efficient. It was in this geometry that the method was first seriously proposed after it had been earlier set aside as unpromising.

In Chapter 3, both the Blending Model II and the Product Mix

Model were graphically solved using as the coordinates of a point the coefficients of a variable in one of the equations and the cost form. For this purpose it was assumed that one of the equations of the model could be written in the form

(1) $$x_1 + x_2 + \ldots + x_n = 1 \qquad\qquad (x_j \geq 0 : \pi_0)$$

leaving, for the case $m = 2$, one other equation and cost form

(2) $$a_1 x_1 + a_2 x_2 + \ldots + a_n x_n = b \qquad\qquad `(: \pi_1)$$

(3) $$c_1 x_1 + c_2 x_2 + \ldots + c_n x_n = z \text{ (Min)}$$

The variables x_j were interpreted as nonnegative weights to be assigned to a system of points $A_j = (a_j, c_j)$ in two-dimensional space (u, v) so that their weighted average (center of gravity) is a point $R = (b, \text{Min } z)$; that is to say the $x_j \geq 0$ are chosen so that the center of gravity lies on the "requirement line" $u = b$ (constant) and such that the v coordinate is minimum (see Fig. 7-3-I).

Convex Hull.

In Fig. 7-3-I, the shaded area C represents the set of all possible centers of gravity G formed by assigning different weights x_j to the points A_j. It is

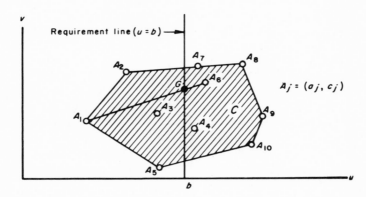

Figure 7-3-I. Geometrically a linear program is a center of gravity problem.

easy to prove these form a convex region C, called the *convex hull* of the set of points A_j. To see this, let G' be any point in C obtained by using nonnegative weights $w_1', w_2', \ldots, w_n'$ and G'' any other point obtained by using nonnegative weights $w_1'', w_2'', \ldots, w_n''$. Let $G^* = \lambda G' + (1 - \lambda)G''$, where $0 \leq \lambda \leq 1$, be any point on the line segment joining G' to G''. G^* must lie in C also because it can be obtained by using weights $w^* = \lambda w_j' + (1 - \lambda)w_j''$ for $j = 1, 2, \ldots, n$; moreover, if $w_j' \geq 0$, $w_j'' \geq 0$, $\Sigma w_j' = 1$, $\Sigma w_j'' = 1$ and $0 \leq \lambda \leq 1$, then $w_i^* \geq 0$, $\Sigma w_j^* = 1$. This establishes the convexity of C.

It is also easy to see that any column (activity) corresponding to a point A_j which is not an extreme point of the convex hull can be dropped from the linear programming problem. Thus the points A_3, A_4, A_6 in the *interior* of C in Fig. 7-3-I and A_7 on an *edge* can be dropped; that is to say, one can set $x_3 = x_4 = x_6 = x_7 = 0$ and still obtain a feasible solution with just as low a minimum value.

A basic feasible solution corresponds to a pair of points, say A_1 and A_6 in Fig. 7-3-I, such that the line joining A_1 to A_6 intersects the constant line $u = b$ in a point G on the line segment between A_1 and A_6. For this to be true we would want

$$\lambda a_1 + (1 - \lambda)a_6 = b_1 \qquad (0 \le \lambda \le 1)$$

But this corresponds to the basic feasible solution to (1) and (2) found by setting $x_1 = \lambda$, $x_6 = (1 - \lambda)$ and $x_j = 0$ for all other j.

To improve the solution, the simplex method first computes the relative cost factors $\bar{c}_j$ by eliminating the basic variables from the cost equation. We shall now show that this is the same as first computing the line joining A_1 to A_6, which we will refer to as the *solution line*, and then substituting the coordinates of a point A_j into the equation of the line to see how much (if any) in the v-direction it is *above* or *below* the line; see Fig. 7-3-II.

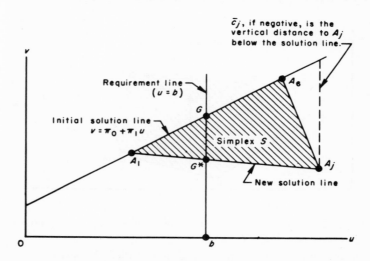

Figure 7-3-II.   The simplex associated with a cycle of the simplex algorithm ($m = 2$).

To eliminate basic variables x_1 and x_6 from (3), suppose equation (1) is multiplied by π_0 and equation (2) by π_1 and subtracted from (3). Then π_0 and π_1 must be chosen so that

(4) $$c_1 - (\pi_0 + \pi_1 a_1) = 0$$

(5) $$c_6 - (\pi_0 + \pi_1 a_6) = 0$$

and the relative cost factors $\bar{c}_j$ are given by

(6) $$\bar{c}_j = c_j - (\pi_0 + \pi_1 a_j)$$

Let us compare this with what would be required to compute the line

(7) $$v = \pi_0 + \pi_1 u$$

where constants π_0 and π_1 are chosen so that the line passes through the points $A_1 = (a_1, c_1)$ and $A_6 = (a_6, c_6)$. Substituting $u = a_1$ and $v = c_1$ into equation (7) gives the condition that A_1 lies on this line, while substituting $u = a_6$, $v = c_6$ yields the condition for A_6 to be on this line. But these are precisely conditions (4) and (5). To determine *how much* a point with coordinates $u = a_j$, $v = c_j$ is above or below the solution line in the v-direction, we first determine the ordinate of the point where the line $u = a_j$ cuts $v = \pi_0 + \pi_1 u$, namely at $v = \pi_0 + \pi_1 a_j$, and then subtract this value from the ordinate c_j of A_j, denoted by $\bar{c}_j$ in (6). Thus A_j is *above, on,* or *below* the line according as $\bar{c}_j > 0$, $\bar{c}_j = 0$, or $\bar{c}_j < 0$.

The condition that a basic feasible solution is minimal is that $\bar{c}_j \geq 0$ for all non-basic variables c_j. *Geometrically* it states that a *basic feasible solution is optimal* if all points A_j lie on or above its solution line. For example, in Fig. 7-3-I, the requirement line $u = b$ cuts the line segment joining A_5 to A_{10}, and all other points A_j lie above the extended line joining these two points; hence the minimal solution is obtained by using x_5 and x_{10} as basic variables.

On the other hand, if there is a point A_j, as in Fig. 7-3-II, *below* the solution line, then join A_j to A_1 and to A_6 and consider the convex figure S formed by $A_1 A_6 A_j$. This is the *convex hull of three points in m = 2 dimensions and is called a two-dimensional simplex.* If A_j is below the solution line, every point of S is also. If G is not at a vertex, there is a segment G^*G on the requirement line belonging to S below the solution line with G^*, the lowest point. Thus there exists a *new solution line* passing through G^*. It is either $A_1 A_j$ or $A_6 A_j$ depending on whether A_j is on the right or left of $u = b$.

In Fig. 7-3-III, we illustrate the steps of the simplex method geometrically on (8) the Product Mix Problem, § 3-5.

(8)
$$
\begin{cases}
y_1 + & y_2 + & y_3 + & y_4 + & y_5 + & y_6 = 1 \qquad (y_j \geq 0) \\
.2y_1 + & .1y_2 + & .3y_3 + & .8y_4 + & 0y_5 + & 1y_6 = .4 \\
-2.4y_1 - & 2.0y_2 - & 1.8y_3 - & .8y_4 + & 0y_5 + & 0y_6 = z \ (\text{Min})
\end{cases}
$$

Let the coordinates of a point A_j in Fig. 7-3-III be the coefficients of y_j in the second and third equations:

$$A_1 = (.2, -2.4), \quad A_2 = (.1, -2.0), \quad A_3 = (.3, -1.8),$$
$$A_4 = (.8, -.8), \quad A_5 = (0, 0), \quad A_6 = (1, 0)$$

[163]

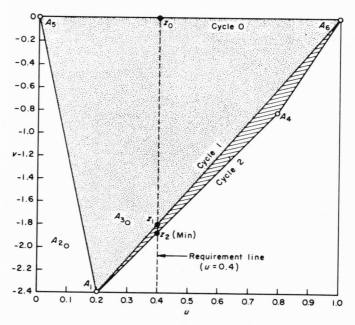

Figure 7-3-III. The simplex algorithm geometrically illustrated on the product mix problem.

The simplex iterations may be summarized as follows:

Iteration	Basic variables	Solution line	Simplex
0	y_5, y_6	$A_5 A_6$	$> A_5 A_6 A_1$
1	y_1, y_6	$A_1 A_6$	$> A_4 A_6 A_1$
2	y_1, y_4	$A_1 A_4$	

Simplex Defined.

In higher dimensions, say m, the convex hull of $m + 1$ points in general position (see definition below) is called an *m-dimensional simplex*; thus

0-dim. simplex is a point
1- ,,   ,,   ,, a line segment
2- ,,   ,,   ,, a triangle and its interior
3- ,,   ,,   ,, a tetrahedron and its interior

DEFINITION: Let $A_j = (a_{1j}, a_{2j}, \ldots, a_{mj})$ be the coordinates of a point A_j in m-dimensional space. A set of $m + 1$ points $[A_1, A_2, \ldots, A_{m+1}]$

is said to be a *general position* if the determinant of their coordinates and a row of ones, as in (9), is non-vanishing,

$$(9) \qquad \begin{vmatrix} 1 & 1 & \dots 1 \\ a_{11} & a_{12} & \cdots a_{1,m+1} \\ \cdot & \cdot & \cdot \\ \cdot & \cdot & \cdot \\ \cdot & \cdot & \cdot \\ a_{m1} & a_{m2} & \cdots a_{m,m+1} \end{vmatrix} \neq 0$$

For $m = 3$ dimensions, consider the problem of finding $x_j \geq 0$ and Min z satisfying

Multipliers

$$(10) \qquad x_1 + x_2 + \dots + x_n = 1 \quad (x_j \geq 0) \qquad : \pi_0$$

and

$$(11) \qquad \begin{aligned} a_{11}x_1 + a_{12}x_2 + \dots + a_{1n}x_n &= b_1 \qquad & : \pi_1 \\ a_{21}x_1 + a_{22}x_2 + \dots + a_{2n}x_n &= b_2 \qquad & : \pi_2 \\ c_1x_1 + c_2x_2 + \dots + c_nx_n &= z \end{aligned}$$

Define as coordinates (u_1, u_2, v) of a point the coefficients of x_j in (11); thus $A_j = (a_{1j}, a_{2j}, c_j)$. The *requirement line* is $u_1 = b_1$, $u_2 = b_2$. A basic feasible solution corresponds to three points, say A_1, A_2, A_3 such that the requirement line intersects the "solution plane" formed by A_1, A_2, A_3 at a point of the two-dimensional simplex formed by A_1, A_2, A_3 as in Fig. 7-3-IV. If

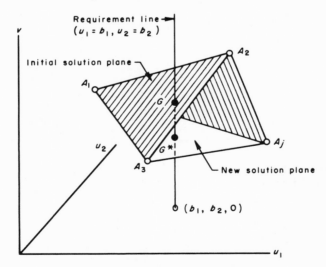

Figure 7-3-IV. The simplex associated with a cycle of the simplex algorithm ($m = 3$).

A_j is a point below the solution plane, $v = \pi_0 + \pi_1 u_1 + \pi_2 v_2$, associated with A_1, A_2, A_3, then $\bar{c}_j = c_j - \pi_0 - \pi_1 a_{1j} - \pi_2 a_{2j} < 0$. In this case, a three-dimensional *simplex* $A_j A_1 A_2 A_3$ can be formed and a point G^* found where the requirement line pierces the simplex at a lower point. G^* is on one of the three faces $A_1 A_2 A_j$, $A_2 A_3 A_j$, $A_1 A_3 A_j$ depending on the position of A_j. In Fig. 7-3-IV, G^* was assumed to be in the face $A_1 A_3 A_j$, and it is these three points that are used to determine the new solution plane.

The simplex criterion used to select a new basic variable x_s does not select an arbitrary x_j corresponding to an A_j below the solution plane, but an $A_s = A_j$ which is a *maximum* distance, $\bar{c}_s = \text{Min } \bar{c}_j$ below the plane. Inspection of figures such as Figs. 7-3-I and 7-3-II give credence to the belief that such a point would have a good chance of being in the optimal solution. Empirical evidence on thousands of problems confirms this and is the reason the simplex method is efficient in practice.

EXERCISE: Study Fig. 7-2-I and § 7-2-(5); construct an example to show for $n = m + 2$ that the simplex criterion $\bar{c}_s = \text{Min } \bar{c}_j$ could cause a maximum number of cycles to be performed.

7-4. PROBLEMS

Convex Regions. (Refer to § 7-1.)

1. Review the relationship between convex sets and linear programming.
2. Determine which of the following are convex sets.

$$\text{(a)} \quad \begin{aligned} x_1 + x_2 + \ x_3 &\geq 6 \\ x_1 - x_2 + 3x_3 &\geq 4 \\ x_j &\geq 0 \end{aligned}$$

$$\text{(b)} \quad x_1^2 + \ x_2^2 \geq 5$$

$$\text{(c)} \quad x_1^2 + 2x_2^2 \leq 3$$

$$\text{(d)} \quad x_2^2 - 2x_1 \leq 2$$

$$\text{(e)} \quad \begin{aligned} x_1 - 2x_2^2 &\geq 3 \\ x_1 + 2x_2 &\leq 4 \\ 2x_1 + 3x_2 &\geq 6 \end{aligned}$$

3. (a) Solve graphically and by the Fourier-Motzkin Elimination Method of § 4-4: maximize $x_1 - x_2$, subject to

$$\begin{aligned} x_1 + \ x_2 &\leq 5 \\ x_1 - 3x_2 &\geq 0 \\ x_1 \qquad &\geq 0 \\ x_2 &\geq 0 \\ 2x_1 + 3x_2 &\geq 6. \end{aligned}$$

(b) State in standard form.

(c) Indicate the convex set of feasible solutions. Why is the optimal solution an extreme point?

(d) Omitting the conditions $x_1 \geq 0$ and $x_2 \geq 0$, reduce to standard form by two methods.

4. Transform the two systems of inequalities (A) and (B) below into systems of equations in nonnegative variables by a change of variables; graph (B) in terms of the original variables. Graph the dual of (A).

$$(A) \begin{cases} 2x_1 + 3x_2 + 4x_3 \geq 5 \\ 4x_1 - 7x_2 + 3x_3 \leq 4 \end{cases} \qquad (B) \begin{cases} x_1 + x_2 \leq 1 \\ 4x_1 + 8x_2 \leq 32 \\ x_1 + x_2 \leq 4 \\ x_1 - 2x_2 \geq 2 \end{cases}$$

5. The process of increasing the variable x_s in the simplex method, while holding the other independent variable fixed at zero, generates a class of solutions corresponding to an edge in a convex polyhedron of feasible solutions if the vertex corresponds to a nondegenerate basic feasible solution. What can happen under degeneracy?

6. If a basic solution is nondegenerate, there are precisely $n - m$ neighbors of its corresponding extreme point and these are generated by increasing one of the $n - m$ independent variables, while holding the remainder fixed at zero. What can happen under degeneracy?

7. Show that if x_k is a variable unrestricted in sign, it is possible to obtain an optimal solution for the system by eliminating x_k from all but one equation, setting this equation aside and optimizing the remaining modified system, and then determining x_k by a back substitution.

8. Suppose that one equation of a linear program in standard form has one positive coefficient, say that of x_k, while all remaining coefficients of the equation are nonpositive and the constant is positive. This implies that $x_k > 0$ for any solution, whatever the values of the remaining $x_j \geq 0$. Pivot on any non-zero term in x_k to eliminate x_k from the remaining equations and set aside the one equation involving x_k. Prove that the resulting linear program in one less equation and one less variable can be solved to find the optimal solution of the original problem.

9. If it is known in advance that a solution cannot be optimal unless it involves a variable x_k at positive value, show that this variable can be eliminated and the reduced system with one less equation and variable solved in its place.

10. Devise a method for finding the second best basic feasible solution. Generalize to the third best, the fourth, etc. Discuss any complications.

11. Show, if r variables have unique and nonnegative values when the remaining variables are set equal to zero, the feasible solution is an extreme point solution.

12. Given an extreme point solution $(v_1, v_2, \ldots, v_n)$, show that if the

[167]

variables x_j are set equal to zero corresponding to $v_j = 0$, then the remaining variables are uniquely determined and $x_j = v_j > 0$.

13. (W. M. Hirsch, unsolved.) Does there exist a sequence of m or less pivot operations, each generating a new basic feasible solution (b.f.s.), which starts with some given b.f.s. and ends with some other given b.f.s., where m is the number of equations? Expressed *geometrically*:

In a convex region in $n - m$ dimensional space defined by n half-planes, is m an upper bound for the minimum-length chain of adjacent vertices joining two given vertices?

14. Prove that a square homogeneous system of m equations always has a nontrivial solution (a solution in which at least one variable is not zero) if there are redundant equations (i.e., if the rank of the system is less than m).

15. (Gale.) Prove that a square homogeneous linear inequality system always has a nontrivial solution.

16. Show that the set of possible values of any variable x_k of a linear program forms a convex set, in this case, a straight line segment $a \le x_k \le b$.

17. Show that the set of possible values of two variables, say (x_1, x_2) or (x_1, z) satisfying a linear program, forms a convex set in two dimensions.

18. As a corollary to problem 17, show, if x_k is treated as a parameter and can take on a range of possible values, that the value of Min z becomes a convex function of x_k.

19. Show, in general, that Min z is a convex function of θ, if the constant terms of a linear program are linear functions of the parameter θ. However, show that the value of some other variable, such as x_4 for Min z in the example below, need not be either a convex or a concave (the negative of a convex) function of θ.

$$
\begin{array}{llllll}
x_1 & & -x_3 + x_4 & & = \theta & \qquad (x_j \ge 0) \\
x_1 + & x_2 & & & = \theta & \\
x_1 & & -x_3 & +x_5 & = 1 & \\
& +x_2 & & +x_6 & = 1 & \\
4x_1 + & 2x_2 & +x_4 & & = z \text{ (Min)} &
\end{array}
$$

20. Show that, if $P = (a_1, a_2, \ldots, a_m)$ is a point in m dimensions, the set of points C with coordinates $a_1\lambda, a_2\lambda, \ldots, a_m\lambda$, where λ can take on any value in the range $0 \le \lambda < \infty$, is convex. This set is called a *ray*. Graph the ray for $P = (1, 1, 1)$.

21. A set of points is called a *cone* if, whenever P is in the set, so is every point in the ray of P. Construct an example to show that a cone, in general, need not be convex.

22. Show that, if $P = (a_1, a_2, \ldots, a_m)$ and $Q = (a_1', a_2', \ldots, a_m')$ are two points in m dimensions, the set of points C with coordinates $X = (\lambda a_1 + \mu a_1', \lambda a_2 + \mu a_2', \ldots, \lambda a_m + \mu a_m')$ for arbitrary λ and μ in

the ranges $0 \leq \lambda < \infty$, $0 \leq \mu < \infty$ forms a convex cone. In vector notation (see § 8-2), X is given by $X = \lambda P + \mu Q$. This set is called the cone generated by two rays λP and μQ. Graph the cone generated by $P = (1, 1, 1)$, and $Q = (1, 1, 0)$.

23. In general, the set generated by forming nonnegative linear combinations of points P_1, P_2, . . ., P_k is called a cone. Thus, C is all points $X = \lambda_1 P_1 + \lambda_2 P_2 + \ldots + \lambda_k P_k$ for arbitrary λ_i in the range $0 \leq \lambda_i < \infty$. Prove C is a convex cone.

24. Show that a convex cone is formed by the set C of all points $P = (b_1, b_2, \ldots, b_m)$ given by choosing $x_1 \geq 0$, $x_2 \geq 0$, . . ., $x_n \geq 0$ in the expressions

$$a_{i1}x_1 + a_{i2}x_2 + \ldots + a_{in}x_n = b_i \qquad (i = 1, 2, \ldots, m)$$

25. Suppose P_1, P_2, . . ., P_k, . . . is an infinite collection of points in m dimensional space. Let C be the set of points generated by forming nonnegative linear combinations of finite subset of these points. Let C' be the set of points generated by forming nonnegative linear combinations of subset of m or less of these points. Show that C and C' are identical convex cones.

Interpretations of the Simplex Method. (Refer to §§ 7-2, 7-3.)

26. Carry out the steps of the simplex method both algebraically and geometrically on (a) the Product Mix Problem and (b) the Blending Problem II and show the correspondence. (Refer to § 3-4 and § 3-5 for the problems.)

27. Take the warehouse problem (§ 3-6) and solve algebraically and geometrically using the simplex method in three dimensions.

28. Using the Fourier-Motzkin elimination procedure, solve

$$\begin{aligned}
2y_1 + y_2 &\leq 2 \\
-3y_1 + y_2 &\leq -3 \\
y_1 - 2y_2 &\leq 6 \\
3y_1 + 9y_2 &\leq 1 \\
- y_1 &\leq -2 \\
3y_1 + 4y_2 &= v \text{ (Max)}
\end{aligned}$$

29. Solve the above, using the following variant of the simplex method: for those with positive right-hand sides introduce *slack* variables $y_j \geq 0$; for those with nonpositive right-hand sides introduce *artificial excess* variables $y_j \geq 0$. Apply the usual simplex method to minimizing the sum of artificial variables, in this case $y_4 + y_7 = w$. However, note that y_1 and y_2 are not restricted in sign. See problem below.

30. Invent a variant of the simplex method which permits specified variables to be unrestricted in sign. Apply this to Problem 28.

31. Solve

$$2y_1 + \;\; y_2 \leq 2 \qquad\qquad (y_1 \geq 0, \, y_2 \geq 0)$$
$$y_1 - 2y_2 \leq 6$$
$$3y_1 + 9y_2 \leq 1$$
$$3y_1 + 4y_2 = v \; (\text{Max})$$

using the simplex method. Interpret geometrically the simplex steps in the 2-dimensional space of y_1 and y_2.

32. Given a system

$$x_1 + \;\; x_2 + \ldots + \;\; x_n = 1 \qquad\qquad (x_j \geq 0)$$
$$a_1 x_1 + a_2 x_2 + \ldots + a_n x_n = b$$
$$c_1 x_1 + c_2 x_2 + \ldots + c_n x_n = z \; (\text{Min})$$

show that the solution line $v = \pi_0^* + \pi_1^* u$ associated with the minimal basic solution must satisfy

(a) $\quad c_j - (\pi_0^* + \pi_1^* a_j) \geq 0$

(b) $\qquad \pi_0^* + \pi_1^* b = \text{Min } z$

33. Prove in the above that the convex hull of points $A_j = (a_j, c_j)$ lies above an arbitrary line $v = \pi_0 + \pi_1 u$, if

$$c_j - (\pi_0 + \pi_1 a_j) \geq 0$$

Use this to show that such a line must cut the requirement line $u = b_1$ in a point, whose ordinate $v \leq \text{Min } z$.

34. Use the results of the above two problems to prove that the values of π_0 and π_1 and Max v, satisfying the (dual) inequality system

$$\pi_0 + \pi_1 a_j \leq c_j \qquad\qquad \text{for } j = 1, 2, \ldots, n$$
$$\pi_0 + \pi_1 b \;\; = v \; (\text{Max})$$

are given by the solution line $v = \pi_0^* + \pi_1^* u$ associated with the minimal basic solution and

$$\text{Max } v = \text{Min } z$$

Review this particular geometrical interpretation of the duality theorem given in § 3-4 and displayed in Fig. 3-4-I.

35. Note that the dual of a standard linear program is a system of inequalities in unrestricted variables. Suppose one is given a system in the latter form; review how its dual may be used as a *third way* to get a standard linear program from a system of linear inequalities. Find the standard linear program of which this is the dual:

$$\pi_0 + .2\pi_1 \leq -2.4$$
$$\pi_0 + .1\pi_1 \geq -2.0$$
$$\pi_0 + .3\pi_1 \leq -1.8$$

[170]

$$\pi_0 + .8\pi_1 \leq - .8$$
$$\pi_0 \qquad \leq \quad 0$$
$$\pi_0 + \quad \pi_1 \leq \quad 0$$
$$\pi_0 \qquad \leq \quad v \text{ (Max)}$$

Solve the dual, by using the simplex method and also by using the elimination method, and prove that Max v = Min z of the dual original system.

36. If $v = \pi_0 + \pi_1 u_1 + \pi_2 u_2$ represents the solution plane associated with A_1, A_2, A_3 in Fig. 7-3-III, interpret the conditions

$$v_j - (\pi_0 + \pi_1 a_{1j} + \pi_2 a_{2j}) = 0 \qquad (j = 1, 2, 3)$$

and the quantities

$$v_j - (\pi_0 + \pi_j a_{1j} + \pi a_{2j}) = \bar{c}_j$$

both algebraically in the simplex method and geometrically.

37. A third geometry of the simplex method can be obtained by regarding a column j as representing a *line* $\pi_0 + a_j \pi_1 = c_j$ in (π_0, π_1) space. Thus, this procedure can be interpreted to be in the same space as the space of independent variables π_0 and π_1 of the *dual linear programming problem* $\pi_0 + a_j \pi_1 \leq c_j$, $\pi_0 + b\pi_1 = v$ (Max) for $j = 1, 2, \ldots, n$. Show that the simplex procedure for solving the dual is different from the interpretation of the simplex procedure for solving the original problem in this geometry. (The procedure of Kelley for solving nonlinear programs is based on this geometry.) See [Wolfe, 1960-1].

38. In the text the relation between the classical gradient procedure and the simplex method is outlined. Show that each iteration of the simplex method expresses the function to be minimized in terms of a different set of independent variables. Show that the direction of maximum decrease of the function under the restrictions $\Sigma x_j = \Delta$, $x_j \geq 0$ is just the one given by the simplex criterion. What would it be if $\Sigma x_j^2 = \Delta^2$ were used instead?

39. (a) Use the "Center of Gravity Method" to find $x_j \geq 0$ and Min z satisfying

$$x_1 + 2x_2 + 3x_3 + 4x_4 = z \text{ (Min)}$$
$$x_1 + \quad x_2 + \quad x_3 + \quad x_4 = 4$$
$$x_1 - 2x_2 + 3x_3 - 4x_4 = -2$$

(b) Dualize and graph the dual problem.

(c) Solve the dual using the Fourier-Motzkin Elimination Method (§ 4-4).

(d) Solve the primal using the simplex method. Trace the steps of the procedure as graphed in (a) and (b).

40. [Minkowski, 1896-1.] *Theorem:* A feasible solution of a bounded linear program can be expressed as a linear nonnegative combination of

basic feasible solutions. Geometrically stated, a point of a bounded convex polyhedron C, defined as the intersection of finitely many half-spaces, can be expressed as a linear nonnegative combination of extreme points of C.

Show that the theorem is false if C is unbounded.

Advanced Problems.

41. *Theorem:* Let M be a given set of points in a Euclidean $(m - 1)$ dimensional space and let Q be in the convex hull of M. It is possible to find m points P_1, P_2, P_3, . . ., P_m (not necessarily different) of M, and m real numbers $x_1 . . . x_m$ so that $x_i \geq 0$, $\sum_1^m x_i = 1$, and $\sum_1^m x_i P_i = Q$. (E. Steinitz, *Reine Angew. Math.*, Vol. 143, 1913, pp. 128–275.)

42. *Theorem:* Let M be a given infinite set of points in Euclidean m-dimensional space and let Q be in the convex cone spanned by M. It is possible to find m points P_1, P_2, . . ., P_m (not necessarily different) of M, and m real numbers $x_1 \geq 0$, . . ., $x_m \geq 0$, so that $\sum_1^m x_i P_i = Q$.

Hint: Establish this theorem for any point Q representable as a nonnegative finite linear combination of points $P_i \in$ M. Show that all such points Q define the convex cone spanned by M.

REFERENCES
Convex Sets and Functions

Beckenbach, 1948-1
Eggleston, 1958-1
Fenchel, 1953-1
Gaddum, 1952-1
Gale, 1951-1, 1956-1, 1962-1
Gerstenhaber, 1951-1
Goldman and Tucker, 1956-1
Hirsch and Hoffman, 1961-1
Klee, 1964-2

Lemke, 1961-1
Minkowski, 1896-1
Motzkin, 1936-1
Saaty, 1955-1
Stokes, 1931-1
Tucker, 1955-1
Weyl, 1935-1
Wolfe, 1960-1
(See also Chapter 4.)

CHAPTER 8

PIVOTING, VECTOR SPACES, MATRICES, AND INVERSES

8-1. PIVOT THEORY[1]

Our purpose is to extend the discussion of § 4-2 regarding properties preserved by pivot operations and characteristics of pivot operations. The first of five important properties concerns redundancy and inconsistency.

THEOREM 1: *If there is a linear combination of equations of a system with non-zero weights which results in a null equation (redundancy), or in an inconsistent equation, then the same is true for a system obtained from it by a sequence of elementary (or pivot) operations.*

PROOF: Let E_0 represent alternatively either a vacuous or an inconsistent equation. Let $E_1, E_2, \ldots, E_k$ denote a subset of the equations of the system that, by the hypothesis, satisfy

$$(1) \qquad \lambda_1 E_1 + \lambda_2 E_2 + \ldots + \lambda_k E_k = E_0 \qquad \text{where } \lambda_i \neq 0$$

If the first of a sequence of elementary operations does not involve these E_i, the same relation will hold in the resulting system. The same is clearly true if an elementary operation replaces E_1 by αE_1, say, where $\alpha \neq 0$. If E_1 is replaced by $E_1 + \alpha E_2 = E_1'$, then $E_1 = E_1' - \alpha E_2$ and the relation

$$(2) \qquad \lambda_1 E_1' + (\lambda_2 - \lambda_1 \alpha) E_2 + \ldots + \lambda_k E_k = E_0$$

holds for the resulting system. Since $\lambda_1 \neq 0$ in this case too, a non-zero linear combination of the equations of the resulting system yields E_0. Finally, if E_1, say, is replaced by $E_1 + \alpha E_t = E_1'$ where $t \neq 1, 2, \ldots, k$, then the relation

$$(3) \qquad \lambda_1 E_1' + \lambda_2 E_2 + \ldots + \lambda_k E_k - \lambda_1 \alpha E_t = E_0$$

holds, and again the result follows since $\lambda_1 \neq 0$. By induction the theorem holds for any number of elementary operations. Since pivot operations are a particular case of the latter, the proof is complete.

The second important property of the pivot operation is its *irreversibility* except in certain situations.

---

[1] I am indebted to A. W. Tucker for his suggestions for developing this section based on the idea of the irreversibility of the pivot operations except when applied to a canonical form.

THEOREM 2: *If a system is in canonical form before a pivot operation, then it is in canonical form after the pivot operation.*

PROOF: Suppose a system is in canonical form with basic variables $x_{j_1}, x_{j_2}, \ldots, x_{j_m}$. Let the pivot term be chosen in equation r using variable x_s. Then, as we have seen in § 5-1, the resulting system is in canonical form with x_s replacing x_{j_r} as a basic variable. In the new system, if a new pivot term is selected in equation r using variable x_r, then a second pivot operation will restore the original system; hence

COROLLARY 1: *If a system is in canonical form, the inverse of a pivot operation is a pivot operation.*

COROLLARY 2: *If a subsystem S is in canonical form before a pivot operation and if the pivot term is selected in an equation of S, then the corresponding subsystem after a pivot operation is in canonical form; the inverse of the pivot operation is a pivot operation (assuming zero coefficients for basic variables in the non-canonical equations).*

COROLLARY 3: *If a subsystem S is in canonical form before a pivot operation and if the pivot term is selected in an equation E not in S, then the subsystem corresponding to $\{S, E\}$ after a pivot operation is in canonical form; the inverse of the pivot operation is not a pivot operation unless $\{S, E\}$ was in canonical form initially.*

The third important property of the pivot operation is that there is a one-to-one correspondence between equations and that easily defined subsets of the original and the derived systems are equivalent.

DEFINITION: The *pivotal subsystem* is that set of equations P of the *original system* corresponding to those selected for pivot terms in a sequence of pivot operations.

It is clear that the number of equations in the pivotal subsystem increases or remains the same during a sequence of pivot operations, depending on whether or not the successive pivot terms are selected from among equations corresponding to the pivotal system or from among the remainder. Let S be any subset of the original equations that includes the pivotal set P and let S' and P' be the corresponding subsets after a sequence of pivot operations.

THEOREM 3: *The system S' is equivalent to S; in particular, P' is equivalent to P and, moreover, P' is in canonical form.*

PROOF: That P' is canonical, follows from Corollaries 2 and 3. To prove S and S' are equivalent systems, note that if the equations not in P are deleted, the same sequence of pivot operations can be performed on those corresponding to P and hence the latter are all equivalent to P.

THEOREM 4: *The pivotal subsystem P is independent and solvable.*

PROOF: P' is in canonical form by Theorem 3 and is therefore solvable and independent. Since P is equivalent to P', it is solvable also. It cannot contain any redundancies because by Theorem 1 the same would have to hold for P'.

THEOREM 5: (*A redundancy and inconsistency tracing theorem.*) *If an equation* E_t' *of a reduced system is vacuous (or inconsistent), then in the original system,* E_t *is either redundant with respect to the pivotal system* P *(or a linear combination of the equations of* P *and* E_t *can form an inconsistent equation).*

PROOF: Note $\{P, E_t\}$ can be generated from $\{P', E_t'\}$ by a reverse sequence of elementary operations, hence applying Theorem 1 there exist weights $\lambda_i \geq 0$ not all zero such that

$$(4) \qquad \lambda_1 E_1 + \lambda_2 E_2 + \ldots + \lambda_k E_k + \lambda_t E_t = E_0 \qquad (\lambda_i \geq 0)$$

where $(E_1, \ldots, E_k)$ are the pivotal equations (not necessarily the first k) and E_0 is alternatively either a vacuous or an inconsistent equation. In either case, $\lambda_t \neq 0$ because of Theorems 3 and 4; hence, if E_0 is vacuous, E_t is dependent on the others.

Testing Systems for Equivalence.

The fourth important property of the pivoting operation is that it provides a way to show whether or not two systems have *the same solution set* by trying to reduce them simultaneously by pivoting step by step, using the *same* pivotal variables. The same process will test the *equivalence* of two systems.

THEOREM 6: *Two solvable systems have the same solution sets if and only if they are equivalent.*

THEOREM 7: *Two systems are equivalent if and only if it is possible to pivot with respect to the same ordered sequence of variables and* (a) *if consistent, the canonical parts of the two systems are identical and the remainder vacuous;* (b) *if inconsistent, the canonical parts are identical except possibly for the constant terms, and the remainder each have one or more inconsistent equations.*

PROOF OF THEOREMS: Let us suppose first that it is possible to reduce two systems using the same set of pivot variables. We assume the equations of the canonical parts are reordered so that both subsystems are canonical with the same set of basic variables. If the two systems are to be *equivalent*, it is necessary that their canonical part be identical, because there is only *one* way to form the left-hand side of an equation of the canonical part of one system as a linear combination of the equations of the reduced system of the other. Their constant terms may not agree if there are inconsistent equations in the non-canonical part (but may be made to agree by adding in a suitable multiple of the latter). If the two systems are solvable with the *same solution set*, the canonical parts are identical; (see proof of Theorem 1 in § 4-2). In general, the non-canonical parts must either both contain an inconsistent equation or both be vacuous because the only way to generate an inconsistent equation of one system from that of the other is as a linear combination of the inconsistent equations of the other.

Now let us suppose that it is *not* possible to reduce two systems using the same set of pivot variables, but that it is possible to pivot on the same variables for the first t steps, say variables $x_1, x_2, \ldots, x_t$ in the first t equations, and that on step $(t + 1)$ it is possible to pivot on the x_{t+1} term in equation $t + 1$ in system I, and it is not possible to use x_{t+1} for pivotal variable in system II because the coefficients of x_{t+1} are zero in *all* the remaining $m - t$ equations of II. Note that it is not possible to generate the $t + 1$st equation of system I from those of system II because the weights on the first t equations must be zero and this makes the coefficient of x_{t+1} automatically zero whatever be the weights on the remaining equations. Hence the two systems cannot be equivalent.

Nor can the two systems, in this case, be solvable with the same solution set. To see this, let $x_1^o, \ldots, x_r^o, x_{r+1}^o, \ldots, x_n^o$ be *any* solution to system I. Either it does not satisfy system II, or if it does, then a solution for system II exists which does not satisfy system I, namely $x_1^*, \ldots, x_r^*; x_{r+1}^*, x_{r+2}^o, \ldots, x_n^o$ obtained by changing x_{r+1}^o to $x_{r+1}^* \neq x_{r+1}^o$ and adjusting the values of $x_1, \ldots, x_r$ in canonical part of the first r equations of system II. Note that this solution satisfies the remaining equations of system II (there are no $x_1, \ldots, x_r, x_{r+1}$ terms) but cannot satisfy system I because it does not satisfy equation $r + 1$ of system I. Hence, in either case, the two systems do not have the same solution set.

The fifth important property of pivoting is that it provides a way to prove a number of interesting theorems concerning the number of independent and dependent equations of a system.

THEOREM 8: *Two equivalent, independent, consistent systems have the same number of equations.*

PROOF: Invoking Theorem 4 it is possible simultaneously to reduce the two systems, and the canonical parts of the reduced systems are identical. No vacuous equations can result because pivoting is actually a sequence of elementary operations, so that, by Theorem 1, the appearance of such equations would imply a redundant equation in the original systems. Therefore, the identical canonical equivalents have the same number of equations as their respective original systems.

The following three theorems are consequences of the above.

THEOREM 9: *Two equivalent canonical systems have the same number of equations.*

THEOREM 10: *If a system has a canonical equivalent with r equations, any partition of the system into an independent set of equations and a set of equations dependent upon them will have exactly r equations in the independent set.*

THEOREM 11: *If a system has a canonical equivalent with r equations, then any r independent equations of the system can generate the remainder by linear combinations.*

DEFINITION: The largest number of independent equations in a solvable system is called its *rank*.

EXERCISE: Prove Theorems 9, 10, and 11. Show that r in Theorem 10 is the rank of the system.

8-2. VECTOR SPACES

Vector Operations.

Many operations that are performed on a system of equations can be viewed as performing a number of operations *in parallel*. For example, we may rewrite the system,

(1)
$$2x_1 + 3x_2 - 4x_3 = 5$$
$$-4x_1 - 2x_2 + 3x_3 = 7$$

in the form

(2)
$$\begin{bmatrix} 2 \\ -4 \end{bmatrix} x_1 + \begin{bmatrix} 3 \\ -2 \end{bmatrix} x_2 + \begin{bmatrix} -4 \\ +3 \end{bmatrix} x_3 = \begin{bmatrix} 5 \\ 7 \end{bmatrix}$$

and interpret this to mean that when the corresponding elements (components) in the column are to be multiplied by the unknowns and added across, their sums give the corresponding elements in the right-hand column. The columns are called *column vectors*. Operations, called "addition" and "scalar multiplication" of vectors, are performed upon them in a manner analogous to ordinary numbers.

The coefficients $[2, 3, -4]$ that appear in the first equation (or $[-4, -2, 3]$ in the second equation) may likewise be considered as an entity called a *row vector*. Vectors whose elements are drawn from a row are usually written with brackets [ ] or parentheses ( ). Often vectors whose elements are from a column are written in text as row vectors to conserve space; when this is the case for us, angle parentheses $\langle \ \rangle$ will be used instead of [ ] or ( ).

Thus $\langle 2, -4 \rangle$ stands for the column vector $\begin{bmatrix} 2 \\ -4 \end{bmatrix}$.

DEFINITION: An m-vector is an ordered set of m numbers called components (elements).

We shall begin by defining two fundamental operations on vectors which are a natural extension of addition and multiplication of numbers to sets of numbers in parallel.

DEFINITION: The *scalar multiple* of an m-vector by a number (scalar) x is an m-vector formed by multiplying each component by x. Thus for a column vector,

(3)
$$\begin{bmatrix} a_1 \\ a_2 \\ \cdot \\ \cdot \\ \cdot \\ a_m \end{bmatrix} x = \begin{bmatrix} a_1 x \\ a_2 x \\ \cdot \\ \cdot \\ \cdot \\ a_m x \end{bmatrix}.$$

DEFINITION: The *sum* of two *m*-vectors is the vector formed by adding the corresponding components. Thus

(4)
$$\begin{bmatrix} a_1 \\ a_2 \\ \cdot \\ \cdot \\ \cdot \\ a_m \end{bmatrix} + \begin{bmatrix} b_1 \\ b_2 \\ \cdot \\ \cdot \\ \cdot \\ b_m \end{bmatrix} \doteq \begin{bmatrix} a_1 + b_1 \\ a_2 + b_2 \\ \cdot \\ \cdot \\ \cdot \\ a_m + b_m \end{bmatrix}$$

DEFINITION: Two *m*-vectors are equal if their corresponding components are equal. Thus

(5)
$$\begin{bmatrix} a_1 \\ a_2 \\ \cdot \\ \cdot \\ \cdot \\ a_m \end{bmatrix} = \begin{bmatrix} b_1 \\ b_2 \\ \cdot \\ \cdot \\ \cdot \\ b_m \end{bmatrix} \text{ means } a_i = b_i \text{ for } i = 1, 2, \ldots, m$$

With this interpretation of operations on vectors it is clear that (2) is the same as (1) because, by the scalar multiplication of vectors, (2) is the same as

(6)
$$\begin{bmatrix} 2x_1 \\ -4x_1 \end{bmatrix} + \begin{bmatrix} 3x_2 \\ -2x_2 \end{bmatrix} + \begin{bmatrix} -4x_3 \\ +3x_3 \end{bmatrix} = \begin{bmatrix} 5 \\ 7 \end{bmatrix}$$

and by addition of vectors (say, by adding the third vector to the sum of the first two)

(7)
$$\begin{bmatrix} 2x_1 + 3x_2 - 4x_3 \\ -4x_1 - 2x_2 + 3x_3 \end{bmatrix} = \begin{bmatrix} 5 \\ 7 \end{bmatrix}$$

and by equality of vectors (7) means (1).

We are now in a position to make the important observation that the so-called *elementary operations on equations are in essence the scalar multiplication and addition of the row vectors formed by detaching the coefficients and constant terms of the equations.* The variables play a passive role throughout. For example, if the first equation of (1) is multiplied by 2 and added to the second, we obtain $0x_1 + 4x_2 - 5x_3 = 17$. This corresponds to the operations $2[2, 3, -4, 5] + [-4, -2, 3, 7] = [0, 4, -5, 17]$.

Linearly Dependent Vectors.

A vector each of whose components is zero is called a *zero vector* (or *null vector*). Thus by a vector $V = 0$ is meant

(8)
$$V = \begin{bmatrix} 0 \\ 0 \\ \cdot \\ \cdot \\ \cdot \\ 0 \end{bmatrix}$$

A vector $V \neq 0$ means that at least one component of V differs from zero.

[178]

A vector $\langle y_1, y_2, \ldots, y_m \rangle$ is said to be *linearly dependent* on n other vectors $P_j = \langle a_{1j}, a_{2j}, \ldots, a_{mj} \rangle$ if one can find numbers (scalars) $x_1, x_2, \ldots, x_n$, such that

$$(9) \qquad \begin{bmatrix} a_{11} \\ a_{21} \\ \cdot \\ \cdot \\ \cdot \\ a_{m1} \end{bmatrix} x_1 + \begin{bmatrix} a_{12} \\ a_{22} \\ \cdot \\ \cdot \\ \cdot \\ a_{m2} \end{bmatrix} x_2 + \ldots + \begin{bmatrix} a_{1n} \\ a_{2n} \\ \cdot \\ \cdot \\ \cdot \\ a_{mn} \end{bmatrix} x_n = \begin{bmatrix} y_1 \\ y_2 \\ \cdot \\ \cdot \\ \cdot \\ y_m \end{bmatrix}$$

EXERCISE: Choose particular values of a_{ij} and y_i, such that there are no x_j that satisfy (9); choose values, such that there are unique x_j that satisfy (9); choose values, such that there are many sets of x_j that satisfy (9).

DEFINITION: A set of r vectors P_i is *linearly independent* if

$$(10) \qquad P_1 x_1 + P_2 x_2 + \ldots + P_r x_r = 0$$

implies $x_1 = x_2 = \ldots = x_r = 0$. If a set of vectors is *not* linearly independent, then (10) holds with at least one $x_i \neq 0$ and the set is said to be *linearly dependent*. It is easy to see that this P_i is linearly dependent on the others.

EXERCISE: Show that the set consisting of a single vector is an independent set unless it is the zero vector. Given any set of vectors show that the null vector is linearly dependent upon them.

An m-vector whose i^{th} element is unity and all other elements are zero is called a *unit vector*. The m *different* unit vectors are denoted by

$$(11) \qquad U_1 = \begin{bmatrix} 1 \\ 0 \\ 0 \\ \cdot \\ \cdot \\ \cdot \\ 0 \end{bmatrix}, U_2 = \begin{bmatrix} 0 \\ 1 \\ 0 \\ \cdot \\ \cdot \\ \cdot \\ 0 \end{bmatrix}, \ldots, U_m = \begin{bmatrix} 0 \\ 0 \\ 0 \\ \cdot \\ \cdot \\ \cdot \\ 1 \end{bmatrix}$$

EXERCISE: Show that the vectors U_i are linearly independent. Show that any other vector can be expressed as a linear combination of the unit vectors U_i.

Vector Equations.

If, as above, we use symbols to denote vectors, we can write a single vector equation to represent m linear equations. For example, let

$$(12) \qquad Q = \begin{bmatrix} y_1 \\ y_2 \\ \cdot \\ \cdot \\ \cdot \\ y_m \end{bmatrix}; \quad P_j = \begin{bmatrix} a_{1j} \\ a_{2j} \\ \cdot \\ \cdot \\ \cdot \\ a_{mj} \end{bmatrix} \qquad (j = 1, 2, \ldots, n)$$

Then (9) becomes the problem of determining weights x_j (if possible) which express a linear dependence between the vectors P_j and Q,

$$(13) \qquad P_1 x_1 + P_2 x_2 + \ldots + P_n x_n = Q$$

Vector Space.

Instead of seeking numbers x_j that satisfy (13), we may reverse the process and generate column vectors $Q = \langle y_1, y_2, \ldots, y_m \rangle$ by varying the values $x_1, x_2, \ldots, x_n$. The set of vectors $\langle y_1, y_2, \ldots, y_m \rangle$ generated by all possible choices of $(x_1, x_2, \ldots, x_n)$ is called a *vector space*.

For example, if we plot in two dimensions the points with coordinates (y_1, y_2) obtained by choosing different values of x_1 and x_2 in (14), it is clear that it will describe the entire (y_1, y_2) plane.

$$(14) \qquad \begin{bmatrix} 1 \\ 2 \end{bmatrix} x_1 + \begin{bmatrix} 2 \\ 1 \end{bmatrix} x_2 = \begin{bmatrix} y_1 \\ y_2 \end{bmatrix}$$

On the other hand, the points (y_1, y_2) of (15) lie on the line $2y_1 = y_2$.

$$(15) \qquad \begin{bmatrix} 1 \\ 2 \end{bmatrix} x_1 = \begin{bmatrix} y_1 \\ y_2 \end{bmatrix}$$

The vector space for (y_1, y_2, y_3) in (16) is the plane $y_3 = y_1 + y_2$ in 3 dimensions,

$$(16) \qquad \begin{bmatrix} 1 \\ 2 \\ 3 \end{bmatrix} x_1 + \begin{bmatrix} 2 \\ 1 \\ 3 \end{bmatrix} x_2 = \begin{bmatrix} y_1 \\ y_2 \\ y_3 \end{bmatrix}$$

It is easy to see that the points (y_1, y_2, y_3) in (17) also lie in the plane $y_3 = y_1 + y_2$, because the column vectors associated with x_3 and x_4 are linearly dependent on those corresponding to x_1 and x_2.

$$(17) \qquad \begin{bmatrix} 1 \\ 2 \\ 3 \end{bmatrix} x_1 + \begin{bmatrix} 2 \\ 1 \\ 3 \end{bmatrix} x_2 + \begin{bmatrix} 3 \\ 3 \\ 6 \end{bmatrix} x_3 + \begin{bmatrix} -1 \\ +1 \\ 0 \end{bmatrix} x_4 = \begin{bmatrix} y_1 \\ y_2 \\ y_3 \end{bmatrix}$$

In fact, substituting in (17) the expressions

$$(18) \qquad \begin{bmatrix} 3 \\ 3 \\ 6 \end{bmatrix} = \begin{bmatrix} 1 \\ 2 \\ 3 \end{bmatrix} + \begin{bmatrix} 2 \\ 1 \\ 3 \end{bmatrix}, \quad \begin{bmatrix} -1 \\ +1 \\ 0 \end{bmatrix} = \begin{bmatrix} 1 \\ 2 \\ 3 \end{bmatrix} - \begin{bmatrix} 2 \\ 1 \\ 3 \end{bmatrix}$$

one obtains

$$(19) \qquad \begin{bmatrix} 1 \\ 2 \\ 3 \end{bmatrix} (x_1 + x_3 + x_4) + \begin{bmatrix} 2 \\ 1 \\ 3 \end{bmatrix} (x_2 + x_3 - x_4) = \begin{bmatrix} y_1 \\ y_2 \\ y_3 \end{bmatrix}$$

and it is clear that the class of vectors $\langle y_1, y_2, y_3 \rangle$ generated by (19) is identical with that generated by (16).

DEFINITION: A *basis* of a vector space is any set of independent vectors in the space such that all other vectors in the space can be generated as linear combinations of the vectors in the set.

It is easy to see that there can be many sets of independent vectors that can generate the same vector space. Thus the vector spaces associated with (14) and with (20) below are the same.

$$\text{(20)} \qquad \begin{bmatrix} 1 \\ 0 \end{bmatrix} x_1 + \begin{bmatrix} 0 \\ 1 \end{bmatrix} x_2 = \begin{bmatrix} y_1 \\ y_2 \end{bmatrix}$$

Rank or Dimensionality of a Vector Space.

The rank of a vector space is the largest number of independent vectors in the space. We shall show that, if a vector space can be generated from r independent vectors, any other set of r independent vectors in the space can also serve as a basis. Moreover, it is not possible to generate the space with fewer than r vectors nor is it possible to find in the space more than r independent vectors. The number r is called the rank or dimensionality of the vector space.

THEOREM 1: *Let Q be any vector in the vector space generated by a set of independent vectors* $(P_1, P_2, \ldots, P_r)$; *then the values* $x_1, x_2, \ldots, x_r$ *such that*

$$\text{(21)} \qquad P_1 x_1 + P_2 x_2 + \ldots + P_r x_r = Q$$

are unique.

PROOF: If not unique then there exists another set of values x' such that

$$\text{(22)} \qquad P_1 x_1' + P_2 x_2' + \ldots + P_r x_r' = Q$$

Subtraction yields

$$\text{(23)} \qquad P_1(x_1 - x_1') + P_2(x_2 - x_2') + \ldots + P_r(x_r - x_r') = 0$$

and we conclude that if not all $(x_i - x_i') = 0$, the vectors $P_1, P_2, \ldots, P_r$ are not independent, contrary to assumption.

DEFINITION: The expression (21) is called the *representation* of the vector Q in terms of the basis $(P_1, P_2, \ldots, P_r)$, and $(x_1, x_2, \ldots, x_r)$ are called the *coordinates* of Q relative to this basis.

EXERCISE: Show that the set of unit vectors (11) constitute a basis in the space E_m of all vectors with m coordinates, and the coordinates of a vector relative to this basis are the same as the components of the vector.

THEOREM 2: *Given a basis and a vector* $R \neq 0$ *in a vector space, it is possible to replace one of the columns of the basis by R to form a new basis.*

PROOF: Let the representation of R in terms of the basis be

$$\text{(24)} \qquad P_1 v_1 + P_2 v_2 + \ldots + P_r v_r = R$$

At least one $v_i \neq 0$ in (24), since $R \neq 0$; then we will show that a new basis can be formed by replacing P_1 by R. First of all,

[181]

P_2, P_3, . . ., P_r; R are linearly independent; for, assuming they are linearly dependent implies that R has a non-zero coefficient and thus can be expressed in terms of the others in a representation different from the *unique* representation (24), a contradiction (see Theorem 1).

Now we only need to show that an arbitrary Q can be expressed in terms of the independent vectors P_2, P_3, . . ., P_r; R to prove these vectors form a basis. In fact, multiplying (24) by an arbitrary constant θ and subtracting from (21) yields

$$(25) \quad P_1(x_1 - \theta v_1) + P_2(x_2 - \theta v_2) + \ldots + P_r(x_r - \theta v_r) + R\theta = Q$$

whence setting

$$(26) \qquad\qquad \theta = x_1/v_1 \qquad\qquad (v_1 \neq 0)$$

shows that Q is linearly dependent upon the others, since $x_1 - \theta v_1 = 0$. Hence, these independent vectors can generate any other vector Q in the space.

THEOREM 3: *Given a basis and k independent non-zero vectors R_1, R_2, . . ., R_k, in the vector space generated by the basis, it is possible to replace k vectors in the basis by R_1, R_2, . . ., R_k.*

PROOF: The proof is inductive. The case $k = 1$ was shown by the previous theorem. Suppose that a new basis can be formed by substituting $k - 1$ vectors R_1, R_2, . . ., R_{k-1} for $k - 1$ vectors in the basis, say, by replacing P_1, P_2, . . ., P_{k-1}, so that the new basis is R_1, R_2, . . ., R_{k-1}; P_k, . . ., P_r. Let the representation of R_k in terms of this basis be

$$(27) \quad R_1v_1 + R_2v_2 + \ldots + R_{k-1}v_{k-1} + P_kv_k + \ldots + P_rv_r = R_k$$

At least one $v_i \neq 0$, for $i \geq k$, otherwise R_k would be linearly dependent on R_1, R_2, . . ., R_{k-1}, contrary to assumption. Let $v_t \neq 0$ for some $t \geq k$. Then, following the argument of the previous theorem, R_k can replace P_t in this basis to form a new basis consisting of vectors R_1, R_2, . . ., R_{k-1}, R_k, P_{k+1}, . . ., P_r (omitting P_t). The following are left as exercises:

THEOREM 4: *If there exists a basis consisting of r vectors, then any r independent vectors in the vector space form a basis.*

THEOREM 5: *If there exists a basis consisting of r vectors, then it is not possible to have more than r independent vectors in the vector space.*

THEOREM 6: *If there exists a basis consisting of r vectors, then it is not possible to find in the vector space a basis with fewer than r vectors.*

EXERCISE: Show that the symbolic operations on equations E_i in § 8-1 may also be viewed as vector relations. Let $\bar{E}_i = (a_{i1}, a_{i2}, \ldots, a_{in}; b_i)$ be the row vector, defined by the coefficients and constant of E_i; then § 8-1-(1) may be interpreted to mean

$$\lambda_1\bar{E}_1 + \lambda_2\bar{E}_2 + \lambda_3\bar{E}_3 + \ldots + \lambda_k\bar{E}_k = \bar{E}_0$$

Interpret the other symbolic relations in § 8-1.

EXERCISE: Show that the rank of a consistent system of equations $E_1, E_2, \ldots$ is the same as the rank of the system of row vectors $\bar{E}_1, \bar{E}_2, \ldots$ associated with these equations. The definition for equations is given at the end of § 8-1.

8-3. MATRICES

Matrix Operations.

A rectangular array of numbers is called a matrix. Thus the detached coefficients of § 8-2-(1)

(1)
$$\begin{bmatrix} 2 & 3 & -4 \\ -4 & -2 & 3 \end{bmatrix}$$

constitute a 2×3 matrix, i.e., a matrix of two rows and three columns. More generally an $m \times n$ matrix is

(2)
$$\begin{bmatrix} a_{11} & a_{12} & \ldots & a_{1n} \\ a_{21} & a_{22} & \ldots & a_{2n} \\ \cdot & & \cdot & \cdot \\ a_{m1} & a_{m2} & \ldots & a_{mn} \end{bmatrix} = A = [a_{ij}]$$

which may be denoted by a single letter, such as A, or by $[a_{ij}]$, where a_{ij} is the symbol for the value in row i and column j. The *transpose* of the matrix A is denoted by A' or A^T and is obtained by interchanging rows and columns. If $A = [a_{ij}]$ and $A^T = [b_{ij}]$, then $b_{ji} = a_{ij}$.

DEFINITION: Two $m \times n$ matrices are *equal* if all corresponding elements are equal. Thus,

(3) $[a_{ij}] = [b_{ij}]$ means $a_{ij} = b_{ij}$ $(i = 1, 2, \ldots, m; j = 1, 2, \ldots, n)$

DEFINITION: The *sum* of two $m \times n$ matrices is the $m \times n$ matrix formed by adding the corresponding elements. Thus,

(4)
$$[c_{ij}] = [a_{ij}] + [b_{ij}]$$

means that for $i = 1, 2, \ldots, m$ and $j = 1, 2, \ldots, n$,

(5)
$$c_{ij} = a_{ij} + b_{ij}$$

For example,

(6)
$$\begin{bmatrix} 2 & 3 & 4 \\ 5 & 6 & 7 \end{bmatrix} + \begin{bmatrix} 1 & 1 & 0 \\ 1 & 0 & 1 \end{bmatrix} = \begin{bmatrix} 3 & 4 & 4 \\ 6 & 6 & 8 \end{bmatrix}$$

It is through the concept of the *multiplication* of two vectors that a significant generalization of operations on numbers is achieved. The basic idea is to consider

(7)
$$2x_1 + 3x_2 - 4x_3$$

[183]

as the product of two vectors $(2, 3, -4)$ and (x_1, x_2, x_3). The convention is to make one of them a row vector and the other a column vector with the row vector preceding the column vector.

DEFINITION: The *(scalar) product* of a row vector by a column vector, each of n components, is a number (scalar) equal to the sum of the products of corresponding components; i.e.,

$$
(8) \qquad [a_1, a_2, \ldots, a_n] \begin{bmatrix} x_1 \\ x_2 \\ \cdot \\ \cdot \\ \cdot \\ x_n \end{bmatrix} = a_1 x_1 + a_2 x_2 + \ldots + a_n x_n
$$

If $n = 1$, (8) becomes ordinary multiplication of two numbers.

DEFINITION: The *product* of an $m \times n$ matrix A by an n-vector X is

$$
(9) \qquad AX = \begin{bmatrix} a_{11} & a_{12} & \ldots & a_{1n} \\ a_{21} & a_{22} & \ldots & a_{2n} \\ \cdot & \cdot & & \cdot \\ \cdot & \cdot & & \cdot \\ \cdot & \cdot & & \cdot \\ a_{m1} & a_{m2} & \ldots & a_{mn} \end{bmatrix} \begin{bmatrix} x_1 \\ x_2 \\ \cdot \\ \cdot \\ \cdot \\ x_n \end{bmatrix}
$$

$$
= \begin{bmatrix} a_{11} x_1 + a_{12} x_2 + \ldots + a_{1n} x_n \\ a_{21} x_1 + a_{22} x_2 + \ldots + a_{2n} x_n \\ \cdot \qquad \cdot \qquad \ldots \qquad \cdot \\ a_{m1} x_1 + a_{m2} x_2 + \ldots + a_{mn} x_n \end{bmatrix}
$$

This definition supersedes § 8-2-(3) and (8) above since the former is obtained if $n = 1$, and the latter is obtained if $m = 1$. According to (9), the product AX is a vector, the ith component of which is the product of the ith row of A (considered as a row vector) by the column vector X. Indeed, if A_i denotes the ith row of the matrix (2), i.e.,

$$
(10) \qquad\qquad A_i = (a_{i1}, a_{i2}, \ldots, a_{in}) \qquad\qquad (i = 1, 2, \ldots, m)
$$

the matrix A may be viewed as a column of row vectors

$$
(11) \qquad A = \begin{bmatrix} a_{11} & a_{12} & \ldots & a_{1n} \\ a_{21} & a_{22} & \ldots & a_{2n} \\ \cdot & \cdot & & \cdot \\ \cdot & \cdot & & \cdot \\ \cdot & \cdot & & \cdot \\ a_{m1} & a_{m2} & \ldots & a_{mn} \end{bmatrix} = \begin{bmatrix} A_1 \\ A_2 \\ \cdot \\ \cdot \\ \cdot \\ A_m \end{bmatrix}
$$

Now letting X symbolize an n-vector,

$$(12) \qquad X = \begin{bmatrix} x_1 \\ x_2 \\ \cdot \\ \cdot \\ \cdot \\ x_n \end{bmatrix}$$

it is seen that, analogous to the multiplication of a column vector by a scalar § 8-2-(3), the multiplication of a matrix by a vector (9) is defined as

$$(13) \qquad AX = \begin{bmatrix} A_1 \\ A_2 \\ \cdot \\ \cdot \\ \cdot \\ A_m \end{bmatrix} X = \begin{bmatrix} A_1 X \\ A_2 X \\ \cdot \\ \cdot \\ \cdot \\ A_m X \end{bmatrix}$$

A matrix may also be viewed as a row of column vectors. Thus, if P_j denotes the jth column of (2), i.e.,

$$(14) \qquad P_j = \begin{bmatrix} a_{1j} \\ a_{2j} \\ \cdot \\ \cdot \\ \cdot \\ a_{mj} \end{bmatrix} \qquad (j = 1, 2, \ldots, n)$$

then

$$(15) \qquad A = \begin{bmatrix} a_{11} & a_{12} & \cdots & a_{1n} \\ a_{21} & a_{22} & \cdots & a_{2n} \\ \cdot & & \cdots & \cdot \\ a_{m1} & a_{m2} & \cdots & a_{mn} \end{bmatrix} = [P_1, P_2, \ldots, P_n]$$

Therefore, analogous to the multiplication of a row vector by a column vector (8), the product of a matrix by a vector (9) is given by

$$(16) \qquad AX = [P_1, P_2, \ldots, P_n] \begin{bmatrix} x_1 \\ x_2 \\ \cdot \\ \cdot \\ \cdot \\ x_n \end{bmatrix} = P_1 x_1 + P_2 x_2 + \ldots + P_n x_n$$

[185]

since

(17) $\quad P_1 x_1 + P_2 x_2 + \ldots + P_n x_n$

$$= \begin{bmatrix} a_{11} \\ a_{21} \\ \cdot \\ \cdot \\ \cdot \\ a_{m1} \end{bmatrix} x_1 + \begin{bmatrix} a_{12} \\ a_{22} \\ \cdot \\ \cdot \\ \cdot \\ a_{m2} \end{bmatrix} x_2 + \ldots + \begin{bmatrix} a_{1n} \\ a_{2n} \\ \cdot \\ \cdot \\ \cdot \\ a_{mn} \end{bmatrix} x_n$$

$$= \begin{bmatrix} a_{11} x_1 + a_{12} x_2 + \ldots + a_{1n} x_n \\ a_{21} x_1 + a_{22} x_2 + \ldots + a_{2n} x_n \\ \cdot \qquad \cdot \qquad \cdots \qquad \cdot \\ a_{m1} x_1 + a_{m2} x_2 + \ldots + a_{mn} x_n \end{bmatrix}$$

We can also define the product of a row vector $\pi = (\pi_1, \pi_2, \ldots, \pi_m)$ of m components by an $m \times n$ matrix by analogy to vectors (see § 8-2-(3)). Thus, we would expect

(18) $\qquad \pi A = \pi[P_1, P_2, \ldots, P_n] = [\pi P_1, \pi P_2, \ldots, \pi P_n]$

DEFINITION: The *product* of a row vector π of m components by an $m \times n$ matrix is a row vector whose j^{th} component is the product of π by the jth column of A (considered as a column vector). Thus

(19) $\quad [\pi_1, \pi_2, \ldots, \pi_m] \begin{bmatrix} a_{11} & a_{12} \ldots a_{1n} \\ a_{21} & a_{22} \ldots a_{2n} \\ \cdot & \cdots \\ a_{m1} & a_{m2} \ldots a_{mn} \end{bmatrix} = [\pi P_1, \pi P_2, \ldots, \pi P_n]$

where

$$\pi P_1 = \pi_1 a_{11} + \pi_2 a_{21} + \ldots + \pi_m a_{m1}$$
$$\pi P_2 = \pi_1 a_{12} + \pi_2 a_{22} + \ldots + \pi_m a_{m2}$$
$$\ldots \ldots \ldots \ldots \ldots \ldots \ldots \ldots \ldots \ldots \ldots$$
$$\pi P_n = \pi_1 a_{1n} + \pi_2 a_{2n} + \ldots + \pi_m a_{mn}$$

This definition supersedes § 8-2-(3) which is obtained by setting $m = 1$; when $n = 1$, it agrees with (8) which is a special case of (9). However, it is possible to generalize the definition of product once more and make both (9) and (19) special cases of the following:

Definition of multiplication of matrices: The *product* of an $(m \times k)$ matrix A by a $(k \times n)$ matrix $\bar{A}$ is an $(m \times n)$ matrix $A\bar{A}$ whose element in row i, column j, is the product of the ith row of A (considered as a row vector) by the jth column of $\bar{A}$ (considered as a column vector).

To illustrate, let

$$
(20) \qquad A =
\begin{bmatrix}
a_{11} & a_{12} & \ldots & a_{1k} \\
a_{21} & a_{22} & \ldots & a_{2k} \\
\cdot & \cdot & & \cdot \\
\cdot & \cdot & & \cdot \\
\cdot & \cdot & & \cdot \\
a_{m1} & a_{m2} & \ldots & a_{mk}
\end{bmatrix}
=
\begin{bmatrix}
A_1 \\
A_2 \\
\cdot \\
\cdot \\
\cdot \\
A_m
\end{bmatrix}
$$

$$
(21) \qquad \bar{A} =
\begin{bmatrix}
\bar{a}_{11} & \bar{a}_{12} & \ldots & \bar{a}_{1n} \\
\bar{a}_{21} & \bar{a}_{22} & \ldots & \bar{a}_{2n} \\
\cdot & & \cdots & \\
\bar{a}_{k1} & \bar{a}_{k2} & \ldots & \bar{a}_{kn}
\end{bmatrix}
= [\bar{P}_1, \bar{P}_2, \ldots, \bar{P}_n]
$$

where we have denoted the columns of $\bar{A}$ by $\bar{P}_j$. Then, by definition,

$$
(22) \qquad A\bar{A} =
\begin{bmatrix}
A_1 \\
A_2 \\
\cdot \\
\cdot \\
\cdot \\
A_m
\end{bmatrix}
[\bar{P}_1, \bar{P}_2, \ldots, \bar{P}_n] =
\begin{bmatrix}
A_1\bar{P}_1 & A_1\bar{P}_2 & \ldots & A_1\bar{P}_n \\
A_2\bar{P}_1 & A_2\bar{P}_2 & \ldots & A_2\bar{P}_n \\
\cdot & \cdot & & \cdot \\
\cdot & \cdot & & \cdot \\
\cdot & \cdot & & \cdot \\
A_m\bar{P}_1 & A_m\bar{P}_2 & \ldots & A_m\bar{P}_n
\end{bmatrix}
$$

where the element in row i, column j of $A\bar{A}$ is

$$
(23) \qquad A_i\bar{P}_j = a_{i1}\bar{a}_{1j} + a_{i2}\bar{a}_{2j} + \ldots + a_{ik}\bar{a}_{kj}
$$

This definition is a natural generalization of the multiplication of a scalar by a row vector; for viewing $A\bar{A}$ as the multiplication of a matrix by a row of column vectors, we would expect

$$
(24) \qquad A\bar{A} = A[\bar{P}_1, \bar{P}_2, \ldots, \bar{P}_n] = [A\bar{P}_1, A\bar{P}_2, \ldots, A\bar{P}_n]
$$

which is clearly the case, since the jth column of $A\bar{A}$ from (22) is $A\bar{P}_j$. Again, by analogy to multiplying a column vector by a scalar, we can view $A\bar{A}$ as the product of a column of row vectors by a matrix

$$
(25) \qquad A\bar{A} =
\begin{bmatrix}
A_1 \\
A_2 \\
\cdot \\
\cdot \\
\cdot \\
A_m
\end{bmatrix}
\bar{A} =
\begin{bmatrix}
A_1\bar{A} \\
A_2\bar{A} \\
\cdot \\
\cdot \\
\cdot \\
A_m\bar{A}
\end{bmatrix}
$$

which again is clearly the case, since the ith row of $A\bar{A}$ is $A_i\bar{A}$.

The Laws of Matrix Algebra.

Just as ordinary numbers (scalars), matrices satisfy the associative and distributive laws with respect to matrix addition and multiplication. The commutative law also holds for matrix addition. However, the commutative law with respect to matrix multiplication does not hold in general even when the matrices are square.

Let $A = [a_{jk}]$, $B = [b_{jk}]$, $C = [c_{jk}]$ each be a $J \times K$ matrix; let $D = [d_{ij}]$ be an $I \times J$ matrix; and $E = [e_{kl}]$ be a $K \times L$ matrix.

1. *The Associative Law for Addition* states:

$$(A + B) + C = A + (B + C)$$

PROOF:

$$[a_{jk} + b_{jk}] + [c_{jk}] = [a_{jk} + b_{jk} + c_{jk}] = [a_{jk}] + [b_{jk} + c_{jk}]$$

2. *The Commutative Law for Addition* states:

$$A + B = B + A$$

PROOF:

$$[a_{jk} + b_{jk}] = [b_{jk} + a_{jk}]$$

3. *The Distributive Law for Multiplication with Respect to Addition* has two forms:

$$D[A + B] = DA + DB; \quad [A + B]E = AE + BE$$

PROOF: To show the first of these, let [ ] indicate matrices, and let the summation (below) be the (i, k) element of a matrix:

$$[d_{ij}][a_{jk} + b_{jk}] = \left[\sum_{j=1}^{J} d_{ij}(a_{jk} + b_{jk}) \right] = \left[\left(\sum_{j=1}^{J} d_{ij}a_{jk} \right) + \left(\sum_{j=1}^{J} d_{ij}b_{jk} \right) \right]$$

$$= \left[\sum_{j=1}^{J} d_{ij}a_{jk} \right] + \left[\sum_{j=1}^{J} d_{ij}b_{jk} \right] = DA + DB$$

4. *The Associative Law for Multiplication* states:

$$D(AE) = (DA)E$$

PROOF: Let $AE = F = [f_{jl}]$ and $DA = G = [g_{ik}]$, then

$$D(AE) = [d_{ij}][f_{jl}] = \left[\sum_{j=1}^{J} d_{ij}f_{jl} \right] = \left[\sum_{j=1}^{J} d_{ij} \left(\sum_{k=1}^{K} a_{jk}e_{kl} \right) \right];$$

$$(DA)E = [g_{ik}][e_{kl}] = \left[\sum_{k=1}^{K} g_{ik}e_{kl} \right] = \left[\sum_{k=1}^{K} \left(\sum_{j=1}^{J} d_{ij}a_{jk} \right) e_{kl} \right]$$

It will be noted that *the order of summation can be interchanged* in the last expression for $(DA)E$ and therefore the value of every (i, l) element is equal to that of $D(AE)$ shown in the equation above it.

DEFINITION: The *rank* of a matrix is the rank of the vector space generated by its columns.

[188]

THEOREM 1: *The rank of the columns of a matrix is the same as the rank of its rows.*

PROOF: Consider a homogeneous system of equations whose coefficients are the elements of the matrix. Its canonical equivalent has the same number of equations as the rank of the matrix *by rows*. Since pivot operations leave invariant any dependent or independent relation among the columns, the rank of the reduced form *by columns* is the same as the original system. But the column rank of the reduced form is the same as the row rank or the number of basic variables because the columns of these variables are unit vectors, are independent, and can be used to generate the columns by linear combinations.

8-4. INVERSE OF A MATRIX

A square $m \times m$ matrix is called *nonsingular* if the columns are *independent*. By § 8-2, Theorem 4, these m columns must form a *basis* in the space of all m-vectors because the m unit vectors form a basis. If it is possible to reduce an m-equation system to canonical form with basic variables $x_{j_1}, x_{j_2}, \ldots, x_{j_m}$, then coefficients of these variables in the *original* system viewed as vectors form a basis. To see this, note that if a set of columns is independent (or dependent) before a pivot operation, the same is true for its corresponding columns after a pivot operation and conversely. It follows that because the unit vector columns of $x_{j_1}, x_{j_2}, \ldots, x_{j_m}$ in the canonical form are obviously independent, the same is true for their correspondents in the original system.

Given any set of m independent columns of coefficients for variables $x_{j_1}, x_{j_2}, \ldots, x_{j_m}$ in an m-equation system, it is always possible to reduce the system to canonical form with these variables basic. To see this, try to reduce the system using $x_{j_1}, x_{j_2}, \ldots, x_{j_r}$. Assume, on the contrary, that it is not possible at the rth stage $(r < m)$ to pivot using $x_{j_{r+1}}$ (because its coefficients are all zero in the equations corresponding to the nonpivotal set). It is obvious that in this partially reduced system, column j_{r+1} can be formed as a linear combination of the r unit vectors in columns $j_1, j_2, \ldots, j_r$. But then the same is true for the corresponding columns of the original system, contradicting the independence assumption. We have therefore established:

THEOREM 1: *A set of m m-vectors is linearly independent if and only if it is possible to reduce an m-equation system to canonical form with m basic variables whose coefficients are the m-vectors.*

The above theorem provides a constructive way to determine whether or not a matrix is nonsingular. Associated with a nonsingular matrix (or basis) is another matrix known as its *inverse*, which we will illustrate below and define later. In particular, the inverse of a basis associated with the kth cycle of the simplex algorithm provides a convenient way to reduce a standard linear programming problem to canonical form and provides the alternative way of performing the computations of the simplex method to be discussed in the next chapter.

An Illustration.

In system (1), x_1 and x_2 may be used for basic variables, since it can be reduced to canonical form using these variables:

$$(1) \qquad 5x_1 - 4x_2 + 13x_3 - 2x_4 + x_5 = 20 \qquad (E_1)$$
$$x_1 - x_2 + 5x_3 - x_4 + x_5 = 8 \qquad (E_2)$$

The array of coefficients of these variables is

$$(2) \qquad \begin{bmatrix} 5 & -4 \\ 1 & -1 \end{bmatrix}$$

and, according to the above definition, constitutes the basis associated with the variables (x_1, x_2).

It is convenient to use a symbol, such as B, to denote a basis. The symbol $[a_{ij}]$ is used where the latter indicates that the element in the ith row and j^{th} column of B is a_{ij}. Thus we may write, for the example above,

$$(3) \qquad B = [a_{ij}] = \begin{bmatrix} 5 & -4 \\ 1 & -1 \end{bmatrix}$$

where $a_{11} = +5$, $a_{12} = -4$, $a_{21} = +1$, $a_{22} = -1$.

To find the inverse of the matrix (basis) B in (3), consider the canonical system of equations with basic variables y_1, y_2:

$$(4) \qquad 5x_1 - 4x_2 + y_1 \qquad = 0$$
$$x_1 - x_2 \qquad + y_2 = 0$$

where the coefficients of x_1 and x_2 constitute the basis B. Solve (4) for x_1 and x_2 in terms of y_1 and y_2; by elimination we obtain

$$(5) \qquad x_1 \qquad + y_1 - 4y_2 = 0$$
$$x_2 + y_1 - 5y_2 = 0$$

It is clear that (5) is equivalent to (4) and is in canonical form with basic variables, x_1 and x_2. The array of coefficients of y_1 and y_2 in (5) is called the *inverse* of the matrix (3) and is written B^{-1}. Hence,

$$(6) \qquad B = \begin{bmatrix} 5 & -4 \\ 1 & -1 \end{bmatrix}; \quad B^{-1} = \begin{bmatrix} 1 & -4 \\ 1 & -5 \end{bmatrix}$$

Conversely, if the coefficients of y_1 and y_2 in (5) are considered as a matrix, then since (4) is equivalent to (5), the coefficients of x_1 and x_2 constitute the inverse of this matrix, and we immediately conclude that the inverse of the inverse of a matrix is the matrix itself. This is the analogue, for a square array of numbers, of the familiar fact that the reciprocal of the reciprocal of a number is the number itself.

The inverse of a basis may be used to reduce a linear programming system, such as (1), to canonical form relative to the associated basic variables. We interpret the first equation of (5), namely, $x_1 + y_1 - 4y_2 = 0$, to mean that if the first equation of (4) is multiplied by 1 and the second equation by -4, and the two summed, all basic variables, except x_1, will be eliminated. (If this were not so, the equating of the two different expressions would lead to a linear relation in x_1 and x_2 contradicting (4) where these variables are independent.) Similarly, from $x_2 + y_1 - 5y_2 = 0$ it follows that, if the first equation of (4) is multiplied by 1 and the second by -5, and the two summed, all basic variables, except x_2, will be eliminated. Now let us see what the effect of these same operations is on the original system, (1). Since the coefficients of x_1 and x_2 are the same as (4), these same operations performed on (1), instead of (4), will reduce (1) to canonical form with basic variables x_1 and x_2:

$$(7) \qquad \begin{aligned} x_1 \quad - \quad 7x_3 + 2x_4 - 3x_5 &= -12 \qquad (E_1' = E_1 - 4E_2) \\ x_2 - 12x_3 + 3x_4 - 4x_5 &= -20 \qquad (E_2' = E_1 - 5E_2) \end{aligned}$$

On the right in (7) are the operations required to obtain (7) from (1); note that the array of coefficients of E_1' and E_2' is the inverse of the basis given in (6).

General Properties of a Matrix and Its Inverse.

Our objective is to formalize and to prove, in general, the assertions made for the illustrative example.

A square array of numbers

$$(8) \qquad B = \begin{bmatrix} a_{11} & a_{12} & \ldots & a_{1m} \\ a_{21} & a_{22} & \ldots & a_{2m} \\ \cdot & \cdot & & \cdot \\ \cdot & \cdot & & \cdot \\ \cdot & \cdot & & \cdot \\ a_{m1} & a_{m2} & \ldots & a_{mm} \end{bmatrix}$$

is nonsingular and its columns constitute a *basis*, by Theorem 1, if the system of equations

$$(9) \qquad \begin{aligned} a_{11} x_1 + a_{12} x_2 + \ldots + a_{1m} x_m + y_1 \qquad\qquad &= 0 \\ a_{21} x_1 + a_{22} x_2 + \ldots + a_{2m} x_m \qquad + y_2 \qquad &= 0 \\ \cdot \qquad \cdot \qquad\qquad \cdot \qquad\qquad \cdot \qquad & \\ \cdot \qquad \cdot \qquad\qquad \cdot \qquad\qquad \cdot \qquad & \\ a_{m1} x_1 + a_{m2} x_2 + \ldots + a_{mm} x_m \qquad\qquad + y_m &= 0 \end{aligned}$$

is equivalent to some system (10) in canonical form, with basic variables

$(x_1, x_2, \ldots, x_m)$; i.e., B is a basis, if we can solve (9) for $x_1, x_2, \ldots, x_m$ in terms of $y_1, y_2, \ldots, y_m$ obtaining

$$
\begin{aligned}
(10) \quad x_1 \quad &+ \beta_{11} y_1 + \beta_{12} y_2 + \ldots + \beta_{1m} y_m = 0 \\
x_2 \quad &+ \beta_{21} y_1 + \beta_{22} y_2 + \ldots + \beta_{2m} y_m = 0 \\
&\qquad\qquad\qquad\cdots \\
x_m &+ \beta_{m1} y_1 + \beta_{m2} y_2 + \ldots + \beta_{mm} y_m = 0
\end{aligned}
$$

It is clear that, if (8) is the array formed by the coefficients of some subset of m variables of an $m \times n$ linear programming problem, it is possible to reduce the problem to canonical form, using the corresponding variables as basic variables.

DEFINITION: The matrix of coefficients of y_i in (10) is the *inverse* of the matrix B of coefficients of x_j in (9). We denote the inverse of B by B^{-1}. By definition

$$
(11) \qquad B^{-1} = \begin{bmatrix} \beta_{11} & \beta_{12} & \cdots & \beta_{1m} \\ \beta_{21} & \beta_{22} & \cdots & \beta_{2m} \\ \cdot & \cdots & & \cdot \\ \beta_{m1} & \beta_{m2} & \cdots & \beta_{mm} \end{bmatrix}
$$

Theorem 1 of § 4-2 establishes the uniqueness of the canonical form, hence the uniqueness of the inverse. Conversely, since (9) is equivalent to (10) and in canonical form relative to $y_1, y_2, \ldots, y_m$, we have established both theorems that follow.

THEOREM 2: *The inverse of a basis is unique.*

THEOREM 3: *The inverse of the inverse of a matrix is the matrix itself.*

If in (10), the values of all independent variables y_i are set equal to zero, except $y_k = -1$, we obtain the obvious solution for the basic variables $x_1 = \beta_{1k}, x_2 = \beta_{2k}, \ldots, x_m = \beta_{mk}$. Since (9) has the same solution set, these values of x_i and y_i must also satisfy it. Substituting in the ith equation of (9) yields a relation between the ith row of a basis B and the kth column of its inverse B^{-1}, namely,

THEOREM 4: *The sum of the products of the corresponding terms in the ith row of B and k^{th} column of B^{-1} are zero or one according as $i \neq k$ or $i = k$:*

$$
(12) \qquad a_{i1}\beta_{1k} + a_{i2}\beta_{2k} + \ldots + a_{im}\beta_{mk} = \begin{cases} 0 \text{ if } i \neq k \\ 1 \text{ if } i = k \end{cases}
$$

For example, for the basis given by (2), we see that

$$
\begin{aligned}
(13) \qquad a_{11}\beta_{11} + a_{12}\beta_{21} &= \quad (5)(1) + \quad (-4)(1) = 1 \quad (i = 1, k = 1) \\
a_{11}\beta_{12} + a_{12}\beta_{22} &= (5)(-4) + (-4)(-5) = 0 \quad (i = 1, k = 2) \\
a_{21}\beta_{11} + a_{22}\beta_{21} &= \quad (1)(1) + \quad (-1)(1) = 0 \quad (i = 2, k = 1) \\
a_{21}\beta_{12} + a_{22}\beta_{22} &= (1)(-4) + (-1)(-5) = 1 \quad (i = 2, k = 2)
\end{aligned}
$$

Having established Theorem 4, we may proceed to interchange the roles of B and B^{-1} to obtain

THEOREM 5: *The sum of the products of corresponding terms in the ith row of B^{-1} and k^{th} column of B are zero or one, according as $i \neq k$ or $i = k$:*

$$(14) \qquad \beta_{i1}a_{1k} + \beta_{i2}a_{2k} + \ldots + \beta_{im}a_{mk} = \begin{cases} 0 \text{ if } k \neq i \\ 1 \text{ if } k = i \end{cases}$$

For our example, we observe that

$$(15) \qquad \begin{aligned} \beta_{11}a_{11} + \beta_{12}a_{21} &= \quad (1)(5) + \quad (-4)(1) = 1 \quad (i = 1, k = 1) \\ \beta_{11}a_{12} + \beta_{12}a_{22} &= (1)(-4) + (-4)(-1) = 0 \quad (i = 1, k \doteq 2) \\ \beta_{21}a_{11} + \beta_{22}a_{21} &= \quad (1)(5) + \quad (-5)(1) = 0 \quad (i = 2, k = 1) \\ \beta_{21}a_{12} + \beta_{22}a_{22} &= (1)(-4) + (-5)(-1) = 1 \quad (i = 2, k = 2) \end{aligned}$$

THEOREM 6: *If a canonical system* (10) *can be formed from a canonical system* (9) *by linear combinations, it is equivalent to* (9), *and the array of coefficients of the y_i in* (10) *is the inverse of the basis, and conversely.*

PROOF: Consider the combined system (9) and (10). By § 8-1, Theorems 8, 9, 10, the rank of the system is m because the first m equations are independent and by hypothesis the remaining m are dependent upon them. However, the last m equations are independent and, since m is the maximum number that can be independent, this implies the first m equations of (9) are dependent on (10). Hence, (10) implies (9) and the two systems are equivalent. The rest of the theorem follows by the definition of the inverse.

Let us now consider another theorem, the *converse* of Theorem 4 (or of Theorem 5). Suppose we are given system (10) with an array of coefficients $[\beta_{ij}]$ and another array of coefficients $[a_{ij}]$ which satisfy the row-column relations (12). We wish to prove that (9) is equivalent to (10) and hence $[a_{ij}]$ is the inverse of $[\beta_{ij}]$.

To see this, multiply the first equation of (10) by a_{i1}, the second by $a_{i2}, \ldots$, the mth equation by a_{im}, and sum; we will obtain the ith relation of (9). Thus (12) and (10) imply (9). Applying Theorem 6, we have shown

THEOREM 7: *A necessary and sufficient condition that the inverse of $[a_{ij}]$ is $[\beta_{ij}]$ is that the row-column relations* (12) *or* (14) *hold.*

Recall that the *transpose* of a basis B is an $m \times m$ array of elements obtained by interchanging rows and columns of B; it is left as an exercise to prove that relations (12) and (14) imply:

THEOREM 8: *The inverse of the transpose of a basis is the transpose of the inverse of a basis.*

The basis B consisting of all ones down the main diagonal and zero elsewhere is called the *identity matrix* and is given the symbol I or I_m: it is so called because for any $m \times n$ matrix M, $I_m M = M$. For example, the identity matrix for $m = 4$ is

$$(16) \qquad B = I_4 = \begin{bmatrix} 1 & 0 & 0 & 0 \\ 0 & 1 & 0 & 0 \\ 0 & 0 & 1 & 0 \\ 0 & 0 & 0 & 1 \end{bmatrix} \qquad (m = 4)$$

It is easy to verify that $B^{-1} = B$ because the associated system (9) is in this case in canonical form with respect to both x_1, x_2, x_3, x_4 and y_1, y_2, y_3, y_4.

Reduction of an $m \times n$ System to Canonical Form.

To reduce

$$(17) \qquad \begin{aligned} a_{11} x_1 + a_{12} x_2 + \ldots + a_{1n} x_n &= b_1 \\ a_{21} x_1 + a_{22} x_2 + \ldots + a_{2n} x_n &= b_2 \\ &\cdots \cdots \\ a_{m1} x_1 + a_{m2} x_2 + \ldots + a_{mn} x_n &= b_m \end{aligned}$$

to canonical form with basic variables x_1, x_2, . . ., x_m, assume that the square array $B = [a_{ij}]$ is a basis and its inverse $B^{-1} = [\beta_{ij}]$ is known. If the first equation of (17) is multiplied by β_{11}, the second by β_{12}, . . ., the mth by β_{1m}, then the weighted sum is

$$(18) \qquad \left(\sum_{k=1}^{m} \beta_{1k} a_{k1} \right) x_1 + \left(\sum_{k=1}^{m} \beta_{1k} a_{k2} \right) x_2 + \ldots$$
$$+ \left(\sum_{k=1}^{m} \beta_{1k} a_{kn} \right) x_n = \sum_{k=1}^{m} \beta_{1k} b_k$$

In general, the rth equation of system (19) can be generated by multiplying the first equation of (17) by β_{r1}, the second by β_{r2}, . . ., the mth by β_{rm} and forming the weighted sum; this will result in the canonical system:

$$(19) \qquad \begin{aligned} x_1 \qquad\qquad &+ \bar{a}_{1,m+1} x_{m+1} + \ldots + \bar{a}_{1n} x_n = \bar{b}_1 \\ &\qquad\qquad \vdots \\ x_r \qquad\qquad &+ \bar{a}_{r,m+1} x_{m+1} + \ldots + \bar{a}_{rn} x_n = \bar{b}_r \\ &\qquad\qquad \vdots \\ x_m &+ \bar{a}_{m,m+1} x_{m+1} + \ldots + \bar{a}_{mn} x_n = \bar{b}_m \end{aligned}$$

where, for $j = 1, 2, \ldots, n$, we have set

$$(20) \qquad \begin{aligned} \bar{a}_{1j} &= \beta_{11} a_{1j} + \beta_{12} a_{2j} + \ldots + \beta_{1m} a_{mj} \\ \bar{a}_{2j} &= \beta_{21} a_{1j} + \beta_{22} a_{2j} + \ldots + \beta_{2m} a_{mj} \\ &\cdots \cdots \\ \bar{a}_{mj} &= \beta_{m1} a_{1j} + \beta_{m2} a_{2j} + \ldots + \beta_{mm} a_{mj} \end{aligned}$$

and

$$(21) \qquad \begin{aligned} \bar{b}_1 &= \beta_{11} b_1 + \beta_{12} b_2 + \ldots + \beta_{1m} b_m \\ \bar{b}_2 &= \beta_{21} b_1 + \beta_{22} b_2 + \ldots + \beta_{2m} b_m \\ &\cdots \cdots \\ \bar{b}_m &= \beta_{m1} b_1 + \beta_{m2} b_2 + \ldots + \beta_{mm} b_m \end{aligned}$$

Note that (19) is in *canonical* form with respect to $x_1, x_2, \ldots, x_m$ because of the row-column relationship between B^{-1} and B; namely by (14), it follows for $j = 1, 2, \ldots, m$, that

(22) $$\bar{a}_{ij} = \begin{cases} 0 & \text{for } i = 1, 2, \ldots, m \text{ and } i \neq j \\ 1 & \text{for } i = j \end{cases}$$

8-5. THE SIMPLEX ALGORITHM IN MATRIX FORM

The central problem in vector notation is to find $x_1 \geq 0$, $x_2 \geq 0$, $\ldots$, $x_n \geq 0$ and Min z, satisfying

(1) $$P_1 x_1 + P_2 x_2 + \ldots + P_n x_n = Q$$

(2) $$c_1 x_1 + c_2 x_2 + \ldots + c_n x_n = z$$

where

(3) $$P_j = \begin{bmatrix} a_{1j} \\ a_{2j} \\ . \\ . \\ . \\ a_{mj} \end{bmatrix}; \quad Q = \begin{bmatrix} b_1 \\ b_2 \\ . \\ . \\ . \\ b_m \end{bmatrix}$$

and a_{ij}, b_i, c_j are constants.

It is required for the simplex algorithm that m of the vectors P_j be independent.[2] Let $P_{j_1}, P_{j_2}, \ldots, P_{j_m}$ be such a set of independent vectors. These form a *basis*, B, in the vector space generated by $P_1, P_2, \ldots, P_n$:

(4) $$B = [P_{j_1}, P_{j_2}, \ldots, P_{j_m}]$$

A *canonical* form is obtained by multiplying (1) by B^{-1}, i.e.,

(5) $$(B^{-1} P_1) x_1 + (B^{-1} P_2) x_2 + \ldots + (B^{-1} P_n) x_n = B^{-1} Q$$

or

(6) $$\bar{P}_1 x_1 + \bar{P}_2 x_2 + \ldots + \bar{P}_n x_n = \bar{Q}$$

where (see § 8-2)

(7) $$B^{-1} P_j = \bar{P}_j; \quad B^{-1} Q = \bar{Q}$$

are the *representations* of P_j and Q, respectively in terms of the basis. Note that from $B^{-1} B = I$ (identity matrix) follows

(8) $$\bar{P}_{j_i} = B^{-1} P_{j_i} = U_i$$

where U_i is a unit vector with unity in component i and zero elsewhere. But the latter, by definition, means (6) is in canonical form with "basic" variables $x_{j_1}, x_{j_2}, \ldots, x_{j_m}$. (See § 4-2.)

[2] Phase I of the simplex algorithm takes care of the situation where this is not true.

The basic solution is obtained by setting non-basic variables $x_j = 0$; thus the values of the basic variables are given by

(9) $$U_1 x_{j_1} + U_2 x_{j_2} + \ldots + U_m x_{j_m} = \bar{Q}$$

or

(10) $$\begin{bmatrix} x_{j_1} \\ x_{j_2} \\ \cdot \\ \cdot \\ \cdot \\ x_{j_m} \end{bmatrix} = \bar{Q}$$

EXERCISE: Show what would be affected by a change in the *ordering* of the basic variables and the basis vectors.

The basic solution is *feasible*, if

(11) $$\bar{Q} \geq 0$$

DEFINITION: $\bar{Q} \geq 0$ means each component $\bar{b}_i$ of $\bar{Q}$ satisfies $\bar{b}_i \geq 0$.

The relative cost factors, $\bar{c}_j$, are obtained by eliminating x_{j_i} from the z-equation. If we define the row vector

(12) $$\gamma = [c_{j_1}, c_{j_2}, \ldots, c_{j_m}]$$

and multiply (6) by γ, we obtain

(13) $$(\gamma \bar{P}_1) x_1 + (\gamma \bar{P}_2) x_2 + \ldots + (\gamma \bar{P}_n) x_n = (\gamma \bar{Q})$$

where $(\gamma \bar{P}_j)$ are *constants* (for each is the product of a row vector by a column vector). In particular, $\gamma \bar{P}_{j_i} = \gamma U_i = c_{j_i}$, so that (13) has the same coefficients for the basic variables as does (2). Hence, by subtracting (13) from (2), we eliminate the basic variables, obtaining

(14) $$(c_1 - \gamma \bar{P}_1) x_1 + (c_2 - \gamma \bar{P}_2) x_2 + \ldots + (c_n - \gamma \bar{P}_n) x_n = z - \gamma \bar{Q}$$

Therefore the relative cost factors are given by

(15) $$\begin{aligned} \bar{c}_j &= c_j - \gamma \bar{P}_j \\ &= c_j - \gamma(B^{-1} P_j) \\ &= c_j - (\gamma B^{-1}) P_j \end{aligned}$$

or

(16) $$\bar{c}_j = c_j - \pi P_j$$

where we have set the row vector

(17) $$\pi = \gamma B^{-1}$$

In words, (16) states that the relative cost coefficients, $\bar{c}_j$, are obtained by subtracting from c_j a weighted sum of the coefficients $a_{1j}, a_{2j}, \ldots, a_{mj}$, where the weights (the same for all j) are the m components $\pi_1, \pi_2, \ldots, \pi_m$

of π. The elements π_i are called *simplex multipliers* (these will be discussed more fully in the next chapter). Multiplying (17) by B, we obtain

$$(18) \qquad\qquad \pi B = \gamma$$

or

$$(19) \qquad\qquad \pi(P_{j_1}, P_{j_2}, \ldots, P_{j_m}) = (c_{j_1}, c_{j_2}, \ldots, c_{j_m})$$

Hence, in particular,

$$(20) \qquad\qquad \pi P_{j_i} = c_{j_i} \qquad\qquad \text{for } i = 1, 2, \ldots, m$$

Thus the weights π_i are just the numbers required to multiply through the *original* equations (1) and sum in order to eliminate the coefficients of the basic variables from (2).

The basic solution is optimal, if all $\bar{c}_j \geq 0$. If not all $\bar{c}_j \geq 0$, then an improved solution is sought by first choosing s, such that

$$(21) \qquad\qquad \bar{c}_s = \text{Min } \bar{c}_j$$

and then increasing the value of x_s as much as possible, keeping other non-basic variables at zero. In order to be nonnegative, the vector of values of the basic variables must satisfy

$$(22) \qquad\qquad (\bar{Q} - \bar{P}_s x_s) \geq 0$$

At some critical value $x_s = x_s^*$, the value of some component r of this vector will change sign while all others remain nonnegative (otherwise $z \to -\infty$ as $x_s \to +\infty$). The components of $\bar{Q}$, $\bar{P}_s$, and r are defined by our earlier notation to be

$$(23) \qquad \bar{Q} = \begin{bmatrix} \bar{b}_1 \\ \bar{b}_2 \\ \cdot \\ \cdot \\ \cdot \\ \bar{b}_m \end{bmatrix}; \quad \bar{P}_s = \begin{bmatrix} \bar{a}_{1s} \\ \bar{a}_{2s} \\ \cdot \\ \cdot \\ \cdot \\ \bar{a}_{ms} \end{bmatrix}; \quad x_s^* = \frac{\bar{b}_r}{\bar{a}_{rs}} = \underset{\bar{a}_{is}>0}{\text{Min}} \frac{\bar{b}_i}{\bar{a}_{is}} \qquad (\bar{a}_{rs} > 0)$$

Hence, P_{j_r} is replaced in the basis by P_s to form the basis B^* of the next cycle. This completes the description of the simplex process in matrix notation. We shall now go deeper into the nature of the transformations from cycle to cycle.

The Transformations from Cycle k to $k + 1$.

The last step of the simplex process is to transform the tableau by pivoting on $\bar{a}_{rs}$. Instead, here we shall use the inverse of the new basis to adjust slightly the representations of P_j and Q in terms of the *old* basis,

B, given by (7) to obtain their representations in terms of the *new* basis, B^*. First, we note that $\bar{P}_j = B^{-1}P_j$ or $P_j = B\bar{P}_j$, so that

(24)

$$P_s = [P_{j_1}, P_{j_2}, \ldots, P_{j_m}] \begin{bmatrix} \bar{a}_{1s} \\ \bar{a}_{2s} \\ \cdot \\ \cdot \\ \cdot \\ \bar{a}_{ms} \end{bmatrix} = P_{j_1}\bar{a}_{1s} + \ldots + P_{j_r}\bar{a}_{rs} + \ldots + P_{j_m}\bar{a}_{ms}$$

where $\langle \bar{a}_{1s}, \bar{a}_{2s}, \ldots, \bar{a}_{ms} \rangle$ is the representation of P_s in terms of B. We may use (24) to express P_{j_r} in terms of the new basis B^*; thus

(25) $$P_{j_r} = P_{j_1}k_1 + \ldots + P_s k_r + \ldots + P_{j_m}k_m = B^*K$$

where we have set $K = \{k_1, k_2, \ldots, k_m\}$, $B^* = [P_{j_1}, \ldots, P_s, \ldots, P_{j_m}]$ and

(26) $$k_i = -\bar{a}_{is}/\bar{a}_{rs} \qquad\qquad (i \neq r)$$

(27) $$k_r = 1/\bar{a}_{rs}$$

For all other $i \neq r$ we may trivially represent P_{j_i} in terms of B^*,

(28) $$P_{j_i} = P_{j_1} \cdot 0 + \ldots + P_s \cdot 0 + \ldots + P_{j_i} \cdot 1 + \ldots + P_{j_m} \cdot 0 = B^*U_i$$

so that *the relation between the old and new basis is given by*

(29) $$B = [P_{j_1}, P_{j_2}, \ldots, P_{j_m}] = B^*[U_1, U_2, \ldots, K, \ldots, U_m]$$

Multiplying through on the right by B^{-1} and by $(B^*)^{-1}$ on the left, we obtain *the relation between the inverse of the new basis and the previous inverse:*

(30) $$(B^*)^{-1} = [U_1, U_2, \ldots, K, \ldots, U_m]B^{-1}$$

Matrix (31) is practically the identity matrix, except that column r consists of k_i values. A matrix that differs from the identity in just one row (or column) is called an *elementary matrix*.

(31) $$[U_1, U_2, \ldots, K, \ldots, U_m] = \begin{bmatrix} 1 & & & & k_1 & & \\ & 1 & & & \cdot & & \\ & & \cdot & & \cdot & & \\ & & & \cdot & \cdot & & \\ & & & & k_r & & \\ & & & & \cdot & \cdot & \\ & & & & \cdot & & \cdot \\ & & & & \cdot & & & 1 \\ & & & & k_m & & & 1 \end{bmatrix}$$

Thus, according to (30), *the new inverse is the product of an elementary matrix and the inverse of the previous basis.* If we now multiply both sides of (30) on the right by any P_j, we can obtain the representation of P_j in terms of the new basis from its representation in terms of the old basis, $\bar{P}_j = B^{-1}P_j$:

$$(32) \qquad (B^*)^{-1}P_j = [U_1, U_2, \ldots, K, \ldots, U_m]\bar{P}_j$$

It is convenient to write matrix (31) as the *sum* of an identity matrix and a null matrix except for one column:

$$(33) \quad [U_1, U_2, \ldots, K, \ldots, U_m] = [U_1, U_2, \ldots, U_r, \ldots, U_m]$$
$$+ [0, 0, \ldots, K - U_r, \ldots, 0]$$

and to write the vector

$$(34) \qquad \bar{K} = K - U_r = \begin{bmatrix} \bar{k}_1 \\ \cdot \\ \cdot \\ \cdot \\ \bar{k}_r \\ \cdot \\ \cdot \\ \bar{k}_m \end{bmatrix} = \begin{bmatrix} k_1 \\ \cdot \\ \cdot \\ \cdot \\ k_r - 1 \\ \cdot \\ \cdot \\ k_m \end{bmatrix}$$

We now have

$$(35) \quad (B^*)^{-1} = [U_1, U_2, \ldots, U_r, \ldots, U_m]B^{-1}$$
$$+ [0, 0, \ldots, K - U_r, 0, \ldots, 0]B^{-1}$$
$$= B^{-1} + [0, 0, \ldots, \bar{K}, \ldots, 0]B^{-1}$$

If now we denote the *rows* of B^{-1} by β_i, so that

$$(36) \qquad B^{-1} = \begin{bmatrix} \beta_1 \\ \cdot \\ \cdot \\ \cdot \\ \beta_r \\ \cdot \\ \cdot \\ \cdot \\ \beta_m \end{bmatrix}$$

and substitute above, we have

$$(37) \qquad (B^*)^{-1} = B^{-1} + [0, 0, \ldots, \bar{K}, \ldots, 0] \begin{bmatrix} \beta_1 \\ \cdot \\ \cdot \\ \cdot \\ \beta_r \\ \cdot \\ \cdot \\ \cdot \\ \beta_m \end{bmatrix}$$

$$(38) \qquad = B^{-1} + \bar{K}\beta_r$$

Note that $(B^*)^{-1}$ *differs from* B^{-1} *by a matrix* $\bar{K}\beta_r$, *which is the product of a column vector* $\bar{K}$ *and a row vector* β_r. Thus

$$(39) \qquad \bar{K}\beta_r = \begin{bmatrix} \bar{k}_1 \\ \cdot \\ \cdot \\ \cdot \\ \bar{k}_i \\ \cdot \\ \cdot \\ \cdot \\ \bar{k}_m \end{bmatrix} [\beta_{r1}, \ldots, \beta_{rj}, \ldots, \beta_{rm}], \quad B^{-1} = [\beta_{ij}]$$

The (i, j) element of $\bar{K}\beta_r$ is simply $\bar{k}_i\beta_{rj}$. Hence, to form the (i, j) element of $(B^*)^{-1}$, we add $\bar{k}_i\beta_{rj}$ to β_{ij}; i.e.,

$$(40) \qquad [B^*]^{-1} = [\beta_{ij}] + [\bar{k}_i\beta_{rj}]$$

Finally, to form the new representation from the old we have from (38)

$$(41) \qquad (B^*)^{-1}P_j = (B^{-1} + \bar{K}\beta_r)P_j = B^{-1}P_j + (\bar{K}\beta_r)P_j$$
$$= \bar{P}_j + \bar{K}\bar{a}_{rj}$$

where we have replaced the constant $\beta_r P_j$ by $\bar{a}_{rj}$, the value of the rth component in the representation of P_j in terms of B. *Thus, the new* $\bar{P}_j$ *differs from the old by a vector proportional to* $\bar{K}$; *the factor of proportionality is the* rth *component of* $\bar{P}_j$.

Product Form of the Inverse.

Relations (30) and (40) are two ways to express the new inverse in terms of the old. It will be noted that (40) requires in general m^2 changes in the components of B^{-1}; whereas (30) shows that the *process* of obtaining $(B^*)^{-1}$ from B^{-1}, by multiplying by the elementary matrix defined by (31), requires only knowledge of the m components of the vector K and its column location r in the matrix.

A. Orden, in the early days of linear programming, proposed that it can be computationally convenient to represent the inverse of the basis as a product of elementary matrices. For example, the inverse of the *initial* basis could always be arranged to be the *identity* by using artificial variables. The inverse of the basis for cycle 1 would then be a single elementary matrix which could be easily recorded on a magnetic tape of an electronic computer as the single vector column K (and its location r). The inverse of the basis for cycle 2 would then be the product of a new elementary matrix and the previous one for cycle 1. This product could be stored by simply recording the new column K *after* the first column K on the same magnetic tape, etc. Both the Orchard-Hays–RAND Code [1956-1] and the Philip Wolfe–RAND Code (using a flexible language medium for the IBM-704 Computer) make use of Orden's suggestion for recording the inverse.

[200]

EXERCISE: Review the relationship between the vector K in (31) and the representation of the new vector P_s entering the basis.

EXERCISE: Suppose the inverse of the basis is given in product form; determine the detailed computational process of representing a vector P_s in terms of a basis by multiplying it on the left by the successive elementary matrices generated by cycle 1, cycle 2, etc.

Block-Pivoting.

Tucker [1960-3] generalizes the notion of pivot by introducing several columns into the basic set at once. With regard to the detached coefficient array (42), let $x_{m+1}, x_{m+2}, \ldots, x_{m+k}$ replace $x_1, x_2, \ldots, x_k$ as basic variables.

$$(42) \quad A = \begin{bmatrix} 1 & & & & \bar{a}_{1m+1} \cdots \bar{a}_{1m+k} & \cdots & \bar{a}_{1n} & \bar{b}_1 \\ & \ddots & & & & & & \vdots \\ & & 1 & & \bar{a}_{km+1} \cdots \bar{a}_{km+k} & & & \\ & & & 1 & & & & \\ & & & & \ddots & & & \\ & & & & 1 \quad \bar{a}_{mm+1} \cdots \bar{a}_{mm+k} & \cdots & \bar{a}_{mn} & \bar{b}_m \end{bmatrix}$$

$$\longleftarrow \text{basis} \longrightarrow \Big|\leftarrow \begin{array}{c}\text{entering the}\\ \text{basis}\end{array} \rightarrow \Big|\leftarrow \begin{array}{c}\text{other}\\ \text{columns}\end{array} \rightarrow \Big| \text{constants} \Big|$$

Note that the new basis has the structure

$$B^* = \begin{bmatrix} P & 0 \\ Q & I_{m-k} \end{bmatrix}$$

where P represents the square block array dotted in (42) called the *block-pivot*. Since the value of the determinant of B^* is the same as the value of the determinant of P, it follows that in order for B^* to be a basis it is necessary that the determinant of P be non-zero. To "pivot," let P^{-1} be the inverse of P. Analogous to the first step of ordinary pivoting (of dividing through by the non-zero pivot coefficient) the first k rows of (42) are multiplied by P^{-1}. Let the original array in matrix form be

$$(43) \qquad A = \begin{bmatrix} I_k & 0 & P & R & e \\ 0 & I_{m-k} & Q & S & f \end{bmatrix}$$

Then multiplying by P^{-1} yields

$$(44) \qquad A' = \begin{bmatrix} P^{-1} & 0 & I_k & P^{-1}R & P^{-1}e \\ 0 & I_{m-k} & Q & S & f \end{bmatrix}$$

[201]

The next step is to "eliminate" the set of variables $x_{m+1}, \ldots, x_{m+k}$ from the remaining equations. To do this, the first k rows are multiplied by $-Q$ on the left and added to the bottom rows, yielding the new array

$$A^* = \begin{bmatrix} P^{-1} & 0 & I_k & P^{-1}R & P^{-1}e \\ -QP^{-1} & I_{m-k} & 0 & S - QP^{-1}R & f - QP^{-1}e \end{bmatrix}$$

Note that the columns corresponding to the new basis when properly ordered are an identity matrix so that A^* is in required canonical form.

8-6. PROBLEMS

Review.

1. Prove the values of $\bar{a}_{ij}$ in the canonical form do not depend, in general, on the order of elimination provided only that the unit coefficient of each basic variable in the canonical system is in the same row. If not, the canonical forms will be identical after proper reordering of the rows.

2. For the following, determine if each system is consistent or inconsistent, and if there are any redundant equations. If consistent, determine its rank.

    (a)
$$\begin{aligned}
2x_1 - 2x_2 + x_3 &= 3 \\
2x_1 + x_2 - 2x_3 &= 2 \\
5x_1 + x_2 + x_3 &= 3 \\
x_2 - x_3 &= 1
\end{aligned}$$

    (b)
$$\begin{aligned}
2x_1 - x_2 + 3x_3 &= 1 \\
-4x_1 + 3x_2 + x_3 &= 3 \\
-5x_1 + 4x_2 + 3x_3 &= 5 \\
x_1 + 2x_2 + x_3 &= 2
\end{aligned}$$

    (c)
$$\begin{aligned}
x_1 + x_2 + 3x_3 + x_4 + x_5 + 6x_6 &= 1 \\
2x_1 - x_2 - x_3 + x_4 - 2x_5 - 2x_6 &= 3 \\
4x_1 + x_2 + 5x_3 + 3x_4 \phantom{{}+ 2x_5} + 10x_6 &= 5 \\
6x_1 - x_2 - 9x_3 + 2x_4 - 7x_5 + 12x_6 &= 5
\end{aligned}$$

3. The classical Hitchcock-Koopmans transportation problem consists in finding nonnegative solutions to the system

$$\sum_{j=1}^{n} x_{ij} = a_i \qquad\qquad (i = 1, 2, \ldots, m; \, a_i \geq 0)$$

$$\sum_{i=1}^{m} x_{ij} = b_j \qquad\qquad (j = 1, 2, \ldots, n; \, b_j \geq 0)$$

$$\sum_{i=1}^{m} \sum_{j=1}^{n} d_{ij} x_{ij} = z \, (\text{Min})$$

Show that $\sum_1^m a_i = \sum_1^n b_j$ is necessary for the equations to be consistent.

4. What is the rank of a transportation problem without slacks? With slacks? Give proof (see Chapter 3, Problems 4 and 5).

5. Given two linear systems, how would you show whether or not they have the same solution set? Are equivalent? Prove that system (A) and (B) are equivalent.

$$\text{(A)} \quad \begin{aligned} 2x_1 + 3x_2 + 4x_3 &= 9 \\ x_1 - x_2 + x_3 &= 1 \\ 4x_1 + 3x_2 + 2x_3 &= 9 \end{aligned} \qquad \text{(B)} \quad \begin{aligned} x_1 + x_2 + x_3 &= 3 \\ 7x_1 - 2x_2 + 5x_3 &= 10 \\ 5x_1 - 2x_2 + 7x_3 &= 10 \end{aligned}$$

6. For solvable systems of rank r, show that there is only one way to form a dependent $(r+1)$st equation as a linear combination of r independent equations.

7. Given a set of r independent equations and a set of $m - r$ dependent equations, prove that the role of any independent equation and any dependent equation can be interchanged providing there is a non-zero weight on the independent equation in forming the dependent equation as a linear combination of the independent equations.

Invariance Properties under Pivoting. (Refer to § 8-1.)

8. Construct an example to show that a sequence of elementary operations does not preserve one-to-one correspondence of solvable independent equations and of the remaining dependent or contradictory equations as does a sequence of pivot operations.

9. Find the rank r of the system below by finding the number of equations in the canonical equivalent. Find the largest number of independent equations of the original system and check if this number is equal to the rank. Show that this is the same as the rank of the matrix of coefficients and constant terms.

$$\begin{aligned} 2x_1 + 3x_2 + 4x_3 &= 9 \\ x_1 - x_2 + x_3 &= 1 \\ 3x_1 + 2x_2 + 5x_3 &= 10 \\ 4x_1 + x_2 + 6x_3 &= 11 \\ 6x_1 + 4x_2 + 10x_3 &= 20 \end{aligned}$$

Show how to generate all solutions to this system of equations.

10. How is the largest number of independent equations of a system generated? How does one determine whether a system is consistent or inconsistent? Does an inconsistent system have rank? Show that if the rank of the matrix of coefficients and constant terms is the same after deletion of the constant terms, the system is solvable.

11. Why does any set of independent equations equivalent to a given solvable system have the same number of equations as the rank of the system?

12. If a given system has a set of k independent equations and the remaining equations are dependent upon them, show that k is the maximum number of independent equations in the system.

13. Show that systems generated by successive elementary transformations from a given system have the same rank.

14. Let $x_1 = x_1^o, \ldots, x_k = x_k^o$ and $x_{k+1} = \ldots = x_n = 0$ be a solution to a system of equations where $x_i^o \neq 0$ for $i = 1, 2, \ldots, k$. Suppose r is the rank of the subsystem formed by dropping terms in $x_{k+1}, \ldots, x_n$. Show there exists a solution involving no more than r variables with non-zero values.

15. Suppose no upper bound on the objective function z for a system of linear equations in nonnegative variables exists; let k be the minimum number of positive variables necessary to achieve a class of solutions in which $z \to +\infty$. Show that $k = r + 1$ where r is the rank of the subsystem formed by dropping all variables of zero value in the above solution.

16. Suppose $\sum_i x_{ijk} = a_{jk}$, $\sum_j x_{ijk} = b_{ik}$, $\sum_k x_{ijk} = c_{ij}$, where $i = 1, 2, \ldots, m$; $j = 1, 2, \ldots, n$; $k = 1, 2, \ldots, p$. What relations must be satisfied by the a_{jk}, b_{ik}, and c_{ij} for the system to be consistent? How many equations are independent?

Vector Spaces. (Refer to § 8-2.)

17. Review the definition of an independent set of vectors; show that a single vector is an independent vector, except the null vector. Show also that the null vector is not part of any independent set.

(a) Show that if $P_1, P_2, \ldots, P_n$ and Q are m-component column vectors and

$$P_1 x_1 + P_2 x_2 + \ldots + P_n x_n = Q$$

where the x_j are scalars, then for any scalar k,

$$P_1(kx_1) + P_2(kx_2) + \ldots + P_n(kx_n) = Qk$$

(b) Show that if $P_1 y_1 + P_2 y_2 + \ldots + P_n y_n = R$ also holds, then

$$P_1(y_1 + kx_1) + P_2(y_2 + kx_2) + \ldots + P_n(y_n + kx_n) = Q + kR$$

18. Show that if a system of linear equations is written in vector form

(a) $$P_1 x_1 + P_2 x_2 + \ldots + P_n x_n = Q$$

where P_j and Q are the jth column vector of coefficients and constant terms respectively, then

(b) $$P_1' x_1 + P_2' x_2 + \ldots + P_n' x_n = Q'$$

where P_j' and Q' are the corresponding columns after an elementary transformation.

[204]

19. Show in Problem 18 that if P_1, P_2, . . ., P_k are linearly independent, then P_1', P_2', . . ., P_k' are also and if there is a linear dependence relation between P_1, P_2, . . ., P_k, the same relation holds for P_1', P_2', . . ., P_k'.

Matrices. (Refer to § 8-3.)

Let $\qquad A_1 = [4, \quad 4, \quad 2] \qquad P_1 = \{1, \quad -2, \quad 3\}$
$\qquad\qquad A_2 = [6, \quad 3, \quad -1]$

20. Show that $A_1 P_1 = 2$ and that $A_2 P_1 = -3$.
21. Find $3A_2$; $A_1 + A_2$; $A_1 + 3A_2$.
22. If $A_1 + A_3 = A_2$, what are the components of A_3?
23. Suppose $A_1 = [2, 1]$, $A_2 = [1, -1]$, and $R = \{x_1, x_2\}$. If $A_1 P_1 = 1$ and $A_2 P_1 = 3$, what are the components of P_1?
24. A buyer for a department store bought 10 dresses at $12.00 each, 15 sweaters at $6.00 each, 3 suits at $40.00 each, and 20 blouses at $4.00 each. Let the vector $A = [10, 15, 3, 20]$ represent the quantities and $P = \{12, 6, 40, 4\}$ the price vector. Show by vector multiplication that the total value of his purchases is $370.
25. A plastics manufacturer discovers that the molding machine set-up time for molding a certain part requires two men for three hours. The pay scale is $20.00 per hour for set-up men. Suppose each part requires 20 seconds for molding. Labor costs, including overhead, are $2.50 per hour. Also the part requires 2 ounces of material which costs $.16 per pound. Write a four component row vector that represents the costs of producing one part, each of two parts, each of three parts, etc. Using vector multiplication, find the cost of producing one part. By vector operations find the total cost of a run of 300 parts.
26. Find the components of $X = \{x_1, x_2\}$ where

$$\begin{bmatrix} 2 & 1 \\ 1 & -1 \end{bmatrix} \begin{bmatrix} x_1 \\ x_2 \end{bmatrix} = \begin{bmatrix} 1 \\ 3 \end{bmatrix}$$

27. If A is a row vector and P a column vector, show that $A(kP) = k(AP)$, where k is a constant.
28. Perform the indicated operations:

(a) $\begin{bmatrix} 2 & 3 \\ 1 & 3 \end{bmatrix} \begin{bmatrix} 1 & -1 \\ 1 & 1 \end{bmatrix}$

(b) $\begin{bmatrix} 2 & 3 \\ 1 & 3 \end{bmatrix} \begin{bmatrix} 2 \\ -1 \end{bmatrix}$

(c) $\begin{bmatrix} 1 & -1 \\ 1 & 1 \end{bmatrix} \begin{bmatrix} 2 & 3 \\ 1 & 3 \end{bmatrix}$

(d) $[2 \quad -1] \begin{bmatrix} 2 & 3 \\ 1 & 3 \end{bmatrix}$

(e) $\begin{bmatrix} 2 & 3 \\ 1 & 3 \end{bmatrix} \begin{bmatrix} 4 & 1 & 3 & -1 \\ 2 & 0 & 2 & 2 \end{bmatrix}$

(f) $3 \begin{bmatrix} 2 & 3 \\ 1 & 3 \end{bmatrix} - 2 \begin{bmatrix} 1 & -1 \\ 1 & 1 \end{bmatrix}$

29. Let I be a 3×3 identity matrix and M any 3×3 matrix. Show that $MI = IM = M$.

30. Let O be a square null matrix (all elements zero). Show that $MO = OM = O$.

31. Let $M = \begin{bmatrix} 3 & 1 & 2 \\ -1 & 0 & 2 \\ 1 & 2 & 1 \end{bmatrix}$, and I and O be defined as in Problems 29 and 30. Find

    (a) M^2, M^3, M^4

    (b) I^2, I^3, I^4

    (c) O^2, O^3, O^4

Inverse of a Matrix. (Refer to § 8-4.)

32. Find the inverse of each of the following matrices:

    (a) $\begin{bmatrix} 1 & 2 \\ 3 & 4 \end{bmatrix}$

    (b) $\begin{bmatrix} 3 & 2 & 1 \\ 1 & -2 & 1 \\ 2 & 2 & 3 \end{bmatrix}$

    (c) $\begin{bmatrix} 1 & 1 \\ 2 & 3 \end{bmatrix}$

33. What are the inverses of each of the bases of examples 1 and 2, § 5-2? For each inverse show that relations (12) and (14) of § 8-4 hold.

34. Each element B_{ij} of the inverse B^{-1} of B can be written as $D_{ji}(-1)^{i+j}/D$, where D is the determinant associated with B, and D_{ji} is the determinant formed by dropping row i and column j of B. Show that this is true.

35. The familiar equations for the rotation of coordinates are given by

$$y_1 = x_1 \cos \theta - x_2 \sin \theta$$
$$y_2 = x_1 \sin \theta + x_2 \cos \theta$$

Solve for x_1 and x_2 in terms of y_1 and y_2. What is the inverse of the basis? Show that relations (12) and (14) of § 8-4 hold.

36. (a) Find the inverse of the coefficients of x_1 and x_2 in

$$3x_1 - 2x_2 + 4x_3 + 2x_4 - x_5 + x_6 = 4$$
$$x_1 + x_2 + x_3 + 3x_4 + x_5 + x_7 = 3$$

(b) Reduce to canonical form relative to x_1 and x_2.

How do the coefficients of x_6 and x_7 compare with the elements of the inverse?

37. Show in general that the elements of the inverse of any set of basic variables of the $m \times n$ system ($m \leq n$) of nonnegative variables

$$
\begin{aligned}
a_{11}x_1 + a_{12}x_2 + \ldots + a_{1n}x_n + x_{n+1} &= b_1 \\
a_{21}x_1 + a_{22}x_2 + \ldots + a_{2n}x_n \quad + x_{n+2} &= b_2 \\
\\
a_{m1}x_1 + a_{m2}x_2 + \ldots + a_{mn}x_n \qquad\qquad + x_{m+n} &= b_m
\end{aligned}
$$

will be the coefficients of x_{n+1}, x_{n+2}, . . ., x_{n+m} when the system is reduced to canonical form.

38. Show that if $x_1, x_2, \ldots, x_m$ is a basic set of variables (so that it is possible to reduce Problem 17 to canonical form relative to these variables by a series of elementary operations) that $P_1, P_2, \ldots, P_m$ are linearly independent and form a basis in m-dimensional coordinate space.

39. Show that the rank of a matrix is the same as the rank of the vector space generated by its row vectors. Compare with the definition given in § 8-2.

40. Show that the determinant of an $m \times m$ matrix vanishes if its rank r is less than m and does not vanish if its rank is m.

41. (a) Given $\sum_{j=1}^{n} a_{ij}x_j = y_i$ for $i = 1, 2, \ldots, m$ (see § 8-2-(2)), show that particular values of a_{ij} and y_i can be chosen so that

   (i) there is *no* set of values of x_j that satisfy the system;
   (ii) there is a *unique* set of values of x_j that satisfy the system;
   (iii) there are *many* sets of values of x_j that satisfy the system.

   (b) Prove: If there is always a unique set of x_j satisfying the system whatever be the choice of $y_1, y_2, \ldots, y_m$, then $n = m$ and $[a_{ij}]$ is a basis.

The Simplex Method in Matrix Form. (Refer to § 8-5.)

42. Show that if $P_1, P_2, \ldots, P_m$ is a basis, then

$$
\begin{aligned}
\bar{a}_{1s}P_1 + \bar{a}_{2s}P_2 + \ldots + \bar{a}_{ms}P_m &= P_s \\
\bar{a}_{1s}c_1 + \bar{a}_{2s}c_2 + \ldots + \bar{a}_{ms}c_m &= c_s - \bar{c}_s
\end{aligned}
$$

where $\bar{a}_{is}$ and $\bar{c}_s$ are the coefficients of the corresponding canonical form.

43. Define linear spaces, vector spaces, dimensionality, affine vector geometry, a basis in a vector space, absolute coordinates, coordinates relative to a basis, convexity, convex hull, convex cone, rays, half-space, supporting half-spaces, hyper-planes. (Some of these terms are not defined in the text.)

[207]

44. Letting a vector $v \geq 0$ mean a vector of all nonnegative components, prove

  (a) The equation $Ax = a$ has no solution $x \geq 0$ if and only if there exists a vector π such that $\pi A \leq 0$, $\pi a > 0$.

  (b) The inequality system $Ax \leq a$ has no solution if and only if there exists a $\pi \geq 0$, such that $\pi A = 0$ and $\pi a < 0$.

  (c) The inequality system $Ax \leq a$ has no solution $x \geq 0$ if and only if $\pi A \geq 0$ and $\pi a < 0$ for some π.

45. *Theorem:* Assume there are 4 sets of basic feasible solutions in a system $\sum_{j=1}^{m+2} P_j x_j = Q$, where P_j are m-component vectors.

(1)
$$
\begin{aligned}
P_1 a_1 + P_2 a_2 + P_3 a_3 &\qquad + P_6 a_6 + \ldots + P_{m+2} a_{m+2} = Q \\
P_2 b_2 + P_3 b_3 + P_4 b_4 &\qquad + P_6 b_6 + \ldots + P_{m+2} b_{m+2} = Q \\
P_3 c_3 + P_4 c_4 + P_5 c_5 &+ P_6 c_6 + \ldots + P_{m+2} c_{m+2} = Q \\
P_1 d_1 \qquad\qquad &+ P_4 d_4 + P_5 d_5 + P_6 d_6 + \ldots + P_{m+2} d_{m+2} = Q
\end{aligned}
$$

Then the basic solution

(2) $$P_1 e_1 + P_2 e_2 + P_5 e_5 + P_6 e_6 + \ldots + P_m e_m = Q$$

is feasible if

(3) $$\frac{c_3 - a_3}{c_4} \leq \frac{b_3 - a_3}{b_4}$$

and

(4) $$\frac{a_3}{c_3} \leq \frac{a_k}{c_k} \qquad\qquad (k = 6, \ldots, m + 2)$$

and not feasible if (3) is false, or if (4) is false for some k and a selected range of values of b_k.

46. Let

$$\sum_{j=1}^{\infty} a_{ij} x_j = b_i \qquad (x_j \geq 0; \; i = 1, 2, \ldots, m)$$

be an infinite linear programming problem, which has a feasible solution. Prove that there is a feasible solution involving no more than m variables with $x_j > 0$.

47. *Theorem:* Let $(P_1, P_2, \ldots, P_m)$ be m linearly independent vectors in m-space and P_0 any other vector. If we let

$$x_1 P_1 + x_2 P_2 + \ldots + P_m x_m = P_0 + \begin{pmatrix} \varepsilon \\ \varepsilon^2 \\ \cdot \\ \cdot \\ \cdot \\ \varepsilon^m \end{pmatrix}$$

then there exists an ε_0 such that for all $0 < \varepsilon < \varepsilon_0$

$$x_i \neq 0 \qquad\qquad (i = 1, 2, \ldots, m)$$

48. (a) Consider a "Markov" system of equations

$$(1) \quad \begin{cases} (-1 + p_{11})x_1 + & p_{12}x_2 + \ldots + & p_{1n}x_n = 0 \\ p_{21}x_1 + (-1 + p_{22})x_2 + \ldots + & p_{2n}x_n = 0 \\ \cdots\cdots\cdots\cdots\cdots\cdots\cdots\cdots\cdots\cdots\cdots\cdots\cdots\cdots\cdots\cdots\cdots\cdots\cdots \\ p_{n1}x_1 + & p_{n2}x_2 + \ldots + (-1 + p_{nn})x_n = 0 \end{cases}$$

$$(2) \qquad x_1 + \qquad x_2 + \ldots + \qquad x_n = 1$$

where $p_{ij} > 0$ and $\sum_{i=1}^{n} p_{ij} = 1$ for $j = 1, 2, \ldots, n$. Prove that the first n equations in n unknowns are redundant; but if each equation i is modified by subtracting from it the last equation multiplied by $\lambda_i > 0$, where λ_i is chosen so that $p_{ij} - \lambda_i > 0$, then the corrected system of n-equations is non-redundant and there is a unique solution which is feasible, in fact, with $x_j > 0$.

(b) A system (1), where $\sum_{i=1}^{n} p_{ij} < 1$ for $j = 1, 2, \ldots, n$, and the constants (column of zeros) are replaced by $b_i < 0$, is referred to as a "Leontief" system. Show that such a system always has a unique feasible solution and that the above process can be used to reduce a Markov system to a Leontief system.

49. Prove or disprove for a three-equation system the conjecture that if x_1, x_2 are in the optimal basic set when the third equation is dropped, x_2, x_3 when the first equation is dropped, and x_1, x_3 when the second equation is dropped, then if x_1, x_2, x_3 forms a feasible basic set, it is optimal.

REFERENCES

Cline, 1963-1
Fox, 1954-1
Fulkerson and Wolfe, 1962-1

Kemeny, Snell, and Thompson, 1957-1
Orden, 1952-1
Tucker, 1950-1, 1960-2, 1960-3

CHAPTER 9

THE SIMPLEX METHOD USING MULTIPLIERS

While each iteration of the simplex method requires that a whole new tableau be computed and recorded, it may be observed that only the modified cost row and the column corresponding to the variable entering the basic set play any role in the decision process. The idea behind the "Simplex Method Using Multipliers" is to use a set of numbers called *simplex multipliers (prices)* and the *inverse of the basis* to generate directly from the original equations just the information required for these decisions. This method is also referred to in the literature as the *revised simplex method* [Dantzig and Orchard-Hays, 1953-1].

The modified cost equation, obtained by eliminating the basic variables from the cost form, can be obtained directly from the original system by multiplying the original equations by weights, summing, and then subtracting from the objective equation. It is these weights that are called simplex multipliers and, in a somewhat broader context (see Chapter 12) are called "prices." From a theoretical point of view they are most important as they are related to the variables of the dual system and they play a role analogous to Lagrange multipliers in the calculus (Chapter 6). They are most valuable, as we shall see in Chapter 12, for determining the bottlenecks in a program, the payoff from increasing availabilities of certain stocks, the effect of an increase in capacity, or the value of a proposed new process.

The computational advantages of this approach are:

(a) Less data is recorded from one iteration to the next, which permits more significant figures to be carried or a larger problem to be solved within the limited memory capacity of an electronic computer.

(b) Where the original data has a high percentage of zero coefficients (90 percent or higher is quite common), there are less multiplications (see the computational remarks at the end of this section).

(c) A simple device exists that avoids degeneracy and hence the possibility of "circling" in the simplex algorithm (see *Lexicographic Rule* at the end of § 9-3). (Because the inverse of the basis is part of the full tableau, this device is equally applicable to the original procedure as well.)

The simplex method using multipliers is based on theory already covered in § 8-5. Accordingly, our purpose will be to bring out its operational features. Because some readers might find that the matrix notation of § 8-5 obscures the computational aspects, we have tended to avoid its use here.

9-1. AN ILLUSTRATION USING MULTIPLIERS

To illustrate the technique, consider problem (1)

Cycle 0

(1)

x_1	x_2	x_3	x_4	x_5	x_6	x_7	x_8	x_9	x_{10}	$-z$	Constants
1		1		1		1					3
	1		1		1		1				2
1			1					1			2
	1			1					1		1
-8	-9	-7	-6	-8	-9					1	-90

Basis B — Cycle-k
Initial Basis

which is in canonical form relative to the variables $(x_7,\ x_8,\ x_9,\ x_{10},\ -z)$. After several iterations of the simplex algorithm, this can be written in equivalent canonical form (2) relative to, say, the variables $(x_1, x_2, x_3, x_4, -z)$.

Cycle k

(2)

Basic Variables	x_1	x_2	x_3	x_4	x_5	x_6	x_7	x_8	x_9	x_{10}	$-z$	Constants
x_1	1				1	-1		-1	1	1		1
x_2		1			1					1		1
x_3			1			1	1	1	-1	-1		2
x_4				1	-1	1		1		-1		1
$-z$					3	-4	7	5	1	4	1	-53

● ● ● ○ ★ Inverse of the Basis $[\beta_{ij}]$
Multipliers $\pi = (-7,\ -5,\ -1,\ -4)$

The basis B for cycle k, see (3), is the square array of coefficients associated with the basic variables in the original system (1) where, for this discussion, we exclude z and the z-equation.

The first column of B corresponds to that basic variable in (2) with unit coefficient in the first row, . . . the kth column of B corresponds to the one with unit coefficient in the kth row, etc. (In other words the columns of B must be ordered to correspond to whatever basic variables are listed in the first column of (2); see § 4-2.) For the case at hand (see § 8-4-(11) for definition of inverse),

[211]

$$(3) \quad B = \begin{bmatrix} 1 & 0 & 1 & 0 \\ 0 & 1 & 0 & 1 \\ 1 & 0 & 0 & 1 \\ 0 & 1 & 0 & 0 \end{bmatrix}; \quad B^{-1} = [\beta_{ij}] = \begin{bmatrix} 0 & -1 & 1 & 1 \\ 0 & 0 & 0 & 1 \\ 1 & 1 & -1 & -1 \\ 0 & 1 & 0 & -1 \end{bmatrix}$$

The inverse of the basis, denoted B^{-1} or $[\beta_{ij}]$, is the square array of coefficients in (2) (excluding the z-equation) associated with the variables (x_7, x_8, x_9, x_{10}) where the latter form the initial set of basic variables in (1). To prove this assertion, let us note, according to (§ 8-4-(20)), that *the inverse of the basis can be used to compute the coefficients $\bar{a}_{ij}$ in any column of (2) from the corresponding column j of the original system (1) by the formulas*

$$(4) \qquad \bar{a}_{1j} = \beta_{11}a_{1j} + \beta_{12}a_{2j} + \beta_{13}a_{3j} + \beta_{14}a_{4j}$$
$$\bar{a}_{2j} = \beta_{21}a_{1j} + \beta_{22}a_{2j} + \beta_{23}a_{3j} + \beta_{24}a_{4j}$$
$$\bar{a}_{3j} = \beta_{31}a_{1j} + \beta_{32}a_{2j} + \beta_{33}a_{3j} + \beta_{34}a_{4j}$$
$$\bar{a}_{4j} = \beta_{41}a_{1j} + \beta_{42}a_{2j} + \beta_{43}a_{3j} + \beta_{44}a_{4j}$$

Since column $\langle a_{17}, a_{27}, a_{37}, a_{47}\rangle = \langle 1, 0, 0, 0\rangle$, substitution into (4) yields $\langle \bar{a}_{17}, \bar{a}_{27}, \bar{a}_{37}, \bar{a}_{47}\rangle = \langle \beta_{11}, \beta_{21}, \beta_{31}, \beta_{41}\rangle$ i.e., the column of coefficients of x_7 in (2) is the *same* as the first column of B^{-1}. In general, if x_j is any variable in (1) whose coefficients form a unit vector with unity in the ith equation, then by substitution in (4), the corresponding column of coefficients in (2) is the same as the ith column of B^{-1}. Hence, the inverse of the basis for cycle k is the set of coefficients in the tableau of cycle k of the variables which were basic in cycle 0.

The simplex multipliers or prices are defined as numbers $\pi_1, \pi_2, \pi_3, \pi_4$ such that the weighted sum formed by multiplying the first equation of (1) by π_1, the second by π_2, etc., and adding, will, when subtracted from the z-equation, eliminate the basic variables and yield the modified z-equation of (2). In particular it is obvious, since the only non-zero coefficient of x_7 in (1) is unity (from the first equation), that the resulting coefficient of x_7 in the z-equation of (2) is $-\pi_1$. Similarly, the coefficients of x_8, x_9, x_{10} in (2) must be $-\pi_2, -\pi_3, -\pi_4$. Thus $\pi_1 = -7, \pi_2 = -5, \pi_3 = -1, \pi_4 = -4$. The fact that these values are correct can be directly verified by multiplying them by the corresponding equations of (1), summing, and subtracting from the z-equation to reproduce the z-equation of (2). Thus the *simplex multipliers $\pi_1, \pi_2, \pi_3, \pi_4$ can be used to compute the relative cost factor $\bar{c}_j$ in (2) from the corresponding column of the original system by the formula* (see § 8-5-(16)):

$$(5) \qquad \bar{c}_j = c_j - (\pi_1 a_{1j} + \pi_2 a_{2j} + \pi_3 a_{3j} + \pi_4 a_{4j})$$

In our discussion so far we have excluded $-z$ from the set of basic variables and the z-equation from the basis and its inverse. If, alternatively, we include them, the basis B^* associated with the basic variables x_1, x_2, x_3, x_4 and $-z$ for some cycle k is composed of the coefficients of these variables in the original system (1).

$$(6) \quad B^* = \begin{bmatrix} 1 & 0 & 1 & 0 & | & 0 \\ 0 & 1 & 0 & 1 & | & 0 \\ 1 & 0 & 0 & 1 & | & 0 \\ 0 & 1 & 0 & 0 & | & 0 \\ \hline -8 & -9 & -7 & -6 & & 1 \end{bmatrix}; \quad [B^*]^{-1} = \begin{bmatrix} 0 & -1 & 1 & 1 & | & 0 \\ 0 & 0 & 0 & 1 & | & 0 \\ 1 & 1 & -1 & -1 & | & 0 \\ 0 & 1 & 0 & -1 & | & 0 \\ \hline 7 & 5 & 1 & 4 & & 1 \end{bmatrix}$$

The inverse of B^* then will be the coefficients of the initial basic variables x_7, x_8, x_9, x_{10}, and $-z$ in the canonical form for cycle k. According to § 8-4-(20), if the elements that appear in the kth row of $[B^*]^{-1}$ are used to multiply respectively the five equations of (1), their sum also will reproduce the kth equation of (2). From this point of view, the equations of (4) should result from using the first m rows of $[B^*]^{-1}$, and (5) should result from using the last row of $[B^*]^{-1}$. This is true because B^* differs from B in (6) by the border column of zeros, the border row of costs, and $+1$ in the lower right hand corner; similarly $[B^*]^{-1}$ differs from B^{-1} by the border column of zeros, the border row of the negative prices, and $+1$ in the lower right hand corner.

In the simplex method using multipliers, only certain key columns of the simplex tableau for cycle k are assumed known at the start of the cycle, namely:

(a) *The inverse of the basis B^* for cycle k*, which numerically is the same as the columns of cycle k corresponding to the basic variables of cycle 0.

(b) *The basic feasible solution for cycle k*, which is expressed as the constant values $\bar{b}_i$, $-\bar{z}_0$ and the basic variables to which they correspond, the values of all other variables being zero. *All other data required to carry out steps of the standard simplex process are computed directly from the initial tableau as needed.*

To illustrate, the unshaded part of (7) shows the *recorded* part of the tableau at the start of cycle k.

Start of Cycle k

(7)

Basic Variables	x_1	x_2	x_3	x_4	x_5	x_6	x_7	x_8	x_9	x_{10}	$-z$	Constants
x_1								-1	1	1		1
x_2										1		1
x_3							1	1	-1	-1		2
x_4								1		-1		1
$-z$							7	5	1	4	1	-53

← Inverse, $[B^*]^{-1}$ →

The next step is to compute the relative cost factors $\bar{c}_j$, which are the values appearing in the bottom row of (2), from the data appearing in the tableau

[213]

of cycle 0 and the known multipliers ($\pi_1 = -7$, $\pi_2 = -5$, $\pi_3 = -1$, $\pi_4 = -4$). From (5) we have, for example,

$$(8) \quad \bar{c}_1 = c_1 - \pi_1 a_{11} - \pi_2 a_{21} - \pi_3 a_{31} - \pi_4 a_{41} =$$
$$-8 + 7 \cdot 1 + 5 \cdot 0 + 1 \cdot 1 + 4 \cdot 0 = 0$$

. . . .

$$\bar{c}_6 = c_6 - \pi_1 a_{16} - \pi_2 a_{26} - \pi_3 a_{36} - \pi_4 a_{46} =$$
$$-9 + 7 \cdot 0 + 5 \cdot 1 + 1 \cdot 0 + 4 \cdot 0 = -4$$

As a check, the values of $\bar{c}_j$ for basic variables computed in this manner should be zero, while for those j corresponding to the basic variables of cycle 0, the values of $\bar{c}_j$ should equal the negative of the price, $-\pi_i$, corresponding to the ith basic variable. If the computed $\bar{c}_j$'s are entered in the tableau and the value of s determined such that $\bar{c}_s = \text{Min } \bar{c}_j$, indicated by a $\star$ entered below column $s = 6$, we are in the situation shown in (9).

Step I of Cycle k

(9)

Basic Variables	x_1	x_2	x_3	x_4	x_5	x_6	x_7	x_8	x_9	x_{10}	$-z$	Constants
x_1								-1	1	1		1
x_2										1		1
x_3							1	1	-1	-1		2
x_4								1		-1		1
$-z$	0	0	0	0	3	-4	7	5	1	4	1	-53

● ● ● ●   ★

We now know that x_6 is the candidate for the new basic variable. To determine which basic variable to drop, the value of $\bar{a}_{i6}$ for each i is computed and entered into column 6 using the coefficients a_{16}, a_{26}, a_{36}, a_{46} appearing in column 6 of the original tableau for cycle 0 and the ith row of the inverse of the basis. According to (4),

$$(10) \quad \bar{a}_{16} = \beta_{11} a_{16} + \beta_{12} a_{26} + \beta_{13} a_{36} + \beta_{14} a_{46}$$
$$= 0 \cdot 0 - 1 \cdot 1 + 1 \cdot 0 + 1 \cdot 0 = -1$$

$$\bar{a}_{26} = \beta_{21} a_{16} + \beta_{22} a_{26} + \beta_{23} a_{36} + \beta_{24} a_{46}$$
$$= 0 \cdot 0 + 0 \cdot 1 + 0 \cdot 0 + 1 \cdot 0 = 0$$

$$\bar{a}_{36} = \beta_{31} a_{16} + \beta_{32} a_{26} + \beta_{33} a_{36} + \beta_{34} a_{46}$$
$$= 1 \cdot 0 + 1 \cdot 1 - 1 \cdot 0 - 1 \cdot 0 = 1$$

$$\bar{a}_{46} = \beta_{41} a_{16} + \beta_{42} a_{26} + \beta_{43} a_{36} + \beta_{44} a_{46}$$
$$= 0 \cdot 0 + 1 \cdot 1 + 0 \cdot 0 - 1 \cdot 0 = 1$$

If the computed $\bar{a}_{i6}$ are entered in the tableau and the value of r determined, such that $\bar{b}_r/\bar{a}_{rs} = \text{Min } \bar{b}_i/\bar{a}_{is}$ for $\bar{a}_{is} > 0$, we are then in the situation shown in (11), where $r = 4$, so that $\bar{a}_{rs} = \bar{a}_{46}$ becomes the *pivot* position.

Step II of Cycle k

(11)

Basic Variables	x_1	x_2	x_3	x_4	x_5	x_6	x_7	x_8	x_9	x_{10}	$-z$	Constants
x_1						-1		-1	1	1		1
x_2										1		1
x_3						1	1		1	-1	-1	2
x_4						1			1		-1	1
$-z$	0	0	0	0	3	-4	7	5	1	4	1	-53

● ● ● ● ★

The next step of the standard simplex method would be to replace x_4 by x_6 as a basic variable by reducing (2) to canonical form by pivoting on $\bar{a}_{46}$. We do the same in (11), except that here we are restricted to the completed columns, namely those corresponding to the pivot, the inverse of the basis B^*, and the constants. After elimination of x_6 in (11) using $\bar{a}_{46}$ as pivot, the situation is as shown in (12). Omitting the computed relative costs of the last cycle and the coefficients of x_6, we are ready to start cycle $k + 1$.

Start of Cycle $k + 1$

(12)

Basic Variables	x_1	x_2	x_3	x_4	x_5	x_6	x_7	x_8	x_9	x_{10}	$-z$	Constants
x_1		Omit all				0		1				2
x_2		entries in the				0			1			1
x_3		shaded portion				0	1		-1			1
x_6						1		1		-1		1
$-z$						0	7	9	1	0	1	-49

● ● ● ●

New Inverse of the Basis

New Multipliers $\pi = (-7, -9, -1, 0)$

Computational Remarks.

In the standard simplex method, each cycle requires the recording of at least $(m + 1)(n + 1)$ entries (or more if there are artificial variables). Here, however, by use of *cumulative multiplications*,[1] the amount of recorded information is reduced to $(m + 1)(m + 2)$ entries, actually $(m + 1)^2$ if we ignore the $(-z)$ column.

To illustrate, the values of $\{-\pi_1, -\pi_2, -\pi_3, -\pi_4, 1\}$ can be placed vertically on a strip of paper and moved alongside the jth column as in (13a). It is now convenient to compute $\bar{c}_j$ by multiplying the corresponding entries and forming the cumulative sum.

DEFINITION: The operation (13a) of multiplying the simplex multipliers

---

[1] Desk calculators and electronic computers have special double-length registers that permit convenient forming of the cumulative products

$$a_1b_1, \quad a_1b_1 + a_2b_2, \quad (a_1b_1 + a_2b_2) + a_3b_3, \ldots$$

to double the number of places of a typical memory register of the machines.

[215]

of the basis by the vector of coefficients of x_j to determine its *coefficient* in the modified objective form is called *pricing out*[2] the jth activity in terms of the basic set of activities.

(13a)

$$
\begin{array}{c|c}
-\pi_1 & a_{1j} \\
-\pi_2 & a_{2j} \\
-\pi_3 & a_{3j} \\
-\pi_4 & a_{4j} \\
1 & c_j
\end{array}
$$

(13b)

$$
\begin{array}{|cccc|}
\hline
a_{16} & a_{26} & a_{36} & a_{46} \\
\hline
\beta_{k1} & \beta_{k2} & \beta_{k3} & \beta_{k4}
\end{array}
$$

Similarly, the values of a_{16}, a_{26}, a_{36}, a_{46} appearing in column $s = 6$ can be placed horizontally on a piece of paper and moved alongside the kth row of the inverse of the basis B. It is now convenient to compute $\bar{a}_{k6}$ by multiplying the corresponding entries and forming their cumulative sum as in (13b).

DEFINITION: The operation of multiplication of the rows of the inverse of the basis by the vector of coefficients of x_j is called *representing the jth activity in terms of the basic set of activities*. (See § 8-2-(21) and following discussion.)

Less machine memory is needed using the multiplier method for recording because the original coefficients are often given in fixed decimal of three to five places. This is considerably less than that required for $\bar{a}_{ij}$, when the standard simplex method is used, for this avoids round-off error difficulties in the passage from iteration to iteration. Moreover, using the multiplier method, it is convenient to cumulate the full products without round-off in the machine for both the pricing and representation operations and then to round the resulting sum. This results usually in considerably less round-off error than with the standard method which must round *each* product before recording.

In order to reduce recording still further, most electronic computer instruction codes compute successive $\bar{c}_j$ values by (13a), but keep a record only of the value and location of the *smallest* $\bar{c}_j$ attained up to that point in the calculations.

Starting with an $m \times n$ system in a feasible canonical form, the total number of multiplications required per iteration is

(14) $t(n - m)(m + 1) + tm(m + 1) + (m + 1)^2 = tn(m + 1) + (m + 1)^2$

where the fraction of non-zero coefficients in the original tableau and in the column entering in the basis are assumed on the average to be both equal to t. The three terms on the left are the number of multiplications (or

___

[2] The reason for this term is that the simplex multipliers can be interpreted as prices (see Chapter 12); multiplying these prices by the input-output coefficients of an activity and summing evaluates or "prices out" the activity in terms of the substitute processes, the basic activities. The sum when compared with the direct cost c_j tells us whether or not it pays to consider introducing a non-basic activity j into the basic set.

divisions) used (a) in "pricing out," (b) in representing the new column, and (c) in pivoting. On the other hand the standard simplex procedure requires

(15) $$\{(n - m) + 1\}(m + 1) = (n - 2m)(m + 1) + (m + 1)^2$$

operations on each cycle. Therefore, if the fraction of non-zeros,

(16) $$t < 1 - 2m/n$$

the simplex method using multipliers will require less effort. For example, if $n > 3m$, the fraction of non-zero coefficients required is $t < \frac{1}{3}$. Fig. 9-1-I

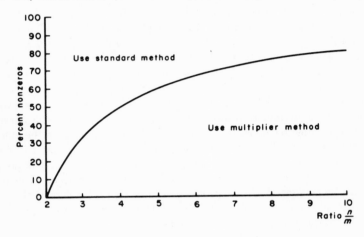

Figure 9-1-I.   Condition for choosing the multiplier method over the standard method (starting in canonical form with no artificial variables).

can be used to decide whether to use the standard simplex or the multiplier method.

9-2. THE GENERAL METHOD USING MULTIPLIERS

Consider the system of equations in *canonical form* for Phase I of the simplex method as in § 5-2-(7), except that we use here m, n for M, N.

Cycle 0

(1)

Admissible Variables	Artificial Variables	
$a_{11}x_1 + a_{12}x_2 + \ldots + a_{1n}x_n$	$+ x_{n+1}$	$= b_1$
$a_{21}x_1 + a_{22}x_2 + \ldots + a_{2n}x_n$	$+ x_{n+2}$	$= b_2$
$\cdot$	$\cdot$	$\cdot$
$a_{m1}x_1 + a_{m2}x_2 + \ldots + a_{mn}x_n$	$+ x_{n+m}$	$= b_m$
$c_1x_1 + c_2x_2 + \ldots + c_nx_n$	$-z$	$= 0$
$d_1x_1 + d_2x_2 + \ldots + d_nx_n$	$-w$	$= -w_0$

[217]

where $b_1, b_2, \ldots, b_m$ are made nonnegative by changing, if necessary, the signs of all terms in the original equations *prior to augmentation with artificial variables*, and where

(2)
$$d_j = - \sum_{i=1}^{m} a_{ij}; \quad w_0 = \sum_{i=1}^{m} b_i$$

Thus, the sum of the first m equations when added to the w-form, implies

(3)
$$x_{n+1} + x_{n+2} + \ldots + x_{n+m} - w = 0$$

The problem is to find w, z, and nonnegative x_j satisfying (1), such that $w = 0$ and z is a minimum. Tableau (4) is the canonical form with basic variables $x_{j_1}, x_{j_2}, \ldots, x_{j_m}, -z, -w$ for the regular simplex method for some cycle k. The basic feasible solution is obtained by setting $x_{j_1} = \bar{b}_1, \ldots, x_{j_m} = \bar{b}_m; z = \bar{z}_0; w = \bar{w}_0;$ and $x_j = 0$ otherwise.

At the start of any cycle, using the multiplier method, the only recorded information from the tableau of the regular simplex method consists of the coefficients of the artificial variables, the constant terms, and the names of their corresponding basic variables. During the cycle, part of the missing data in the simplex tableau is generated as required; these are the values of $\bar{c}_j$ or $\bar{d}_j$ for $j = 1, 2, \ldots, n$ and the values in column $j = s$. The purpose of this section is to review, in general, how parts of the simplex tableau for cycle k can be generated *directly* from cycle 0 using the *inverse* of the basis. In the next section, we shall make use of this to give the computational rules of the simplex method using multipliers.

Tableau of Regular Simplex Method—Cycle k

(4)

Basic Variables	Admissible Variables			Artificial Variables		$-z$	$-w$	Constants
	$x_1 \cdots x_s \cdots x_n$			$x_{n+1} \cdots x_{n+m}$				
x_{j_1}	$\bar{a}_{11} \cdots$	$\bar{a}_{1s}$	$\cdots \bar{a}_{1n}$	$\bar{a}_{1,n+1} \cdots \bar{a}_{1,n+m}$				$\bar{b}_1$
x_{j_r}	$\bar{a}_{r1} \cdots$	$\bar{a}_{rs}$	$\cdots \bar{a}_{rn}$	$\bar{a}_{r,n+1} \cdots \bar{a}_{r,n+m}$				$\bar{b}_r$
x_{j_m}	$\bar{a}_{m1} \cdots$	$\bar{a}_{ms}$	$\cdots \bar{a}_{mn}$	$\bar{a}_{m,n+1} \cdots \bar{a}_{m,n+m}$				$\bar{b}_m$
$-z$	$\bar{c}_1 \cdots$	$\bar{c}_s$	$\cdots \bar{c}_n$	$\bar{c}_{n+1} \cdots \bar{c}_{n+m}$		1		$-\bar{z}_0$
$-w$	$d_1 \cdots$	d_s	$\cdots d_n$	$d_{n+1} \cdots d_{n+m}$			1	$-\bar{w}_0$

$$B^{-1} = [\bar{a}_{i,n+j}], \quad -\pi = [\bar{c}_{n+1}, \ldots, \bar{c}_{n+m}]$$
$$-\sigma = [d_{n+1}, \ldots, d_{n+m}]$$

Since the first m equations of (1) are in canonical form with respect to

$x_{n+1}, x_{n+2}, \ldots, x_{n+m}$ and the equivalent system (4) is in canonical form with respect to $x_{j_1}, x_{j_2}, \ldots, x_{j_m}$, it follows from (9) and (10) of § 8-4:

(a) if the basis, B, is the coefficient matrix of $x_{j_1}, x_{j_2}, \ldots, x_{j_m}$ in (1), then its inverse, B^{-1}, is the coefficient matrix of $x_{n+1}, x_{n+2}, \ldots, x_{n+m}$ in (4), excluding the z- and w-equations.

excluding the z- and w-equations. Moreover, since the entire system (1) is in canonical form with respect to $x_{n+1}, x_{n+2}, \ldots, x_{n+m}, -z, -w$ and the entire system (4) is in canonical form with respect to $x_{j_1}, x_{j_2}, \ldots, x_{j_m}, -z, -w$, it also follows that:

(b) if the basis, B^*, is the coefficient matrix of $x_{j_1}, x_{j_2}, \ldots, x_{j_m}, -z, -w$ in (1), then its inverse, $[B^*]^{-1}$, is the coefficient matrix of $x_{n+1}, x_{n+2}, \ldots, x_{n+m}, -z, -w$ in (4).

According to § 8-4-(20), an element in a given row and column of (4) can be generated from (1) by forming the scalar product of the corresponding row in the inverse and the corresponding column of (1). Thus $\bar{a}_{ij}$ can be generated for, say, $j = s$ by forming the scalar product of the ith row of the inverse B by the jth column of (1) excluding the z- and w-equations, i.e.,

$$(5) \qquad \bar{a}_{ij} = \beta_{i1}a_{1j} + \beta_{i2}a_{2j} + \ldots + \beta_{im}a_{mj}$$

where we have designated the elements of B^{-1} by β_{ij} and have shown by (a) and (b) above

$$(6) \qquad \beta_{ik} = \bar{a}_{i,n+k} \qquad\qquad (i, k = 1, 2, \ldots, m)$$

Similarly, $\bar{c}_j$ or $\bar{d}_j$ can be generated by the scalar product of the z- or w-row of the inverse $[B^*]^{-1}$ with the jth column of (1) including the z- and w-rows. Upon rearrangement of terms

$$(7) \qquad \bar{c}_j = c_j - (\pi_1 a_{1j} + \pi_2 a_{2j} + \ldots + \pi_m a_{mj})$$
$$(8) \qquad \bar{d}_j = d_j - (\sigma_1 a_{1j} + \sigma_2 a_{2j} + \ldots + \sigma_m a_{mj})$$

where we have designated by $-(\pi_1, \pi_2, \ldots, \pi_m)$ and $-(\sigma_1, \sigma_2, \ldots, \sigma_m)$, the coefficients of the artificial variables in the z- and w-equations of (4); thus

$$(9) \qquad \pi_k = -\bar{c}_{n+k}, \; \sigma_k = -\bar{d}_{n+k} \qquad (k = 1, 2, \ldots, m)$$

Finally, the constants $\bar{b}_i, \bar{z}_0, \bar{w}_0$ can be generated by forming the scalar product of the corresponding row of the inverse with the constant column of (1):

$$(10) \qquad \bar{b}_i = \beta_{i1}b_1 + \beta_{i2}b_2 + \ldots + \beta_{im}b_m$$
$$\bar{z}_0 = \pi_1 b_1 + \pi_2 b_2 + \ldots + \pi_m b_m$$
$$\bar{w}_0 = \sigma_1 b_1 + \sigma_2 b_2 + \ldots + \sigma_m b_m + w_0$$

Since the pivoting process of the multiplication method generates new values for the basic variables, formulas (10) are not used, except for *check* purposes.

DEFINITION: Multipliers $\pi = (\pi_1, \pi_2, \ldots, \pi_m)$ are called "simplex multipliers" *relative to the z-equation*, if multiplying the first equation of (1) by π_1, the second equation by $\pi_2, \ldots$, the mth equation by π_m and subtracting their sum from the z-equation, eliminates the basic variables. A set of simplex multipliers *relative to the w-equation* is denoted $\sigma = (\sigma_1, \sigma_2, \ldots, \sigma_m)$.

THEOREM 1: *The simplex multipliers are unique, and are equal to the negative of the coefficients of the artificial variables of the z- and w-equation of the canonical form* (4).

PROOF: Using the particular values of $\pi_k = -\bar{c}_{n+k}$, $\sigma_k = -\bar{d}_{n+k}$ for $(k = 1, \ldots, m)$, the coefficients $\bar{c}_j$ and $\bar{d}_j$ of x_j, as given by the right-hand side of (7) and (8), vanish for columns j corresponding to basic variables. Hence these values satisfy the definition of simplex multipliers.

To show uniqueness, suppose for convenience that $x_1, x_2, \ldots, x_m$ are the basic variables; then π_i must be chosen so that

$$(11) \qquad \begin{aligned}
\pi_1 a_{11} + \pi_2 a_{21} + \ldots + \pi_m a_{m1} &= c_1 \\
\pi_1 a_{12} + \pi_2 a_{22} + \ldots + \pi_m a_{m2} &= c_2 \\
\cdots\cdots\cdots\cdots\cdots\cdots\cdots\cdots \\
\pi_1 a_{1m} + \pi_2 a_{2m} + \ldots + \pi_m a_{mm} &= c_m
\end{aligned}$$

This system of m equations in m unknowns should be contrasted with the system of m equations in m unknowns that the basic variables must satisfy

$$(12) \qquad \begin{aligned}
x_1 a_{11} + x_2 a_{12} + \ldots + x_m a_{1m} &= b_1 \\
x_1 a_{21} + x_2 a_{22} + \ldots + x_m a_{2m} &= b_2 \\
\cdots\cdots\cdots\cdots\cdots\cdots\cdots\cdots \\
x_1 a_{m1} + x_2 a_{m2} + \ldots + x_m a_{mm} &= b_m
\end{aligned}$$

System (11) interchanges rows and columns in (12) and replaces the constants by cost coefficients of the basic variables. The coefficients of x_j in (12) form the basis B (in this case) and hence the coefficients of π_i in (11) form the *transpose of the basis*. By § 8-4, Theorem 7, the inverse of the transpose of the basis exists and is the transpose of B^{-1}. This implies that $\pi_1, \pi_2, \ldots, \pi_m$ can be expressed uniquely in terms of $c_1, c_2, \ldots, c_m$ by

$$(13) \qquad \begin{aligned}
\pi_1 &= \beta_{11} c_1 + \beta_{21} c_2 + \ldots + \beta_{m1} c_m \\
\pi_2 &= \beta_{12} c_1 + \beta_{22} c_2 + \ldots + \beta_{m2} c_m \\
\cdots\cdots\cdots\cdots\cdots\cdots\cdots\cdots \\
\pi_m &= \beta_{1m} c_1 + \beta_{2m} c_2 + \ldots + \beta_{mm} c_m
\end{aligned}$$

where $x_1, x_2, \ldots, x_m$ are basic variables or, more generally, if $x_{j_1}, \ldots, x_j$

are the basic variables, by replacing c_i above by the cost coefficient of the ith basic variable $c_{j_i} = \gamma_i$ (see § 8-5-(17)).

9-3. COMPUTATIONAL RULES USING MULTIPLIERS

Preliminary Remarks.

Write out the system of equations in canonical form for Phase I of the simplex method, as described in § 9-2-(1). The full system is written in detached coefficient form in Table 9-3-Ia at the end of this section.

The *tableau of the simplex method using multipliers*, Table 9-3-IIb, changes from cycle to cycle. [The entries for the starting cycle 0 are shown in Table 9-3-IIa.] Its entries, excluding the last column, are the coefficients of the artificial variables $x_{n+1}, x_{n+2}, \ldots, x_{n+m}$, of $-z$, and $-w$, and the constant terms of the tableau of the regular simplex method for that cycle. It may also be interpreted as composed of the "Inverse of the Basis," $[\beta_{ij}]$, two rows for the negative of the "simplex multipliers," π_i and σ_i, a column for the values of the basic variables in the basic solution, and a column for a variable x_s. At the start of a cycle, all entries in the tableau except the last column "x_s" are known.

During some cycle, say cycle t, the values of the relative cost factors $\bar{d}_j$ for Phase I or $\bar{c}_j$ for Phase II are computed and entered in Table 9-3-Ib. Except at the end of Phase I or Phase II, this is followed by the computation of each $\bar{a}_{is}$, which are entered in the last column of Table 9-3-IIb. At the end of the cycle the entries of this tableau are used to compute the corresponding starting tableau of the next cycle, cycle $t + 1$. Table 9-3-IIc shows how the starting tableau of cycle $t + 1$ is related to the ending tableau of cycle t.

Computational Rules.

These apply to all cycles but differ slightly depending on whether the computations are in Phase I or in Phase II. They are the same as the standard method given in § 5-2 with the following modifications:

Step Ia: Use values of σ_i (if Phase I) or π_i (if Phase II) from Table 9-3-IIb to compute relative cost factors $\bar{d}_j$ (Phase I) or $\bar{c}_j$ (Phase II) for $j = 1, 2, \ldots, n; \ldots, n + m$ by (7), (8), (9) and record in Table 9-3-Ib in the row corresponding to the cycle.

Step Ib: Same as Step I of Standard Method.

Step IIa: Compute for $i = 1, 2, \ldots, m$, the coefficients $\bar{a}_{is}$ of x_s in the canonical form by (5) and (6) and record in the last column of tableau, Table 9-3-IIb.

Step IIb: Same as Step II of Standard Method. Instead of the *random rule* for resolving ties, one may use as an *alternative, the lexicographic rule* given below Step III.

[221]

Step III: Same as Step III of the Standard Method, except: Pivot using pivot element in $\bar{a}_{rs}$ in Table 9-3-IIb (instead of Table 5-2-II) and record entries in Table 9-3-IIc. Leave column "x_s" blank. Leave the list of basic variables in the left column the same as Table 9-3-IIb except change j_r to the value of s determined in Step I. *Return to Step Ia to initiate cycle* $t + 1$.

Lexicographic Rule for Resolving Degeneracy.

If two or more indices r_1, r_2, . . . are tied for the minimum, form the ratios of the corresponding entries in the *first column of the inverse* to $\bar{a}_{r_1 s}$, $\bar{a}_{r_2 s}$, . . ., respectively:

$$\beta_{r_1,1}/\bar{a}_{r_1 s}$$
$$\beta_{r_2,1}/\dot{a}_{r_2 s}$$
$$\cdot$$
$$\cdot$$
$$\cdot$$

and take the index of the row with the minimizing ratio for r. If there still remain ties, repeat for those indices that are still tied using instead the ratio of the corresponding entries in the *second column of the inverse* to their respective $\bar{a}_{r_s s}$. In this manner, ratios are formed from successive columns of the inverse until all ties are resolved uniquely (this always occurs on or before the last column is reached). A proof that the simplex algorithm always terminates in a finite number of steps using this rule will be the subject of the next chapter. (The proof that the random rule terminates in a finite number of steps with probability one was given at the end of § 6-1.)

TABLE 9-3-Ia

SIMPLEX METHOD USING MULTIPLIERS

Detached Coefficients, Original System

Equation i	Admissible Variables					Artificial Variables				$-z$	$-w$	Constants
	x_1	x_2	... x_j	...	x_n	x_{n+1}	x_{n+2}	...	x_{n+m}			
1	a_{11}	a_{12}	... a_{1j}	...	a_{1n}	1						b_1
2	a_{21}	a_{22}	... a_{2j}	...	a_{2n}		1					b_2
$\cdot$	$\cdot$	$\cdot$	$\cdot$		$\cdot$							$\cdot$
$\cdot$	$\cdot$	$\cdot$	$\cdot$		$\cdot$							$\cdot$
$\cdot$	$\cdot$	$\cdot$	$\cdot$		$\cdot$							$\cdot$
m	a_{m1}	a_{m2}	... a_{mj}	...	a_{mn}				1			b_m
z-form	c_1	c_2	... c_j	...	c_n	0 0		...	0	1		0
w-form	d_1	d_2	... d_j	...	d_n	0 0		...	0		1	$-\sum_1^m b_i$

$$d_j = -\sum_{i=1}^{m} a_{ij}; \ b_1 \geq 0, \ . \ . \ ., b_m \geq 0$$

[222]

TABLE 9-3-Ib

Relative Cost Factors d_j or $\bar{c}_j$

		Variable j			
		1, 2, ...	$n,\quad n+1$	...	$n+m$
Cycle					
Phase I $\left\{\begin{array}{l}0\\1\\ \cdot\\ \cdot\\ \cdot\\k\end{array}\right.$		$d_1\quad d_2\quad \cdots$	$d_n,\qquad 0$	$\cdots$	0
		Using $\left\{\begin{array}{c}\sigma_i \text{ if in Phase I}\\ \text{or}\\ \pi_i \text{ if in Phase II}\end{array}\right\}$ from Table 9-3-IIb, same cycle,			
Phase II $\left\{\begin{array}{l}k\\k+1\\ \cdot\\ \cdot\\ \cdot\end{array}\right.$		*compute* $\left\{\begin{array}{c}\bar{d}_j = d_j - [a_{1j}\sigma_1 + a_{2j}\sigma_2 + \ldots + a_{mj}\sigma_m]\\ \text{or}\\ \bar{c}_j = c_j - [a_{1j}\pi_1 + a_{2j}\pi_2 + \ldots + a_{mj}\pi_m]\end{array}\right\}$			
		record $\quad d_j$ or $\bar{c}_j$ on row corresponding to cycle and choose			
		pivot column s such that $\left\{\begin{array}{c}\bar{d}_s = \text{Min } \bar{d}_j \text{ (Phase I)}\\ \bar{c}_s = \text{Min } \bar{c}_j \text{ (Phase II)}\end{array}\right\}$			

TABLE 9-3-IIa

SIMPLEX METHOD USING MULTIPLIERS

Tableau Start of Cycle 0

Basic Variables	(Columns of Canonical Form)					Value of Basic Variable	x_s (see note)
	x_{n+1}	...	x_{n+m}	$-z$	$-w$		
	← Inverse of Basis →						
x_{n+1}	1					b_1	
$\cdot$		$\cdot$				$\cdot$	
$\cdot$			$\cdot$			$\cdot$	
$\cdot$						$\cdot$	
x_{n+r}		1				b_r	
$\cdot$			$\cdot$			$\cdot$	
$\cdot$						$\cdot$	
$\cdot$						$\cdot$	
x_{n+m}			1			b_m	
$-z$	0	...	0	1		0	
$-w$	0	...	0		1	$-\sum_1^m b_i$	

Note: The x_s column is blank at start of cycle 0.

TABLE 9-3-IIb
SIMPLEX METHOD USING MULTIPLIERS
Tableau End of Some Cycle t

Basic Variables	(Columns of Canonical Form)		$-z$ $-w$	Value of Basic Variable	x_s (see note)
	x_{n+1} $\quad\cdots\quad$ x_{n+m}				
	$[\beta_{jk}] = [\bar{a}_{j,n+k}]$ $\longleftarrow$ Inverse of Basis $\longrightarrow$				Compute $\downarrow$
x_{j_1}	β_{11} $\quad\cdots\quad$ β_{1m}			$\bar{b}_1$	$\sum_1^m \beta_{1i} a_{is} = \bar{a}_{1s}$
x_{j_r}	β_{r1} $\quad\cdots\quad$ β_{rm}			$\bar{b}_r$	$\sum_1^m \beta_{ri} a_{is} = \bar{a}_{rs}$
x_{j_m}	β_{m1} $\quad\cdots\quad$ β_{mm}			$\bar{b}_m$	$\sum_1^m \beta_{mi} a_{is} = \bar{a}_{ms}$
$-z$	$(-\pi_k = \bar{c}_{n+k})$ $-\pi_1$ $\quad\cdots\quad$ $-\pi_m$		1	$-\bar{z}_0$	$c_s - \sum_1^m \pi_i a_{is} = \bar{c}_s$
$-w$	$(-\sigma_k = \bar{d}_{n+k})$ $-\sigma_1$ $\quad\cdots\quad$ $-\sigma_m$		1	$-\bar{w}_0$	$d_s - \sum_1^m \sigma_i a_{is} = \bar{d}_s$

Note: Last column is blank at start of cycle; see Table 9-3-Ib for choice of s; see Step IIb for r; Table 9-3-IIc is obtained by pivoting on $\bar{a}_{rs}$ and omitting entries in last column. The bold-faced $\bar{a}_{rs}$ indicates position of pivot.

TABLE 9-3-IIc
Tableau Start of Cycle $t + 1$

x_{j_1}	$\beta_{11} - \bar{a}_{1s}\beta_{r1}^*$ $\cdots$ $\beta_{1m} - \bar{a}_{1s}\beta_{rm}^*$			$\bar{b}_1 - \bar{a}_{1s}\bar{b}_r^*$	(see note above)
x_s	β_{r1}^* $\quad\cdots\quad$ β_{rm}^*			b_r^*	
x_{j_m}	$\beta_{m1} - \bar{a}_{ms}\beta_{r1}^*$ $\cdots$ $\beta_{mm} - \bar{a}_{ms}\beta_{rm}^*$			$\bar{b}_m - \bar{a}_{ms}\bar{b}_r^*$	
$-z$	$-\pi_1 - \bar{c}_s\beta_{r1}^*$ $\cdots$ $-\pi_m - \bar{c}_s\beta_{rm}^*$		1	$-\bar{z}_0 - \bar{c}_s\bar{b}_r^*$	
$-w$	$-\sigma_1 - d_s\beta_{r1}^*$ $\cdots$ $-\sigma_m - d_s\beta_{rm}^*$		1	$-\bar{w}_0 - d_s\bar{b}_r^*$	

$$\beta_{r1}^* = \beta_{ri}/\bar{a}_{rs} \ (i = 1, 2, \ldots, m); \ \bar{b}_r^* = \bar{b}_r/\bar{a}_{rs}$$

EXAMPLE: To illustrate the computational procedures of the simplex method using multipliers, let us return again to the example of § 5-2, Table 5-2-V. In tableau form, the problem is given by Table 9-3-IIIa.

TABLE 9-3-IIIa

Detached Coefficients of Original System

x_1	x_2	x_3	x_4	x_5	x_6	x_7	$-z$	$-w$	Constants
5	−4	13	−2	1	1				20
1	−1	5	−1	1		1			8
1	6	−7	1	5			1		0
−6	5	−18	3	−2				1	−28

TABLE 9-3-IIIb

Cycle		Relative Cost Factors							
		(1)	(2)	(3)	(4)	(5)	(6)	(7)	
d_j	0	−6	5	−18 ★	3	−2	0 ●	0 ○	
	1	12/13	−7/13	0 ●	3/13	−8/13 ★	18/13 ○	0	
	2	0	0	0 ●	0	0 ●	1	1	End of Phase I
$\bar{c}_j$	2	12	−1 ★	0 ●	2	0 ○			
	3	72/7	0 ●	0 ●	11/7	8/7	Drop		End of Phase II

TABLE 9-3-IV

Cycle 0

Basic Variables		Columns of Canonical Form					
		x_6	x_7	$-z$	$-w$	Constants	$x_s = x_3$
x_6		1				20	**13**
x_7			1			8	5
$-z$				1		0	−7
$-w$					1	−28	−18

Cycle 1 $(x_s = x_5)$

x_3		1/13				20/13	1/13
x_7		−5/13	1			4/13	**8/13**
$-z$		7/13	0	1		140/13	72/13
$-w$		18/13	0		1	−4/13	−8/13

[225]

TABLE 9-3-IV (continued)

Cycle 2 $\qquad$ $(x_s = x_2)$

x_3	1/8	$-1/8$				3/2	$-3/8$	End of Phase I,
x_5	$-5/8$	13/8				1/2	**7/8**	$d_j \geq 0$, $w = 0$
$-z$	$+4$	-9	1			8	-1	Drop x_6 and x_7 since
$-w$	1	1		1		0	0	$(d_6, d_7) = (1, 1) > 0$; drop w-row

Cycle 3

x_3	$-1/7$	4/7		12/7		End of Phase II,
x_2	$-5/7$	13/7		4/7		$\bar{c}_j \geq 0$.
$-z$	23/7	$-50/7$	1	60/7		
$-w$		(w-row dropped)				

9-4. PROBLEMS

1. Solve by the simplex method using multipliers:

$$3x_1 - 3x_2 + 4x_3 + 2x_4 - x_5 + x_6 \qquad\qquad = 0$$
$$x_1 + x_2 + x_3 + 3x_4 + x_5 \qquad + x_7 = 2$$
$$2x_1 + 3x_2 + 2x_3 - x_4 + x_5 \qquad\qquad = z$$
$$x_6 + x_7 = w$$

and minimize z, where $x_j \geq 0$ and $w = 0$.

2. Solve, using the simplex method using multipliers:

$$x_1 \qquad + 2x_3 - x_4 \qquad \geq 3 \qquad\qquad (x \geq 0)$$
$$2x_1 + x_2 \qquad + 2x_4 - 2x_5 \leq 1$$
$$+ x_2 - x_3 \qquad\qquad \geq 0$$
$$-x_1 \qquad\qquad + 3x_5 \leq 2$$
$$-x_1 - x_2 - x_3 \qquad + x_5 = \text{Min } z$$

3. Discuss the relationships between the regular simplex method and the revised simplex method.

4. Set up the dual of the problem of finding x_j that minimizes $x_1 + x_2 = z$ subject to

$$x_1 + 2x_2 \geq 3$$
$$x_1 - 2x_2 \geq -4$$
$$x_1 + 7x_2 \leq 6$$

where $x_1 \geq 0$, and x_2 is unrestricted in sign. Determine the simplex multipliers of the optimum solution of the primal, and verify that it satisfies the dual and gives the same value for the objective form.

5. Solve the Blending Problem II, § 3-4, by the revised simplex method.

6. Solve Waugh's problem using simplex multipliers. (See Problem 28, Chapter 5.)

7. Prove that

$$c_1 \bar{a}_{1j} + c_2 \bar{a}_{2j} + \ldots + c_m \bar{a}_{mj} = \pi_1 a_{1j} + \pi_2 a_{2j} + \ldots + \pi_m a_{mj}$$

where $\pi_1, \pi_2, \ldots, \pi_m$ are simplex multipliers associated with the basic set of variables $x_1, x_2, \ldots, x_m$. See Chapter 12 for an economic interpretation of this relation.

8. Prove that if P_s replaces P_{j_r}, the rth column in a basis, and if π^* is the new vector of simplex multipliers, then

$$\pi^* = \pi + k\beta_r, \qquad k = \bar{c}_s/\bar{a}_{rs}$$

where β_r is the row of B^{-1} corresponding to P_{j_r}.

9. In § 8-5, the product form of the inverse was developed. Review this discussion and rework the exercises. Discuss how you would compute the simplex prices, π^*, if the inverse of the basis in product form were given.

REFERENCES

Dantzig, Harvey, and McKnight, 1964-1
Dantzig and Orchard-Hays, 1953-1
Dantzig, Orden, and Wolfe, 1954-1
Fredrick, 1964-1
Garvin, 1960-1
Gass, 1964-1

Hadley, 1961-2
Orchard-Hays, 1955-1, 1956-1
Orden, 1952-1
Mueller-Merbach, 1964-3
Spurkland, 1963-2
Smith and Orchard-Hays, 1963-1

CHAPTER 10

FINITENESS OF THE SIMPLEX METHOD UNDER PERTURBATION

10-1. THE POSSIBILITY OF CIRCLING IN THE SIMPLEX ALGORITHM

We have seen that if degeneracy does occur, then it is possible to have a sequence of iterations with no decrease in the value of z. Under such circumstances, may it not happen that a basic set will be repeated, thereby initiating an endless circle of such repetitions? If so, can we devise an efficient procedure to prevent such a circling possibility? In the early days of linear programming this was an unsolved problem.

In 1951, A. J. Hoffman constructed an example, shown in Table 10-1-I, involving three equations and eleven variables. He showed that if one *resolved* the ambiguity of choice regarding which variable to drop from the basic set *by selecting the first among them*, then the tableau at cycle 9 would be the same as at cycle 0. It follows in this case that the same basic set would be repeated every nine iterations and the simplex method would never terminate. This phenomenon is usually referred to as *cycling in the simplex algorithm*. We prefer, however, the term "circling," because we use the term "cycle" for a single iteration of the simplex algorithm.

Later, E. M. L. Beale [1955-1] constructed a second example, a version of which is shown in Table 10-1-II, that is remarkable for its simplicity. It also has three equations but only seven variables. Using the same rule for resolving a tie, the tableau at cycle 6 is the same at cycle 0. It is conjectured that this is the simplest example; to be precise, it is believed that no other example of circling can be constructed involving fewer variables regardless of the number of equations.

Since circling in the simplex algorithm is only possible under degeneracy, it is pertinent to ask how degeneracy can occur, how frequently it is encountered in practice and how often it implies circling. Degenerate solutions are possible only when the constants, b_i, of the original right-hand side bear a special relation to the coefficients of the basic variables. This is clear since the process of reduction to one of the finite set of canonical forms depends only on the coefficients and *not* on the right-hand side; the final values, $\bar{b}_i$, are weighted sums of the original b_i's where the weights depend only on the coefficients. If all the b_i's were selected at random, it would be something of a miracle if one or more of the constants $\bar{b}_i$ of the canonical system should vanish.

[228]

TABLE 10-1-I

A. J. Hoffman's Example of Circling in the Simplex Algorithm

$$[\theta = 2\pi/5,\ \ w > (1 - \cos\theta)/(1 - 2\cos\theta)]$$

(Cycle 0)

	x_1	x_2	x_3	x_4	x_5	x_6	x_7	x_8	x_9	x_{10}	x_{11}	Constant
	1	1	1	$\boxed{\cos\theta}$	$-w\cos\theta$	$\cos 2\theta$	$-2w\cos^2\theta$	$\cos 2\theta$	$2w\cos^2\theta$	$\cos\theta$	$w\cos\theta$	1
				$\sin\theta\tan\theta/w$	$\cos\theta$	$\tan\theta\sin 2\theta/w$	$\cos 2\theta$	$-2\sin^2\theta/w$	$\cos 2\theta$	$-\tan\theta\sin\theta/w$	$\cos\theta$	0
												0
				$-(1-\cos\theta)/\cos\theta$	$+w$		$+2w$	$+4\sin^2\theta$	$-2w\cos 2\theta$	$+4\sin^2\theta$	$w(1-2\cos\theta)$	z (Min)

(Cycle 1)

	x_1	x_2	x_3	x_4	x_5	x_6	x_7	x_8	x_9	x_{10}	x_{11}	Constant
	1	$\sec\theta$	1	1	$-w$	$4\cos^2\theta - 3$	$-2w\cos\theta$	$4\cos^2\theta - 3$	$2w\cos\theta$	1	w	1
		$-\tan^2\theta/w$			$\boxed{\sec\theta}$	$\tan^2\theta/w$	1	$2\sin\theta\tan\theta/w$	$4\cos^2\theta - 3$	$-2\sin\theta\tan\theta/w$	$4\cos^2\theta - 3$	0
												0
		$(1-\cos\theta)/\cos^2\theta$			$w(2\cos\theta-1)/\cos\theta$	$-2\sin\theta\tan\theta$	$2w\cos\theta$	$(\cos\theta-1)/\cos\theta$	$3w$	$2\sin\theta\tan\theta$	$-w(4\cos^2\theta - 3)$	z

(Cycle 2)

	x_1	x_2	x_3	x_4	x_5	x_6	x_7	x_8	x_9	x_{10}	x_{11}	Constant
	1	$\cos\theta$	$w\cos\theta$	1	1	$\boxed{\cos\theta}$	$-w\cos\theta$	$\cos 2\theta$	$-2w\cos^2\theta$	$\cos 2\theta$	$2w\cos^2\theta$	1
		$-\tan\theta\sin\theta/w$	$\cos\theta$			$\sin\theta\tan\theta/w$	$\cos\theta$	$\tan\theta\sin 2\theta/w$	$\cos 2\theta$	$-2\sin^2\theta/w$	$\cos 2\theta$	0
												0
		$4\sin^2\theta$	$w(1-2\cos\theta)$			$-(1-\cos\theta)/\cos\theta$	$+w$		$+2w$	$+4\sin^2\theta$	$-2w\cos 2\theta$	z

Notice that columns (2, 3, 4, . . ., 11) of cycle 0 are the same as columns (4, 5, 6, . . ., 11; 2, 3) respectively of cycle 2; hence, 8 more iterations will repeat cycle 2. The □ indicates the position of the pivot.

TABLE 10-1-II

BEALE'S EXAMPLE OF CIRCLING IN THE SIMPLEX ALGORITHM

x_1	x_2	x_3	x_4	x_5	x_6	x_7	$-z$	Constant
				(Cycle 0)				
1/4	−60	−1/25	9	1				0
1/2	−90	−1/50	3		1			0
		1				1		1
−3/4 ★	150	−1/50	6	●	●	●	1	0
				(Cycle 1)				
1	−240	−4/25	36	4				0
	30	3/50	−15	−2	1			0
		1				1		1
●	−30 ★	−7/50	33	3	●	●	1	0
				(Cycle 2)				
1		**8/25**	−84	−12	8			0
	1	1/500	−1/2	−1/15	1/30			0
		1				1		1
●	●	−2/25 ★	18	1	1	0 ●	1	0
				(Cycle 3)				
25/8		1	−525/2	−75/2	25			0
−1/160	1		**1/40**	1/120	−1/60			0
−25/8			525/2	75/2	−25	1		1
1/4	●	●	−3 ★	−2	3	●	1	0
				(Cycle 4)				
−125/2	10,500	1		**50**	−150			0
−1/4	40		1	1/3	−2/3			0
125/2	−10,500			−50	150	1		1
−1/2	120	●	●	−1 ★	1	●	1	0
				(Cycle 5)				
−5/4	210	1/50		1	−3			0
1/6	−30	−1/150	1		**1/3**			0
		1				1		1
−7/4	330	1/50	●	●	−2 ★	●	1	0

Note: Cycle 6 must be the same as Cycle 0, as it has the same basic variables in the same order.

Nevertheless, it is common experience, based on the solutions of thousands of practical linear programming problems by the simplex method, that nearly every problem at some stage of the process is degenerate. It might be thought that, since degeneracy happens all the time, there would be many observed cases of circling. However, to date, there has not been one single case of circling, except in the specially constructed examples of Hoffman and Beale. Apparently, circling is a very rare phenomenon in practice. For this reason, most instruction codes for electronic computers use no special device for perturbing the problem to avoid degeneracy and the possibility of circling. The cells of the computer's high-speed memory, when not entirely reserved for the data of a large problem, are occupied by subroutines designed to increase accuracy by means of arithmetical checks and multiple precision arithmetic.

From a mathematical point of view, the phenomenon of circling is an interesting one. Long before Hoffman discovered his example, simple devices were proposed to avoid degeneracy. The main problem was to devise a way of avoiding degeneracy that involved *as little extra work as possible*. The first proposal along these lines was presented by the author in the fall of 1950 in his Linear Programming Course at the Graduate School of the U.S. Department of Agriculture. Students were assigned exercises involving the proofs of the method along the lines given in this section [Edmondson, 1951-1; Dantzig, 1951-2]. Later A. Orden, P. Wolfe, and the author published a proof of this method based on the concept of *lexicographic ordering* of vectors [Dantzig, Orden, and Wolfe, 1954-1]. A. Charnes [1952-1] independently developed a technique of perturbation that is described in one of the problems at the end of the chapter.

As an alternative to the random choice rule established in § 6-1, we shall show in the next section that it is possible to perturb slightly the constant terms in such a way that

(a) *the basic feasible solutions become nondegenerate, and*
(b) *moreover, the corresponding basic solutions for the unperturbed problem will remain feasible.*

In effect, the perturbation simply *guides* the proper choice of variables to drop from the basic set in case of ties.

10-2. PERTURBING CONSTANTS TO AVOID DEGENERACY[1]

Let us begin with Phase I of the simplex method and assume, as in § 9-2, that all $b_i \geq 0$ and that a set of variables has been augmented by the

---

[1] The method given in this section is based on perturbing the constant terms. In [Dantzig, Orden, and Wolfe, 1954-1] an alternative proof, based on *lexicographic ordering*, closely parallels the one given here. For further discussion, see Problems 11, 12, and 13 at the end of this chapter and § 13-4.

artificial variables x_{n+1}, x_{n+2}, . . ., x_{n+m}, so that the basic problem of Phase I is to find $x_j \geq 0$ and Min w, such that

(1)
$$\sum_{j=1}^{n} a_{ij}x_j + x_{n+i} = b_i \quad (b_i \geq 0; i = 1, 2, . . ., m)$$

$$\sum_{i=1}^{m} x_{n+i} = w$$

Let the initial basic set of variables be x_{n+1}, x_{n+2}, . . ., x_{n+m}. If one or more of the constants, b_i, equal zero, the corresponding solution will be degenerate. We shall avoid this by considering the *perturbed problem*:

(2)
$$\sum_{j=1}^{n} a_{ij}x_j + x_{n+i} = b_i + \varepsilon^i \quad (b_i \geq 0; \varepsilon > 0 \; i; = 1, 2, . . ., m)$$

$$\sum_{i=1}^{m} x_{n+i} = w \text{ (Min)}$$

It is obvious that the initial basic solution is nondegenerate, because for all i

(3)
$$x_{n+i} = b_i + \varepsilon^i > 0 \qquad\qquad (b_i \geq 0; \varepsilon > 0)$$

and that, by setting $\varepsilon = 0$, the basic solution is feasible for the *unperturbed* problem.

On subsequent iterations, the values of basic variables will become general polynomial expressions in ε. Indeed, suppose for cycle t that $(x_{j_1}, x_{j_2}, . . ., x_{j_m})$ is some basic set of variables, then by § 8-4-(21), the values of the basic variables which we denote by $\bar{b}_i(\varepsilon)$ are

(4)
$$\bar{b}_i(\varepsilon) = \sum_{k=1}^{m} \beta_{ik}(b_k + \varepsilon^k) \qquad\qquad (i = 1, 2, . . ., m)$$

$$= \bar{b}_i + \beta_{i1}\varepsilon + \beta_{i2}\varepsilon^2 + . . . + \beta_{im}\varepsilon^m$$

where $[\beta_{ij}]$ is the inverse of the basis and $\bar{b}_i$ are the values of x_{j_i} for $\varepsilon = 0$.

EXERCISE: Show for each i there exists a $\beta_{ik} \neq 0$.

EXERCISE: Show that it is not possible for two rows of the inverse of a matrix to be proportional.

In (4) it is no longer possible to guarantee that the values of the basic variables will remain positive for *all* positive ε and nonnegative for $\varepsilon = 0$. However, we shall prove the following:

LEMMA 1: *Given a polynomial*

(5)
$$f(\varepsilon) = a_0 + a_1\varepsilon + . . . + a_m\varepsilon^m$$

then $f(\varepsilon) > 0$ for all $0 < \varepsilon <$ some h_0, if and only if it has a non-zero term and the first such has a positive coefficient.

[232]

PROOF: Let the first term of $f(\varepsilon)$ with non-zero coefficient (called the *leading term*) be k; then by assumption

$$(6) \qquad a_0 = a_1 = \ldots = a_{k-1} = 0 \quad \text{and} \quad a_k > 0$$

Let, for $j = k + 1, \ldots, m$,

$$(7) \qquad M = \text{Max}\,(0, \underset{j}{\text{Max}} - a_j)$$

Then for $0 < \varepsilon < 1$ and $p \geq 1$,

$$a_j \varepsilon^p \geq -M\varepsilon^p \geq -M\varepsilon \qquad (j = k + 1, \ldots, m)$$

and, therefore,

$$(8) \qquad \begin{aligned} f(\varepsilon) &= \varepsilon^k[a_k + a_{k+1}\varepsilon + \ldots + a_m\varepsilon^{m-k}] \\ &\geq \varepsilon^k[a_k - M\varepsilon - M\varepsilon - \ldots - M\varepsilon] \\ &\geq \varepsilon^k[a_k - M(m - k)\varepsilon] \end{aligned}$$

If we let

$$(9) \qquad h_0 = \text{Min}\,[1, a_k/M(m - k)]$$

where $h_0 = 1$ if $M = 0$ or $M = k$, then it follows from (8) that $f(\varepsilon) > 0$ for all ε in the interval $0 < \varepsilon < h_0$.

EXERCISE: Prove the "only if" part of Lemma 1; see Problem 4.

LEMMA 2: *Given two polynomials $f(\varepsilon)$ and $g(\varepsilon)$, where*

$$(10) \qquad f(\varepsilon) = \sum_{i=0}^{m} a_i\varepsilon^i, \qquad g(\varepsilon) = \sum_{i=0}^{m} b_i\varepsilon^i$$

such that

$$(11) \qquad \begin{aligned} a_i &= b_i \quad \text{for } i = 1, 2, \ldots, k - 1 \\ a_k &< b_k \\ a_i, \quad b_i &\quad \text{arbitrary for } i \neq k \end{aligned}$$

then for some $h_0 > 0$, $f(\varepsilon) < g(\varepsilon)$ for all $0 < \varepsilon < h_0$.

PROOF: This will follow from Lemma 1, since conditions (11) are a restatement of conditions (6) for $g(\varepsilon) - f(\varepsilon)$. Hence, there must exist an h_0, such that

$$(12) \qquad g(\varepsilon) - f(\varepsilon) = \sum_{i=0}^{m} (b_i - a_i)\varepsilon^i > 0 \qquad \text{for all } 0 < \varepsilon < h_0$$

THEOREM 1: *For cycle t, each polynomial expression in ε in (4) has at least one non-zero term; if the first such is positive for every i, then there is some range of values $0 < \varepsilon < h_t$, such that for any fixed ε in the range, the values of all basic variables are positive.*

The first part of the theorem holds because not all $\beta_{ij} = 0$ for fixed i. The second part follows from Lemma 1 and the fact that, if there are different ranges of values for ε within which the values of the various basic variables stay positive as a function of ε, then the smallest of these ranges will do for all x_{j_i}.

For our purposes, it is only important for cycle t that a range of values $0 < \varepsilon < h_t$ exists for which all basic variables remain positive as a function of ε. An explicit value for h_t is not needed, so that, *in computing work, h_t is never evaluated.*

THEOREM 2: *There exists a common range of values $0 < \varepsilon < h_t^*$ such that for any finite number of iterations of the simplex method as applied to any perturbed problem within the range, the values of all basic variables remain positive and the choice of the variable entering and leaving the basic set is unique and independent of the particular value of ε in the range.*

PROOF: For some cycle t let us apply the simplex algorithm to improve a basic solution for a perturbed problem (1), in which we assume for *inductive purposes,* that $\bar{b}_i(\varepsilon)$ will be positive for some range $0 < \varepsilon < h_t$ (hence, its leading term has a positive coefficient). Clearly the assumption is true for cycle 0 by (3). The choice of the *new variable x_s* entering the basic set depends only on the coefficients of the variables in the basic set and is *independent* of $\bar{b}_i$ and ε. On the other hand, the choice of the rth basic variable *to be dropped is dependent on $\bar{b}_i$ and ε.* However, we shall now show that for the class of perturbed problems whose ε is within a sufficiently small range, the same variable x_r will be dropped from the basic set. In fact, by § 5-1-(21), the maximum value x_s^* of the variable x_s entering the basic set and the choice of the rth basic variable to drop is determined through the relations

$$(13) \qquad x_s^* = \frac{\bar{b}_r(\varepsilon)}{\bar{a}_{rs}} = \underset{\bar{a}_{is}>0}{\text{Min}} \{(\bar{b}_i + \beta_{i1}\varepsilon + \beta_{i2}\varepsilon^2 + \ldots + \beta_{im}\varepsilon^m)/\bar{a}_{is}\}$$

where x_s^* is positive for any ε in some range $0 < \varepsilon < h_t$ by the assumption that $\bar{b}_i(\varepsilon) > 0$ in this range.

The Lexicographic Rule.

Applying Lemma 2, the minimum of the several polynomial expressions (for sufficiently small range of values for ε) is found by first comparing their constant terms, i.e., by choosing r, such that

$$(14) \qquad \frac{\bar{b}_r}{\bar{a}_{rs}} = \text{Min} \frac{\bar{b}_i}{\bar{a}_{is}} \qquad\qquad (\bar{a}_{rs} > 0 \,;\, \bar{a}_{is} > 0)$$

If, however, there are several $i = r_1, r_2, \ldots$ satisfying (14), then for these i, choose $i = r$, such that

$$(15) \qquad \frac{\beta_{r1}}{\bar{a}_{rs}} = \text{Min} \frac{\beta_{i1}}{\bar{a}_{is}} \qquad\qquad \text{for } i = r_1, r_2, \ldots$$

That is to say, the coefficients of the ε^1 power terms of these various polynomials are compared for those i that are tied in (15). If again r is not unique, then for those remaining i which are again tied for the minimum, the corresponding coefficients of ε^2; ε^3; and as many powers as necessary are compared *in turn* until a *unique* r is determined. This will always occur *on or before* comparison of the coefficients of ε^m because, if two (or more) polynomial expressions had equal coefficients for all powers, it would mean that *two (or more) rows of the inverse of the basis were constant multiples of each other*, which is *not* possible; see earlier exercise and Problem 2. By this means a unique r can be chosen corresponding to the unique smallest ratio (13) where the *same* choice of r can be made for all $\varepsilon > 0$ in some range. This also means that the values of *all* the basic variables for the next iteration, as given by the polynomial expressions in ε, must remain positive (zero excluded) in some range $0 < \varepsilon < h_{t+1}$, thereby completing the induction. Theorem 2 follows, if we let h_t^* be the smallest h_p for all $0 \leq p \leq t$.

THEOREM 3: *The simplex algorithm as applied to the perturbed problem terminates in a finite number of iterations.*

PROOF: For any fixed number of iterations, N, the values of the basic variables are all positive for *any* fixed ε in some range $0 < \varepsilon < h_N^*$. It follows that *there is a positive (zero excluded) decrease in the value of the objective form.* Therefore, *no basic set of variables could be the same as one obtained in earlier iterations.* Since there are only a finite number of basic sets of variables, not larger than the number of combinations of n things taken m at a time, $\binom{n}{m} = \dfrac{n!}{(n-m)!\, m!}$, it is not possible that $N > \binom{n}{m}$.

It is easy to see also

THEOREM 4: *The minimal basic feasible solution of the perturbed problem will yield the corresponding solution for the unperturbed problem by setting* $\varepsilon = 0$ *in* (4).

Phase I—Phase II Considerations.

The perturbed problem for Phase II must be suitably chosen so as to be a natural extension of Phase I. At the same time, the setup must be such that any artificial variables remaining in the basis must have zero values in basic solutions in subsequent iterations, when $\varepsilon = 0$. Let $d_j \geq 0$ be the relative coefficients of the infeasibility form at the end of Phase I; then the perturbed problem for Phase II for $i = 1, 2, \ldots, m$ becomes

(16)
$$\sum_{j=1}^{n} a_{ij}x_j + \delta_i x_{n+i} = b_i + \varepsilon^i$$

$$\sum_{j=1}^{n} d_j x_j + (-w) = + \varepsilon^{m+1}$$

$$\sum_{j=1}^{n} c_j x_j = z \text{ (Min)}$$

where for $i = 1, 2, \ldots, m$, $\delta_i = 1$ or 0 according to whether or not x_{n+i} is in the basic set at the end of Phase I. It will be noted that, if B is the basis associated with the first m equations, and we now include the w-equation of (16) and $(-w)$ as a basic variable, the extended basis and its inverse for the first $(m + 1)$ equations become, respectively,

$$(17) \qquad \begin{bmatrix} B & 0 \\ 0 & 1 \end{bmatrix} \quad \text{and} \quad \begin{bmatrix} B^{-1} & 0 \\ 0 & 1 \end{bmatrix}$$

The values of the basic variables for the *initial solution* for Phase II are now

$$(18) \qquad \begin{aligned} x_{j_i} &= \bar{b}_i + \beta_{i1}\varepsilon + \beta_{i2}\varepsilon^2 + \ldots + \beta_{im}\varepsilon^m + 0\,\varepsilon^{m+1} > 0 \\ (-w) &= \varepsilon^{m+1} \end{aligned}$$

where the leading terms are positive by Theorem 2.

During Phase II all variables $x_j \geq 0$, $x_{n+i} \geq 0$, and $(-w) \geq 0$ are treated as admissible variables and z is minimized. This, of course, follows precisely the procedure of Phase I. It remains only to show that if ε is set equal to zero, the value of any artificial basic variable is *zero* in any feasible solution. Let σ_i be the simplex multipliers associated with the final basis of Phase I; then, recalling that $d_j = -\sum_i a_{ij}$,

$$(19) \qquad \bar{d}_j = d_j - \sum_{i=1}^{m} a_{ij}\sigma_i = -\sum_{i=1}^{m} a_{ij}(\sigma_i + 1)$$

Hence, if the ith equation of (16) is multiplied by $(\sigma_i + 1)$ and their sum for $i = 1, 2, \ldots, m$ is *added* to the w-equation of (16), one obtains, using (19) and the fact that $\sigma_i = -\bar{d}_{n+i}$

$$(20) \qquad \sum_{i=1}^{m} \delta_i x_{n+i} + (-w) = \sum_{i=1}^{m} (\sigma_i + 1)b_i + \sum_{i=1}^{m} (\sigma_i + 1)\varepsilon^i + \varepsilon^{m+1}$$

Now the constant term in the polynomial in ε of the right member of (20) vanishes and the leading term is positive.

PROOF: Equation (20) must hold for *every* solution of Phase II; in particular, it must hold for the values given to the artificial variables in the initial solution for Phase II given by (18); but these have the property that their constant terms are all zero and their leading terms are positive. Hence, substituting their polynomial expressions on the *left* in (20), and noting $\delta_i \geq 0$, the same property must hold for the polynomial expressions on the right. Conversely, if the expression on the right has a zero constant term, then so do x_{n+i} and $(-w)$ in any subsequent solution, because their leading terms are maintained positive. It follows that $x_{n+i} = 0$, if $\varepsilon = 0$.

THEOREM 5: *If a minimal feasible solution $x_j = x_i^*$, $z = z^*$ exists, then* at the end of Phase II, a system of multipliers $\pi_i = \pi_i^*$ is obtained with the properties that

(21)
$$\bar{c}_j^* = c_j - \sum_{i=1}^m \pi_i^* a_{ij} \geq 0 \qquad (j = 1, 2, \ldots, n)$$

$$\bar{c}_j^* > 0 \Rightarrow x_j^* = 0, \ x_j^* > 0 \Rightarrow \bar{c}_j^* = 0$$

$$\text{Min } z = z^* = \sum_{i=1}^m \pi_i^* b_i$$

Note: The symbol $\Rightarrow$ means "implies."

PROOF: The simplex multipliers π_i obtained at the end of Phase II for the extended problem satisfy the above conditions, *providing* a multiplier k is included for the w-equation of (16). However, dropping the artificial variables and the perturbation, the w-equation, $\Sigma d_j x_j$, can be formed from the first m equations, using the multipliers σ_i obtained at the end of Phase I; noting (19), the required multipliers are

(22)
$$\pi_j^* = \pi_i - k(\sigma_i + 1)$$

10-3. PROBLEMS

1. Prove the exercise in § 10-2 that at least one element of each row and each column of the inverse of a basis is non-zero.
2. Prove the exercise in § 10-2 that it is impossible for the elements in a row of the inverse of a basis to be proportional to the elements of another row. (By use of the transpose, prove that the same is true for columns.)
3. Prove that if $\bar{b}_i(\varepsilon) \geq 0$ for $0 < \varepsilon < h$, then there exists an $h' < h$, such that $\bar{b}_i(\varepsilon)$ is *positive* for $0 < \varepsilon < h'$, where $\bar{b}_i(\varepsilon) = \bar{b}_i + \sum_j \beta_{ij} \varepsilon^j$ and $B^{-1} = [\beta_{ij}]$.
4. If $a_k < 0$ and $a_0 = a_1 = \ldots = a_{k-1} = 0$, prove there exists an $h > 0$, such that
$$f(\varepsilon) = a_0 + a_1 \varepsilon + a_2 \varepsilon^2 + \ldots + a_m \varepsilon^m$$
is negative for *all* $0 < \varepsilon < h$.
5. Prove that if all basic variables for perturbed solutions for each cycle t remain positive in a range $0 < \varepsilon < h_t$, then there exists a common range for all cycles up to t within which all basic variables for the first t iterations remain positive.
6. Solve Hoffman's example using a perturbation method. (See § 10-1, Table 10-1-I.)
7. Solve Beale's example using a perturbation method. (See § 10-1, Table 10-1-II.)
8. (a) Is it possible to construct a class of perturbed problems which are infeasible, but the corresponding class of unperturbed problems are feasible?

(b) Can the class of perturbed problems be feasible, but the unperturbed problem infeasible?

(c) Can the class of perturbed problems have a finite lower bound for z, but not the unperturbed?

(d) Can the class of perturbed problems have a lower bound of $-\infty$ for z, but not the unperturbed?

9. (Charnes.) Develop an alternative perturbation procedure based on replacing b_i by $b_i(\varepsilon) = b_i + \sum_j a_{i_j} \varepsilon^j$ for $i = 1, 2, \ldots, m$. Express the selection rules in terms of the full tableau of the regular simplex method.

10. (Unsolved.) It is conjectured that Beale's example has the least number of variables of any for which circling can occur in the simplex algorithm. Is this true? If not, construct an example with the least.

Problems Based on the Lexicographic Method. [Dantzig, Orden, and Wolfe, 1954-1]

11. An m-component vector A is said to be *lexico-positive*, denoted $A \succ 0$ (see § 13-3), if at least one component is non-zero and the first such is positive. The term "lexico" is short for "lexicographically." A vector A is said to be "lexico-greater" than B, written $A \succ B$, if $A - B \succ 0$. The smallest of several vectors will be denoted Lexico-Min. Prove that this lexicographic ordering of vectors is transitive, in other words

$$A \succ B \text{ and } B \succ C \Rightarrow A \succ C$$

12. Instead of perturbing constants, suppose the constants, b_i, in § 9-2-(1), are replaced by vectors

$$b_1^v = [b_1, 1, 0, \ldots, 0] \qquad (b_i \geq 0)$$
$$b_2^v = [b_2, 0, 1, \ldots, 0]$$
$$\cdot$$
$$\cdot$$
$$\cdot$$
$$b_m^v = [b_m, 0, 0, \ldots, 1]$$

where the superscript v denotes "vector."

(a) Show, analogous to § 9-2-(4), that the values of the basic variables on some subsequent iteration are replaced by

$$\bar{b}_i^v = [\bar{b}_i, \beta_{i1}, \beta_{i2}, \ldots, \beta_{im}] \qquad (i = 1, 2, \ldots, m)$$
$$z^v = [\bar{z}_t, \pi_1, \pi_2, \ldots, \pi_m]$$

(b) Show, analogous to § 9-2-(10), that the variable chosen to be dropped is selected so that

$$\bar{b}_r^v / \bar{a}_{rs} = \text{Lexico-Min} \{ \bar{b}_i^v / \bar{a}_{is} \} \succ 0 \qquad (\bar{a}_{is} > 0)$$

where $\bar{b}_i^v/\bar{a}_{is}$ is a vector formed by dividing the components of $\bar{b}_i^v$ by the scalar $\bar{a}_{is}$.

Prove $\bar{b}_i^v > 0$ for all iterations and $z_0^v > z_1^v > z_2^v \ldots \ldots$

13. Define a partial order relation between n-component vectors as follows:

If $x = (\xi_1, \ldots, \xi_n)$ and $y = (\eta_1, \ldots, \eta_n)$, then $x \geq y$ and $y \leq x$ if $\xi_i \geq \eta_i$ for $i = 1, \ldots, n$.

Letting x, y, x_1, y_1, a, denote n-component vectors, prove:

If $x \geq y$ and $y \geq z$, then $x \geq z$;

If $x_1 \geq y_1$ and $x_2 \geq y_2$, then $x_1 + x_2 \geq y_1 + y_2$;

If $x \geq y$, then $\lambda x \geq \lambda y$, where $\lambda \geq 0$ is a scalar and $\lambda x \leq \lambda y$, if $\lambda \leq 0$;

If $x \geq y$ and $a \geq 0$, then $a^T x \geq a^T y$, where a^T is the transpose of a.

REFERENCES

Beale, 1955-1
Charnes, 1952-1
Dantzig, 1951-2, 3, 1959-1
Dantzig, Orden, and Wolfe, 1954-1
Edmondson, 1951-1

Hadley, 1961–2
Hoffman, 1953-1
Nelson, 1957-1
Simonnard and Hadley, 1959-1
Wolfe, 1963-3

CHAPTER 11

VARIANTS OF THE SIMPLEX ALGORITHM

Introduction.

By a *variant* of the simplex method (in this chapter) is meant an algorithm consisting of a sequence of pivot steps in the primal system, but using alternative rules for the selection of the pivot. Historically these variants were developed to take advantage of a situation where an infeasible basic solution of the primal is available. Often in applications, for example, there occurs a set of problems differing from one another only in their constant terms and cost factors. In such cases, it is convenient to omit Phase I and to use the optimal basis of one problem as the initial basis for the next.

Several methods have been proposed for varying the simplex algorithm so as to reduce the number of iterations. This is especially needed for problems involving many equations in order to reduce the cost of computation. It is also needed for problems involving a large number of variables n, for the number of iterations appears to grow proportionally to n.

As an alternative to using the selection rule $\bar{c}_s = \mathrm{Min}\ \bar{c}_j$ one could select $j = s$ such that introducing x_s into the basic set gives the largest decrease in the value of z in the next basic solution. This rule is obviously not practical when using the simplex method with multipliers; see Chapter 9. Even using the standard canonical form, considerably more computations would be required per iteration. It is possible, however, to develop a modification of the canonical form in which the coefficient of the ith basic variable is allowed to be different from unity in the ith equation but $\bar{b}_i = 1$. In this form the selection of s by the steepest descent criterion would require little effort; moreover (by means of a special device), no more effort than that for the standard simplex algorithm would be required to maintain the tableau in proper form from cycle to cycle.

Starting in 1960-1961, a number of investigations have been systematically gathering empirical data on the comparative efficiency of various proposals such as the above. Harold Kuhn of Princeton and Philip Wolfe of RAND have been particularly active. Based on their preliminary findings, criteria independent of the units of the activities or of the items appear to be well worth the additional effort.

An important sub-case occurs when a new problem differs from the original in the constant terms alone. The optimal basis of the first problem will still "price out" optimal for the second (i.e., $\bar{c}_j \geq 0$), but the associated solution may not be feasible. Note, however, that optimality implies that the associated solution of the dual is feasible. For this situation, C. Lemke [1954-1] developed the *Dual-Simplex* algorithm as a variant of the standard primal simplex; see § 11-2. Computationally similar variants, the "Method of Leading Variables," by E. M. L. Beale [1954-1] and "PLP (Parametric Linear Programming)," by W. Orchard-Hays [1956-1], [Orchard-Hays, Cutler, and Judd, 1956-1] were developed. These are subsumed in the *Primal-Dual* method of § 11-4 developed first by Ford and Fulkerson for transportation problems (see Chapter 20), and later extended to the general linear program [Dantzig, Ford, and Fulkerson, 1956-1]. These alterations of the algorithm apply when the old basis still prices out optimally in the new system, and thus constitutes a feasible starting solution for the new dual. In contrast Gass and Saaty [1955-1], in their paper on the parametric objective, studied the case of fixed constant terms and varying cost coefficients.

However, when the problems differ by more than just the constant terms, the old basis may not price out optimal in the new problem, and other methods must be sought. When neither the basic solution nor the dual solution generated by its simplex multipliers remains feasible, the corresponding algorithm is called *composite* [Orchard-Hays, 1954-1 and 1956-1]. The *Self-Dual* algorithm of § 11-3 is an example of this.

11-1. COMPLEMENTARY PRIMAL AND DUAL BASES

Lemke [1954-1] discovered a certain complementarity between bases of the primal and dual systems that made it possible to interpret the simplex algorithm as applied to the dual as a sequence of basis changes in the primal; in this case, however, the associated basic solutions of the primal are not feasible, but the simplex multipliers continue to price out optimal (hence, yield a basic feasible solution to the dual). It is well to understand this complementarity, for it provides a means of easily dualizing a problem without the formality of actually restating it.

It will be convenient to take $x_1, x_2, \ldots, x_m$ as basic variables for the primal problem and to show that $(\pi_1, \pi_2, \ldots, \pi_m)$ and $(\bar{c}_{m+1}, \bar{c}_{m+2}, \ldots, \bar{c}_n)$ constitute a basic feasible solution for the dual. This may be shown clearly by use of a Tucker Diagram, Table 11-1-I. The smaller, bold-line square contains the basis, B, of the primal system, while the larger, double-line square gives the transpose of the dual basis, $\bar{B}$. It may easily be shown (and this is left as an exercise) that the determinant of B has the same absolute value as that of $\bar{B}$, so that if B^{-1} exists, then $\bar{B}^{-1}$ exists. With the aid of Table 11-1-I it is easy to see the correspondences given in Table 11-1-II.

TABLE 11-1-I

TUCKER DIAGRAM OF THE PRIMAL DUAL-SYSTEMS

		Primal			
	Variables	x_1 x_2 ... x_m	x_{m+1} .... x_n	Relation	Constants
	$\bar{c}_1 \geq 0$	1		$\geq$	0
	$\bar{c}_2 \geq 0$	$\quad 1$		$\geq$	0
	·	$\quad\quad 1$		·	·
	·			·	·
	$\bar{c}_{m+1} \geq 0$		1	$\geq$	0
Dual	·			·	·
	·			·	·
	$\bar{c}_n \geq 0$		$\qquad\qquad 1$	$\geq$	0
	π_1	a_{11} a_{12} ... a_{1m}	a_{1m+1} .... a_{1n}	$=$	b_1
	π_2	a_{21} a_{22} ... a_{2m}	a_{2m+1} .... a_{2n}	$=$	b_2
	·	....	....	·	·
	π_m	a_{m1} a_{m2} ... a_{mm}	a_{mm+1} .... a_{mn}	$=$	b_m
	Relation	$=$ $=$ ... $=$	$=$ .... $=$		$\leq$ Max v
	Constants	c_1 c_2 ... c_m	c_{m+1} .... c_n	$\geq$ Min z	

TABLE 11-1-II

PRIMAL-DUAL CORRESPONDENCES

	Primal	Dual
Basis	B	$\bar{B}$
Basic Variables	$x_1, x_2, \ldots, x_m$	$\bar{c}_{m+1}, \ldots, \bar{c}_n;\ \pi_1, \pi_2, \ldots, \pi_m$
Non-Basic Variables	$x_{m+1}, \ldots, x_n$	$\bar{c}_1, \bar{c}_2, \ldots, \bar{c}_m$
Feasibility Condition	$x_i = \bar{b}_i \geq 0 \qquad$ for all i	$\bar{c}_j \geq 0 \qquad$ for all j

	Primal Simplex Method	Dual Simplex Method
Optimality Criterion	$\bar{c}_j \geq 0 \qquad$ for all j	$\bar{b}_i \geq 0 \qquad$ for all i
Introduction Rule (selection of the new basic variable)	if $\bar{c}_s = $ Min $c_j < 0$, then choose x_s (pivot in *column s*)	if $\bar{b}_r = $ Min $\bar{b}_i < 0$, then choose $\bar{c}_r$ (pivot in *row r*)
Representation of the new vector in terms of the basis	$\bar{a}_{1s}, \bar{a}_{2s}, \ldots, \bar{a}_{ms}$	$-\bar{a}_{r,m+1}, -\bar{a}_{r,m+2}, \ldots, -\bar{a}_{r,n};$ $\beta_{r1}, \beta_{r2}, \ldots, \beta_{rm}$
Rejection Rule (choice of the variable to be dropped from basis)	if $\bar{b}_r/\bar{a}_{rs} = \underset{\bar{a}_{is}>0}{\text{Min}}\ b_i/\bar{a}_{is} \geq 0$ drop x_r (pivot in *row r*)	if $\bar{c}_s/-\bar{a}_{rs} = \underset{-\bar{a}_{rj}>0}{\text{Min}}\ \bar{c}_j/-\bar{a}_{rj} \geq 0$ drop $\bar{c}_s$ (pivot in *column s*)
Pivot Element	$\bar{a}_{rs}$	$\bar{a}_{rs}$
Effect on the Objective Function	z decreases	v increases

11-2. THE DUAL SIMPLEX METHOD

The dual simplex operates with the same tableau as the primal method. However, the relative cost factors are nonnegative from iteration to iteration ($\bar{c}_j \geq 0$ instead of $\bar{b}_i \geq 0$). If it also happens that all the $\bar{b}_i$ are nonnegative, the associated solution will be *optimal* as well as feasible. If not, a pivot row r is chosen where $\bar{b}_r = \text{Min } \bar{b}_i < 0$; secondly, the pivot column s, is chosen so that $\bar{c}_s/-\bar{a}_{rs} = \text{Min } \bar{c}_j/-\bar{a}_{rj}$ for $\bar{a}_{rj}$ negative. If all $\bar{a}_{rj}$ are non-negative, it is easy to see that the primal has no feasible solution. Thus, in the dual simplex method, when viewed in terms of the primal variables, one decides first which basic variable to *drop* and then decides which non-basic variable to *introduce*.

EXAMPLE: Suppose a system has been transformed to yield

Cycle 0

$$
(1) \qquad
\begin{aligned}
x_1 \quad\quad\; + 4x_4 - 5x_5 + 7x_6 &= 8 \\
x_2 \quad - 2x_4 + 4x_5 - 2x_6 &= -2 \\
x_3 + \; x_4 - 3x_5 + 2x_6 &= 2 \\
\hline
x_4 + 3x_5 + 2x_6 &= z - 4
\end{aligned}
$$

● ○ ● ★

Since all $\bar{c}_j$, but not all constant terms, are nonnegative, drop the basic variable, x_2, corresponding to $\bar{b}_2 = \text{Min } \bar{b}_i = -2$; and introduce x_4 into the next basic set, since $j = 4$ is determined by the criterion, $\text{Min } \bar{c}_j/-\bar{a}_{2j} = \bar{c}_4/-\bar{a}_{24} = \frac{1}{2}$, for $\bar{a}_{2j} < 0$. After pivoting, the system becomes (2). Since all $\bar{b}_i$ and $\bar{c}_j$ are nonnegative, the basic solution is now optimal.

Cycle 1

$$
(2) \qquad
\begin{aligned}
x_1 + 2x_2 \quad\quad\quad + 3x_5 + 3x_6 &= 4 \\
- \tfrac{1}{2}x_2 \quad + x_4 - 2x_5 + \; x_6 &= 1 \\
+ \tfrac{1}{2}x_2 + x_3 \quad\quad - \; x_5 + \; x_6 &= 1 \\
\hline
+ \tfrac{1}{2}x_2 \quad\quad\quad\quad + 5x_5 + \; x_6 &= z - 5
\end{aligned}
$$

● ● ●

Artificial Variables in the Dual Simplex.

Suppose, for the preceding example, that x_2 and x_3 are artificial; we shall proceed as before; we shall, however, disregard all artificial variables once they drop out of the basic set. Thus, x_2 will be dropped from the system in (2). The basic solution is still not feasible because x_3 is artificial. Conceptually, any artificial basic variable, x_j, whose value is positive in the basic solution, may be replaced by $-x_j' = x_j$, so that the basic solution becomes "infeasible," allowing application of the dual simplex rules.

[243]

It is clear that the algorithm cannot terminate as long as artificial variables with non-zero values remain in the basic solution. It must terminate either with a proof of the primal's infeasibility or with a primal feasible solution whose artificial variables are all zero or dropped.

In practice, it is probably better not to make the formal substitution, $x_j = -x'_j$, for artificial variables of positive value, but to modify the rules of procedure to produce the same effect. Proceeding with the example, however, dropping x_2 from the system and replacing x_3 by $-x'_3$, we have

Cycle 1 (x_2 dropped, $x'_3 = -x_3$ artificial)

(3)

$$x_1 \qquad\quad + 3x_5 + 3x_6 = 4$$
$$+ x_4 - 2x_5 + x_6 = 1$$
$$+ x'_3 \qquad + x_5 - 1x_6 = -1$$

$$\rule{6cm}{0.4pt}$$

$$5x_5 + x_6 = z - 5$$

● ○ ● ★

Cycle 2 (Optimal)

(4)

$$x_1 + 3x'_3 \qquad\quad + 6x_5 \qquad = 1$$
$$+ x'_3 + x_4 - x_5 \qquad = 0$$
$$- x'_3 \qquad - x_5 + x_6 = 1$$

$$\rule{6cm}{0.4pt}$$

$$x'_3 \qquad + 6x_5 \qquad = z - 6$$

● ● ●

As we have pointed out, many problems have a feasible solution to the dual readily available. For example, if the equations are weighted by the multipliers of a previously optimized system having the same matrix of coefficients, a_{ij}, and if the weighted sum is subtracted from the z-equation, the coefficients, c'_j, of the transformed z-equation are nonnegative. Upon augmentation of the new system with artificial variables, the system is (a) in canonical form with respect to the artificial basis, and (b) its relative cost factors, c'_j, are nonnegative. Hence, optimizing via the dual algorithm provides an optimum to the primal system without the usual Phase I.

Even in cases where the minimizing form has a *few* negative coefficients, it would appear expedient to replace each negative c_j by $c'_j = 0$ and then optimize. This will provide a basic feasible solution to the original system (not necessarily optimum) which may then be used with the true values of c_j to initiate the usual Phase II of the simplex process.

EXERCISE: Discuss how to recover the true values of $\bar{c}_j$ in this case.

EXERCISE: Prove that no more than k iterations are required to eliminate k artificial variables from a basic set while maintaining feasibility of the dual.

11-3. A SELF-DUAL PARAMETRIC ALGORITHM

Suppose that neither the basic solution nor its complementary dual is feasible. It is a simple matter to increase all the negative $\bar{b}_i$ and $\bar{c}_j$ to nonnegative values by adding some constant θ to all of them.

The modified problem is now optimal. Next we will consider ways to maintain the feasibility of the primal and dual systems as the constants and cost coefficients are gradually changed toward their original values. Either the primal or the dual choice criterion will be employed, depending upon whether the basic solutions of the dual or the primal become infeasible.

For example, in the canonical system below, the original problem is obtained by setting $\theta = 0$; the associated basic solutions are infeasible for both the primal and dual.

$$
\begin{aligned}
(1) \qquad x_1 \qquad\quad + 2x_4 + 2x_5 \qquad\quad &= 10 \\
x_2 \quad - \quad x_4 + 1x_5 \qquad\quad &= -1 + \theta \\
x_3 + \quad x_4 - 2x_5 \qquad\quad &= -1 + \theta
\end{aligned}
$$

$$
3x_4 + (-3 + \theta)x_5 = z
$$

$$\bullet \quad \bullet \quad \bullet \qquad \star$$

On the other hand, if $\theta \geq 3$, the associated solutions are both feasible. If we start with $\theta = 4$, say, and then let θ approach zero, the associated solutions will remain feasible down to the critical value $\theta = 3$. Just below $\theta = 3$, the primal solution still remains feasible, but the dual solution becomes infeasible since $\bar{c}_3 = -3 + \theta$ is negative. Hence, for θ less than 3 but "very close" to it, we use the *primal* simplex algorithm, introducing x_5 while maintaining the feasibility of both systems. The variable to be dropped is determined from the minimum of the ratios $\bar{b}_i/\bar{a}_{is}$ for $\bar{a}_{is}$ positive. Since

$$\bar{b}_1/\bar{a}_{15} = 5, \qquad \bar{b}_2/\bar{a}_{25} = -1 + \theta$$

in the neighborhood of $\theta = 3$ the second ratio is minimal; thus x_2 is to be dropped from the basic set in the next cycle. The new canonical system is

$$
\begin{aligned}
(2) \qquad x_1 \quad - 2x_2 \qquad + 4x_4 \qquad &= 12 - 2\theta \qquad\qquad (1 \leq \theta \leq 3) \\
x_2 \quad - \quad x_4 + x_5 &= -1 + \theta \\
2x_2 + x_3 - 1x_4 \qquad &= -3 + 3\theta
\end{aligned}
$$

$$
(3 - \theta)x_2 \qquad + \theta x_4 \qquad = z + (3 - \theta)(\theta - 1)
$$

$$\bullet \qquad\qquad \circ \quad \star \quad \bullet$$

which remains feasible in the range, $1 \leq \theta \leq 3$. *Below* the critical value $\theta = 1$, the primal basic solution becomes infeasible. Hence, for θ less than 1 but very close to it, we use the *dual* simplex algorithm to drop x_3 as a basic variable and maintain the feasibility of both systems. The variable to be introduced is given by the minimum of the ratios $\bar{c}_j/-\bar{a}_{3j}$ for $\bar{a}_{3j}$ negative;

in this case, the only variable with a negative coefficient is x_4. Pivoting, we obtain

$$(3) \quad x_1 \; + 6x_2 + 4x_3 \qquad\qquad\quad = 0 + 10\theta \qquad\qquad (0 \le \theta \le 1)$$
$$- \; x_2 - \; x_3 \qquad + x_5 = 2 - 2\theta$$
$$- 2x_2 - \; x_3 + x_4 \qquad = 3 - 3\theta$$

$$(\theta + 3)x_2 + \theta x_3 \qquad\qquad\quad = z + (3 - \theta)(\theta - 1) + \theta(3\theta - 3)$$

which is feasible for both the primal and dual systems at $\theta = 0$. Hence, the *optimal* solution is obtained by setting $\theta = 0$.

In general, it is not necessary to add the same parameter, θ, to all of the negative constants, $\bar{b}_i$ and $\bar{c}_j$, as was done in (1). Several different parameters could be added and each allowed *separately* to tend toward zero. Either way, the net result is the successive application of either the primal or dual simplex rules to change the basis.

How can one be certain that such a process will terminate in a finite number of steps? To answer this, we prove two theorems for the case of a single parameter, θ. First, we note that the values of a basic variable are linear functions of θ, so that, clearly, when a variable is nonnegative for both $\theta = \theta_1$ and $\theta = \theta_2$, then it is nonnegative throughout the interval $\theta_1 \le \theta \le \theta_2$; therefore

THEOREM 1: *It is not possible to have the same basis feasible in the primal and dual for two values of θ, with $\theta_1 < \theta_2$, unless it is also feasible for all values in the range, $\theta_1 \le \theta \le \theta_2$.*

Second, note that, if a change to basis B permits at some critical value $\theta = \theta_1$ a positive (non-zero) decrease in θ, this B is not a repeat of an earlier basis associated with some $\theta_2 > \theta_1$ because at the critical value of θ_1 where the basis change occurred, B would give an infeasible basic solution just above θ_1. Hence, also,

THEOREM 2: *If each change in basis is accompanied by a positive decrease in θ, there can only be a finite number of iterations.*

THEOREM 3: *If there is only one degeneracy in the primal and dual solutions before and after pivoting at a critical value of θ, there will be a positive decrease in θ.*

The latter theorem is due to Gass and Saaty [1955-1] for the case of degeneracy in the *dual* basic solution and to Orchard-Hays [1956-1] for degeneracy in the *primal*. If we prove one of them, the other will follow by duality. Suppose that, corresponding to x_s at a critical value of $\theta = \theta_0$, we have $\bar{c}_s = k(\theta - \theta_0) = \varepsilon$; however, for all *other* non-basic x_j, let $\bar{c}_j$ be expressed linearly in ε by $\bar{c}_j = \alpha_j + \varepsilon\beta_j$ where, by hypothesis, α_j is *positive* (not zero) for $j \ne s$. Also, assume that, for $\varepsilon = 0$, the primal solution is *nondegenerate* before and after x_s displaces some variable, x_{j_r}, in the basic set (actually, we need only require that the basic solution of the primal remain feasible for some *positive* decrease of ε). Under these conditions the new values of the relative cost factors $\bar{c}_j^*$ will be

(4)
$$\bar{c}_j^* = \bar{c}_j - (\bar{a}_{rj}/\bar{a}_{rs})\varepsilon = \alpha_j + [\beta_j - \bar{a}_{rj}/\bar{a}_{rs}]\varepsilon$$
$$\bar{c}_{j_r}^* = -(1/\bar{a}_{rs})\varepsilon$$

Since α_j is positive for all non-basic x_j except x_s, there is a range of values, $\varepsilon_0 < \varepsilon < 0$, with $\varepsilon_0 < 0$, for which $\bar{c}_j^*$ remains positive. In this range $c_{j_r}^* > 0$, and the theorem follows.

THEOREM 4: *If a feasible solution to the primal and dual systems exists for* $\theta = \theta_0$ *and* $\theta = 0$, *then feasible solutions exist for all* θ *in the interval* $0 \leq \theta \leq \theta_0$.

EXERCISE: Prove Theorem 4. This theorem also implies that the solution set generated by all vectors of constant terms, b_i, and cost terms, c_j, for which both the primal and dual problems remain feasible simultaneously, is a convex polyhedron. Prove this too.

11-4. THE PRIMAL-DUAL ALGORITHM

Experiments indicate that the "primal-dual" technique, developed by Fulkerson and Ford (Chapter 20) is very efficient for solving distribution problems. It is closely related to the work of H. Kuhn, who developed a special routine for solving assignment problems called the "Hungarian Method," based on investigations by the Hungarian mathematician Egerváry [1931-1]; see [Kuhn, 1955-1]. Our purpose is to extend this process to the solution of general linear programming problems. As stated here, it is a simplex variant whose number of iterations is quite often fewer than that required by the dual simplex [Dantzig, Ford, and Fulkerson, 1956-1].

Any feasible solution to the dual system may be used to initiate the proposed method. Associated with the dual solution is a *restricted primal* requiring optimization. When the solution of the restricted primal problem has been accomplished, an improved solution to the dual system can be obtained. This in turn gives rise to a *new* restricted primal to be optimized. After a finite number of improvements, an optimal solution is obtained for the original, unrestricted problem.

What markedly distinguishes the Ford-Fulkerson algorithm for distribution problems from the more general case discussed here is that the former method uses a method of optimization of the restricted primal, which appears to be more efficient than the simplex process, whereas the generalization uses the simplex process because it appears to be the most efficient one available. [According to R. Gomory, the former is actually a condensed sequence of simplex pivot steps.]

As in the preceding sections, the entire process may be considered to be a way of starting with an infeasible basic solution and using a feasible solution to the dual already at hand to *decrease the infeasibility form* of the primal in such a manner that, when a feasible basic solution is obtained, it will already be optimal.

The initial canonical form for the primal-dual algorithm is the same as for Phase I of the regular simplex method; see § 5-2-(7). Let

$$(1) \qquad
\begin{aligned}
a_{11} x_1 + \ldots + a_{1n} x_n + x_{n+1} &= b_1 \\
&\cdots\cdots\cdots \\
a_{m1} x_1 + \ldots + a_{mn} x_n \qquad\qquad + x_{n+m} &= b_m \\
d_1 x_1 + \ldots + d_n x_n &= w - w_0 \\
c_1 x_1 + \ldots + c_n x_n &= z - z_0
\end{aligned}$$

where b_i are made nonnegative before insertion of artificial variables, and

$$(2) \qquad\qquad d_j = - \sum_i a_{ij}, \text{ and } w_0 = \sum_i b_i$$

so that the sum of the first $m + 1$ equations yields

$$(3) \qquad\qquad x_{n+1} + x_{n+2} + \ldots + x_{n+m} = w$$

As before, it is *assumed* that a feasible solution to the dual is available and that, by applying the associated multipliers and summing, *the c_j have been adjusted before augmentation by artificial variables*, so that now

$$(4) \qquad\qquad c_j \geq 0 \qquad\qquad \text{for } j = 1, 2, \ldots, n$$

The problem is to find $x_j \geq 0$, $w = 0$, and Min z satisfying (1).

Suppose that on cycle t, the tableau has the format of Table 11-4-I

TABLE 11-4-I

TABLEAU OF THE PRIMAL-DUAL ALGORITHM

Cycle t

Basis									Constants	π	σ
x_1 $\ldots$ x_q	x_{q+1} $\ldots$ x_m	x_{m+1}	$\ldots$	x_{m+p}	x_{m+p+1}	$\ldots$	x_{n+q}				
1		$\bar{a}_{1,m+1}$	$\ldots$	$\bar{a}_{1,m+p}$	$\ldots\ldots\ldots$		$\bar{a}_{1n+q}$	$b_1 \geq 0$	π_1	σ_1
. 1								.	.	.
. 1		.		.	.			.	.	.
.		.		.	.			.	.	.
	1	$\bar{a}_{m,m+1}$	$\ldots$	$\bar{a}_{m,m+p}$	$\ldots\ldots\ldots$		$\bar{a}_{m,n+q}$	$b_m \geq 0$	π_m	σ_m
0 $\ldots$ 0	0 $\ldots$ 0	d_{m+1}	$\ldots$	d_{m+p}	d_{m+p+1}	$\ldots$	d_{n+q}	$w - \bar{w}_0$		
* $\ldots$ *	0 $\ldots$ 0	0	$\ldots$	0	$\bar{c}_{m+p+1}$	$\ldots$	$\bar{c}_{n+q}$	$z - z_0$		
Artificial		$\bar{c}_j = 0$			$\bar{c}_j > 0$					
	Restricted primal									

after relabeling and rearrangement of variables. Artificial variables not in the basic set are dropped from the system. We remark that

(a) The associated primal solution, including artificial variables, is feasible; $\bar{b}_i \geq 0$.

(b) The multipliers, σ, *are* simplex multipliers of the basis relative to the infeasibility form and generate $\bar{d}_j$.

(c) The multipliers, π, are *not* the simplex multipliers of the basis.

(d) The multipliers π constitute a feasible solution to the dual *excluding* artificial x_j and hence generate $\bar{c}_j \geq 0$.

(e) The values of $\bar{c}_j$ for artificial basic x_j may have either sign and may be omitted; otherwise $\bar{c}_j = 0$ for x_j basic.

THEOREM 1: *If $\bar{w}_0 = 0$, then the basic solution is optimal.*

When $\bar{w}_0 = 0$, the artificial variables all have zero values in the basic solution. Upon dropping them, the feasible solution has $\bar{c}_j$ equal to zero for x_j positive, which fulfills the condition for optimality.

Step 1: Minimizing Infeasibility of the Restricted Primal. At the start of cycle t, it is assumed that there are one or more non-basic x_j whose $\bar{c}_j = 0$. These x_j, together with the basic variables, constitute the *restricted primal* problem. Using only these variables for pivot choice, the simplex algorithm is applied to minimize w. Usually artificial variables are dropped from the system when they become non-basic. During this subroutine, the values of the multipliers, π_i, are not modified. The simplex multipliers, σ_i, change, of course, at each iteration until w is "minimized," that is, until $\bar{d}_j$ is nonnegative for each x_j of the *restricted primal*.

Step 2: (a) If $\bar{w}_0 = 0$, terminate—the basic solution is feasible and minimal; (b) if $\bar{w}_0 > 0$ and all $\bar{d}_j \geq 0$ $(j = 1, 2, \ldots, n)$, terminate—no primal feasible solution exists. Otherwise, take Step 3.

Step 3: Improving the Dual Solution (Finding a New Restricted Primal). An improved solution of the dual and a new restricted primal is found by using new multipliers,

$$(5) \qquad\qquad \pi_i^* = \pi_i + k\sigma_i \qquad\qquad (i = 1, 2, \ldots, m)$$

which generate nonnegative cost factors,

$$(6) \qquad\qquad \bar{c}_j^* = \bar{c}_j + k\bar{d}_j$$

where k is a positive number defined by

$$(7) \qquad\qquad k = \bar{c}_s/(-\bar{d}_s) = \operatorname*{Min}_{d_j < 0} \bar{c}_j/(-\bar{d}_j) > 0$$

The new restricted primal is obtained by using all the basic variables and those non-basic variables whose cost factors, $\bar{c}_j^*$, are zero. This completes the steps of the algorithm.

It should be noted under Step 3 that at least one new variable appears in the restricted primal, namely, x_s, as determined by (7). Note also that $\bar{d}_s < 0$, so that at least one iteration must take place before w is minimized within the new restricted primal. Assuming nondegeneracy, each iteration will decrease infeasibility; hence, no basis can be repeated, and an optimal solution will be obtained in a finite number of iterations.

It should also be noted under Step 2b, that, if the infeasibility factors, $\bar{d}_j$, are all nonnegative, *but $\bar{w}_0$ is still positive*, then (5) and (6) constitute a class of feasible solutions to the dual whose objective,

$$(8) \qquad\qquad v = \bar{z}_0 + k\bar{w}_0$$

tends to $+\infty$ with increasing k. At the same time, the nonnegativity of *all* the $\bar{d}_j$ and $\bar{w}_0 > 0$ implies that Min w is positive, so that no feasible solutions to the primal exist.

The Initial Restricted Primal.

At first glance it may appear that (1) is not in proper form to initiate the algorithm if *all c_j* are positive. However, if $c_j > 0$ for $j = 1, 2, \ldots, n$, let $\pi = 0$ and view the basic set of artificials as the full set of variables of the restricted primal with multipliers $\sigma = (1, 1, \ldots, 1)$. The algorithm, in this case, is initiated with the finding of an improved dual solution by means of Step 3.

To illustrate the procedure, we consider the problem of finding $x_1 \geq 0$, $x_2 \geq 0, \ldots, x_5 \geq 0$, Min z, and artificial variables, $x_6 = x_7 = x_8 = w = 0$, satisfying

$$(9) \qquad \begin{aligned} x_1 + 4x_2 - 5x_3 + 7x_4 - 4x_5 + x_6 &= 8 \\ -4x_2 + 4x_3 - 4x_4 + 4x_5 + x_7 &= 2 \\ x_2 - 3x_3 + 4x_4 - 2x_5 + x_8 &= 2 \\ -x_1 - x_2 + 4x_3 - 7x_4 + 2x_5 &= w - 12 \\ x_1 + 4x_2 + 8x_3 + 8x_4 + 23x_5 &= z \end{aligned}$$

The w-equation is generated in a manner such that the sum of the first four equations is

$$(10) \qquad\qquad x_6 + x_7 + x_8 = w$$

The first step is to determine the largest number, k, such that $z + kw$ has all its coefficients nonnegative. In this case, $k = 1$ according to (7), so that by simply adding the z and w equations, we obtain (11); for convenience, we have dropped the letter w, since all we are really doing is adding to the z-equation a linear combination of the original equations without the artificial variables.

$$(11) \qquad\qquad 0x_1 + 3x_2 + 12x_3 + x_4 + 25x_5 = z - 12$$

The first *restricted primal* is obtained by choosing our variables *only* among x_6, x_7, x_8; and x_1 (since the first three are already basic and since only x_1 has a relative cost factor of zero in (11)); we now proceed to minimize w.

[250]

Cycle 0 (First Restricted Primal: $(x_6, x_7, x_8; x_1)$)

(12)
$$
\begin{aligned}
x_1 + 4x_2 - 5x_3 + 7x_4 - 4x_5 + x_6 &= 8 \\
-4x_2 + 4x_3 - 4x_4 + 4x_5 \quad\quad\ + x_7 &= 2 \\
x_2 - 3x_3 + 4x_4 - 2x_5 \quad\quad\quad\quad\ + x_8 &= 2 \\
-x_1 - x_2 + 4x_3 - 7x_4 + 2x_5 \quad\quad\quad &= w - 12
\end{aligned}
$$

Pivoting on x_1 and dropping x_6 from further consideration (since it is artificial), we obtain the next cycle, (13). The value of w has been minimized on the restricted primal $(x_6, x_7, x_8; x_1)$ since all the corresponding d_j are nonnegative. This terminates our concern with the first restricted primal.

(13)   Cycle 1 $\begin{bmatrix} \text{First Restricted Primal, } (x_6, x_7, x_8; x_1), \text{ is terminated} \\ \text{Second Restricted Primal, } (x_1, x_7, x_8; x_3), \text{ is initiated} \end{bmatrix}$

$$
\begin{aligned}
x_1 + 4x_2 - 5x_3 + 7x_4 - 4x_5 \quad\quad &= 8 \\
-4x_2 + 4x_3 - 4x_4 + 4x_5 + x_7 &= 2 \\
x_2 - 3x_3 + 4x_4 - 2x_5 \quad\ + x_8 &= 2 \\
+ 3x_2 - x_3 \quad\quad\quad - 2x_5 \quad\quad &= w - 4
\end{aligned}
$$

To determine the new restricted primal, we adjust the z-equation again by determining the largest value of k such that $z + kw$, for z and w as given in (11) and (13), has all its coefficients nonnegative. We find that $k = 12$ is such a value, so that the new cost equation (upon omitting artificial variables as explained above) is

(14)
$$0x_1 + 39x_2 + 0x_3 + x_4 + x_5 = z - 60$$

Since $\bar{c}_3 = 0$ in this equation, the variables of the new restricted primal are x_1, x_7, x_8; and x_3. Introducing x_3 and dropping x_7 from the basic set (and from the system because it is artificial), we have (15). We have now minimized w for the restricted primal, $(x_1, x_7, x_8; x_3)$.

(15)   Cycle 2 $\begin{bmatrix} \text{Second Restricted Primal, } (x_1, x_7, x_8; x_3), \text{ is terminated} \\ \text{Third Restricted Primal, } (x_1, x_3, x_8; x_4, x_5), \text{ is initiated} \end{bmatrix}$

$$
\begin{aligned}
x_1 - x_2 \quad\quad + 2x_4 + x_5 \quad\quad &= 10\tfrac{1}{2} \\
- x_2 + x_3 - x_4 + x_5 \quad\quad &= \tfrac{1}{2} \\
- 2x_2 \quad\quad + 1x_4 + x_5 + x_8 &= 3\tfrac{1}{2} \\
+ 2x_2 \quad\quad\quad - x_4 - x_5 \quad\quad &= w - 3\tfrac{1}{2}
\end{aligned}
$$

Once more we are ready to adjust the z-equation, so as to determine a new restricted primal, this time by determining the largest value of k such that $z + kw$, for z and w as given in (14) and (15), has nonnegative coefficients. This value turns out to be $k = 1$, giving (upon dropping of artificial variables)

(16)
$$0x_1 + 41x_2 + 0x_3 + 0x_4 + 0x_5 = z - 63\tfrac{1}{2}$$

[251]

The corresponding restricted primal is $(x_1, x_3, x_8; x_4, x_5)$, since both x_4 and x_5 have zero cost factors. Incidentally, we see that, except for x_2, all the original variables have been brought back into the problem.

To minimize w for the new restricted primal, we now introduce x_4 into the basic set, obtaining the system

Cycle 3 (Optimal)

$$(17) \qquad \begin{aligned} x_1 + 3x_2 \qquad\qquad - \ x_5 &= 3\tfrac{1}{2} \\ -\ 3x_2 + \ x_3 \qquad + 2x_5 &= 4 \\ -\ 2x_2 \qquad\quad + \ x_4 + \ x_5 &= 3\tfrac{1}{2} \\ 0x_1 + 0x_2 + 0x_3 + 0x_4 + 0x_5 &= w - 0 \end{aligned}$$

whose associated solution, $(3\tfrac{1}{2}, 0, 4, 3\tfrac{1}{2}, 0)$, and $w = 0$ is feasible for the original *unrestricted* problem. Since the coefficients of the z-equation have been kept nonnegative throughout our procedure, this solution is evidently minimal.

Note in (15) that if x_5 had been introduced instead of x_4, it would have taken *two* iterations to minimize w, since x_3 would have dropped out instead of x_8.

The minimum value of z, $63\tfrac{1}{2}$, is obtained from (16).

11-5. AN ALTERNATIVE CRITERION FOR PHASE I

This criterion, first suggested informally by H. Markowitz, has many points in common with the primal-dual algorithm [Dantzig, Ford, and Fulkerson, 1956-1] treated in the last section and with the dual algorithm [Lemke, 1954-1].

Like the standard simplex, this method uses basic feasible solutions but changes the criterion for choice of new basic variables in Phase I. The standard criterion selects x_s in such a way that w, which measures primal infeasibility, decreases at the maximum rate when x_s is increased. Since this criterion is not influenced by the objective form, z, the feasible solution provided by Phase I may be quite different from the one required to minimize z. To correct this, *it is proposed that x_j be chosen in such a way that there is a maximum decrease (least increase) of the objective form per unit decrease of the infeasibility form.*

For some iteration, let the canonical tableau be the same as (3). The variables $x_1, x_2, \ldots, x_m$, some of which will be artificial, are assumed by rearrangement and relabeling to constitute the basic set. The standard criterion for Phase I chooses s in such a way that

$$(1) \qquad\qquad \bar{d}_s = \text{Min } \bar{d}_j < 0$$

Instead, the present proposal is to choose $j = s$ such that

$$(2) \qquad\qquad \bar{c}_s/(-\bar{d}_s) = \underset{\bar{d}_j < 0}{\text{Min }} \bar{c}_j/(-\bar{d}_j) \qquad\qquad (\bar{d}_s < 0)$$

with no other change in the algorithm. In the event that several j minimize this ratio, the choice is made among those tied by the standard criterion, (1). For Phase II, s is chosen in the usual manner (i.e., such that $\bar{c}_s = \text{Min } \bar{c}_j < 0$).

(3)

x_1	x_2	. . .	x_m	x_{m+1} . . .	x_n	. . .	x_{n+m}	Constants
1				$\bar{a}_{1,m+1}$ . . .	$\bar{a}_{1,n}$	. . .	$\bar{a}_{1,n+m}$	$\bar{b}_1$
	1			$\bar{a}_{2,m+1}$ . . .	$\bar{a}_{2,n}$	. . .	$\bar{a}_{2,n+m}$	$\bar{b}_2$
		.		.	.		.	.
		.		.	.		.	.
			.	.	.		.	.
			1	$\bar{a}_{m,m+1}$ . . .	$\bar{a}_{m,n}$	. . .	$\bar{a}_{m,n+m}$	$\bar{b}_m$
				$\bar{c}_{m+1}$ . . .	$\bar{c}_n$	. . .	$\bar{c}_{n+m}$	$z - z_0$
				d_{m+1} . . .	d_n	. . .	d_{n+m}	$w - w_0$

11-6. PROBLEMS

1. Review the following results from § 6-3:

   (a) Show that if a linear programming problem has a finite lower bound for some given set of constant terms, then it has a finite lower bound for *any* set of constant terms, providing a feasible solution exists.

   (b) Suppose that a linear programming problem is augmented with artificial variables whose sum is bounded by a constant (not necessarily zero). If z is minimized, allowing the artificial variables to enter the basic set with nonnegative value, prove that the minimum is finite or infinite, depending on whether Min z of the *original* problem is finite or infinite.

2. Show that no basis can re-occur in the parametric linear programming procedure. What assumption is made about degeneracy?

3. Develop lexicographic (perturbation) schemes for the dual simplex; for the self-dual parametric algorithm. What is a lexicographic scheme for the primal-dual algorithm and the Phase I alternative of Markowitz?

4. Re-solve the blending problem illustrated in § 5-2 (see Table 5-2-V), applying the different variants discussed in this chapter.

5. Show that, if no artificial variables remain in the basic set using the primal-dual algorithm, the solution is optimal.

REFERENCES

Beale, 1954-1
Dantzig, 1954-1, 2
Dantzig, Ford, and Fulkerson, 1956-1
Egerváry, 1931-1
Gass and Saaty, 1955-1
Graves, 1963-1

Gunther, 1955-1
Kuhn, 1955-1
Lemke, 1954-1
Orchard-Hays, 1954-1, 1956-1
Orchard-Hays, Cutler, and Judd, 1956-1
Orden, 1952-1

Wolfe and Cutler, 1963-1

CHAPTER 12

THE PRICE CONCEPT IN LINEAR PROGRAMMING

In previous chapters we have frequently referred to the simplex multipliers as "prices." In this chapter, we shall discuss economic examples, which not only show how this viewpoint of the multipliers arises naturally, but also how it permits an economic interpretation of the simplex method itself. As we have seen, these multipliers are themselves the solution to a second linear programming problem which is called the *dual* of the first. The first example shows how a price can arise in a situation where there are no prices to begin with; the second and third examples, in § 12-2, show how the dual system of competitive prices for new items arises "naturally" in a situation where prices for old products and methods already exist. A fuller treatment of the relation of linear programming to economic theory can be found in several excellent books; see references at the end of this chapter.

12-1. THE PRICE MECHANISM OF THE SIMPLEX METHOD

The Manager of the Machine Tool Plant.[1]

Consider the problem of a manager of a machine tool plant, say, in an economy which has just been socialized. The central planners have allocated to this manager *input* quantities $+b_1, \ldots, +b_k$ of materials which we designate by $1, \ldots, k$ and have instructed this manager to produce *output* quantities $-b_{k+1}, \ldots, -b_m$ of the machine tools numbered $k+1$ through m (the $b_{k+1}, \ldots, b_m$, being outputs, are negative numbers by our conventions). The planners further direct the manager that he shall use as little labor as possible to meet his required production goals and that he must pay the workers with labor certificates, one certificate for each hour of labor. The central planners have declared old prices of items to be of no use and have not provided any new prices to the manager to guide him.

The manager has at his disposal many production activities, say, n of them, each of which he can describe by a column vector, $\langle a_{1j}, \ldots, a_{mj} \rangle$. If the jth process inputs a_{ij} units of the ith item per unit level of operation, a_{ij} is positive. If, on the other hand, the jth process outputs a_{ij} units of item i per unit level of operation, a_{ij} is negative. The jth process also requires c_j

---

[1] This subsection was contributed by C. Almon, Jr.

units of labor per unit level of operation. The manager's problem then is to find levels of operation for all the processes, $x_1, \ldots, x_n$, which satisfy

$$(1) \qquad \begin{aligned} a_{11} x_1 + a_{12} x_2 + \ldots + a_{1n} x_n &= b_1 \\ a_{21} x_1 + a_{22} x_2 + \ldots + a_{2n} x_n &= b_2 \\ \cdots\cdots\cdots\cdots\cdots\cdots\cdots\cdots\cdots \\ a_{m1} x_1 + a_{m2} x_2 + \ldots + a_{mn} x_n &= b_m \end{aligned}$$

and minimize the total amount of labor used,

$$c_1 x_1 + c_2 x_2 + \ldots + c_n x_n = z \text{ (Min)}$$

The x's must, of course, be nonnegative. In matrix notation $Ax = b$, $cx = z$.

The manager knows of m old reliable processes, namely $1, \ldots, m$, with which he is sure he can produce the required outputs with the given inputs though the labor requirements may be considerable. Thus, he knows he can find nonnegative $x_1, \ldots, x_m$, such that

$$(2) \qquad \begin{aligned} a_{11} x_1 + a_{12} x_2 + \ldots + a_{1m} x_m &= b_1 \\ a_{21} x_1 + a_{22} x_2 + \ldots + a_{2m} x_m &= b_2 \\ \cdots\cdots\cdots\cdots\cdots\cdots\cdots\cdots\cdots \\ a_{m1} x_1 + a_{m2} x_2 + \ldots + a_{mm} x_m &= b_m \end{aligned}$$

or, in matrix notation, $Bx = b$. We shall assume that B is a feasible basis for (1).

This manager has learned, however, that his workers are prone to be extravagant with materials, using far more inputs than are called for in (1). Unless he can keep this tendency in check, he knows he will fail to meet his quotas. Formerly, he deducted the cost of the extra materials from the workers' wages; but now that all prices have been swept away, he lacks a common denominator for materials and wages. Suddenly, in a moment of genius, it occurs to him that he can make up his own prices in terms of labor certificates, charge the operators of each process for the materials they use, credit them for their products, and give them the difference as their pay. Being a fair man, he wants to set prices such that the efficient workers can take home a certificate for each hour worked. That is, he wants to set product and raw material prices $\pi_1, \ldots, \pi_m$, such that the net yield on a unit level of each basic activity j is equal to the amount of labor c_j which it requires:

$$(3) \qquad \begin{aligned} \pi_1 a_{11} + \pi_2 a_{21} + \ldots + \pi_m a_{m1} &= c_1 \\ \pi_1 a_{12} + \pi_2 a_{22} + \ldots + \pi_m a_{m2} &= c_2 \\ \cdots\cdots\cdots\cdots\cdots\cdots\cdots\cdots\cdots \\ \pi_1 a_{1m} + \pi_2 a_{2m} + \ldots + \pi_m a_{mm} &= c_m \end{aligned}$$

or, using matrix notation,

$$\pi B = c$$

where π and c are row vectors.

The manager now proceeds to solve (2) for x by finding B^{-1} and setting

$$x = B^{-1}b = \bar{b}$$

Turning to (3), he notes that the solution is almost at hand, for

$$\pi = cB^{-1}$$

Common sense tells the manager that by using his pricing device he would have to pay out exactly as many labor certificates as he would if he paid the labor by the hour and all labor worked efficiently. Indeed, this is easily proved since the total cost using his calculated prices for all activities is $\pi b = cB^{-1}b = cx$, where $c\bar{x}$ is the cost of paying wages directly.

The manager harbors one qualm about his pricing device, however. He remembers that there are other processes besides the m he is planning to use and suspects that among the remainder there may be some for which his pricing device would require him to pay

(4) $$c'_j = \pi_1 a_{1j} + \pi_2 a_{2j} + \ldots + \pi_m a_{mj}$$

which is greater than the direct wages c_j. If such a process comes to the attention of the workers, they will see that by using it they can, if they work efficiently, get more than one labor certificate for one hour's work. The wily men will then try to substitute these processes in such a way as not to affect the material inputs, yet achieve the same outputs. If they can do so, they will pocket excess wages, and before long, the secret will be out that he is paying for labor not performed. On looking over the list of processes in (1), the manager finds several for which the inequality $c'_j > c_j$ holds. Denoting the excess wages of the jth process by $\bar{c}_j$,

$$\bar{c}_j = c_j - (\pi_1 a_{1j} + \pi_2 a_{2j} + \ldots + \pi_m a_{mj})$$

the manager singles out process s, the one offering the most excess wages:

(5) $$\bar{c}_s = \text{Min } \bar{c}_j < 0$$

Before devising repressive measures to keep the workers from using processes that yield excess wages, the manager, a meditative sort of fellow, pauses to reflect on the meaning of these excess wages. Having always had a bent for mathematics, he soon discovers a relation which, mathematically, we express by saying that the vector of coefficients $\bar{a}_{ij}$, for any activity j in the canonical form, can be used as weights to form a linear combination of the *original* vectors of the basic activities, which has the *same* input and output coefficients as that of activity j for all items, except possibly the cost item. In particular, he finds that he can represent activity s, the one yielding the most excess wages, as a linear combination of his "old reliables" as follows:

$$(6) \quad \begin{bmatrix} a_{11} \\ a_{21} \\ \cdot \\ \cdot \\ \cdot \\ a_{m1} \end{bmatrix} \bar{a}_{1s} + \begin{bmatrix} a_{12} \\ a_{22} \\ \cdot \\ \cdot \\ \cdot \\ a_{m2} \end{bmatrix} \bar{a}_{2s} + \ldots \begin{bmatrix} a_{1m} \\ a_{2m} \\ \cdot \\ \cdot \\ \cdot \\ a_{mm} \end{bmatrix} \bar{a}_{ms} = \begin{bmatrix} a_{1s} \\ a_{2s} \\ \cdot \\ \cdot \\ \cdot \\ a_{ms} \end{bmatrix}$$

where $\bar{a}_{is}$ are the coefficients of x_s in the canonical form. In words, (6) tells him that x_s units of activity s can be *simulated* by a combination of $\bar{a}_{1s}x_s$, $\bar{a}_{2s}x_s$, . . ., $\bar{a}_{ms}x_s$ units of the basic set of activities (1, 2, . . ., m). Thus, if the workers introduce x_s units of activity s, the levels of the basic activities must be *adjusted* by these amounts (up or down, depending on sign) if the material constraints and output quotas are to remain satisfied. Now the labor cost of simulating one unit of activity s by the m old reliables is

$$c_1\bar{a}_{1s} + c_2\bar{a}_{2s} + \ldots + c_m\bar{a}_{ms}$$

This amount is precisely what the manager would pay for the various inputs and outputs of one unit of the real activity s if he were to use the prices π_i. For, considering the vector equation (6) as m equations and multiplying the first equation through by π_1, the second by π_2, etc., and summing, one obtains immediately from (3)

$$(7) \quad c_1\bar{a}_{1s} + c_2\bar{a}_{2s} + \ldots + c_m\bar{a}_{ms} = \pi_1a_{1s} + \pi_2a_{2s} + \ldots + \pi_ma_{ms}$$

It is now readily shown that the fact that the process s yields excess wages means to the manager that it takes less labor to operate s directly than to simulate it with the m old activities. This is clear from (4), (5), and (7), which yield

$$(8) \quad c_1\bar{a}_{1s} + \ldots + c_r\bar{a}_{rs} + \ldots + c_m\bar{a}_{ms} > c_s$$

Hence, he reasons, s must be in a sense more efficient than at least one of these old processes. Recalling that the planners instructed him to use as little labor as possible, the manager decides to use activity s in place of one of the original m. He soon discovers that if he wishes to avoid the non-sensical situation of planning to use some activity at a negative level, the process r to be replaced by process s must be chosen, as we have seen in § 5-1-(18), so that

$$\bar{b}_r/\bar{a}_{rs} = \text{Min } \bar{b}_i/\bar{a}_{is} \qquad (\bar{a}_{is}, \bar{a}_{rs} > 0)$$

Because $\bar{a}_{rs} > 0$, it follows from (8) that

$$(9) \quad \{(c_1\bar{a}_{1s} + \ldots + c_{r-1}\bar{a}_{r-1,s} + c_{r+1,s}\bar{a}_{r+1,s} + \ldots \\ + c_m\bar{a}_{ms} - c_s)/(-\bar{a}_{rs})\} < c_r$$

The coefficients of c_1, c_2, . . ., c_s, . . ., c_m in (9) are precisely the weights required to simulate activity r out of the activities in the new basis, as can be seen by re-solving (6) for column r in terms of the others. But, e.g.,

$c_1 \bar{a}_{1s}/-\bar{a}_{rs}$ is the labor cost of the first activity in the simulation of activity r, so that the left-hand side of (9) represents the total labor cost of simulating a unit level of activity r by the activities in the new basis, while c_r is of course the labor cost of one unit of the real activity r. Hence (9) shows that activity r is indeed less efficient in its use of labor than those in the new basis.

In summary, the manager now knows that, if there exist processes for which his pricing device yields more labor certificates than are actually required, then he can substitute one of these processes for one in the original set and thereby bring about a more efficient use of labor. Since the planners instructed him to use as little labor as possible, it is clearly wise for him to plan production using activity s instead of one of the m he had originally intended to use, to readjust the levels of use of the remaining ones, and to change the prices, so that none of the processes that will then be in use gives excess wages.

Having learned this lesson, the manager proceeds again to look for processes offering excess wages, to put into operation the worst offender, to readjust prices, to look for excess wages, and so on until he finds a set of prices π^0 under which no process offers excess wages. Fortunately for him, it turns out (as we know) that in a finite number of steps he will find such a set of prices.

Let us pause for a moment to consider the meaning of one of these prices, say π_i. Suppose we introduce into the manager's (A) matrix equation (1), a fictitious activity which consists simply of increasing his allotment of item i if $b_i > 0$ or of decreasing his quota on i if $b_i < 0$. Such an activity will be represented by a column which has all zeros except for a one in the ith row. Thus the labor cost of simulating this activity with those of the final basis is, by (4), precisely π_i. Thus, π_i is the *labor value*, the labor which can be replaced by one additional unit of item i.

The manager has now achieved his objective of finding a set of prices to charge for raw materials and to pay for finished goods which will keep his workers from wasting inputs and yet offer no possibilities for excess wages. But he now begins to wonder if he is truly safe from the planners' criticism for the amount of labor he uses. He begins by specifying explicitly what he intends to do. His operating plan consists of a set of activity levels $x^o = (x_1^o, x_2^o, \ldots, x_n^o)$ satisfying

(10)
$$Ax^o = b \qquad\qquad (x_j^o \geq 0)$$
$$cx^o = z^o$$

a set of prices $\pi^o = (\pi_1^o, \pi_2^o, \ldots, \pi_m^o)$, and, for each activity, an excess labor cost

(11)
$$\bar{c}_j^o = c_j - \sum_{i=1}^{m} a_{ij}\pi_i^o \geq 0$$

with the property that,

$$(12) \qquad \text{if} \quad \bar{c}_j^o = c_j - \sum_{i=1}^{m} \pi_i^o a_{ij} > 0, \qquad \text{then } x_j^o = 0$$

We shall now prove that the manager's operating plan has minimized his labor costs. Writing $\bar{c}^o = (c - \pi^o A) = (\bar{c}_1^o, \bar{c}_2^o, \ldots, \bar{c}_n^o)$, we have from (10) that

$$(13) \qquad \bar{c}^o x^o = (c - \pi^o A) x^o = z^o - \pi^o b$$

where by (10), z^o is the total labor requirement of the manager's operating plan. But because of (12), $\bar{c}^o x^o = 0$, and therefore

$$(14) \qquad z^o = \pi^o b$$

Now let $x = (x_1, x_2, \ldots, x_n)$ be *any other feasible operating plan, and let z be its labor requirements; then*

$$(15) \qquad Ax = b \qquad\qquad (x_j \geq 0)$$
$$cx = z$$

It follows by multiplying $Ax = b$ by π^o and subtracting from $cx = z$ and noting (14):

$$(16) \qquad (c - \pi^o A)x = z - \pi^o b = z - z^o$$
$$\text{or} \quad \sum_j \bar{c}_j^o x_j = z - z^o$$

But the left member is the sum of nonnegative terms and therefore $z \geq z^o$. Hence, no other feasible operating plan exists whose labor requirement is less than the one found by the manager.

At this point, we can imagine the manager's delight at his genius, for *as a by-product of his search for prices that will cause his workers to work efficiently, he has also discovered those processes which minimize his labor requirements.* Without explicitly trying, he has solved his assigned task of keeping his use of labor to a *minimum*!

The Dual Problem.

Let us review the requirements satisfied by the prices found by the manager. First, there will be no excess wages in any activity; that is

$$(17) \qquad \pi A \leq c$$

Second, the total amount of wages to be paid for all activities should be the same whether they are paid directly or by use of the pricing device; that is

$$(18) \qquad z^o = cx^o = \pi b$$

where x^o is an optimal solution to (1).

[259]

Let us now show that these prices, π, themselves represent the optimal solution to another linear programming problem—specifically, to the dual problem of our manager's original production problem. By multiplying the jth equation of (17) by x_j^o and summing, we find that

$$(19) \qquad \pi_1 \sum_{j=1}^{n} a_{1j}x_j^o + \pi_2 \sum_{j=1}^{n} a_{2j}x_j^o + \ldots + \pi_m \sum_{j=1}^{n} a_{mj}x_j^o \leq \sum_{j=1}^{n} c_j x_j^o$$

Substituting from (1)

$$(20) \qquad b_i = \sum_{j=1}^{n} a_{ij}x_j^o \qquad (i = 1, 2, \ldots, m)$$

gives

$$\pi_1 b_1 + \pi_2 b_2 + \ldots + \pi_m b_m \leq c_1 x_1^o + c_2 x_2^o + \ldots + c_n x_n^o$$

Thus, $\pi b \leq cx^o$ for any π that satisfies (17). The prices, π^o, found by the manager give $\pi^o b = cx^o$ and thus π^o maximizes πb, subject to the constraints (17). Hence, $\pi = \pi^o$ may be viewed as an optimal solution to the *dual* linear programming problem, namely,

$$(21) \qquad \pi A \leq c$$
$$\pi b = v \text{ (Max)}$$

The relation $\pi^o b = cx^o$, where π^o is an optimal solution to (21), and x^o, an optimal solution to (1), agrees with the *duality theorem* established in § 6-3, Theorem 1. The reader should interpret for himself the economic meaning of maximizing πb in the case of the tool plant manager.

Let us now consider two other examples showing how the dual problem arises in other ways and how it may be interpreted.

12-2.   EXAMPLES OF DUAL PROBLEMS

The Scheme of the Ambitious Industrialist.

In this section we shall formulate a problem whereby the dual problem arises "naturally." Consider a defense plant which has just been built by the government. The plant has been designed to produce certain definite amounts, $-b_i$, $i = k + 1, \ldots, m$, of certain defense items and to use only certain definite amounts, $+b_i$, $i = 1, 2, \ldots, k$, of certain scarce materials which will be provided without cost by other government plants. The consulting engineers who designed the plant provided the government with a list of the various processes available in the plant and their input and output coefficients. Somewhat confused by this mass of data, the civil servants who were supposed to operate the plant decide to call in a private industrialist to consult on how they should plan their production. The industrialist realizes that it would be good training for his men and a feather in his cap actually to operate the plant. Accordingly, once he gets the information and studies the data, he proposes a flat fee for which he will manage the plant, turn over to the government the required amounts of output. and use no more than the alloted quantities of the scarce materials. The civil service men declare that, all other things being equal, they think it would be best for the government to operate the plant, but if he can convince them that his proposal is a good one (meaning that if the government operates the plant, it is unlikely it could do so less expensively), they will accept his offer.

The industrialist takes the data back to his office, gets out his linear programming book, and uses the data on input-output coefficients to form a matrix, A, similar to that of the manager of the machine tool plant, but with this difference: he includes the cost of purchased materials needed per unit of process j in the process cost, c_j.

To determine the minimum fee for which he can afford to operate the defense plant, the industrialist has only to solve the following linear program: find $x \geq 0$, such that

$$(1) \qquad\qquad Ax = b$$
$$cx = z \text{ (Min)}$$

He calls in his computer man, gives him the problem, and the next morning the results are on his desk: z^o is the minimum cost and x^o is the vector of optimal process utilization levels. His first thought is to explain the linear programming technique to his civil service friends, show them the final tableau, and thereby convince them that they can do no better than to accept his offer and pay him z^o. But then he realizes that this plan will give away his secret; the civil servants will have no further need for him; they will take his x^o vector and operate the plant themselves. Hence, he must convince them that z^o is minimal without giving away his plan x^o.

To this end, he decides to invent a system of prices which he will offer to pay for the materials, provided he is paid certain prices for outputs. He wants these prices to be such that there are no profits on any individual activity, for if there were profits, the government would spot them and would want to run this particular activity itself. On the other hand, given these restraints, he wants to make as much money as possible. That is, he wants his price vector π, a row, to satisfy

$$(2) \qquad\qquad \pi A \leq c$$

and

$$\pi b = v \text{ (Max)}$$

Again he calls the computer man, who recognizes this problem as the dual of the one he solved the night before and immediately produces the solution: optimal $\pi = \pi^o$, the simplex multipliers from the last stage of the previous problem, and maximal $v = v^o$. Fortunately, they note with relief, $v^o = z^o$.

[261]

With these results under his arm, the industrialist goes back to see the civil servants and presents his offer in price terms. The bureaucrats check to be sure that every one of the inequalities (2) is satisfied, and, of course, calculate the total cost using these prices: $\pi^o b = v^o$. The industrialist then invites them to consider any program, x, satisfying (1). Its cost to them, if they operate the plant themselves, is cx. But, replacing π by π^o in (2) and multiplying both sides by any *feasible* x yields

$$\text{(3)} \qquad\qquad \pi^o A x \leq cx$$

or, by (1),

$$\text{(4)} \qquad\qquad \pi^o b \leq cx$$

Hence,

$$\text{(5)} \qquad\qquad v^o \leq cx$$

so that the cost of the program will be at least v^o. This argument convinces the civil servants that they can do no better than to accept the industrialist's flat fee offer of v^o. With one last hope of operating the plant themselves, they try to pry out of him just how much of each process he intends to operate; but he feigns ignorance of such details and is soon happily on his way with his contract signed.

The Nutrition Pill Manufacturer.[2]

A housewife can buy foods in the grocery which vary in cost and nutritional elements. For simplicity, let us assume five foods and only two nutritional elements, calories and vitamins. The housewife's problem is to determine a minimum cost diet that has at least 21×100 calories and 12×100 vitamin units per person per day. The data for the simple linear programming model for this problem are given in Table 12-2-I.

TABLE 12-2-I

PRIMAL PILL PROBLEM

Items	Activities							Constants
	Buying Food					Having Excess		
						Cal.	Vit.	
	x_1	x_2	x_3	x_4	x_5	x_6	x_7	
Calories	-1		-1	-1	-2	1		$-21 \times (100)$
Vitamins		-1	-2	-1	-1		1	$-12 \times (100)$
Cost	20	20	31	11	12			z (Min)

[2] This example is a variant of one given in the book, *Linear Programming and Economic Analysis*, by Dorfman, Samuelson, and Solow [1958-1]. Our discussion can be regarded as a supplement to theirs.

A nutrition pill manufacturer wishes to supply the entire dietary requirements by marketing in the drug stores a pure calorie pill and a pure vitamin
pill at prices that will not only compete with similar "foods" 1 and 2 offered
in the grocery store but will be a cheaper source of nutritional needs than
any food on the market. What prices should he charge in order to maximize
his revenues?

Let π_1 be the price he charges per calorie pill and π_2 be the price per
vitamin pill (each pill $= 100$ units). Then the dual problem takes the form
shown in (6a). By substituting for π_i,

$$\pi_i = -y_i$$

it takes on the form (6b) which is more convenient for plotting; see Fig.
12-2-I.

Dual Pill Problem

(6a)
$$
\begin{aligned}
-\pi_1 & & &\le 20 \\
& - & \pi_2 &\le 20 \\
-\pi_1 & - & 2\pi_2 &\le 31 \\
-\pi_1 & - & \pi_2 &\le 11 \\
-2\pi_1 & - & \pi_2 &\le 12 \\
\pi_1 & & &\le 0 \\
& & \pi_2 &\le 0 \\
\end{aligned}
$$
$$-21\pi_1 - 12\pi_2 = v \text{ (Max)}$$

(6b)
$$
\begin{aligned}
y_1 & & &\le 20 \\
& & y_2 &\le 20 \\
y_1 & + & 2y_2 &\le 31 \\
y_1 & + & y_2 &\le 11 \\
2y_1 & + & y_2 &\le 12 \\
y_1 & & &\ge 0 \\
& & y_2 &\ge 0 \\
\end{aligned}
$$
$$21y_1 + 12y_2 = v \text{ (Max)}$$

In (6b) the sum of the terms to the left of the inequality (such as $y_1 + 2y_2$
in the third constraint) represents the cost to the housewife if she *simulates*
the type of food in question by purchasing nutrition pills with equal amounts
of nutritional elements; the quantity to the right represents the cost to her
if, instead, she buys the food. In each case it is required that it cost no more
to buy the simulated food.

The inequalities (6b) are plotted in Fig. 12-2-I, and it is evident that the
optimum choice of prices is to charge 1 cost unit for the calorie pill and 10
cost units for the vitamin pill.

(7) Optimum Prices: $\pi_1^* = -1,\ \pi_2^* = -10$
     Maximum Revenue: $v^* = \pi_1^* b_1 + \pi_2^* b_2 = -(-21) - 10(-12) = 141$

It should be noted that there is a built-in assumption that the drug
manufacturer will supply all dietary needs. Granted this, it is clear that his
prices must be competitive with the price of each food, for otherwise the
housewife would buy part of the diet in the grocery store and part in the
drug store. Another point worth noting is that foods 4 and 5 are still
competitive with the pills; that is to say, no more costly than the pills, as
can be seen by substituting these values of π_i^* in (6a). Thus, pill prices must

[263]

be set slightly below the optimum in order to overcome any residual bias toward pills and thereby guarantee the market. In the nutrition case, it is obvious from Fig. 12-2-I (and true in general when all $a_{ij} \leq 0$) that a slight

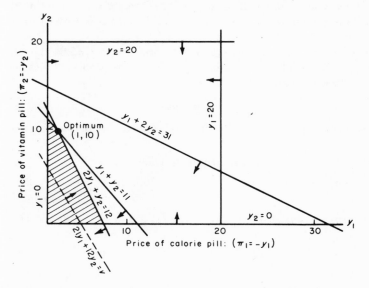

Figure 12-2-I.   The dual pill problem.

decrease in all y_i (or increase in π_i) from the optimum is sufficient to guarantee the entire market, if the decisions of all housewives are determined strictly by minimum cost. Let us hope that this is not the case.

12-3.   THE SIGN CONVENTION ON PRICES

DEFINITION: The *price* of an item is its exchange ratio relative to some standard item. If the item measured by the objective function is taken as a standard, then the price π_i of item i is the change it induces in the objective z per change of b_i, for small changes of b_i. *Asset* items will have *negative values* for prices because an increase in their quantity should bring about a *decrease* in the objective function, since we are minimizing.

The optimal dual "prices" π_i satisfy the relation

$$\bar{z}_0 = \pi_1 b_1 + \pi_2 b_2 + \ldots + \pi_m b_m$$

where Min $z = \bar{z}_0$. This same relation yields the value of z in any basic solution if π_i are the corresponding simplex multipliers. If the basic solution *is nondegenerate*, then, for small changes in any b_i, the basis and hence the simplex multipliers will remain constant. Thus the change in value of z per change of b_i for small changes in b_i is clearly π_i; hence by the above definition, π_i can be interpreted as the price.

Let us introduce into the program a fictitious "procurement" activity— "increasing the allotment of item i" whose coefficients are zero except for minus unity in row i and p_i in the cost row. Query: How low must the cost p_i be before it pays to increase the allotment of i? Pricing out this activity, we see it pays if

$$p_i + \pi_i < 0 \text{ or } p_i < -\pi_i$$

Hence, $-\pi_i$ is the break-even cost of the item i procurement activity.

Now, according to our interpretation of the price scheme developed in § 12-1 and § 12-2, for each unit of activity j, the input, $a_{ij} > 0$, would induce a payment to the manager of $\pi_i a_{ij}$. If the item is an asset, $\pi_i < 0$ and $\pi_i a_{ij} < 0$. In other words, *the flow of money is out* (negative). Similarly, if $a_{ij} < 0$, then the flow of money is toward the activity $\pi_i a_{ij} > 0$.

The total flow of money into the activity by the price device is given by pricing it out, i.e.,

$$\sum_i \pi_i a_{ij}$$

If this value exceeds c_j, the amount that would be received by the alternative of direct payment, then this activity (or some other with the same property) will, as we have seen for the example of § 12-1, be used in lieu of a basic activity now in use. This in turn will generate a new set of prices, etc.

12-4. SENSITIVITY ANALYSIS ILLUSTRATED[3]

The term *sensitivity analysis* refers to an analysis of the effect on the optimal solution to a linear programming problem of changes in the input-output coefficients, cost coefficients, and constant terms. We shall discuss these effects in terms of an illustration. The reader will find no difficulty in extending the results to the general case.

Consider the product mix problem as stated in § 3-5-(6):

$$(1) \quad \begin{aligned} 4x_1' + 9x_2' + 7x_3' + 10x_4' + x_5' &= 6000 \quad \text{Carpentry Shop} \\ x_1' + x_2' + 3x_3' + 40x_4' + x_6' &= 4000 \quad \text{Finishing Dept.} \\ -12x_1' - 20x_2' - 18x_3' - 40x_4' &= z' \text{ (Min)} \end{aligned}$$

For computational ease, let us scale the problem so that the production activities are stated in units of 1,000's of desks, the capacities in units of 1,000's of hours, and cost in units of $1,000. Letting $x_j' = 1,000x_j$, $z' = 1,000z$, system (1) in simplex tableau form, becomes (2).

[3] This section was contributed by W. O. Blattner.

(2)

Basic Variables	Admissible Variables (Including Slacks)							Constants
	x_1	x_2	x_3	x_4	x_5	x_6	$-z$	
x_5	4	9	7	10	1	0	0	6
x_6	1	1	3	40	0	1	0	4
$-z$	-12	-20	-18	-40	0	0	1	0

● ● ●

Since this is already in canonical form, addition of artificial variables is unnecessary, and we can proceed directly with Phase II of the simplex method. After several cycles we arrive at the optimum solution (3).

(3)

Basic Variables	Admissible Variables (Including Slacks)							Constants
	x_1	x_2	x_3	x_4	x_5	x_6	$-z$	
x_1	1	7/3	5/3	0	4/15	$-1/15$	0	4/3
x_4	0	$-1/30$	1/30	1	$-1/150$	2/75	0	1/15
$-z$	0	20/3	10/3	0	44/15	4/15	1	56/3

● ● ●

From the information contained in this tableau (3) we see that the optimum product mix for the problem as stated is at the rate of $1{,}333\frac{1}{3}$ desks of type 1 and $66\frac{2}{3}$ desks of type 4 per time period for a total profit rate of $z' = \$18{,}667$ per period.

In addition to giving us the point of most profitable operation, it is possible to obtain from the optimum tableau a wealth of information concerning a wide range of operations in the neighborhood of this optimum by making a sensitivity analysis. In many applications, the information thus obtained is as valuable as the specification of the optimum solution itself.

Sensitivity analysis is important for several reasons:

(a) Stability of the optimum solution under changes of parameters may be critical. For example, using the old optimum solution point, a slight variation of a parameter in one direction may result in a large unfavorable difference in the objective function relative to the new minimum, while a large variation in the parameter in another direction may result in only a small difference. In an industrial situation where there are certain inherent variabilities in processes and materials not taken account of in the model, it may be desirable to move away from the optimum solution in order to achieve a solution less likely to require essential modification.

(b) Values of the input-output coefficients, objective function coefficients, and/or constraint constants may be to some extent *controllable*, and in this case we want to know the effects which would result from changing these values.

(c) Even though the input-output and objective function coefficients and constraint constants are *not* controllable, the estimates for their values may be only approximate, making it important to know for what ranges of these values the solution is still optimum. If it turns out that the optimum solution is extremely sensitive to their values, it may become necessary to obtain better estimates.

Optimality Range for Cost Coefficients: Non-Basic Activities.

Problem 1: A new desk called Type 7 has been designed which will require 6 man hours of Carpentry Shop time and 2 man hours of Finishing Department labor per desk. Based on an estimated profit of $18 per desk, would it pay to produce this desk?

Note that the negatives of the values of the simplex multipliers, $\frac{44}{15}$, $\frac{4}{15}$, 1, for the last iteration can be obtained from the bottom row vector of the inverse of the final basis, and it is obvious that these are simply the updated relative cost factors corresponding to the initial basic variables x_5, x_6, $(-z)$. This yields, after pricing out, $\bar{c}_7 = \frac{44}{15}(6) + \frac{4}{15}(2) - 18 = \frac{2}{15}$. Since $\bar{c}_7 > 0$, it does *not* pay to produce this desk.

Problem 2: How much would the profit for desk Type 7 have to change before it becomes worthwhile to produce?

In order for a non-basic activity to be a candidate to enter the basis, its relative cost factor must be ≤ 0. If any non-basic activity has a relative cost factor exactly equal to zero it can be brought into the basis without changing the value of the objective function. Therefore, if the cost coefficient c_j for any non-basic activity is decreased by the value of its relative cost factor $\bar{c}_j$ in the optimum solution, it becomes a candidate to enter the basis. In this case, desk Type 7 becomes a candidate for production if its *profit* per unit can be increased by $\bar{c}_7 = \frac{2}{15}$.

EXERCISE: How much must the profit on desk Type 2 be increased to bring it into an optimum solution? How much would you have to raise the selling price on desk Type 3 in order to make its production profitable, assuming that all desks of Type 3 produced can be sold at the new price? How would you modify the model if the amount that can be sold is a function of selling price? See Chapter 18; see also Chapter 24.

Effect of Changing Input-Output Coefficients: Non-Basic Activities.

Problem 3: How much would the Carpentry Shop labor requirement for desk Type 7 have to change for it to become profitable to produce?

For non-basic activities the effect of changing the input-output coefficients or a_{ij} in the initial tableau can be easily calculated using the negative of the

[267]

simplex multipliers. Replacing the original value of $a_{17}^o = 6$ by the parameter $a_{1,7}$ in the $\bar{c}_j$ calculation, we have

$$(4) \qquad \bar{c}_7 = [\tfrac{44}{15} \quad \tfrac{4}{15} \quad 1] \cdot \begin{bmatrix} a_{17} \\ 2 \\ -18 \end{bmatrix} = \tfrac{44}{15}a_{1,7} - \tfrac{262}{15}$$

In order for activity $j = 7$ to become a candidate to enter the solution, $\bar{c}_7$ must be ≤ 0 or $a_{17} \leq \tfrac{131}{22}$.

EXERCISE: To what value would the Carpentry Shop hours for desk Type 2 have to be reduced to make it competitive?

Problem 4: Suppose that we are not really sure of either the labor requirements *or* profit for desk Type 2. Give a formula for these parameters that may be used to determine if it is profitable to produce desk Type 2.

For activity $j = 2$ to become a candidate to enter the solution:

$$\bar{c}_2 = [\tfrac{44}{15} \quad \tfrac{4}{15} \quad 1] \cdot \begin{bmatrix} a_{12} \\ a_{22} \\ c_2 \end{bmatrix} = \tfrac{44}{15}a_{12} + \tfrac{4}{15}a_{22} + c_2 \leq 0$$

If, for example, it turns out that $a_{12} = 8$, $a_{22} = 2$, $c_2 = -25$, substitution in the above formula gives $\bar{c}_2 = -1$ so that it pays to produce desk Type 2.

The Substitution Effect of Non-Basic Activities on Basic Activities.

Problem 5: How many units of the entering activity $j = s$ can be brought into the solution and what will be the effect upon the quantities of the other basic activities? Here again the answer is given by the simplex method:

$$(5) \qquad \text{Max } x_s = \underset{\bar{a}_{is} > 0}{\text{Min}} \left(\frac{\bar{b}_i}{\bar{a}_{is}} \right)$$

Let us review the information directly available from the optimum tableau (3). The rows express the basic variables in terms of the non-basic variables, while the columns express the non-basic activities in terms of the basic activities. The column vector of matrix coefficients, $\bar{a}_{ij}$, under each variable x_j can be interpreted as "substitution" factors. For example, for each unit of activity $j = 2$ we bring into the solution we must remove $\tfrac{2}{3}$ units of basic activity $j = 1$ and add $\tfrac{1}{30}$ unit of basic activity $j = 4$ for a resulting net increase of $\tfrac{20}{3}$ units in the objective function. From (5), when (Max x_2) units of activity $j = 2$ are brought into the solution, then the corresponding i^{th} basic activity drops out.

Observe that the relative cost factor $\bar{c}_j$ for each variable can be calculated from the "substitution" factors, $\bar{a}_{ij}$, and the original cost coefficients c_j; namely

$$(6) \qquad \bar{c}_j = c_j - \sum_i \bar{a}_{ij} c_{j_i}$$

where j_i is the index of the ith basic activity. This is an alternative way to do the "pricing out" calculations. For each unit of $j = 2$ added, the following changes in the basic variables result:

(7)

Variable	Quantity Change		Cost per Unit	=	Cost Change
x_1:	$(-\tfrac{7}{3})$	$\cdot$	(-12)	=	$+28$
x_4:	$(+\tfrac{1}{30})$	$\cdot$	(-40)	=	$-\tfrac{4}{3}$
x_2:	$(+1)$	$\cdot$	(-20)	=	-20

Relative cost factor: $\bar{c}_2 = +\tfrac{20}{3}$ per unit of x_2 introduced

EXERCISE: If the profit on desk Type 2 is increased by exactly $\bar{c}_2 = \tfrac{20}{3}$ per desk, show that up to $571\tfrac{3}{7}$ desks of Type 2 can be produced per period without reducing total profit. What is the resulting product mix?

Effect of Changing Constraint Constants.

Problem 6: What is the effect of increasing Finishing Department capacity?

An increase in the value of a constraint constant can be considered equivalent to introducing a fictitious procurement activity with coefficients equal to but opposite in sign to the corresponding slack variable in the original formulation (2). It follows that the effect of increasing Finishing Department capacity is to *increase* net profit by $\$\tfrac{4}{15}$ per hour of increase, up to 20,000 hours increase in the period, because the value of $\bar{c}_6 = \tfrac{4}{15}$ for the corresponding slack variable.

EXERCISE: If Finishing Department capacity is increased by 20,000 hours per time period, what is the resulting product mix? Which basic activity has dropped out of the solution?

EXERCISE: Necessary equipment to increase the capacity of the Carpentry Shop by 10 per cent can be rented for $5,000. Also, overtime hours up to 20 per cent of the rated capacity of either shop can be obtained at a premium of $1.50 per hour. Above this figure the premium is estimated to be about $3.00 per hour because of loss of productive efficiency. What would you do?

EXERCISE: Show that if a slack variable is in the basic set with value $\hat{x}_j$ in the optimum solution, then the corresponding constraint constant b_i in the initial tableau can take on any value $b_i \geq b_i^o - \hat{x}_j$ where b_i^o was its original value, with no change in the values of the objective function or the other basic variables in the optimum solution. In this range, is b_i actually constraining the solution?

Optimality Range for Cost Coefficients: Basic Activities.

Problem 7: For what range of costs of the basic activities does the present optimum solution still remain optimum?

In particular, consider basic activity $j = 1$. The present solution will remain optimal until cost coefficient c_1 is increased or decreased sufficiently so that the relative cost factor on one of the non-basic activities goes to zero, at which point that non-basic activity becomes a candidate to enter the solution.

Referring to (6) we have

$$(8) \qquad \bar{c}_2 = -20 - [+\tfrac{7}{3}(c_1) - \tfrac{1}{30}(-40)] = -\tfrac{7}{3}c_1 - \tfrac{64}{3}$$

We see that the value of the cost coefficient c_1 of $-(64/3)/(7/3)$ is required to make the relative cost factor $\bar{c}_2 = 0$. We must, however, also investigate the effect of a c_1 change on all *other* non-basic activities; we find in general that the *change* in c_1 necessary to make the value of $\bar{c}_j = 0$ is given by

$$(9) \qquad\qquad c_1 - c_1^o = \frac{\bar{c}_j^o}{\bar{a}_{1j}} \qquad\qquad (c_1^o = -12)$$

Hence,

$$\bar{c}_2 = 0 \text{ if } c_1 \text{ is increased by } \frac{\frac{20}{3}}{\frac{7}{3}} = \frac{20}{7}$$

$$\bar{c}_3 = 0 \text{ if } c_1 \text{ is increased by } \frac{\frac{10}{3}}{\frac{5}{3}} = 2$$

$$\bar{c}_5 = 0 \text{ if } c_1 \text{ is increased by } \frac{\frac{44}{15}}{\frac{4}{15}} = 11$$

$$\bar{c}_6 = 0 \text{ if } c_1 \text{ is increased by } \frac{\frac{4}{15}}{-\frac{1}{15}} = -4$$

Thus the present solution (3) is still optimal, for $-12 - 4 \leq c_1 \leq -12 + 2$ where $c_1^o = -12$ was the original value of c_1. The computational rule can be summarized:

$$(10) \qquad \text{Max } c_{j_i} = c_{j_i}^o + \underset{\bar{a}_{ij}>0}{\text{Min}} \left(\frac{\bar{c}_j}{\bar{a}_{ij}} \right) \qquad\qquad j \text{ non-basic}$$

$$\text{Min } c_{j_i} = c_{j_i}^o + \underset{\bar{a}_{ij}<0}{\text{Max}} \left(\frac{\bar{c}_j}{\bar{a}_{ij}} \right) \qquad\qquad j \text{ non-basic}$$

EXERCISE: For what range of profit for desk Type 4 is the present solution (3) still optimal? Determine what activity enters the solution if c_1 is decreased to -20, increased to $-\tfrac{19}{2}$. What activity leaves the solution in each case?

EXERCISE: Construct an example by changing b_1 in the original problem (2) to show that if c_1 is increased to $-\tfrac{19}{2}$, desk Type 1 is not necessarily the activity that leaves the solution.

EXERCISE: Prove that if the cost of a basic activity is reduced, it will not be dropped from the optimum solution.

EXERCISE: The reason for the Irish Rebellion. The average Irishman has 27 pence per day to spend on food and requires a diet of 2,000 calories to live. Irish potatoes cost 3 pence per 1,000 calories and meat costs 24 pence per 1,000 calories. Since he detests potatoes, he eats 1,000 calories of meat and 1,000 calories of potatoes per day. Show that if the price of potatoes goes up to 10 pence per 1,000 calories (which will, of course, be blamed on the English), the average Irishman must increase his daily potato consumption by 50 per cent.

Effect of Changing Input-Output Coefficients: Basic Activities.

Problem 8: What happens if the Carpentry Shop requirements for desk Type 1 change? Changing an input-output coefficient for a basic activity results in changes to the negatives of the simplex multipliers and other elements of the updated inverse of the initial basis. To evaluate the effect of varying a_{11} we must find:

$$
(11) \qquad [\tilde{B}]^{-1} = \begin{bmatrix} a_{11} & 10 & 0 \\ 1 & 40 & 0 \\ -12 & -40 & 1 \end{bmatrix}^{-1}
$$

already knowing that

$$
(12) \qquad [B]^{-1} = \begin{bmatrix} 4 & 10 & 0 \\ 1 & 40 & 0 \\ -12 & -40 & 1 \end{bmatrix}^{-1} = \begin{bmatrix} \frac{4}{15} & -\frac{1}{15} & 0 \\ -\frac{1}{150} & \frac{2}{75} & 0 \\ \frac{44}{15} & \frac{4}{15} & 1 \end{bmatrix}
$$

We can write $[\tilde{B}]$ as $[A] \cdot [B]$, where the matrix

$$
(13) \qquad [A] = [\tilde{B}] \cdot [B]^{-1} = \begin{bmatrix} \dfrac{4a_{11}-1}{15} & \dfrac{4-a_{11}}{15} & 0 \\ 0 & 1 & 0 \\ 0 & 0 & 1 \end{bmatrix}
$$

Since $[A]$ is an elementary matrix (see § 8-5) we can easily find its inverse. Let the reciprocal of the diagonal element in the first row be γ, thus

$$
(14) \qquad \gamma = \frac{15}{4a_{11}-1} \quad \text{and} \quad a_{11} = \frac{15+\gamma}{4\gamma}
$$

We shall show that $[A]^{-1}$ and hence $[\tilde{B}]^{-1}$ are *linear* in γ.

$$
(15) \qquad [A] = \begin{bmatrix} \dfrac{1}{\gamma} & \left(\dfrac{1}{4}-\dfrac{1}{4\gamma}\right) & 0 \\ 0 & 1 & 0 \\ 0 & 0 & 1 \end{bmatrix} \quad \text{and} \quad [A]^{-1} = \begin{bmatrix} \gamma & \dfrac{1-\gamma}{4} & 0 \\ 0 & 1 & 0 \\ 0 & 0 & 1 \end{bmatrix}
$$

Then

$$(16) \quad [\tilde{B}]^{-1} = [[A][B]]^{-1} = [B]^{-1} \cdot [A]^{-1} = \begin{bmatrix} \dfrac{4\gamma}{15} & \dfrac{-\gamma}{15} & 0 \\[2mm] \dfrac{-\gamma}{150} & \dfrac{\gamma+15}{600} & 0 \\[2mm] \dfrac{44\gamma}{15} & \dfrac{15-11\gamma}{15} & 1 \end{bmatrix}$$

where by (14) $\gamma^o = 1$ corresponds to $a_{11}^o = 4$. Note that in order for $[\tilde{B}]$ to be a basis, $[\tilde{B}]^{-1}$ must exist. This means that $[A]^{-1}$ must exist which requires $1/\gamma \neq 0$, $\gamma \neq 0$. We shall show later that for feasibility $\gamma \geq 0$. Together these two restrictions require $\gamma > 0$. The question now becomes one of finding for what range of γ the present basic activities are still optimal. We first determine what values of γ will insure $\bar{c}_j \geq 0$ for each of the non-basic activities.

$$(17) \quad \bar{c}_2 = \begin{bmatrix} \dfrac{44\gamma}{15} & \dfrac{15-11\gamma}{15} & 1 \end{bmatrix} \begin{bmatrix} 9 \\ 1 \\ -20 \end{bmatrix} = \dfrac{77\gamma}{3} - 19 \geq 0 \text{ if } \gamma \geq \dfrac{57}{77}$$

$$\bar{c}_3 = \begin{bmatrix} \dfrac{44\gamma}{15} & \dfrac{15-11\gamma}{15} & 1 \end{bmatrix} \begin{bmatrix} 7 \\ 3 \\ -18 \end{bmatrix} = \dfrac{55\gamma}{3} - 15 \geq 0 \text{ if } \gamma \geq \dfrac{9}{11}$$

$$\bar{c}_5 = \begin{bmatrix} \dfrac{44\gamma}{15} & \dfrac{15-11\gamma}{15} & 1 \end{bmatrix} \begin{bmatrix} 1 \\ 0 \\ 0 \end{bmatrix} = \dfrac{44\gamma}{15} \geq 0 \text{ if } \gamma \geq 0$$

$$\bar{c}_6 = \begin{bmatrix} \dfrac{44\gamma}{15} & \dfrac{15-11\gamma}{15} & 1 \end{bmatrix} \begin{bmatrix} 0 \\ 1 \\ 0 \end{bmatrix} = -\dfrac{11\gamma}{15} + 1 \geq 0 \text{ if } \gamma \leq \dfrac{15}{11}$$

In order to maintain *feasibility* we must *also* determine what range of values of γ will maintain each of the elements $\bar{b}_i \geq 0$:

$$(18) \quad \begin{bmatrix} \bar{b}_1 \\[2mm] \bar{b}_2 \\[2mm] -z \end{bmatrix} = \begin{bmatrix} \dfrac{4\gamma}{15} & -\dfrac{\gamma}{15} & 0 \\[2mm] -\dfrac{\gamma}{150} & \dfrac{\gamma+15}{600} & 0 \\[2mm] \dfrac{44\gamma}{15} & \dfrac{15-11\gamma}{15} & 1 \end{bmatrix} \begin{bmatrix} 6 \\[2mm] 4 \\[2mm] 0 \end{bmatrix} = \begin{bmatrix} \dfrac{4\gamma}{3} \\[2mm] \dfrac{3-\gamma}{30} \\[2mm] \dfrac{12+44\gamma}{3} \end{bmatrix}$$

From this we see that $\bar{b}_1 \geq 0$ if $\gamma \geq 0$; and $\bar{b}_2 \geq 0$ if $\gamma \leq 3$. Noting that the first row of $[\tilde{B}]^{-1}$ is simply γ times the first row of $[B]^{-1}$, we see that $\bar{b}_1 = \gamma \bar{b}_1^o$.

Assuming nondegeneracy, $\bar{b}_1^o > 0$. Then the requirement $\bar{b}_1 \geq 0$ requires $\gamma \geq 0$. Since $\gamma \neq 0$, $\gamma > 0$ and $\bar{b}_1 > 0$. Taking the most restrictive of the γ calculated by (17) and (18) above we find that the objective function z, and the values, $\bar{b}_i$, of the basic variables are all *linear* in γ and the adjusted basic solution is feasible and optimal for the range $\frac{9}{11} \leq \gamma \leq \frac{15}{11}$ or $\frac{29}{6} \geq a_{11} \geq 3$.

EXERCISE: What is the effect of increasing Carpentry Shop time on desk Type 1 to $4\frac{1}{2}$ hours per desk? To 5 hours per desk?

EXERCISE: Under what conditions can the value of an input-output coefficient for a basic activity be changed without any cost effect?

Problem 9: What is the effect of simultaneous changes to Carpentry Shop and Finishing Department requirements and profit for desk Type 1? Here the problem is to find

$$(19) \qquad [\tilde{B}']^{-1} = \begin{bmatrix} a_{11} & 10 & 0 \\ a_{21} & 40 & 0 \\ c_1 & -40 & 1 \end{bmatrix}^{-1}$$

Writing $[\tilde{B}']$ this time as $[B] \cdot [A']$ we have

$$(20) \qquad [A'] = [B]^{-1} \cdot [\tilde{B}'] = \begin{bmatrix} \dfrac{4a_{11} - a_{21}}{15} & 0 & 0 \\ \dfrac{4a_{21} - a_{11}}{150} & 1 & 0 \\ \dfrac{44a_{11} + 4a_{21} + 15c_1}{15} & 0 & 1 \end{bmatrix}$$

Letting $\dfrac{4a_{11} - a_{21}}{15} = p$, $\dfrac{4a_{21} - a_{11}}{150} = q$, and $\dfrac{44a_{11} + 4a_{21} + 15c_1}{15} = r$

$$(21) \qquad [A']^{-1} = \begin{bmatrix} \dfrac{1}{p} & 0 & 0 \\ \dfrac{-q}{p} & 1 & 0 \\ \dfrac{-r}{p} & 0 & 1 \end{bmatrix}$$

and

$$(22) \qquad [\tilde{B}']^{-1} = [A']^{-1}[B]^{-1} = \begin{bmatrix} \dfrac{4}{15p} & \dfrac{-1}{15p} & 0 \\ \dfrac{-p - 40q}{150p} & \dfrac{2p + 5q}{75p} & 0 \\ \dfrac{44p - 4r}{15p} & \dfrac{4p + r}{15p} & 0 \end{bmatrix}$$

where, as before, the pivot element $p \neq 0$ and $1/p \neq 0$.

[273]

Observe that $p^o = 1$, $q^o = r^o = 0$ corresponds to $a_{11}^o = 4$, $a_{21}^o = 1$, $c_1^o = -12$. We now determine what values of p, q, r will insure $\bar{c}_j \geq 0$ for each of the non-basic activities,

$$(23) \quad [\bar{c}_2] = \begin{bmatrix} \dfrac{44p - 4r}{15p} & \dfrac{4p + r}{15p} & 1 \end{bmatrix} \begin{bmatrix} 9 \\ 1 \\ -20 \end{bmatrix} = \frac{20}{3} - \frac{7r}{3p} \geq 0 \text{ if } \frac{r}{p} \leq \frac{20}{7}$$

$$[\bar{c}_3] = \begin{bmatrix} \dfrac{44p - 4r}{15p} & \dfrac{4p + r}{15p} & 1 \end{bmatrix} \begin{bmatrix} 7 \\ 3 \\ -18 \end{bmatrix} = \frac{10}{3} - \frac{5r}{3p} \geq 0 \text{ if } \frac{r}{p} \leq 2$$

$$[\bar{c}_5] = \begin{bmatrix} \dfrac{44p - 4r}{15p} & \dfrac{4p + r}{15p} & 1 \end{bmatrix} \begin{bmatrix} 1 \\ 0 \\ 0 \end{bmatrix} = \frac{44}{15} - \frac{4r}{15p} \geq 0 \text{ if } \frac{r}{p} \leq 11$$

$$[\bar{c}_6] = \begin{bmatrix} \dfrac{44p - 4r}{15p} & \dfrac{4p + r}{15p} & 1 \end{bmatrix} \begin{bmatrix} 0 \\ 1 \\ 0 \end{bmatrix} = \frac{4}{15} + \frac{r}{15p} \geq 0 \text{ if } \frac{r}{p} \geq -4$$

and also maintain each of the elements $\bar{b}_i \geq 0$:

$$(24) \quad \begin{bmatrix} \bar{b}_1 \\ \bar{b}_2 \\ -z \end{bmatrix} = \begin{bmatrix} \dfrac{4}{15p} & \dfrac{-1}{15p} & 0 \\ \dfrac{-p - 40q}{150p} & \dfrac{2p + 5q}{75p} & 0 \\ \dfrac{44p - 4r}{15p} & \dfrac{4p + r}{15p} & 1 \end{bmatrix} \begin{bmatrix} 6 \\ 4 \\ 0 \end{bmatrix} = \begin{bmatrix} \dfrac{4}{3p} \\ \dfrac{1}{15} - \dfrac{4q}{3p} \\ \dfrac{56}{3} - \dfrac{4r}{3p} \end{bmatrix}$$

whence $\bar{b}_1 \geq 0$ if $\dfrac{1}{p} \geq 0$, $\bar{b}_2 \geq 0$ if $\dfrac{q}{p} \leq \dfrac{1}{20}$, and the value of the objective function $z = -\dfrac{56}{3} + \dfrac{4r}{3p}$. Note that assuming nondegeneracy as before, $\bar{b}_1 = \dfrac{1}{p}\bar{b}_1^o > 0$ and $\dfrac{1}{p} > 0$.

Taking the most restrictive of the limits calculated above, we see that z and the $\bar{b}_i$ are *linear* in $\dfrac{1}{p}$, $\dfrac{q}{p}$, and $\dfrac{r}{p}$ for the range $\dfrac{1}{p} > 0$, $\dfrac{q}{p} \leq \dfrac{1}{20}$, and $2 \geq \dfrac{r}{p} \geq -4$. These restrictions are equivalent to $p > 0$, $p \geq 20q$, and $2p \geq r \geq -4p$, which upon substitution yield the conditions on the input-output coefficients and cost coefficients of basic activity $j = 1$ for which the basic variables given in (3) remain in the optimum solution:

[274]

(25)
$$4a_{11} - a_{21} \geq 0$$
$$2a_{11} - 3a_{21} \geq 0$$
$$-\frac{12a_{11} + 2a_{21}}{5} \geq c_1 \geq -4a_{11}$$

The effect of varying the a_{11} and c_1 within these limits upon the $\bar{b}_i$ and z of the optimum solution is given by (24).

EXERCISE: Show that if a_{11} and a_{21} are varied within the limits of the first two inequalities in (25) and if c_1 is correspondingly varied so that $c_1 = -\dfrac{44a_{11} + 4a_{21}}{15}$, then there will be no change in the value of the objective function.

EXERCISE: Prove the following:

THEOREM: *Given a general linear program, the domain of all possible variations of a column P in an optimal feasible basis is convex in the space of the components of P.*

12-5. PROBLEMS

1. Show in § 12-1 that if, in an optimal solution, there are surpluses of certain items, their prices are zero. Show that the price of an item is zero if there is no cost associated with the activity of storing it and there is a surplus of the item.
2. Show that the above case might lead to excessive use of the raw material inputs, unless the central planners place some value on excess raw material in terms of labor.
3. Show that it would be better to also introduce activities for procurement of additional inputs and to place a labor value on these as well.
4. (Review) Show that the price π_i represents the change in the total costs z per infinitesimal change in the availability of item i.
5. Which of the various properties associated with the duality theorems of Chapter 6 explains why the manager of the tool plant discovered the process which minimizes his labor requirements in the course of developing a pricing system ?
6. Given an optimal basic feasible solution and the corresponding system in canonical form, show that $\bar{c}_j$ represents the change necessary in the unit cost of the jth non-basic activity before it would be a candidate to enter the basis. If the other coefficients as well as cost coefficients can vary, show that
$$\bar{c}_j = c_j - \sum_i \pi_i a_{ij}$$
is the amount of change where π_i are the prices associated with the basic set of variables.

7. Develop a formula for the change in cost c_j of a basis activity before it is a candidate for being dropped from the basis. Which activity would enter in its place?

REFERENCES

Allen, 1959-1
Arrow, 1951-1
Arrow, Karlin, and Suppes, 1960-1
Baumol, 1961-1
Beckmann, 1955-1
Boulding and Spivey, 1960-1
Dantzig, 1955-2
Dorfman, 1951-1
Dorfman, Samuelson, and Solow, 1958-1
Fisher and Schruben, 1953-1
Gale, 1960-1
Gale, Kuhn, and Tucker, 1950-1, 2, 1951-1
Hicks, 1960-1

Karlin, 1959-1
Koopmans, 1951-1, 2
Leontief, 1951-1
Massé, 1946-1
Massé and Gibrat, 1957-1
Mills, 1956-1
Morgenstern, 1954-1
Solow, 1952-1
Uzawa, 1960-1
von Neumann, 1937-1
Wagner, 1957-1
Wald, 1935-1
Walras, 1874-1

CHAPTER 13

GAMES AND LINEAR PROGRAMS

13-1. MATRIX GAMES

Background.[1]

According to Gale [1960-1, p. 216], "One of the most striking events in connection with the emergence of modern linear economic model theory was the simultaneous but independent development of linear programming on the one hand and game theory on the other, and the eventual realization of the very close relationship that exists between these two subjects."

This relationship between linear programming and games was first pointed out by J. von Neumann in the fall of 1947 in informal discussions with the author. He showed that the central mathematical problem associated with a matrix game could be stated as a linear program and he conjectured that the converse was true. A. W. Tucker and his group at Princeton in early 1948 undertook a systematic study of the interrelations between the two fields in order to place the theory on a rigorous foundation [Gale, Kuhn, and Tucker, 1951-1]. It is the purpose of this chapter to bring out these connections.

Game theory is concerned with finding the best "strategies" for solving conflict situations. In the abstract these may be characterized as situations where the participants of the contest each control some but not all the actions that can take place. This, together with chance events (if present), determines the outcome upon which the participants may place widely differing values. The mathematical foundations of game theory are found in certain papers by J. von Neumann in 1928 and 1937 and less conclusive contributions by Borel in the early 1920's [von Neumann, 1928-1, 1937-1; Borel, 1921-1, 1924-1, and 1927-1]. Actually, until 1944 there were almost no papers; it was then that von Neumann and Morgenstern [1944-1] published their famous book, *Theory of Games and Economic Behavior*.

Matrix Games Defined.

In a matrix game there are two players whom we will refer to as "R" and "C." Each is supposed to make one choice from a set of possible choices

[1] For a popular explanation of Game Theory, the reader is referred to *The Compleat Strategyst* by John D. Williams [Williams, 1954-1]; a more formal introduction can be found in Luce and Raiffa, *Games and Decisions* [Luce and Raiffa, 1957-1] and in M. Dresher, *Games of Strategy: Theory and Applications* [Dresher, 1961-1]. Fundamental papers on the subject can be found in *Annals of Mathematics Studies*, Nos. 24 (1950) and 28 (1953) entitled "Contributions to the Theory of Games," edited by Kuhn and Tucker, [Kuhn and Tucker, 1950-1, and 1953-1].

without knowledge as to the choice of the other player. For each such choice by the two players, say i for R and j for C, there is a resulting outcome that can be specified by a single number a_{ij}, the *payoff* R stands to receive (positive, negative, or zero) according as R wins from C, loses, or draws; at the same time, C is in *diametric opposition* to R and stands to receive what R loses—namely $-a_{ij}$. If choices i for R range from $i = 1, 2, \ldots, m$ and choices j for C from $j = 1, 2, \ldots, n$, the possible payoff to R may be displayed as a matrix:

Payoff to R
_____

if R chooses row i and C chooses column j
_____

$$\begin{bmatrix} a_{11} & a_{12} & \cdots & a_{1n} \\ a_{21} & a_{22} & \cdots & a_{2n} \\ \cdot & \cdot & & \cdot \\ \cdot & \cdot & & \cdot \\ \cdot & \cdot & & \cdot \\ a_{m1} & a_{m2} & \cdots & a_{mn} \end{bmatrix}$$

The problem for each player is this: What choice should he make in order that his partial influence over the outcome benefits him the most?

Our immediate purpose is to show that a variety of competitive situations can be cast into the form of a matrix game if we interpret "choice" in these cases to mean a selection among the "pure strategies" available to each player.

DEFINITION: *A pure strategy* is a plan so complete that it cannot be upset by the opponent or nature [Williams, 1954-1]. It is a complete set of advance instructions that specifies a definite choice for every conceivable situation in which the player may be required to act [Kuhn and Tucker, 1955-1].

Example 1, A Calling Game: Player R has two cards, one black and one red. He selects one. Without showing it to his opponent, he lays it down on the table. Player C then calls it. The card is turned over. If the card is called, R pays C a penny, otherwise he loses a penny. The pure strategies open to R are listed in the left *row* margin of the two-way array (1); we refer to R for this reason as the *row player*. In a similar manner, those for C are listed in the *column* margin, shown across the top, and C is called the *column player*. The table entries are the payoff to R if C calls the card correctly or incorrectly.

(1)

Player R's Pure Strategies	Player C's Pure Strategies	
	Call Black	Call Red
Choose black	-1	$+1$
Choose red	$+1$	-1

This matrix game points up how important it is to both R and C that their plans not be discovered in advance. The result could be disastrous. No matter how R chooses, his highest "floor," the maximum gain that R can guarantee himself, if he is discovered, is -1. Similarly, C's lowest "ceiling," the minimum loss that C can guarantee himself, if he is discovered, is $+1$. We shall show, however, that there is a way to play this game so that R can have an expected gain of 0, and C can have an expected loss of 0.

Example 2, Morra [Williams, 1954-1]: Two players simultaneously throw out one or two fingers and call out their guess as to what the total sum of the outstretched fingers will be. If a player guesses right, but his opponent does not, he receives payment equal to his guess. In all other cases, it is a draw.

The pure strategies open to each player are show 1, call 2; show 1, call 3; show 2, call 3; show 2, call 4. If we abbreviate these combinations $(1, 2)$, $(1, 3)$, etc., the matrix game takes the (skew-symmetric) form

(2)

		C			
		$(1, 2)$	$(1, 3)$	$(2, 3)$	$(2, 4)$
R	$(1, 2)$	0	2	-3	0
	$(1, 3)$	-2	0	0	3
	$(2, 3)$	3	0	0	-4
	$(2, 4)$	0	-3	4	0

The maximum floor for R, if his pure strategy is discovered, is -2 and similarly the minimum ceiling for C is $+2$. Again we see how important it is not to reveal the pure strategy in advance.

Example 3, The Campers: John D. Williams [1954-1] in his humorous elementary introduction to game theory, *The Compleat Strategyst*, supplies the following example and discussion, which we quote with minor changes.[2]

"It may help to fix these ideas if we give a specific physical realization. When the payoffs are all positive, we may interpret them as the altitudes of points in a mountainous region. The various R and C strategies then correspond to the latitudes and longitudes of these points.

"To supply some actors and motivation for a game, let's suppose that a man and wife—Ray and Carol—are planning a camping trip, and that Ray likes high altitudes and Carol likes low altitudes.[3] The region of interest to them is criss-crossed by a network of fire divides, or roads, four running in each direction. The campers have agreed to camp at a road junction.

[2] We have changed the actress' name to Carol to correspond to C and have deleted a few phrases.

[3] Williams implicitly assumes that the interests of the man and wife, as far as altitude is concerned, are diametrically opposed and the "payoff" to R can be measured in feet of altitude.

[279]

They have further agreed that Ray will choose the east-west road and that Carol will choose the north-south road, which jointly identify the junction.

"Let us suppose the junctions on the roads i available to Ray and roads j available to Carol have the following altitudes, in thousands of feet:

(3)

		Carol (j)			
		(1)	(2)	(3)	(4)
Ray (i)	(1)	7	2	5	1
	(2)	2	2	3	4
	(3)	5	3	4	4
	(4)	3	2	1	6

Ray, being a reasonable person, who simply wants to have as much as possible, is naturally attracted to the road Ray 1—with junctions at altitudes of 7, 2 5, and 1—for it alone can get him the 7-thousand-foot peak. However, he does not dare undertake a plan which would realize him a great deal if it succeeds, but which would lead to disaster if Carol is skillful in her choice. Not anticipating that she will choose carelessly, his own interests compel him to ignore the peaks; instead, he must attend particularly to the sinks and lows which blemish the region. This study leads him finally to the road Ray 3, which has as attractive a low as the region affords, namely, one at an altitude of 3-thousand feet. By choosing Ray 3, he can ensure that the camp site will be at least 3-thousand feet up; it will be higher, if Carol is a little careless.

"His wife—as he feared—is just as bright about these matters as he is. As she examines these, she knows better than to waste time mooning over the deep valleys of Carol 3 and Carol 4, much as she would like to camp there. Being a realist, she examines the peaks which occur on her roads, determined to choose a road which contains only little ones. She is thus led, finally, to Carol 2, where a 3-thousand-foot camp site is the worst that can be inflicted on her.

"We now note that something in the nature of a coincidence has occurred. Ray has a strategy (Ray 3) which guarantees that the camp site will have an altitude of 3-thousand feet or more, and Carol has one (Carol 2) which ensures that it will be 3-thousand feet or less. In other words, either player can get a 3-thousand-foot camp site by his own efforts, in the face of a skillful opponent; and he will do somewhat better than this if his opponent is careless."

DEFINITION: When the guaranteed maximum floor for R and the minimum ceiling for C are exactly equal (as they are above), the game is said to have a *saddle point* and is also called a *strictly determined game* because the players should use the strategies which correspond to it. If either alone departs from the saddle-point strategy, he will suffer unnecessary loss. If both depart from it, the situation becomes completely fluid and someone will suffer. Note too, this consequence of having a saddle point: security measures are not strictly necessary. Either can openly announce a choice (if it is the proper one), and the other will be unable to exploit the information and force the other beyond the guaranteed maximum floor or minimum ceiling.

EXERCISE: Show for a general matrix game that the maximum floor for R is less than or equal to the minimum ceiling for C.

Example 4, Chance and Bluffing: A deck consisting of one Ace, one King, one Queen is shuffled and the three cards are dealt face down one to each player and the last card placed in the middle of the table. R inspects his card and can either bet an amount b (including the ante) that he has the higher card or he can "fold." In the latter case, he loses an amount a, the ante, to his opponent. Player C can then inspect the card in the middle of the table and can either call the bet or he can fold, in which case he loses an amount a. If C calls, the player with the higher card receives the amount b from his opponent

The pure strategies for R are four in number (if we assume he always bets if he has an Ace). For example, he might state (to himself) two of his four complete alternative plans this way:

Abbreviation

Pure Strategy (1) $\left\{\begin{array}{l}\text{"If I receive Ace,\quad I will bet."}\\ \quad\text{,,}\qquad\text{,,}\quad\text{King,}\qquad\text{,,}\qquad\text{,,}\\ \quad\text{,,}\qquad\text{,,}\quad\text{Queen,}\qquad\text{,,}\qquad\text{,,}\end{array}\right\}$ (b, b, b)

Pure Strategy (2) $\left\{\begin{array}{l}\quad\text{,,}\qquad\text{,,}\quad\text{Ace,}\qquad\text{,,}\qquad\text{,,}\\ \quad\text{,,}\qquad\text{,,}\quad\text{King,}\qquad\text{,,}\qquad\text{,,}\\ \quad\text{,,}\qquad\text{,,}\quad\text{Queen, I will fold."}\end{array}\right\}$ (b, b, f)

The pure strategies for C depend on whether R folds *or*, if he does not, on the outcome of the middle card. He has eight pure strategies, two of which he might state (to himself) as follows:

Abbreviation

(1) $\left\{\begin{array}{l}\text{"If R folds, I will collect ante."}\\ \text{"If R bets, and middle card is Ace,\quad I will call."}\\ \quad\text{,,}\qquad\text{,,}\qquad\text{,,}\qquad\text{,,}\quad\text{King,}\qquad\text{,,}\qquad\text{,,}\\ \quad\text{,,}\qquad\text{,,}\qquad\text{,,}\qquad\text{,,}\quad\text{Queen,}\qquad\text{,,}\qquad\text{,,}\end{array}\right\}$ (b, b, b)

(2) $\left\{\begin{array}{l}\text{"If R folds, I will collect ante."}\\ \text{"If R bets, and middle card is Ace,\quad I will call."}\\ \quad\text{,,}\qquad\text{,,}\qquad\text{,,}\qquad\text{,,}\quad\text{King,}\qquad\text{,,}\qquad\text{,,}\\ \quad\text{,,}\qquad\text{,,}\qquad\text{,,}\qquad\text{,,}\quad\text{Queen, I will fold."}\end{array}\right\}$ (b, b, f)

[281]

Let us now turn to the payoff under the pure strategy (b, b, b) for R and (b, b, b) for C. We examine the payoffs in the six cases arising out of the random shuffle.

R receives	Middle Card	Probability	The Play		The Payoff
			R	C	
Ace,	King	$\frac{1}{6}$	bet	bet	b
Ace,	Queen	$\frac{1}{6}$	bet	bet	b
King,	Ace	$\frac{1}{6}$	bet	bet	b
King,	Queen	$\frac{1}{6}$	bet	bet	$-b$
Queen,	Ace	$\frac{1}{6}$	bet	bet	$-b$
Queen,	King	$\frac{1}{6}$	bet	bet	$-b$

Expected Payoff: $\dfrac{0}{6} = 0$

In this problem, the payoff for given pure strategies for R and C cannot be stated with certainty because of the random elements which are beyond the control of either player. In this situation, the *expected payoff* is defined to be the "payoff" entry in the game matrix.

With this definition the game matrix (multiplied by 6 to avoid fractions) can be calculated to be

(4)

C

		(bbb)	(bbf)	(bfb)	(bff)	(fbb)	(fbf)	(ffb)	(fff)
R	(bbb)	0	$2a$	$2a$	$4a$	$2a$	$4a$	$4a$	$6a$
	(bbf)	$2b - 2a$	$2b$	$b - a$	$b + a$	$b - a$	$b + a$	0	$2a$
	(bfb)	$-2a$	$-b - a$	0	$-b + a$	$b - a$	0	$a + b$	$2a$
	(bff)	$2b - 4a$	$b - 3a$	$b - 3a$	$-2a$	$2b - 4a$	$b - 3a$	$b - 3a$	$-2a$

EXERCISE: Verify the entries in the game matrix. Which player has the advantage?

EXERCISE: Introduce the full set of pure strategies for R into the matrix game, i.e., include (fbb), (fbf), (ffb), (fff). Do you feel R's decision not to consider the latter possibilities was a good one?

Mixed Strategies.

As R weighs the consequences of various courses of action open to him in a matrix game, he becomes more aware of the need to keep secret his choice of pure strategy. In situations where there will be many repetitions of the same game, any obvious pattern of choice could lead to disastrous consequences.

If R is *completely pessimistic*, i.e., assumes that C knows his plan and will counter it to limit his gain to a bare minimum, then R will select his

Max-Min pure strategy, namely the row r whose row minimum is maximum. As we have seen in the matrix game

(5)
$$
\begin{array}{cc}
(j = 1) & (j = 2)
\end{array}
$$
$$
\begin{array}{c}
(i = 1) \\
(i = 2)
\end{array}
\left[
\begin{array}{cc}
-1 & +1 \\
+1 & -1
\end{array}
\right]
$$

this highest floor is -1 attained when R chooses either $(i = 1)$ or $(i = 2)$. If C is also *completely pessimistic*, he will employ his Min-Max pure strategy, namely the column s whose column maximum is minimum, in this case $+1$. The payoff of a matrix game between two complete pessimists is a_{rs} which is somewhere in between R's highest floor and C's lowest ceiling, i.e.,

(6)
$$
\operatorname*{Max}_{i} \left(\operatorname*{Min}_{j} a_{ij} \right) \leq a_{rs} \leq \operatorname*{Min}_{j} \left(\operatorname*{Max}_{i} a_{ij} \right)
$$

When there is a *saddle point* so that Max-Min = Min-Max, the pure strategy choices r, s are completely satisfactory as a solution to the game because whether R is pessimistic and assumes his opponent knows his choice or, if R is pessimistic and it turns out that his opponent is also, R can do no better. In any case, C can *force* R to accept a maximum gain of a_{rs} and if R deviates, he can only lose and if C deviates, R can only gain in general.

When there is *no saddle point*, the contradictory assumptions on the part of the two players lead to an *unstable* situation. In the event of repetitions of the same game with the same players, we can expect sooner or later one of the players will become bold and change his assumptions about his opponent's finding out and taking advantage of his plan. *Depending on what assumptions are made by the opponents about each other's knowledge of their respective plans, there can be, in general, different solutions to the game.*

If R is less than completely pessimistic (we will call him *conservative*) i.e., assumes that C can never be sure what his plan is, but can guess with what *probabilities* he will use one or the other pure strategy, then R will select the row probabilities so that the smallest "average" payoff in a column is a maximum. (For example, in repeated trials of the same game, R may seek to protect his plan by varying his choice of row and is willing to assume that his opponent cannot discover his particular selection, but at best can only detect his frequency of choice of the various rows.)

In the matrix game above, if row 1 is selected by R with probability x_1 and row 2 with probability $1 - x_1$, and if his opponent chooses strategy j, the *expected payoffs* are

(7)
$$
\begin{array}{cc}
(j = 1) & (j = 2) \\
-1x_1 + 1(1 - x_1), & 1x_1 - 1(1 - x_1)
\end{array}
$$

which simplifies to $1 - 2x_1$, and $-1 + 2x_1$. From $0 \leq x_1 \leq \frac{1}{2}$ the right term is the smaller and its largest value 0 occurs at $x_1 = \frac{1}{2}$. From $\frac{1}{2} < x_1 \leq 1$

the left term is the smaller and its largest value 0 also occurs at $x_1 = \frac{1}{2}$. Hence, in this case if R selects his pure strategies with equal probability, and if C should discover these probabilities, then R can assure himself an expected gain of at least 0.

Because of symmetry, it is obvious that if C makes the same kinds of assumptions with regard to his opponent, C can assure himself an expected payoff of no more than 0 if he randomizes his selections by choosing columns $j = 1$ and $j = 2$ with equal probability. Since the expected maximum floor for R equals the expected minimum ceiling for C, it is clear to C that even if he changes his mind and assumes that R is playing conservatively against him, he cannot take advantage and pay less than zero, and may have to pay more if he deviates. On the other hand, C also notes that he may pay less if he sticks to his optimal conservative mix of pure strategy choices and R deviates from his.

DEFINITION: A *mixed strategy* is a selection among pure strategies with fixed probabilities.

DEFINITION: A *conservative* player is one who assumes that his mixed strategy is known to his opponent.

As a second example of the optimal selection of probabilities for a mixed strategy, let us change the value of $a_{42} = 2$ to $a_{42} = 6$ in Williams' example (3) to avoid a saddle-point solution. Let us now consider the simpler problem of determining an optimal mix between two strategies $i = 3$ and $i = 4$ for the matrix

(8)

	$(j = 1)$	$(j = 2)$	$(j = 3)$	$(j = 4)$	Probabilities
$(i = 3)$	5	3	4	4	x_3
$(i = 4)$	3	6	1	6	$1 - x_3$

It is clear that any choice of a pure strategy on the part of R which becomes known to C (say through many repetitions of the same game using the same pure strategy each time) could at best achieve 3 units (strategy $i = 3$) because his opponent will surely choose $j = 2$. On the other hand, if he chooses $i = 3$ with probability x_3 and $i = 4$ with probability $1 - x_3 = x_4$, then his expected payoff for various j of his opponent would be the weighted average of his former payoffs:

(9)

$(j = 1)$	$(j = 2)$	$(j = 3)$	$(j = 4)$

$$5x_3 + 3(1 - x_3), \ 3x_3 + 6(1 - x_3), \ 4x_3 + 1(1 - x_3), \ 4x_3 + 6(1 - x_3)$$

If $x_3 = 1$, then his opponent will select road $j = 2$ and his payoff will be 3; if $x_3 = 0$, then his opponent will select road $j = 3$ and his payoff will be 1. However, if $\frac{2}{3} < x_3 < 1$, then the *expected value* for any j will be greater than 3. To determine the best value we plot these expectations for different j strategies as a function of x_3. It is clear that C will choose $j = 3$ for $0 \leq x_3 < \frac{5}{6}$ and will choose $j = 2$ for $\frac{5}{6} < x_3 \leq 1$. For $x_3 = \frac{5}{6}$ he can choose either $j = 2$ or $j = 3$ and the expected payoff to R will be $\frac{7}{2}$ which is the best he can do if C knows his mixed strategy. See Fig. 13-1-I.

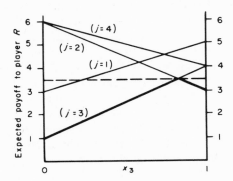

Figure 13-1-I.   Graphical solution of a 2 × 4 matrix game.

On the other hand, if C randomizes his pure strategies, choosing j with probability y_j where $y_2 = y_3 = \frac{1}{2}$ and $y_1 = y_4 = 0$, then all the alternatives facing R reduce to a single dotted line at *constant* height $\frac{7}{2}$. In other words, C can limit his maximum gain to $\frac{7}{2}$ without knowing R's mixed strategy and could very well limit his gain to less if R deviates from his optimal mixed strategy.

The Mathematical Problem.

It thus appears that a conservative player can increase his expectation against an opponent who (he believes) knows he is conservative, by choosing at random among his pure strategies with certain *probabilities* $x_1, x_2, \ldots, x_m$. Any particular choice of x_i values is called a *mixed strategy* for player R. The mathematical problem for him thus becomes one of choosing $x_i \geq 0$, $\Sigma x_i = 1$, so that his expected payoff is maximum. This is referred to as the *optimum mixed strategy* for R. Just how to choose the x_i in general will be the subject of the next section. We will consider also mixed strategies for C which will be denoted by $(y_1, y_2, \ldots, y_n)$ where $y_j \geq 0$ and $\Sigma y_j = 1$.

A remarkable theorem due to von Neumann states that R can always assure himself a value v, the *value* of the game, if he plays his optimal mixed strategy and cannot hope to get more than this same value v even when playing to take advantage of a conservative opponent. What is more, any deviation by R, the other holding firm, runs the risk of a loss. The same statement holds, of course, for C and so we can expect that both players will play their optimal mixed strategies.

[285]

13-2. EQUIVALENCE OF MATRIX GAMES AND LINEAR PROGRAMS; THE MINIMAX THEOREM

Let $x_1, x_2, \ldots, x_m$ denote the probabilities that the row player R selects his pure strategies $i = 1, 2, \ldots, m$. We *assume* that R is *conservative*, that is to say R believes that C knows only R's probability of choice (but not his particular choice) and that C will play to take full advantage of this knowledge. If C chooses pure strategy $j = 1, 2, \ldots, n$, for any particular choice of x_i the expected *payoff* to R is $\sum_{i=1}^{m} a_{ij}x_i$ where, by definition, a_{ij} is the payoff to R if he chooses i and C chooses j. Thus R expects C to choose that pure strategy j corresponding to the *minimum* of these n expressions. Alternatively, if we *let L be any lower bound* for these expressions so that $\sum_{i=1}^{m} a_{ij}x_i \geq L$, then another way to state this is to say that C will choose (for fixed x_i) his pure strategy j to correspond to $j = j_0$ such that $\sum_{i=1}^{m} a_{ij_0}x_i = \text{Max } L$. Since R is interested that L be as large as possible, he will try to choose his x_i such that this Max L is as large as possible. Thus Max L is the largest floor that R can assure himself.

The Row Player's Problem: Choose $x_i \geq 0$ and Max L satisfying

$$
\begin{aligned}
a_{11}x_1 + a_{21}x_2 + \ldots + a_{m1}x_m &\geq L \\
a_{12}x_1 + a_{22}x_2 + \ldots + a_{m2}x_m &\geq L \\
&\cdots \cdots \cdots \cdots \cdots \cdots \cdots \cdots \\
a_{1n}x_1 + a_{2n}x_2 + \ldots + a_{mn}x_m &\geq L \\
x_1 + x_2 + \ldots + x_m &= 1
\end{aligned}
$$
(1) $(x_i \geq 0)$

It is clear that we have reduced the solution of a matrix game for a conservative row player to a linear program. Let us now suppose that his opponent C also plays conservatively. In an analogous manner C is interested in choosing M as small as possible in the problem below. Thus Min M is the smallest ceiling that C can assure himself.

The Column Player's Problem: Choose $y_j \geq 0$ and Min M satisfying

$$
\begin{aligned}
a_{11}y_1 + a_{12}y_2 + \ldots + a_{1n}y_n &\leq M \\
a_{21}y_1 + a_{22}y_2 + \ldots + a_{2n}y_n &\leq M \\
&\cdots \cdots \cdots \cdots \cdots \cdots \cdots \cdots \\
a_{m1}y_1 + a_{m2}y_2 + \ldots + a_{mn}y_n &\leq M \\
y_1 + y_2 + \ldots + y_n &= 1
\end{aligned}
$$
(2) $(y_j \geq 0)$

THEOREM 1: *If each player plays conservatively, each solves a linear program that i the dual of the other; this implies that the largest floor for R equals the lowest ceiling for C.*

PROOF: To see that (1) and (2) are duals of one another, transpose L and M to the left and let $M = z$ be the objective equation for (2) where z is to be minimized and $L = \underline{z}$ be the objective equation for (1) where $\underline{z}$ is to be maximized. Because any values $x_i \geq 0$, $\Sigma x_i = 1$; $y_j \geq 0$, $\Sigma y_j = 1$

may be used to obtain *feasible solutions* to the primal and dual problems, the *duality theorem states that optimal solutions exist* and Max L = Min M (§ 6-3, Theorem 1).

In substance, Theorem 1 tells us that if C plays conservatively, he can always hold R to the maximum assured gain whether or not R plays his optimal mixed strategy. Any deviation by R from his optimal runs risk of loss if C sticks to his optimal mixed strategy and there is a possibility of gain to R if C deviates from his. In such a situation we can expect that both players will use their optimal mixed strategies.

DEFINITIONS: The pair of optimal mixed strategies, if both players play conservatively, is called *the solution of the matrix game*; the resulting guaranteed expected payoff to the row player is called *the value of the game*.

THEOREM 2 (*von Neumann's Minimax Theorem*): Given $\Sigma x_i = \Sigma y_j = 1$, $x_i \geq 0$, $y_j \geq 0$,

$$(3) \qquad \operatorname*{Max}_{x} \operatorname*{Min}_{y|x} \sum_i \sum_j a_{ij} x_i y_j = \operatorname*{Min}_{y} \operatorname*{Max}_{x|y} \sum_i \sum_j a_{ij} x_i y_j$$

The symbol $y|x$ is to be read "y given x." The left-hand side of (3) means: For some fixed (given) x, minimize the sum with respect to y; this results in a value that is a function of x; now choose x so that this value is maximum. Part of the term appearing on the right above may be rewritten (because $\Sigma x_i = 1$, $x_i \geq 0$),

$$\operatorname*{Max}_{x|y} \sum_i x_i \sum_j a_{ij} y_j = \operatorname*{Max}_i \sum_j a_{ij} y_j$$

and is the payoff to R if R knows C's mixed strategy and makes use of it. If C plays conservatively, he minimizes the entire right expression. Hence the right-hand side is a restatement of C's problem, and its value is Min M. Similarly, the left side is a restatement of R's problem and its value is Max L. In short, Theorem 2 is a concise statement of Theorem 1, since it includes (1) and (2).

COROLLARY 1: *If C's optimal strategy yields a strict inequality in the ith relation of (2), then R's optimal strategy must have $x_i = 0$; if R's optimal strategy yields a strict inequality in the jth relation of (1), then C's optimal strategy must have $y_j = 0$.* (For proof see Theorem 4, § 6-4.)

Equivalent Linear Programs.

We will now discuss various linear programs equivalent to the game problem [Dantzig, 1951-1; Gale, Kuhn, and Tucker, 1951-1]. Introducing into (2) slack variables $y_{n+i} \geq 0$, we have

$$(4) \qquad a_{11} y_1 + a_{12} y_2 + \ldots + a_{1n} y_n + y_{n+1} = M$$
$$\cdots\cdots\cdots\cdots\cdots\cdots\cdots\cdots\cdots\cdots\cdots\cdots$$
$$a_{m1} y_1 + a_{m2} y_2 + \ldots + a_{mn} y_n + y_{n+m} = M$$
$$y_1 + y_2 + \ldots + y_n = 1$$

By subtracting the first equation from each of the others (except the last), the resulting system is equivalent to a linear program in standard form. Find $y_j \geq 0$ and Min M satisfying

$$
\begin{aligned}
(5) \quad & a_{11}y_1 + a_{12}y_2 + \ldots + a_{1n}y_n + y_{n+1} = M \\
& (a_{21} - a_{11})y_1 + (a_{22} - a_{12})y_2 + \ldots + (a_{2n} - a_{1n})y_n + (y_{n+2} - y_{n+1}) = 0 \\
& \ldots\ldots\ldots\ldots\ldots\ldots\ldots\ldots\ldots\ldots\ldots\ldots\ldots\ldots\ldots\ldots\ldots\ldots\ldots\ldots \\
& (a_{m1} - a_{11})y_1 + (a_{m2} - a_{12})y_2 + \ldots + (a_{mn} - a_{1n})y_n + (y_{n+m} - y_{n+1}) = 0 \\
& y_1 + y_2 + \ldots + y_n = 1
\end{aligned}
$$

EXERCISE: Show that solutions to primal and dual systems of (1), (2) and hence to (5) always exist.

EXERCISE: Show that if a constant K is added to each element of the payoff matrix, the optimal mixed strategy for either player is unchanged.

Another more symmetric way of effecting the reduction to standard form is found by substituting $y_j'M = y_j$ in (2), thus obtaining

$$
\begin{aligned}
(6) \quad & a_{11}y_1' + a_{12}y_2' + \ldots + a_{1n}y_n' \leq 1 & (y_j' \geq 0) \\
& \ldots\ldots\ldots\ldots\ldots\ldots\ldots\ldots\ldots\ldots\ldots\ldots\ldots \\
& a_{m1}y_1' + a_{m2}y_2' + \ldots + a_{mn}y_n' \leq 1 \\
& y_1' + y_2' + \ldots + y_n' = \frac{1}{M} \ (\text{Max})
\end{aligned}
$$

Note $y_j' \geq 0$. *This substitution is valid* only if the value of the game, M, is known to be positive. However, since an arbitrary constant K can be added to all the elements of a payoff matrix without affecting the optimal mixed strategy, the restriction $M > 0$ presents no difficulties.

EXERCISE: How large must K be to guarantee $M > 0$?

Reduction of a Game to a Symmetric Game.

A two-person game is symmetric if the *same* number of pure strategies is open to both players and if the payoff to player R, when he selects his strategy i and his opponent selects j, is the same as the payoff to player C when the latter selects i and his opponent selects j. In other words, if $a_{ij} = -a_{ji}$ for all i, j. A matrix with this property is called *skew-symmetric*.

EXERCISE: Prove that the value of a symmetric matrix game is zero.

Von Neumann and Morgenstern [1944-1] first showed how to find a symmetric game matrix which is equivalent to any given game matrix. Later Gale, Kuhn, and Tucker [1951-1] showed a more compact way to symmetrize a game based on the same device by which a linear program is reduced to a game (see (11)). To reduce a game with matrix A to another game which is symmetric, we assume all $a_{ij} > 0$ (by adding a sufficiently large constant if necessary) and consider the dual programs which yield the optimum mixed strategies x and y of the two players:

(7)
$$\begin{cases} u^T x = 1 \\ A^T x \geq vL \\ L = \underline{z} \ (\text{Max}), \end{cases} \qquad \begin{cases} v^T y = 1 \qquad (x \geq 0, \ y \geq 0) \\ Ay \leq Mu \\ M = \bar{z} \ (\text{Min}) \end{cases}$$

where T, as in Chapter 8, denotes the transpose and $u^T = (1, 1, \ldots, 1)$, $v^T = (1, 1, \ldots, 1)$ are m- and n-component row vectors; thus $u^T x = \Sigma x_i = 1$ and $v^T y = \Sigma y_j = 1$.

We now consider a new matrix game with skew-symmetric matrix (8) of $m + n + 1$ columns and rows, and with a *new* pair of players:

(8)
$$\begin{array}{c} \begin{array}{ccc} \bar{x} & \bar{y} & t \end{array} \\ \begin{array}{c} \bar{x} \\ \bar{y} \\ t \end{array} \left[\begin{array}{ccc} 0 & A & -u \\ -A^T & 0 & v \\ u^T & -v^T & 0 \end{array} \right] \end{array}$$

where $(\bar{x}, \bar{y}, t) = (\bar{x}_1, \ldots, \bar{x}_m; \bar{y}_1, \ldots, \bar{y}_n; t)$ denotes the optimal mixed strategy of either new player, and $\Sigma \bar{x}_i + \Sigma \bar{y}_j + t = 1$.

EXERCISE: Prove that if $\bar{x}, \bar{y}, t$ is optimal for player R, it is also optimal for player C.

THEOREM 3: *If a game with matrix A has all positive elements, then any optimal mixed strategy $(\bar{x}, \bar{y}, t)$ for either player of the symmetric game (8) will yield optimal mixed strategies x, y and payoff M for players of the original game, namely*

(9a)
$$y = \bar{y} / \sum \bar{y}_j, \qquad x = \bar{x} / \sum \bar{x}_i, \qquad M = 2t/(1 - t)$$

or conversely,

(9b)
$$\bar{y} = y/(M + 2), \qquad \bar{x} = x/(M + 2), \qquad t = M/(M + 2)$$

PROOF: Since the value of the symmetric game must necessarily be zero, the optimal mixed strategy satisfies

(10)
$$\begin{aligned} A\bar{y} \quad - ut \quad &\leq 0; \qquad (\bar{x} \geq 0, \ \bar{y} \geq 0, \ t \geq 0) \\ -A^T\bar{x} + vt \quad &\leq 0; \\ \sum \bar{x}_i \quad - \sum \bar{y}_j \quad &\leq 0; \\ \sum \bar{x}_i \quad + \sum \bar{y}_j + t &= 1; \end{aligned}$$

where (10) is a special case of (2) when the skew-symmetric S replaces the A matrix of (2) and the value of the game is replaced by zero. We now observe that $t > 0$ if matrix A has all positive elements, because $t = 0$ implies $\bar{y} = 0$ from the first inequality, but then $\Sigma \bar{x}_i = 0$ by the next to the last inequality and $\Sigma \bar{x}_i = 1$ by the last equation—a contradiction. Next we observe from Corollary 1 that $\Sigma \bar{x}_i = \Sigma \bar{y}_j$ because $t > 0$ implies

[289]

the "first" player of the symmetric game selects the last row with *positive* probability which means the expected payoff $\Sigma \bar{x}_i - \Sigma \bar{y}_j$ is maximal, i.e., zero. Finally, we note that $\bar{x} \neq 0$, for assuming $\bar{x} = 0$ would contradict the second equality; from $\Sigma \bar{x}_i = \Sigma \bar{y}_j$ follows $\bar{y} \neq 0$, and thus $t < 1$ from the last equality. It is therefore possible to define mixed strategies x and y and $M = L$ by (9) and observe that (10) reduces to (7) with $M = L$; hence x and y are optimal solutions to the dual programs and therefore optimal mixed strategies for the matrix A. Q.E.D.

Reduction of a Program to a Symmetric Game.

Analogous to the above we consider the dual programs

$$(11) \qquad \begin{cases} A^T x \leq c \\ b^T x = \underline{z} \text{ (Max)} \end{cases} \qquad \begin{cases} Ay \geq b \\ c^T y = z \text{ (Min)} \end{cases} \qquad (x \geq 0, y \geq 0)$$

where b and c are column vectors and study their relationship to the skew-symmetric game matrix,

$$(12) \qquad \begin{array}{c} \\ \bar{x} \\ \bar{y} \\ t \end{array} \begin{array}{ccc} \bar{x} & \bar{y} & t \\ \begin{bmatrix} 0 & -A & +b \\ +A^T & 0 & -c \\ -b^T & c^T & 0 \end{bmatrix} \end{array}$$

THEOREM 4: *A necessary and sufficient condition that solutions to linear programs* (11) *exist is that there exists an optimal mixed strategy* $(\bar{x}, \bar{y}, t)$ *to the symmetric game* (12) *with* $t > 0$. *The optimal solution to the programs is* $x = \bar{x}/t$, *and* $y = \bar{y}/t$.

The reduction of a linear program to a game was first established in 1948, based on conversations between the author and G. W. Brown. Soon thereafter, both Brown and Tucker noted its skew-symmetric game matrix [Dantzig, 1951-1].

PROOF: The optimal mixed strategy satisfies

$$(13) \qquad \begin{aligned} -A\bar{y} + bt &\leq 0 \\ A^T\bar{x} \qquad - ct &\leq 0 \\ -b^T\bar{x} + c^T\bar{y} \qquad &\leq 0 \end{aligned} \qquad (\bar{x} \geq 0, \bar{y} \geq 0)$$

Setting $\bar{y} = yt$, $\bar{x} = xt$, and noting $t > 0$, yields

$$(14) \qquad \begin{aligned} Ay &\geq b \\ A^T x &\leq c \\ c^T y &\leq b^T x \end{aligned} \qquad (x \geq 0, y \geq 0)$$

However, if the first inequality of (14) is multiplied on the left by x^T and the second by y^T, we obtain $b^T x \leq x^T A y \leq c^T y$. This together with the last inequality of (14) implies

$$(15) \qquad z = c^T y = b^T x = \underline{z}$$

Hence, by the Duality Theorem (§ 6-3, Theorem 1), x and y are optimal solutions to the dual programs.

Conversely, if optimal solutions x, y exist for the dual programs, then we can reverse our steps by defining $t > 0$ by

(16)
$$t \left(\sum x_i + \sum y_j + 1 \right) = 1$$

and setting $tx = \bar{x}$ and $ty = \bar{y}$.

The reduction of a linear program to a game depends on finding a solution of a game with $t > 0$. If $t = 0$ in a solution, it does not necessarily mean that an optimal feasible solution to the linear program does not exist. See Problems 3 through 7 at the end of the chapter.

13-3. CONSTRUCTIVE SOLUTION TO A MATRIX GAME (ALTERNATIVE PROOF OF MINIMAX THEOREM)

The matrix game is solved by a sequence of pivot operations on the linear program representing either the row or column player's problem. The rules of pivot choice will be reviewed so that the reader is provided with a constructive proof of the Minimax Theorem independent of the earlier chapters.[4]

The linear program § 13-2-(4) is set up in detached coefficient form (1) with constant terms in the first column; next, the columns y_{n+i} corresponding to slack variables; next, $(-M)$, the variable to be maximized, and then the main variables y_j.

(1)

Constants	y_{n+1}	$\cdots$	y_{n+m-1}	y_{n+m}	$(-M)$	y_1	y_2	$\cdots$	y_n
1					0	1	1	$\ldots$	1
0	1				1	a_{11}	a_{12}	$\cdots$	a_{1n}
.		.			.	.	.		.
.			.		.	.	.		.
.					.	.	.		.
0			1		1	$a_{m-1.1}$	$a_{m-1.2}$	$\cdots$	$a_{m-1.n}$
0				1	1	a_{m1}	a_{m2}	$\cdots$	a_{mn}

For convenience we assume the rows and columns of (1) are arranged so that

$$a_{m1} = \underset{j}{\text{Min}} \, [\underset{i}{\text{Max}} \, a_{ij}]$$

By multiplying the last row by -1 and the first row by $(a_{m1} - a_{k1})$ and adding their sum to row $k = 2, 3, \ldots, m - 1$ results in the equivalent tableau (2), where $a'_{kj} = a_{kj} - a_{mj} - a_{k1} + a_{m1}$. The last row is obtained

---

[4] Material in this section is drawn from Dantzig [1956-1], Tucker [1960-3], and Dorfman [1951-2].

by multiplying the top row by $-a_{m1}$ and adding to the last row. Heavy dots are placed below the unit vector columns $y_{n+1}, \ldots, y_{n+m-1}, (-M), y_1$.

(2)

Cycle 0

Constants	y_{n+1}	$\cdots$	y_{n+m-1}	y_{n+m}	$-M$	y_1	y_2	$\cdots$	y_n
1				0		1	1	$\ldots$ 1	
$a_{m1} - a_{11}$	1			-1		0	a'_{12}	$\ldots$	a'_{1n}
$\cdot$		$\cdot$		$\cdot$		$\cdot$	$\cdot$		$\cdot$
$\cdot$			$\cdot$	$\cdot$		$\cdot$	$\cdot$		$\cdot$
$a_{m1} - a_{m-1,1}$			1	-1		0	$a'_{m-1,2}$	$\ldots$	$a'_{m-1,n}$
$-a_{m1}$				1	1	0	$a_{m2} - a_{m1}$	$\cdots$	$a_{mn} - a_{m1}$

Each cycle provides an improved mixed strategy for the column player C. The probability of choosing column j of the matrix game is zero, unless the corresponding column for y_j in some cycle is a unit vector column with a dot below. The value of y_j for such a column with a unit coefficient in row i is the ith component of the constant column. Thus for cycle 0, $y_1 = 1$. Let us suppose the equivalent system in tableau form for cycle p is given by (3) which always includes some $m + 1$ unit vector columns (usually indicated by dots below these columns).

Cycle p

(3)

Constants	y_{n+1}	y_{n+2}	$\cdots$	y_{n+m}	$-M$	y_1	$\cdots$	y_s	$\cdots$	y_n
$\bar{b}_1$	β_{11}	β_{12}	$\cdots$	β_{1m}	0	$\bar{a}_1$	$\cdots$	$\bar{a}_{1s}$	$\cdots$	$\bar{a}_{1n}$
$\cdot$	$\cdot$			$\cdot$	$\cdot$			$\cdot$		$\cdot$
$\cdot$	$\cdot$	$\cdot$		$\cdot$	$\cdot$	$\cdot$		$\cdot$		$\cdot$
$\bar{b}_r$	β_{r1}	β_{r2}	$\cdots$	β_{rm}	0	$\bar{a}_{r1}$	$\cdots$	$\bar{a}_{rs}$	$\cdots$	$\bar{a}_{rn}$
$\cdot$	$\cdot$	$\cdot$		$\cdot$	$\cdot$	$\cdot$		$\cdot$		$\cdot$
$\cdot$	$\cdot$	$\cdot$		$\cdot$	$\cdot$	$\cdot$		$\cdot$		$\cdot$
$\bar{b}_m$	β_{m1}	β_{m2}	$\cdots$	β_{mm}	0	$\bar{a}_{m1}$	$\cdots$	$\bar{a}_{ms}$	$\cdots$	$\bar{a}_{mn}$
$-M_0$	$\bar{c}_{n+1}$	$\bar{c}_{n+2}$	$\cdots$	$\bar{c}_{n+m}$	1	$\bar{c}_1$	$\cdots$	$\bar{c}_s$	$\cdots$	$\bar{c}_n$

THEOREM 1: *If $\bar{c}_j \geq 0$ for all j and $\bar{b}_i \geq 0$ for all i, then an optimal mixed strategy for R is $x_i = \bar{c}_{n+i}$ for $i = 1, 2, \ldots, m$, and an optimal mixed strategy for C is to choose columns j of the matrix game with probability 0 unless the corresponding j in (3) is a dotted i^{th} unit column, $j = j_i$, in which case $y_{j_i} = \bar{b}_i$; moreover, M_0 is the value of the matrix game.*

PROOF: Note that the linear combination of rows of (1) with weights $M, x_1, x_2, \ldots, x_m$ that forms the last equation of (3) is $-M_0, \bar{c}_{n+1}, \ldots, \bar{c}_{n+m}$. These weights applied to the coefficients of $-M$ yield $\Sigma x_i = 1$, and to any other column j yield $\Sigma x_i a_{ij} = \bar{c}_j + M_0 \geq M_0$. Since $y_{j_i} = \bar{b}_i$ obviously solves C's problem and the payoff is also equal to M_0, the solutions are optimal.

Rules for Pivoting.

Step 1. Choose pivot column s (and dot column) by

$$(4) \qquad \bar{c}_s = \text{Min } \bar{c}_j \qquad (j = 1, 2 \ldots, n + m)$$

If $\bar{c}_s \geq 0$ exit via step 4.

Step 2. Choose pivot row r (and remove dot from column with unity in row r) from among rows i with $\bar{a}_{is} > 0$ such that the row vector

$$(5) \qquad [\bar{b}_r, \beta_{r1}, \beta_{r2}, \ldots, \beta_{rm}]/\bar{a}_{rs}$$

is the *lexicographic minimum* of the row vectors

$$(6) \qquad [\bar{b}_i, \beta_{i1}, \beta_{i2}, \ldots, \beta_{im}]/\bar{a}_{is}$$

This is done by first comparing the leading components of these vectors, thus

$$\bar{b}_r/\bar{a}_{rs} = \text{Min } \bar{b}_i/\bar{a}_{is} \qquad (\bar{a}_{rs}, \bar{a}_{is} > 0)$$

where $\bar{a}_{is} = \beta_{ik}$ if $s = n + k$.

The Rule for Resolving Ties

> If the choice of r is not unique so that $r = r_1, r_2, \ldots$ yields the minimum ratio above, then pass to column y_{n+1} and choose pivot row r by
>
> $$\frac{\beta_{r1}}{\bar{a}_{rs}} = \text{Min } \frac{\beta_{i1}}{\bar{a}_{is}} \qquad (r, i = r_1, r_2, \ldots)$$
>
> If the choice of r is still not unique so that $r = r_1', r_2', \ldots$ minimizes both ratios above, pass to column y_{n+2} and choose row r by
>
> $$\frac{\beta_{r2}}{\bar{a}_{rs}} = \text{Min } \frac{\beta_{i2}}{\bar{a}_{is}} \qquad (r, i = r_1', r_2', \ldots)$$
>
> Continue in this manner, passing to columns $y_{n+3}, y_{n+4}, \ldots$ until r is uniquely chosen.

Step 3. Pivot; cycle p is complete. Return to Step 1.

Step 4. Terminate by computing an *optimal mixed strategy* for player R:

$$(7) \qquad x_1 = \bar{c}_{n+1}, \, x_2 = \bar{c}_{n+2}, \ldots, x_m = \bar{c}_{n+m}$$

and an optimal mixed strategy for player C: choose column j of the matrix game with probability 0 for $j = 1, 2, \ldots, n$ unless corresponding to j in cycle p is a dotted ith unit vector column, in which case for each such i

$$(8) \qquad y_{j_i} = \bar{b}_i$$

[293]

Note on Lexicographic Ordering.

We now digress for a moment and discuss a way to arrange or order a set of vectors (each with the same number of components) in sequence in much the same way that one orders a set of words in a dictionary; we will therefore refer to this way of ordering vectors as "lexicographic." We define a vector R as greater than zero in the lexicographic sense or, more simply, *lexico-positive*[5] and denoted $R \succ 0$, if it has at least one non-zero component, the first of which is positive. We next define a vector R to be *greater than* S in the lexicographic sense, denoted $R \succ S$, if $R - S \succ 0$.

EXERCISE:

(1) Show that the lexicographic ordering relation is transitive, i.e., $R \succ S$, $S \succ T$, implies $R \succ T$.

(2) Show that any two vectors R and S with the same number of components satisfy either $R \succ S$, $S \succ R$, or $R = S$; show also that $R \succ S$ implies $R \neq S$.

(3) Let $R \succeq S$ mean that either $R \succ S$ or $R = S$; show that $R \succeq S$ and $S \succeq R$ implies $R = S$.

(4) If $R \succ 0$ and $S \succ 0$, then $R + S \succ 0$. If $k > 0$ is a scalar and $R \succ 0$, then $kR \succ 0$.

Example: A. W. Tucker in his [1960-3] paper, "Solving a Matrix Game by Linear Programming," provides us with the following matrix game

$$(9) \qquad \begin{bmatrix} 1 & -1 & 0 \\ -6 & 3 & -2 \\ 8 & -5 & 2 \end{bmatrix}$$

The column players problem in detached coefficient form is:

(10)

Constants	y_4	y_5	y_6	$-M$	y_1	y_2	y_3
1				0	1	1	1
0	1			1	1	−1	0
0		1		1	−6	3	−2
0			1	1	8	−5	2*

By analogy with (2), the starred entry $a_{33} = 2$ is Min [Max a_{ij}], hence the
$\quad\quad\quad\quad\quad\quad\quad\quad\quad\quad\quad\quad\quad\quad\quad\quad\quad j \quad\quad i$
cycle-0 tableau (11) is obtained from (10) by two easy pivot operations such that the y_4, y_5, $-M$, y_3 columns are unit vectors.

---

[5] The abbreviated term is due to A. W. Tucker.

Cycle 0

(11)

Constants	y_4	y_5	y_6	$-M$	y_1	y_2	y_3	
1					1	1	1	
2	1		-1		-5	6		Tie
4		1	-1		-10	12		Tie
-2			1	1	6	-7		

● ● ● ★ ●

Note that $r = 2$ and $r = 3$ are both tied for pivot since $\frac{2}{6} = \frac{4}{12}$. However, lexicographically the vector $\frac{1}{6}[2\ 1\ 0\ \text{-}1\ 0] > \frac{1}{12}[4\ 0\ 1\ \text{-}1\ 0]$. Hence $r = 3$ is chosen for pivot row. Pivoting on 12 yields

Cycle 1

(12)

Constants	y_4	y_5	y_6	$-M$	y_1	y_2	y_3
8/12		$-1/12$	1/12		22/12		1
0	1	$-6/12$	$-6/12$		0		
4/12		1/12	$-1/12$		$-10/12$	1	
$+4/12$		7/12	5/12	1	2/12		

● ● ● ●

Since all entries in the bottom row are nonnegative, the cycling is terminated. The optimal solution for R is taken from the bottom row in the y_4, y_5, y_6 columns; it is $x_1 = 0$, $x_2 = \frac{7}{12}$, $x_3 = \frac{5}{12}$. The optimal solution for C is taken from the constant column; it is $y_3 = \frac{8}{12}$, $y_2 = \frac{4}{12}$ and all other non-slack y_j are zero. The value of the game is $M_0 = -\frac{4}{12}$.

Proof of Algorithm.

In (2), the tableau for cycle 0, entries in columns for y_1, y_{n+1}, y_{n+2}, · · ·, y_{n+m-1}, $-M$ form an identity matrix. The effect of a pivot operation in column s, row r is to transform column s into a unit vector with unity in the rth position. The effect of several cycles is to shift the position of the identity matrix into the columns y_{j_1}, y_{j_2}, · · ·, y_{j_m} and the $-M$ column. (The column for $-M$ remains the same from cycle to cycle.) The set of columns of the cycle-0 tableau corresponding to these unit columns in the cycle p tableau is referred to as the *basis* for cycle p. We shall denote it by B. It is easy to see that B is non-singular and, because under the pivot operations B transforms into the identity matrix (see § 8-4-(9), (10), and sequel), the identity matrix consisting of the first $m + 1$ columns of cycle 0 transforms into B^{-1} of cycle p.

We now show that the choice of pivot row r given in Step 2 always results in a unique value for r. Since r must be chosen among i such that $\bar{a}_{is} > 0$ we first show that at least one $\bar{a}_{is}$ is positive (so that this class is

[295]

non-empty). Notice in the tableau of cycle p that the columns corresponding to $y_{j_1}, y_{j_2}, \ldots, y_{j_m}, -M$, form an identity matrix; hence, the linear combination of these columns using weights $\bar{a}_{is}$ results in column s and therefore this same relation among columns must hold also for the original tableau (1) (since pivoting does not effect a linear-combination relation among columns). However, assuming on the contrary that all $\bar{a}_{is} \leq 0$ would imply that some nonpositive linear combination of certain columns of (1) could yield column s. But this is clearly impossible since each column $j = 1, 2, \ldots, n$ has unity in the top row and the linear combination must include at least one such j.

We now show that the rule for deciding in which row to choose the pivot term results in a unique choice because non-uniqueness would imply at least two row vectors (5) and (6) to be equal component by component; but then, the square submatrix of (3) consisting of the first $m + 1$ rows and columns (starting with the constants column) would be singular—a contradiction, since this submatrix is obtained from (1) by a sequence of pivot operations and the corresponding submatrix of (1) is an identity matrix and, hence, non-singular.

The rule for selection of r also prevents the repetition of a basis obtained on an earlier cycle. To demonstrate this, let us denote for cycle p the rows of the tableau by $R_1, R_2, \ldots, R_m; R_{m+1}$, and those for cycle $p + 1$ by $R_1^*, R_2^*, \ldots, R_m^*; R_{m+1}^*$. We will now show

LEMMA 1: $R_i \succ 0$ for all i and any cycle p.

LEMMA 2: $R_{m+1}^* \succ R_{m+1}$.

The Proof is Inductive. The relation between R_i and R_i^* is

$$(13) \qquad R_i^* = R_i - R_r \frac{\bar{a}_{is}}{\bar{a}_{rs}} \qquad (i \neq r)$$

$$R_r^* = R_r \frac{1}{\bar{a}_{rs}}$$

$$R_{m+1}^* = R_{m+1} - R_r \frac{\bar{c}_s}{\bar{a}_{rs}} \qquad \text{where } \bar{c}_s < 0$$

where r is the pivot row and $\bar{a}_{rs} > 0$. It follows at once that $R_r^* \succ 0$ if $R_r \succ 0$; moreover if $\bar{a}_{is} \leq 0$, then $R_i^* \succ 0$ since R_i and $-R_r(\bar{a}_{is}/\bar{a}_{rs})$ are each lexico-positive by our inductive assumptions (the same argument applies to R_{m+1}^* since $\bar{c}_s < 0$ and thus establishes Lemma 2). On the other hand, if $\bar{a}_{is} > 0$, then we write

$$R_i^* = [R_i/\bar{a}_{is} - R_r/\bar{a}_{rs}]\bar{a}_{is}$$

We now observe that the rule for selecting the pivot row in Step 2 is the same as selecting the lexico-smallest vector $R_i/\bar{a}_{is}$ among i such that $\bar{a}_{is} > 0$.

[296]

Thus $R_i^* \succeq 0$. As observed earlier, the square submatrix of the first $m + 1$ rows and columns of (3) is non-singular so that a non-zero component exists for each vector R_i somewhere among its first $m + 1$ components and hence on the next iteration for $R_i^* \neq 0$ also. Since we have already shown $R_i^* \succeq 0$ it follows that $R_i^* \succ 0$.

To show finiteness of the algorithm note that the last row is strictly increasing in the lexicographic sense; hence *no tableau can be the same as one obtained earlier*. We get a contradiction by assuming an infinite number of iterations because *the number of different bases is finite*, and, therefore, on some iteration, there would be a basis that is the same as one obtained earlier. But in this case the entire tableau would have to be repeated because the $\bar{a}_{ij}$ in the tableau simply express the combination of columns in the basis that form column j and this linear combination is unique and invariant under pivoting.

13-4. PROBLEMS

1. Suppose each of two players has a penny, a nickel, and a dime that he can select from as his pure strategies. If both players select the same type coin, Player 1 wins Player 2's coin; if the two coins *are not the same type*, then Player 2 wins Player 1's coin. How much should Player 2 give Player 1 before the game in order to make the game fair?

2. What is the analogue for a linear program of the saddle point solution of a game, if it exists?

3. (a) Show that, if $t = 0$ in Theorem 4 of § 13-2, this does not imply that a program does not have a solution.

   (b) Show that, if $t = 0$ and if the optimal solution has *positive slack* in the complementary relation of the dual system using the solution to the symmetric game, then there exists no solution to the linear program.

   (c) Show that, if $t = 0$ and there is *zero slack* in the complementary relation, it does not imply that a program does not have a solution.

   (d) If the coefficients $a_{ij} > 0$, show that $t > 0$.

   (e) (Shapley) Show that no feasible solution exists for the primal program below but that $t = 0$ and its complementary slack is zero for the equivalent game.

$$\text{Primal Program:} \begin{cases} 0y_1 \geq +1 \\ 0y_1 = z \text{ (Min)} \end{cases}$$

Solution → 0 1 0

$$\text{Equivalent Game:} \begin{bmatrix} 0 & 0 & 1 \\ 0 & 0 & 0 \\ -1 & 0 & 0 \end{bmatrix} \begin{matrix} 0 \\ 1 \\ 0 \end{matrix}$$

↑
Solution

(f) (Shapley) Show that feasible solutions exist and no lower bound for v exists for the dual of the above program (shown below) but that $t = 0$ and its complementary slack is zero for the equivalent game.

$$\text{Solution} \to 1 \quad 0 \quad 0$$

$$\begin{array}{cc}
\text{Dual} \\
\text{Program:}
\end{array}
\left\{
\begin{array}{l}
0x_1 \leq 0 \\
+1x_1 = v \ (\text{Max})
\end{array}
\right.
\qquad
\begin{array}{c}
\text{Equivalent} \\
\text{Game:}
\end{array}
\begin{bmatrix}
0 & 0 & 0 \\
0 & 0 & -1 \\
0 & 1 & 0
\end{bmatrix}
\begin{array}{c}
1 \\
0 \\
0
\end{array}$$

$$\uparrow$$
$$\text{Solution}$$

where $x_1 \geq 0$, $y_1 \geq 0$.

4. Construct an example to show that feasible solutions to both the primal and dual systems can exist, but that the solution to the equivalent game can have $t = 0$.

5. Prove false: If a solution to a game is unique when variables corresponding to positive complementary slack values are dropped, then the remaining variables have positive values.

6. (Wolfe) Prove the following theorem: *All solutions of the corresponding game have $t > 0$ if, and only if, there exist u, $x > 0$ such that $uA > c$ and $Ax < b$.*

7. (Wolfe) Prove the following theorem: *If the set of $x \geq 0$, $Ax \leq b$ is non-empty, bounded and has an interior, and A has no zero row, then any solution $[x, u, t]$ of the corresponding game has $t > 0$.*

REFERENCES

Blackwell and Girshick, 1954-1
Bohnenblust, Karlin, and Shapley, 1950-1
Borel, 1921-1, 1924-1, 1927-1, 1953-1
Brown, 1951-1
Candler, 1960-1
Dantzig, 1951-1, 1956-1
Dorfman, 1951-2
Dresher, 1961-1
Dresher, Shapley, and Tucker, 1964-1
Dresher, Tucker, and Wolfe, 1957-1
Flood, 1962-1
Gale, 1960-1
Gale, Kuhn, and Tucker, 1951-1
Gass, 1964-1
Karlin, 1959-1
Kemeny, Snell, and Thompson, 1957-1
Kuhn and Tucker, 1950-1, 1953-1, 1955-1, 1958-1
Luce and Raiffa, 1957-1
McKinsey, 1952-1
Mills, 1956-1, 1960-1
Morgenstern, 1949-1
Radner, 1959-1
Raiffa, Thompson, and Thrall, 1952-1
Robinson, 1951-1
Schelling, 1960-1
Shapley and Snow, 1950-1
Shubik, 1959-1
Shubik, 1964-1
Tucker, 1950-1, 1960-3
Tucker, and Luce, 1959-1
Vajda, 1956-1
Ville, 1938-1
von Neumann, 1928-1, 1937-1
von Neumann and Morgenstern, 1944-1
Williams, 1954-1

CHAPTER 14

THE CLASSICAL TRANSPORTATION PROBLEM

14-1. HISTORICAL SUMMARY

An important class of linear programming problems of economic and physical origin can be formulated in terms of a network composed of points (nodes) connected by routes (arcs), over which various kinds of transport (flow) take place (see Chapter 19).

The classical transportation problem arises when we must determine an optimal schedule of shipments that:

(a) originate at sources (supply depots) where fixed stockpiles of a commodity are available;

(b) are sent directly to their final destinations (demand depots) where various fixed amounts are required;

(c) exhaust the stockpiles and fulfill the demand; hence, total demand equals total supply;

and finally, the cost must

(d) satisfy a linear objective function; that is, the cost of each shipment is proportional to the amount shipped, and the total cost is the sum of the individual costs.

In this chapter we will take up this problem and show how it may be solved by the simplex method. (Succeeding chapters will explore some of its important variations.)

Although he awakened little interest at the time, L. V. Kantorovich [1939-1] showed that a class of problems closely related to the classical transportation case has a remarkable variety of applications concerned typically with the allotment of tasks to machines whose costs and rates of production vary by task and machine type. He gave a useful but incomplete algorithm for solving such problems (see Chapter 21). Again, in 1942, he wrote a mathematical paper concerned with a *continuous* version of the transportation problem, and in 1948, he authored an applicational study, jointly with Gavurin, on the *capacitated* transportation problem (see Chapter 18).

The now standard form of the problem was first formulated, along with a constructive solution, by Frank L. Hitchcock [1941-1]. His paper, "The Distribution of a Product from Several Sources to Numerous Localities," sketched out the partial theory of a technique foreshadowing the simplex method; it did not exploit special properties of the transportation problem except in finding starting solutions. This paper also failed to attract much attention.

Still another investigator, T. C. Koopmans, as a member of the Combined Shipping Board during World War II, became concerned with using solutions of the transportation problem to help reduce over-all shipping times, for the shortage of cargo ships constituted a critical bottleneck.

In 1947, Koopmans began to spearhead research on the potentialities of linear programs for the study of problems in economics. His historic paper, "Optimum Utilization of the Transportation System" [1947-1], was based on his wartime experience. Because of this and the work done earlier by Hitchcock, the classical case is often referred to as the Hitchcock-Koopmans Transportation Problem.

Another whose work anticipated the recent era of development in linear programming was E. Egerváry, a mathematician. His 1931 paper considered the problem of finding a permutation of ones in a matrix composed of zero and one elements. Based on this investigation, Kuhn [1955-1] developed an efficient algorithmic method for solving assignment problems (see § 15-1). Kuhn's approach, in its turn, underlies the Ford-Fulkerson Method for solution of the classical transportation problem (Chapter 20).

The method to be described in this chapter was developed independently, by specializing the general simplex method [Dantzig, 1951-2].

14-2. ELEMENTARY TRANSPORTATION THEORY

Suppose that m warehouses (origins) contain various amounts of a commodity which must be allocated to n cities (destinations). Specifically, the ith warehouse must dispose of exactly the quantity a_i, while the jth city must receive exactly the quantity b_j. It is assumed that the *total demand equals the total supply*, that is,

(1)
$$\sum_{i=1}^{m} a_i = \sum_{j=1}^{n} b_j$$

Besides the numbers, a_i and b_j, which are *nonnegative*, we are also given a set of numbers, c_{ij}, which may be *unrestricted* (although usually nonnegative under the present interpretation). The number c_{ij} represents the cost (or profit, if negative) of shipping a unit quantity from origin i to destination j. Our problem is to determine the number of units to be shipped from i to j in order that stockpiles will be depleted and needs satisfied at an over-all minimum cost.

[300]

The special structure of the matrix is evident when the equations are written in standard form, as in (2).

(2)

$$
\begin{array}{l}
x_{11} + x_{12} + \ldots + x_{1n} \hspace{6cm} = a_1 \\
\hspace{1.5cm} + x_{21} + x_{22} + \ldots + x_{2n} \hspace{3.5cm} = a_2 \\
\cdots\cdots\cdots\cdots\cdots\cdots\cdots\cdots\cdots\cdots\cdots\cdots\cdots\cdots\cdots\cdots\cdots\cdots \\
\hspace{5cm} x_{m1} + x_{m2} + \ldots + x_{mn} = a_m \\
\hline
x_{11} \hspace{2.5cm} + x_{21} \hspace{2.5cm} + x_{m1} \hspace{2cm} = b_1 \\
\hspace{0.7cm} + x_{12} \hspace{2.3cm} + x_{22} \hspace{2.5cm} + x_{m2} \hspace{1.5cm} = b_2 \\
\cdots\cdots\cdots\cdots\cdots\cdots\cdots\cdots\cdots\cdots\cdots\cdots\cdots\cdots\cdots\cdots\cdots\cdots \\
\hspace{0.7cm} + x_{1n} \hspace{2.3cm} + x_{2n} \hspace{2.5cm} + x_{mn} = b_n \\
\hline
c_{11}x_{11} + \ldots + \quad c_{1n}x_{1n} + c_{21}x_{21} + \ldots + c_{2n}x_{2n} \ldots + c_{m1}x_{m1} + \ldots \quad + c_{mn}x_{mn} = z
\end{array}
$$

EXERCISE: Condition (1) renders the system dependent since the sum of the first m-equations is the same as the sum of the last n. Prove that the rank of the system is exactly $m + n - 1$. Also show that each equation is a linear combination of the other $m + n - 1$ so that any one equation may be called redundant and discarded.

The Standard Transportation Array.

An important feature of this model is that it can be abbreviated in the form of a rectangular array, which displays the values of x_{ij} and c_{ij} in row i and column j, and the values of the constants and corresponding multipliers for the first m equations in a marginal column and for the remaining n equations in a marginal row.

(3)

					Row Totals
x_{11}	x_{12}	x_{13}	x_{14}	x_{15}	a_1
c_{11}	c_{12}	c_{13}	c_{14}	c_{15}	u_1
x_{21}	x_{22}	x_{23}	x_{24}	x_{25}	a_2
c_{21}	c_{22}	c_{23}	c_{24}	c_{25}	u_2
x_{31}	x_{32}	x_{33}	x_{34}	x_{35}	a_3
c_{31}	c_{32}	c_{33}	c_{34}	c_{35}	u_3
b_1	b_2	b_3	b_4	b_5	Column Totals
v_1	v_2	v_3	v_4	v_5	Implicit ← Prices ↑

At any stage of the algorithm, the square (i, j), situated in the ith row and the jth column, contains c_{ij} in its lower right-hand corner while, at its upper left corner, we find x_{ij}^o, the current numerical *value* assigned to x_{ij}. The lack of such an entry implies that x_{ij} is non-basic and hence of zero value. Zero-valued *basic* variables are indicated by a zero entry (degeneracy).

Any square along the right-hand or bottom margin, however, differs in that it contains the row or column *totals*, a_i or b_j, at upper left, and the corresponding current value, u_i^o or v_j^o, of the simplex multipliers at lower right. Each row and column of the array represents an equation. Specifically,

(4) The Row Equations:
$$\sum_{j=1}^{n} x_{ij} = a_i$$
   $(i = 1, 2, \ldots, m)$

(5) The Column Equations:
$$\sum_{i=1}^{m} x_{ij} = b_j$$
   $(j = 1, 2, \ldots, n)$

In order that these equations continue to be satisfied during the course of the algorithm, we must keep the sum of the entries in each row and column equal to the appropriate row or column total, a_i or b_j, which appear in the margins.

Finding a Basic Feasible Solution.

As candidate for the first basic variable, choose any variable, x_{pq}, and make it as large as possible, consistent with row and column totals, i.e., set

$$x_{pq} = \text{Min}\,[a_p, b_q]$$

Case 1: If a_p is less than b_q, then all the other variables in the pth row are to be given the value zero and designated as non-basic. Next delete the pth row, reduce the value of b_q to $(b_q - a_p)$, and proceed in the same manner to evaluate a variable in the *reduced array* composed of the $m - 1$ rows and n columns remaining.

Case 2: If a_p is greater than b_q, then, similarly, the qth column is to be deleted and a_p replaced by $(a_p - b_q)$, etc.

Case 3: If a_p equals b_q, then delete either the row or the column, but *not both*. However, if several columns, but only one row, remain in the reduced array, then drop the qth column, and conversely, if several rows and one column, drop the pth row.

This rule will select as many variables for the basic set as there are rows plus columns, less one, $m + n - 1$, since on the last step, when one row and one column remain, both must be dropped after the last variable is evaluated. The important fact is that, as we shall show, *all basic solutions are of this form*, so that in defining a specific algorithm for achieving optimality, it is unnecessary to consider other forms of solution.

EXERCISE: We have assumed that $\sum_{i=1}^{m} a_i = \sum_{j=1}^{n} b_j$. Show that every reduced array retains this property, so that the last remaining variable can acquire a value consistent with the totals for the single row and column still remaining in the final reduced array.

EXERCISE: Let B be a square matrix. Show that B is nonsingular if and only if $Bx = b$ has a unique solution for every b.

THEOREM 1: *The candidate variables chosen by the rule for initial solution constitute a basic set.*

PROOF: Since the rank of the system is $m + n - 1$, a set of variables, x_{pq}, constitutes a basic set if its values, satisfying all $m + n$ equations, are given *uniquely* as linear combinations of any $m + n - 1$ of the $m + n$ marginals $a_1, a_2, \ldots, a_m; b_1, b_2, \ldots, b_n$, when the remaining variables are set equal to zero. Now, the value given each basic variable by the starting rule is the same as a marginal total of some reduced array, but this total, because of the way in which it was derived, is equal to the difference between partial sums of the original row and column totals. This shows the values are uniquely determined by some *particular* set of $m + n - 1$ marginals. However, because of condition (1), any one of these totals may be re-expressed as a linear combination of the others; for example,

$$b_n = \sum_{i=1}^{m} a_i - \sum_{j=1}^{n-1} b_j$$

COROLLARY 1: *The row totals of each reduced array are expressible as partial sums of the a_i minus partial sums of the b_j, whereas every column total is expressible as the negative of such a difference.*

EXERCISE: Show the above by induction.

The Property of Basis Triangularity.

When a system has the property that every basis is triangular (see § 4-2), then basic solutions are easily obtained. Let numbers, for example zeros, be substituted for all the non-basic variables. The resulting system of equations will, of course, involve only the basic variables. By definition, if triangular, the subsystem will contain at least one equation having exactly one variable, and this variable may, of course, be immediately evaluated by means of a single division. When the value so determined is substituted in the remaining equations, there will again be at least one equation with exactly one variable in the reduced system, and so forth. Thus, all of the basic variables may be evaluated in an analogous way. In particular, since each equation corresponds to a row or a column, this is the same thing as saying that all basic sets of variables can be generated by the starting rule of solution [Dantzig, 1951-2].

THEOREM 2: *Fundamental Theorem for the Transportation Problem: All bases are triangular.*

PROOF: Suppose we have a standard transportation array, similar to (3), with m rows and n columns and with arbitrary constants, a_i and b_j. Consider any particular set of basic variables and substitute the value zero for each of the non-basic variables.

Contrary Assumption: Assume that no row or column has exactly one basic variable. We discount the possibility that some row or column might have no basic variables since this would mean that the left member of the corresponding equation would be zero while the marginal total, presumed arbitrary, could be non-zero. Hence, all columns under our assumption must have two or more basic entries. If k is the total number of basic entries in the array, then, since there are at least two such entries per column, we must have

$$k \geq 2n$$

Similarly, we have

$$k \geq 2m$$

since there are at least two basic variables per row. Summing, we get

(6) $$k \geq m + n$$

Now, there are $m + n$ equations, but since condition (1) renders one of these redundant, the number of basic variables, k, must also satisfy

(7) $$k < m + n$$

in direct contradiction to (6). Thus, we have proved

LEMMA 1: *Some row or column has exactly one basic entry.*

Now to establish the triangularity of the basis, we must show

LEMMA 2: *The subsystem resulting by the exclusion of any redundant equation from the original system still contains an equation in exactly one basic variable.*

Suppose we drop some equation as redundant, say, the last row equation, and again make the contrary assumption, then

(8) $$k \geq 2n$$

$$k' \geq 2(m - 1)$$

where k' is the total number of basic variables in all but the last row. However, since there is at least one basic entry in the last row, we have

(9) $$k \geq k' + 1$$

Hence, adding both relations in (8) and (9), we have

(10) $$2k \geq 2m + 2n - 1 \qquad \text{or}$$

$$k \geq m + n - \tfrac{1}{2}$$

contradicting the fact that at least one equation is redundant. This proves the lemma.

Now, starting with the original array, we delete the row or column having a single entry and repeat the argument for the reduced array, etc., thereby establishing the theorem.

THEOREM 3: *The values of all basic variables are integers if the row and column totals are integers.*

PROOF: The value of each basic variable is the same as a marginal total of some reduced array, but this is expressible as the difference between partial sums of the original row and column totals (see Corollary 1).

Simplex Multipliers.

Instead of using the symbol π_i, we represent the multiplier of the ith row equation as u_i, and that of the jth column equation as v_j. Since *any equation may be considered redundant, we can assign an arbitrary value to one of the simplex multipliers* and then evaluate the set of multipliers, thereby rendered unique, which will cause the vanishing of all the relative cost factors corresponding to basic variables. For the present, we will suppose that

$$(11) \qquad\qquad v_n = 0$$

After multiplying the ith row equation of (2) by u_i and the jth column equation by v_j, we subtract the weighted sum from the objective form, to obtain a modified z-equation,

$$(12) \qquad\qquad \sum_{i,j} \bar{c}_{ij} x_{ij} = z - z_0$$

where

$$(13) \qquad\qquad \bar{c}_{ij} = c_{ij} - (u_i + v_j) \quad \text{for } i = 1, 2, \ldots, m; \text{ and} $$
$$ j = 1, 2, \ldots, n$$

and

$$(14) \qquad\qquad z_0 = \sum_{i=1}^{m} a_i u_i + \sum_{j=1}^{n} b_j v_j$$

The values for u_i and v_j are chosen to make the coefficients of the basic variables vanish, i.e.,

$$(15) \qquad\qquad c_{ij} = u_i + v_j \qquad \text{for } x_{ij}, \text{ a basic variable}$$

Note that (15) defines a *system* of equations in which the simplex multipliers play the part of variables. This system of equations has a matrix which is the *transpose* of the particular basis for which we desire simplex multipliers. (The *basis*, it will be recalled, is the matrix of coefficients belonging to the basic set of variables (§ 4-2 and § 8-2).)

EXERCISE: Show that u_i and v_j may be replaced by $(u_i + k)$ and $(v_j - k)$ without affecting the value of $\bar{c}_{ij}$ and z_0 in (13) and (14); hence, any one of $m + n$ multipliers may be given an arbitrary value in determining the remainder.

THEOREM 4: *When the unit costs, c_{ij}, are integers and one multiplier is given an arbitrary integral value, then all the simplex multipliers will be integers.*

PROOF: Since the basis is triangular, so is its transpose. Moreover, the transpose is also of rank $m + n - 1$. This means that the values of u_i and v_j satisfying (15) can be obtained uniquely, after one of them is arbitrarily assigned, in the same manner as the values of the basic variables; i.e., by looking for one equation in one unknown, etc. Since the coefficients in the basis are either unity or zero, the values of u_i and v_j will be sums and differences of c_{ij} corresponding to basic variables.

Finding an Improved Basic Solution.

The simplex criterion for optimality is $\bar{c}_{ij} \geq 0$ for all (i, j), i.e.,

$$(16) \qquad c_{ij} \geq u_i + v_j, \qquad \text{for } i = 1, 2, \ldots, m; \text{ and}$$
$$j = 1, 2, \ldots, n$$

On the other hand, if for some s and t

$$(17) \qquad c_{st} < u_s + v_t$$

then a new basic solution is obtained by increasing the value of the non-basic variable, x_{st}, if possible, and adjusting the values of the basic variables so as to compensate.

To determine the effect of increasing x_{st}, the terms involving x_{st} are moved to the right in (2), and the values of the basic variables are redetermined.

THEOREM 5: *If the value of a non-basic variable, x_{st}, is allowed to increase, with the other non-basic variables remaining at zero, the value of any basic variable, x_{ij}, will change from x_{ij}^o to*

$$(18) \qquad x_{ij} = x_{ij}^o \pm \delta x_{st}, \qquad \text{where } \delta = 0 \text{ or } 1$$

PROOF: When, in the *general* simplex process, the non-basic variable, x_s, is allowed to increase while the other independent variables remain at zero, the value of the ith basic variable is given by

$$x_{j_i} = \bar{b}_i - \bar{a}_{is} x_s$$

where $\bar{b}_i$ is obtained by solving the basic system of equations when the right-hand side of the ith equation is b_i. The value of $\bar{a}_{is}$ is obtained by solving the same system when the right-hand side is a_{is}. In this case, the coefficient of x_{st}, as given in (2), is unity for the sth row equation and for the tth column equation, and *zero* elsewhere. *Hence, the coefficient of x_{st} in the canonical form is obtained by solving for the values imposed on the basic variables when the constants are replaced by $a_s = 1$ and $b_t = 1$, while all other a_i and b_j are zero.* By Corollary 1, the value of a basic variable is the difference (positive or negative) between some partial sum of the a_i (which in this case can only be unity or zero), and some partial sum of the b_j (also unity or zero). This difference must clearly be $+1$, 0, or -1; (18) is thus established.

Degeneracy.

If all a_i are positive, then degeneracy in the transportation problem can be avoided by considering the class of perturbed problems:

(19)

$$
\begin{array}{ccccc}
x_{11} & x_{12} & \cdots x_{1n} & a_1 \\
x_{21} & x_{22} & \cdots x_{2n} & a_2 \\
\cdot & \cdot & \cdot & \cdot \\
\cdot & \cdot & \cdot & \cdot \\
\cdot & \cdot & \cdot & \cdot \\
x_{m-1,1} & x_{m-1,2} & \cdots x_{mn} & a_{m-1} \\
x_{m1} & x_{m2} & \cdots x_{mn} & a_m + n\varepsilon \\
\end{array}
$$

$$ b_1 + \varepsilon \quad b_2 + \varepsilon \ldots b_n + \varepsilon $$

For our discussion, *we shall assume that the last row equation has been omitted as redundant.* An arbitrary basic solution is chosen by the process of Theorem 1, except that basic variables are not selected in the last row until all other rows have been eliminated. If, at any step, there is a tie for $\varepsilon = 0$ between a reduced row and column total, then that total with the smallest coefficient of ε is selected for the minimum.

THEOREM 6: *It is not possible that there be a tie for minimum and thus a degeneracy in the basic solution for the subsequent perturbed problem.*

PROOF: The coefficient of ε in any row total of the reduced array is either zero or negative, since it is composed of a non-vacuous partial sum of the a_i (excluding $a_m + n\varepsilon$), minus a (possibly vacuous) partial sum of the $b_j + \varepsilon$. Similarly, the coefficient of ε for any column total of the reduced array is always positive, since it is composed of a (non-vacuous) partial sum of the $b_j + \varepsilon$, minus a (possibly vacuous) partial sum of the a_i (excluding $a_m + n\varepsilon$).

The adjusted row totals in each reduced array will always remain positive (non-zero) for $\varepsilon = 0$, while the column totals will be nonnegative. We can see this inductively. Assume all a_i are positive and all b_j are nonnegative. Suppose this is still true for some reduced array, so that $a_i' = \alpha - p\varepsilon$ (where α is positive and p is nonnegative), and that $b_j' = \beta + q\varepsilon$ (where β is nonnegative and q is positive). Now, if x_{ij} becomes a basic variable, then its value is Min $[(\alpha - p\varepsilon), (\beta + q\varepsilon)]$. For $\alpha \leq \beta$, the row total is satisfied and the new column total becomes $(\beta - \alpha) + (p + q)\varepsilon$, where $(\beta - \alpha)$ is nonnegative and $(p + q)$ is positive. On the other hand, if $\beta < \alpha$, then, for ε in some range, $0 < \varepsilon < \varepsilon_0$, the column total is satisfied, and the new row total becomes $(\alpha - \beta) - (p + q)\varepsilon$, with $(\alpha - \beta)$ and $(p + q)$ both positive.

This establishes the assertion that the *initial* basic solution is nondegenerate for a positive range of ε in the neighborhood of $\varepsilon = 0$. If we now perform an iteration of the simplex method, the new basic solution is feasible for some positive range of ε. Since the basis (formed by excluding the last row equation) is *triangular*, we have (by a repetition of the same argument as above) that the values of the new basic variables are of the form $\alpha + \varepsilon\beta$, where either α is positive or it is zero and β is positive. Hence, the new basic solution must be nondegenerate for some range of ε, $0 < \varepsilon < \varepsilon_1$ and the first two basic solutions remain feasible and nondegenerate for any $0 < \varepsilon < \text{Min}(\varepsilon_0, \varepsilon_1)$.

In general, for any sufficiently small ε, there will be a positive (non-zero) decrease in the value imposed on z after each cycle. Orden [1956-1] has shown that no basic feasible solution can be degenerate if $0 < \varepsilon < 1/n$. (See Problems 14 and 15.) Thus, no basis can be repeated, and the algorithm will terminate in a finite number of steps.

14-3. COMPUTATIONAL ALGORITHM FOR THE TRANSPORTATION PROBLEM

A notable feature of this problem is that, whereas linear programs typically require hand-operated calculators or, for larger problems, high-speed computing machinery, the transportation problem frequently is best solved by nothing more sophisticated than pencil and paper, since additions and subtractions are the only calculations required.

The standard transportation array § 14-2-(3) is repeated here for convenience. The array appearing here, however, is slightly different in that it contains certain Theta symbols. These are part of the computational procedure and will be explained later in this section.

(1)

x_{11}	$x_{12} - \theta$			$+\theta*$ (enter)	a_1
c_{11}	c_{12}	c_{13}	c_{14}	c_{15}	u_1
	$x_{22} + \theta$		$x_{24} - \theta$		a_2
c_{21}	c_{22}	c_{23}	c_{24}	c_{25}	u_2
		x_{33}	$x_{34} + \theta$	$x_{35} - \theta$	a_3
c_{31}	c_{32}	c_{33}	c_{34}	c_{35}	u_3
b_1	b_2	b_3	b_4	b_5	
v_1	v_2	v_3	v_4	v_5	Implicit ← Prices ↑

Finding a Good Starting Solution.

Computationally, the starting rule of solution given in the last section is not too practical, since usually the number of iterations required to achieve optimality can be greatly reduced if the basic set is selected with some reference to the values of the coefficients in the objective form. Several rules for selection can be found in the literature; one is

The Least-Cost Rule: Scan the

$$(2) \quad \text{Unit Cost Array:} \quad \begin{bmatrix} c_{11} & c_{12} & \cdots & c_{1n} \\ c_{21} & c_{22} & \cdots & c_{2n} \\ \cdots & \cdots & \cdots & \cdots \\ c_{m1} & c_{m2} & \cdots & c_{mn} \end{bmatrix}$$

for the *smallest* c_{ij} and choose the first basic variable, x_{pq}, such that

$$(3) \quad c_{pq} = \underset{(i,\,j)}{\text{Min}}\, c_{ij}$$

The value of x_{pq} is chosen to be the minimum of its row or column total, and the row or column where the minimum is attained is then ineligible for the assumption of further increases in the values of its variables; if both the row and the column totals are minimum simultaneously, then either the row or the column is made ineligible, but not both. For subsequent entries, find the smallest cost factor, c_{ij}, among those remaining in eligible squares, and set the corresponding value of x_{ij} as large as is consistent with row and column totals (and with the values already entered). In all, $m + n - 1$ entries will be made. If any of these $m + n - 1$ values is zero, it is important that a zero symbol be entered to distinguish this zero of a basic variable from the zero of a non-basic variable (the latter being indicated by the lack of any numerical entry). The steps that follow apply to the initial or to any subsequent basic solution.

Computing the Values of the Implicit Prices (Simplex Multipliers).

First of all, since one equation must be redundant, we may set one of the prices at an arbitrary value. A good convention is to find a row or column having a great many basic variables and to set its corresponding price at zero. The remaining u_i and v_j are then so chosen that

$$(4) \quad c_{ij} - u_i - v_j = 0, \quad \text{if } x_{ij} \text{ is basic}$$

We can determine such prices by scanning the squares corresponding to basic variables until one is found for which either the row price, u_i, or the column price, v_j, has already been evaluated; subtracting either price from c_{ij} determines the other price. The fundamental theorem on the triangularity of the basis guarantees that repeated scanning will result in the evaluation of all u_i and v_j.

Optimality Criterion: By inspection, every unit cost, c_{ij}, is compared with the sum of the implicit prices of its row and column. If their differences, which are the relative cost factors, are all nonnegative, that is, if we have

$$(5) \qquad \bar{c}_{ij} = c_{ij} - (u_i + v_j) \geq 0$$

for every square in the array, then the basic solution is *optimal* and the problem is finished.

Finding a Better Basic Solution.

If some $\bar{c}_{ij}$ is negative, then a non-basic variable, x_{st}, is *entered* into the basic set, replacing one of the $m + n - 1$ basic variables which is dropped from the basic set and becomes just another non-basic variable.

Choose x_{st} to be the new basic variable, where

$$(6) \qquad c_{st} - u_s - v_t = \underset{(i,\,j)}{\text{Min}} \left[(c_{ij} - u_i - v_j) < 0 \right]$$

The symbol, $+\theta$, is entered in square (s, t) to indicate that a value, called θ, will be given to the non-basic variable, x_{st}. Next, assuming that $x_{st} = \theta$, the basic entries are symbolically adjusted to compensate; we will append $(+\theta)$ to some, $(-\theta)$ to others, and leave the rest unchanged. *Because of the property of basis triangularity, it will always be possible to evaluate the basic variables, whatever be the values assigned to the non-basic variables, by repetitive scanning of the rows and columns for one in which only a single basic entry remains undetermined.* This entry is symbolically adjusted (if necessary), and the scanning is repeated until all entries have been considered.

The symbol, θ, is replaced by the largest numerical value which does not require any basic entries to be nonnegative; that is, θ takes on the value, x_{pq}^o, of the smallest entry to which the symbol $(-\theta)$ is appended, so that $x_{pq}^o - \theta$ becomes zero. Thus, x_{pq} is the variable to be dropped from the basic set. (If several variables are tied for smallest entry,[1] only one of them is selected for rejection; the choice can be made randomly (see § 6-1) or by the special perturbation procedure given in § 14-2-(19).)

Using the value of θ so determined, all the basic entries are recomputed and will constitute a new basic solution. Thereafter, as necessary, we repeat the cycle.

Three examples follow. The first is the original example due to Hitchcock, the second is an "assignment" problem (a transportation problem in which each x_{ij} equals zero or one, while all a_i and b_j are unity (see Chapter 15)); the third illustrates the perturbation method for avoiding degeneracy.

---

[1] This is the case of degeneracy. It is not known whether circling can occur in the transportation case, but a simple procedure for avoiding degeneracy is illustrated in Example 3 and represents only a trivial amount of extra work.

TABLE 14-3-I
Example 1 (Hitchcock)
Cycle 0

				Row Totals
			25	**25**
10	5	6	7	−1
	20 − θ		**5 + θ**	**25**
8	2	7	6	−2
15	**+θ*** (enter)	**30**	**5 − θ** (drop)	**50**
9	3	4	8	0
15	**20**	**30**	**35**	Implicit
9	4	4	8	← Prices ↑

Column Totals

Cycle 1 (*Optimal*)

			25	**25**
10	5	6	7	0
	15		**10**	**25**
8	2	7	6	−1
15	**5**	**30**		**50**
9	3	4	8	0
15	**20**	**30**	**35**	Implicit
9	3	4	7	← Prices ↑

TABLE 14-3-II
Example 2 (4 × 4 Assignment Problem)
Cycle 0

Row Totals

				Row Totals
14	**0 + θ** / 5	**0 − θ** (drop) / 8	**1** / 5	**1** / 0
1 / 2	12	6	7	**1** / −1
7	8	**1** / 3	9	**1** / −5
0 / 2	**1 − θ** / 4	**θ*** (enter) / 6	10	**1** / −1
1 / 3	**1** / 5	**1** / 8	**1** / 5	Implicit ← Prices ↑

Column Totals (bottom row)

Cycle 1 (*Optimal*)

				Row Totals
14	**0** / 5	8	**1** / 5	**1** / 0
1 / 2	12	6	7	**1** / −1
7	8	**1** / 3	9	**1** / −4
0 / 2	**1** / 4	**0** / 6	10	**1** / −1
1 / 3	**1** / 5	**1** / 7	**1** / 5	Implicit ← Prices ↑

TABLE 14-3-III
Example 3 (Perturbation)
Cycle 0

				Row Totals
14	5	8	**1** 5	**1** −5
1 − θ 2	12	6	**+θ*** (enter) 7	**1** 0
7	8	**1** 3	9	**1** −3
ε + θ 2	**1 + ε** 4	**ε** 6	**ε − θ** (drop) 10	**1 + 4ε** 0
1 + ε 2	**1 + ε** 4	**1 + ε** 6	**1 + ε** 10	Implicit ← Prices ↑

Column Totals

Cycle 1 (*Optimal*)

				Row Totals
14	5	8	**1** 5	**1** −2
1 − ε 2	12	6	**ε** 7	**1** 0
7	8	**1** 3	9	**1** −3
2ε 2	**1 + ε** 4	**ε** 6	10	**1 + 4ε** 0
1 + ε 2	**1 + ε** 4	**1 + ε** 6	**1 + ε** 7	Implicit ← Prices ↑

14-4. PROBLEMS

1. (Review.) Prove that $\sum_{i=1}^{m} a_i = \sum_{j=1}^{n} b_j$ is a necessary and sufficient condition for the feasibility of a transportational problem.

2. (Review.) Prove there are $m + n - 1$ independent equations in the classical transportation problem, and that any equation can be dropped as the redundant equation.

3. (Review.) What is the dual of the transportation problem?

4. (Review.) Prove that any basis of the transportation problem's dual is triangular.

5. (Review.) Show that the simplex multipliers u_i and v_j are integers if c_{ij} are integers and u_1 is an integer.

6. Prove that in a regular transportation problem ($u_m = 0$) the values of the implicit prices are always $+1$ or 0 or -1 if all $c_{ij} = 0$ except $c_{11} = 1$.

7. Prove for the classic transportation problem that the unit costs c_{il} of any column l can be replaced by $c_{il} + c_l$ without affecting the optimal solution; similarly, for any row k, c_{kj} may be replaced by $c_{kj} + r_k$ where c_l and r_k are arbitrary.

8. Prove that the classic transportation problem with some (or all) $c_{ij} < 0$ can be replaced by an equivalent problem where all $c_{ij} > 0$.

9. Suppose corresponding values of c_{ij} in two rows differ by a constant; show that the two rows can be combined into a single row.

10. (a) Solve Example 1 (Table 14-3-I) using the perturbation method.
    (b) Solve the transportation problem given in Fig. 16-1-I.

11. Prove every $k \times k$ sub-determinant of coefficients of a transportation problem has value $+1$, 0, or -1.

12. Solve the transportation problem of Chapter 1.

13. Solve the transportation problem of Chapter 3.

14. (Orden [1956-1].) Prove that if a_i, b_j are integers for $i = 1, 2, \ldots, m$; $j = 1, 2, \ldots, n$ and if b_j are replaced by $b_j + (1/n)$ and a_m by $a_m + 1$, then the new problem is never degenerate for a basic feasible solution and the corresponding solution for the unperturbed problem is always feasible. How can this be used to guard against the possibility of circling?

15. (Orden [1956-1].) With reference to Problem 14, show that fractions can be avoided in applying the simplex algorithm if the original b_j are replaced by $nb_j + 1$ and the a_i by na_i except a_m by $na_m + n$.

16. (Unsolved.) Can a degenerate transportation problem ever circle? (See Chapter 10.) If the answer is no, is a perturbation scheme required such as that described in Chapter 10 or such as the simpler one given in § 14-2-(19) and in Problems 14 and 15?

REFERENCES

Balas, 1962-1, 1963-1

Beckmann, McGuire, and Winsten, 1956-1

Berge, 1962-1

Charnes and Cooper, 1959-1

Charnes, Cooper, and Thompson, 1964-1

Dantzig, 1951-2

Dantzig and Fulkerson, 1954-1

Dennis, 1959-1

Dwyer, 1955-1

Flood, 1960-1

Ford and Fulkerson, 1955-1, 1956-1, 1960-1

Gale, 1960-1

Garvin, 1960-1

Gass, 1964-1

Gassner, 1964-1

Gerstenhaber, 1958-1

Gol'shieyn and Yudin, 1961-1

Gross, 1962-1

Hadley, 1961-2

Heller, 1964-1

Heller and Tompkins, 1956-1

Hills, 1961-1

Hitchcock, 1941-1

Hoffman and Markowitz, 1963-1

Iri, 1960-1

Kantorovich, 1939-1, 1942-1

Kantorovich and Gavurin, 1949-1

Koopmans, 1947-1

Koopmans and Reiter, 1951-1

Kuhn, 1955-1

Lourie, 1964-1

Maghout, Comes, and Steinberg, 1962-1

McIllroy, 1962-1

Motzkin, 1952-1

Munkres, 1957-1

Prager, 1957-1

Shetty, 1959-1

Simonnard and Hadley, 1959-1

Totschek and Wood, 1961-1

Tucker, 1950-1

Williams, 1962-1, 1963-1

CHAPTER 15

OPTIMAL ASSIGNMENT AND OTHER DISTRIBUTION PROBLEMS

The transportation problem, as set forth in the preceding chapter, appears to treat a rather narrow situation. However, the method developed for dealing with the problem may be extended to certain cases which are different in appearance but which can all be shown to be equivalent to the classical case:

1. *Optimal Assignment*

   We shall take up the problem of optimally assigning tasks to operators.

2. *Allocation When Surplus and Deficit Are Allowed*

   We shall give a means for dealing with the transportation array when the assumption of exact sums for the rows and columns is relaxed.

3. *Fixed Values*

   We shall explore the problems that arise when some of the variables in the array must assume certain predetermined values (e.g., zero).

15-1. THE OPTIMAL ASSIGNMENT PROBLEM

The term "assignment" describes the problem concerned, typically, with finding the best way to assign n persons to n jobs, assuming that the individuals vary in their suitability for a particular job. We shall assume that, by means of performance tests, the "value" of assigning the ith person to the jth job can in some sense be determined. The negative of this value (i.e., the unit cost) will be denoted by c_{ij}. Suppose for each i the ith person has been assigned to job p_i; the total cost, z, for this assignment of personnel will be, we assume, the sum of the individual costs, that is,

$$z = \sum_{i=1}^{n} c_{ip_i}$$

The numbers $p_1, p_2, \ldots, p_n$ constitute a *permutation* of $1, 2, \ldots, n$; hence, the optimal assignment problem is to find a minimizing permutation.

Stated in this form the problem is evidently combinatorial. There are n ways in which to choose p_1, $(n-1)$ ways remaining to choose p_2, . . ., or

$$n! = (n)(n-1)(n-2) \ldots . (2)(1)$$

different possibilities. For $n = 6$, $n! = 720$, and one might pick the smallest value of z after calculating the costs of all the 720 possible assignments. But the number of possibilities grows rapidly. For example, $12! \cong 4.79 \times 10^8$. To attempt the solution of even a 12×12 assignment problem by seeking all the permutations is not very practical even on present-day computers. However, the problem can be reformulated as a 12×12 transportation problem which, through the procedures described earlier, can be solved by hand in a few minutes. For this purpose, let

(1) $\qquad x_{ij} = \begin{cases} 1 \text{ if the } i^{\text{th}} \text{ individual is assigned to the } j^{\text{th}} \text{ job} \\ 0 \text{ if not} \end{cases}$

Because (we assume) each person can be assigned only one job, we have

(2) $$\sum_{j=1}^{n} x_{ij} = 1 \qquad\qquad \text{for } i = 1, 2, \ldots, n$$

and, because each job is assigned to only one person,

(3) $$\sum_{i=1}^{n} x_{ij} = 1 \qquad\qquad \text{for } j = 1, 2, \ldots, n$$

Square arrays of nonnegative numbers, x_{ij}, with the property that all row and all column sums are unity, frequently appear in statistical theory. They are called *doubly stochastic* matrices, and the x_{ij} are interpreted as probabilities (not necessarily zero or one). When such arrays have all x_{ij} zero or one, they are called *permutation matrices*.

The objective of the assignment problem is to choose x_{ij}, satisfying (1), (2), and (3), in such a way that the total cost,

(4) $$z = \sum_{i=1}^{n} c_{ip_i} = \sum_{i=1}^{n} \sum_{j=1}^{n} c_{ij} x_{ij}$$

is minimized.

Condition (1), however, forestalls the direct application of linear programming methods to this formulation. Conditions of this type can, in themselves, make a problem very difficult to solve. The condition, "$x_{ij} = 0$ or 1," assigns x_{ij} a *disconnected* range composed of *discrete* values, as diagrammed in (5).

$$\qquad\qquad 0 \qquad\qquad 1$$

(5) $\qquad\qquad$ ...... ● ...... ● ...... x_{ij}

Another example of a disconnected range which can take a problem out of the direct reach of linear programming methods is the condition, "$x_{ij} = 0$ or $1 \leq x_{ij} \leq 2$," depicted in (6).

(6)

In Chapter 26, we shall develop general methods for handling conditions such as these, which generate variables having disconnected or discrete ranges.

In lieu of the assignment problem formulated above, we shall show that we can obtain an equivalent transportation problem simply by replacing (1) with the condition,

(7) $$0 \leq x_{ij}$$

Garrett Birkhoff [1946-1] showed that the set of permutation matrices is given by the extreme points of the convex set defined by the conditions for a doubly stochastic matrix with nonnegative entries; i.e.,

THEOREM 1: *An optimal solution of the assignment problem $\{(1), (2), (3),$ and $(4)\}$ is the same as an optimal solution of the linear programming problem given by $\{(2), (3), (4), and (7)\}$.*

PROOF: Each basic feasible solution has the property that the x_{ij} values are either zero or one, for Theorem 3, § 14-2, states that if the row and column totals are integers, then so are the values of the basic variables, and it is clear from (7) and (2), or (7) and (3), that the only integer values possible for x_{ij} are zero and one. It follows that an optimal basic feasible solution will be a permutation. Since all permutation solutions satisfy conditions (2), (3), (4), and (7), and since the minimizing solution is a permutation, it must also be a minimizing solution for the original assignment problem. Von Neumann [1953-1] establishes Birkhoff's theorem by reducing an assignment problem to an interesting matrix game. See also [Marcus, 1960-1].

Degeneracy.

Degeneracy, as earlier defined, occurs whenever one or more of the basic variables are zero. The linear program equivalent to an assignment problem has the property that every basic solution is degenerate, since exactly n basic variables must receive unit value, and the remaining $n - 1$ basic variables must, therefore, all be zero. If the number of basic variables with zero value is taken as measuring the "extent" of degeneracy, the equivalent linear program is seen to be highly degenerate. As pointed out earlier, it is not known whether circling can occur in transportation problems. (See Chapter 10.)

In practical work where, because of degeneracy, there is ambiguity as to which basic variable should be dropped, various procedures can be adopted. A simple rule would be to choose the variable, x_{rs}, whose corresponding c_{rs}

is maximal. The special ε-perturbation method developed in § 14-2-(19) for avoiding degeneracy in transportation problems, requires but a trivial amount of extra work and can be used whenever insurance against circling is necessary. A second method, guaranteed with probability one, is simply to resolve the degeneracy by random choice (see § 6-1).

Equivalence of Transportation and Assignment Problems.

We have already seen that the assignment problem is but a special case of the transportation problem. We shall now show that, *mutatis mutandis*, the transportation problem is, in its turn, a special case of the assignment problem, so that the two problems are completely equivalent. We shall assume that a_i and b_j are integers; if they were rational fractions, then, through a change of units, they could immediately be replaced by integers, while if irrational, they could be rationally approximated and then replaced.

A constructive proof will be indicated by example. Consider the transportation problem defined by tableau (8).

(8)

x_{11} $c_{11} = 10$	x_{12} $c_{12} = 5$	x_{13} $c_{13} = 6$	x_{14} $c_{14} = 7$	$2 = a_1$
x_{21} $c_{21} = 8$	x_{22} $c_{22} = 2$	x_{23} $c_{23} = 7$	x_{24} $c_{24} = 6$	$3 = a_2$
x_{31} $c_{31} = 9$	x_{32} $c_{32} = 3$	x_{33} $c_{33} = 4$	x_{34} $c_{34} = 8$	$1 = a_3$
$2 = b_1$	$1 = b_2$	$1 = b_3$	$2 = b_4$	

The first row equation

$$x_{11} + x_{12} + x_{13} + x_{14} = 2$$

is replaced by two equations (since $a_1 = 2$),

$$x'_{11} + x'_{12} + x'_{13} + x'_{14} = 1$$
$$x''_{11} + x''_{12} + x''_{13} + x''_{14} = 1$$

The second row equation

$$x_{21} + x_{22} + x_{23} + x_{24} = 3$$

is, similarly, replaced by three row equations (since $a_2 = 3$),

$$x'_{21} + x'_{22} + x'_{23} + x'_{24} = 1$$
$$x''_{21} + x''_{22} + x''_{23} + x''_{24} = 1$$
$$x'''_{21} + x'''_{22} + x'''_{23} + x'''_{24} = 1$$

Since $a_3 = 1$, the third row equation is left untouched. This results in an equivalent transportation problem with all row totals unity, as given in (9).

(9)

x'_{11} $\quad c'_{11} = 10$	x'_{12} $\quad 5$	x'_{13} $\quad 6$	x'_{14} $\quad 7$	$1 = a'_1$
x''_{11} $\quad c''_{11} = 10$	x''_{12} $\quad 5$	x''_{13} $\quad 6$	x''_{14} $\quad 7$	$1 = a''_1$
x'_{21} $\quad 8$	x'_{22} $\quad 2$	x'_{23} $\quad 7$	x'_{24} $\quad 6$	$1 = a'_2$
x''_{21} $\quad 8$	x''_{22} $\quad 2$	x''_{23} $\quad 7$	x''_{24} $\quad 6$	$1 = a''_2$
x'''_{21} $\quad 8$	x'''_{22} $\quad 2$	x'''_{23} $\quad 7$	x'''_{24} $\quad 6$	$1 = a'''_2$
x_{31} $\quad 9$	x_{32} $\quad 3$	x_{33} $\quad 4$	x_{34} $\quad 8$	$1 = a_3$
2	1	1	2	

In this table, $c_{11} = 10$ has been replaced by ($c'_{11} = 10$ *and* $c''_{11} = 10$), etc. Any solution of (9) yields a solution of (8) upon setting

$$x'_{11} + x''_{11} = x_{11} \qquad x'_{21} + x''_{21} + x'''_{21} = x_{21}$$
$$x'_{12} + x''_{12} = x_{12} \qquad x'_{22} + x''_{22} + x'''_{22} = x_{22}$$
$$x'_{13} + x''_{13} = x_{13} \qquad x'_{23} + x''_{23} + x'''_{23} = x_{23}$$
$$x'_{14} + x''_{14} = x_{14} \qquad x'_{24} + x''_{24} + x'''_{24} = x_{24}$$

Because of the linearity of this relationship and the equality of the corresponding cost coefficients in (9), it is clear that the same values of z are obtained for (8). Moreover, if the original problem has a solution, then a solution of (9) can be obtained by apportioning the x_{ij} between the rows in any arbitrary manner, provided the row totals are unity. For example, the x_{ij} values in the first row of (8) can be divided equally between the two corresponding rows of (9); the second row values can be divided into three equal parts. The same value of z is obtained. From these observations, it follows that a minimizing solution of the first problem corresponds to a minimizing solution of the second, and conversely. Hence, the two problems are equivalent.

So far, however, only the row equations of (9) have been modified. To obtain the corresponding assignment problem, it is necessary to modify the column equations in a similar manner. The result is the assignment array given below, with y_{ij} denoting the new variables.

(10)

y_{11}		y_{12}		y_{13}		y_{14}		y_{15}		y_{16}		1
	10		10		5		6		7		7	
y_{21}		y_{22}		y_{23}		y_{24}		y_{25}		y_{26}		1
	10		10		5		6		7		7	
y_{31}		y_{32}		y_{33}		y_{34}		y_{35}		y_{36}		1
	8		8		2		7		6		6	
y_{41}		y_{42}		y_{43}		y_{44}		y_{45}		y_{46}		1
	8		8		2		7		6		6	
y_{51}		y_{52}		y_{53}		y_{54}		y_{55}		y_{56}		1
	8		8		2		7		6		6	
y_{61}		y_{62}		y_{63}		y_{64}		y_{65}		y_{66}		1
	9		9		3		4		8		8	
1		1		1		1		1		1		

Some Typical Uses of the Assignment Model.

Machine Set-up Time (See Problem 1). A job has n tasks to be assigned concurrently to n different machines. Each machine must receive an adjustment so as to adapt it to the particular task assigned. Cost is the time it takes to do this, and total cost is the sum of the man-hours thus consumed. The time it takes to set up a machine depends on what the machine was doing previously; if the same kind of task, it will not be necessary to reset the machine, or if the same raw material is used, it may not be necessary to remove residual material, and so forth.

The Marriage Game (See Problem 2). A pioneering colony of 10 bachelors is joined by 10 prospective brides. After a short period of courting, it is decided to have an immediate ceremony. Each bride is given a list of 10 names on which she is to list her preferences in a scale of 10, e.g., she may assign her first choice the number 10, her second choice the number 9, etc. She may also cross out names unacceptable to her. We assume that the sum of the assigned numbers constitutes a valid measure of the anticipated "happiness" of the colony in marital bliss [Halmos and Vaughan, 1950-1].

In taking leave of this example the reader may be amused by the following story:

In 1955, at the summer meeting of the Operations Research Society in Los Angeles, I (the author) was interviewed by the press. The reporter turned out to be the brother of my small daughter's piano teacher, and so we became quite friendly. I explained to him that linear programming models originated in the Air Force, and I described their growing application to industrial problems. It became obvious that this veteran Hollywood reporter was having a hard time seeing how to make the material into exciting news copy. In desperation I suggested, "How about something with sex appeal?" "Now you're talking," he said. "Well," I continued, "an interesting by-product of our work with linear programming models is a mathematical proof that of all the possible forms of marriage (monogamy, bigamy, polygamy, etc.), monogamy is the best." "You say monogamy is the best of all possible relations?" he queried. "Yes," I replied. "Man," he said, shaking his head in the negative, "you've been working with the wrong kind of models."

15-2. ALLOCATION WITH SURPLUS AND DEFICIT

It is often possible to identify one set of totals, say a_i, as the amount *available at origins* and b_j as the amount *required at destinations*, but in some applications it may be impossible (or unprofitable) to supply all that is required or to ship all that is available. Accordingly, the array takes the form (1), with $\Sigma a_i \geq \Sigma b_j$,

(1)

Origins i	Destinations j			Row Totals Available
	1	2 . . . n		
1	x_{11}	x_{12} . . . x_{1n}		$\leq a_1$
2	x_{21}	x_{22} . . . x_{2n}		$\leq a_2$
. . .		. . . .		. . .
m	x_{m1}	x_{m2} . . . x_{mn}		$\leq a_m$
Column Totals Required	$\leq$ b_1	$\leq$ b_2	. . . $\leq$ b_n	

where the inequality symbols indicate that the row and column sums do not exceed the corresponding totals, a_i and b_j.

Let x_{i0} denote the *surplus* at the ith origin and x_{0j} the *shortage* at the jth destination, and let x_{00} be the total amount shipped from all origins to all destinations, so that

(2)
$$x_{00} = \sum_{i=1}^{m} \sum_{j=1}^{n} x_{ij}$$

Upon augmentation with a surplus column and a shortage row, to accommodate the slack variables, x_{i0} and x_{0j}, array (1) takes the form (3).

(3)

	Surplus Column	Destinations	Row Totals Available
Shortage Row	x_{00}	$x_{01} \cdots x_{0n}$	$= \sum_1^n b_j$
Origins	x_{10} $\cdots$ x_{m0}	$x_{11} \cdots x_{1n}$ $\cdots\cdots\cdots$ $x_{m1} \cdots x_{mn}$	$= a_1$ $\cdots$ $= a_m$
Column Totals Required	$\sum_1^m a_i$	$b_1 \cdots b_n$	

This is a standard transportation array, because it is clear from the way we have defined the variables that

$$(4) \qquad \sum_{i=1}^m a_i - \sum_{i=1}^m x_{i0} = \sum_{j=1}^n b_j - \sum_{j=1}^n x_{0j} = \sum_{i=1}^m \sum_{j=1}^n x_{ij} = x_{00}$$

We have thus converted (1) to the standard format, but it should be noted that if there is no penalty associated with failure to deliver the required amounts, then there is really no problem at all; simply ship nothing. A meaningful problem exists only where failure to ship means a loss of revenue or good will, i.e., where positive cost factors, c_{i0} or c_{0j}, are assigned to surplus or shortage.

Surplus only: In case the availabilities exceed the requirements (i.e., $\Sigma a_i > \Sigma b_j$), but requirements must be met exactly, the array takes the form (5).

(5)

	Surplus Column	Destinations	Row Totals Available
Origins	x_{10} x_{20} $\cdots$ x_{m0}	$x_{11} \quad x_{12} \cdots x_{1n}$ $x_{21} \quad x_{22} \cdots x_{2n}$ $\cdots\cdots\cdots$ $x_{m1} \quad x_{m2} \cdots x_{mn}$	$= a_1$ $= a_2$ $\cdots$ $= a_m$
Column Totals Required	$\Sigma a_i - \Sigma b_j$	$b_1 \quad b_2 \cdots b_n$	

[323]

Shortages only: In case the requirements exceed the availabilities (i.e., $\Sigma b_j > \Sigma a_i$), but all available supplies must be shipped, the transportation array takes the form (6).

(6)

	Destinations	Row Totals Available
Shortage Row	$x_{01} \quad x_{02} \ldots x_{0n}$	$= \Sigma b_j - \Sigma a_i$
Origins	$x_{11} \quad x_{12} \ldots x_{1n}$ $\ldots\ldots\ldots\ldots\ldots$ $x_{m1} \quad x_{m2} \ldots x_{mn}$	$= a_1$ $\ldots$ $= a_m$
Column Totals Required	$=\quad = \ldots =$ $b_1 \quad b_2 \ldots b_n$	

Theoretical Background.

Upon introduction of slack variables, x_{i0} and x_{0j}, the surplus-shortage problem may be displayed as in (7).

(7)

$$
\begin{array}{c|ccc|c}
 & x_{01} & x_{02} \ldots x_{0n} & \\
\hline
x_{10} & x_{11} & x_{12} \ldots x_{1n} & = a_1 \\
\ldots & \multicolumn{2}{c}{\ldots\ldots\ldots\ldots} & \ldots \\
x_{m0} & x_{m1} & x_{m2} \ldots x_{mn} & = a_m \\
\hline
 & = & = \ldots = & \\
 & b_1 & b_2 \ldots b_n & \\
\end{array}
$$

All $m + n$ equations are independent, in contrast to the classical transportation case, in which only $m + n - 1$ are independent. For example, it is easy to see that the slack variables constitute a basic set of $m + n$ variables.

Moreover, every basis is triangular. Proceeding as in the proof given earlier for the basic triangularity of transportation problems, let f be the number of basic variables among the surplus variables, x_{i0}, g among the shortage variables, x_{0j}, and h among the non-slack variables, so that

(8)
$$ n + m = f + g + h $$

$$
\begin{array}{|c|c|}
\hline
 & g \\
\hline
f & h \\
\hline
\end{array}
$$

THEOREM 1: *Every basis contains at least one slack variable, i.e.,* $f + g \geq 1$.

PROOF: If some basis has no slack, then it would also constitute a basis for the analogous transportation problem, *without* slack. This can only happen if $\Sigma a_i = \Sigma b_j$, but in this case we know that the number of basic variables cannot exceed $m + n - 1$. We conclude that

$$(9) \qquad\qquad f + g \geq 1$$

THEOREM 2: *Every basis is triangular.*

PROOF: If not, then every row (except the shortage row) and every column (except the surplus column) has two or more basic variables. Thus,

$$(10) \qquad\qquad 2m \leq h + f, \quad \text{and}$$
$$2n \leq h + g, \quad \text{so that}$$

$$(11) \qquad\qquad n + m \leq h + \tfrac{1}{2}(f + g)$$

Since, according to (9), $f + g$ is *positive*, (11) implies the *strict* inequality,

$$(12) \qquad\qquad n + m < h + f + g$$

which contradicts (8).

Thus, the assumption that all non-slack rows and columns contain at least two basic variables apiece must be false, and at least one of them must therefore contain exactly one variable. Upon deleting such a row or column, adjusting the totals as necessary, we may repeat the foregoing argument for the reduced system so derived, so that Theorem 2 is established by mathematical induction.

Pricing.

If u_i and v_j are the simplex multipliers (or "prices") associated with row i, column j, then the relative cost factors are

$$(13) \qquad \bar{c}_{ij} = c_{ij} - (u_i + v_j) \qquad \text{for } i \neq 0, j \neq 0,$$
$$\bar{c}_{0j} = c_{0j} - v_j \qquad\qquad \text{for } j \neq 0, \text{ and}$$
$$\bar{c}_{i0} = c_{i0} - u_i \qquad\qquad \text{for } i \neq 0$$

It may be noted that we need not define slack multipliers, u_0 or v_0, since there is no equation pertaining to row zero or to column zero. For uniformity, however, it is convenient to assign fictitious prices,

$$(14) \qquad\qquad u_0 = v_0 = 0$$

We can then characterize the choice of prices as a selection of u_i and v_j such that, if x_{ij} is a basic variable, then

$$(15) \qquad\qquad u_i + v_j = c_{ij}$$

Optimal Allocation of Receivers to Transmitters. (An example of allocation with slack.)

A certain engine-testing facility is fully using four kinds of instruments: two hundred thermocouples, fifty pressure gauges, fifty accelerometers, and forty thrust meters. Each is measuring one type of characteristic and transmitting data about it over a separate communication channel. There are four types of receivers, each capable of recording one channel of information: two hundred cameras, one hundred fifty oscilloscopes, two hundred fifty-six test instruments called "Idiots," and fifty others called "Hathaways." The set-up time per channel varies among the different types and also according to the kind of data to be recorded. Assuming that all data must be recorded, the problem is to find an allocation of receivers to transmitters which minimizes the total set-up time.

The allocation table takes the form (16).

(16)

Recording Instrument i	Measuring Instrument j				Total Recording Channels Available
	Temp. 1	Pressure 2	Accel. 3	Thrust 4	
Cameras 1	x_{11} 1	x_{12} 3	x_{13} ∞	x_{14} 1	≤ 200
Oscilloscopes 2	x_{21} .5	x_{22} .5	x_{23} .5	x_{24} .5	≤ 150
"Idiots" 3	x_{31} 2	x_{32} 2	x_{33} 10	x_{34} 2	≤ 256
"Hathaways" 4	x_{41} 1.5	x_{42} 1.5	x_{43} 1.5	x_{44} 1.5	≤ 50
Total Channels to be recorded	200	50	50	40	

The number, c_{ij}, appearing at the lower right of square (i, j) is "cost" or set-up time of assigning a recording channel of the ith type to a measuring channel of the jth type The condition that $c_{13} = \infty$ means a camera is not to be used to record acceleration data. From a procedural point of view, square $(1, 3)$ is to be avoided, if possible, in forming a starting solution, and if avoided initially, it will not thereafter be considered as a candidate in the basic set. (See § 15-3 for further details concerning inadmissible squares.) The objective is to choose nonnegative x_{ij} so as to minimize

(17)
$$\sum_{i=1}^{m} \sum_{j=1}^{n} c_{ij} x_{ij}$$

If slack variables are introduced to measure the number of unused recording channels, we have the transportation array (18).

(18)

Recording Instrument	Surplus 0	Measuring Instrument				a_i	
		Temp. 1	Pressure 2	Accel. 3	Thrust 4		u_i
1	10	190				200	
	0	1	3	∞	1		.5
2		10	50	50	40	150	
	0	.5	.5	.5	.5		0
3	256					256	
	0	2	2	10	2		.5
4	50					50	
	0	1.5	1.5	1.5	1.5		.5
b_j	316	200	50	50	40		
v_j	$-.5$	.5	.5	.5	.5		

The total of the surplus column is the same as the number of channels available minus the number of channels required, i.e.,

$$(200 + 150 + 256 + 50) - (200 + 50 + 50 + 40) = 316$$

The costs for this column, c_{i0}, are all zero, because there is no set-up cost involved in not using a channel.

The basic solution shown was generated by using the rule discussed earlier in this section for choosing a good starting solution. When several c_{ij} were tied for minimum, squares were chosen which caused rows or columns having high c_{ij} values to be deleted. For example, because the set-up costs for recording most transmissions are highest with the instruments in rows *3* and *4*, allocations to surplus were made in these rows first. This left rows *1* and *2*, and columns *1*, *2*, *3*, and *4*. Because the costs in the second row are all exceeded by the corresponding first-row costs for these columns, allocations to surplus were made next in row *1*. The remaining allocations

[327]

follow the rule given earlier. Computing the implicit prices, one can easily establish that this basic solution is optimal.

When recording instruments are in short supply (or are not of the most suitable types), a decision must be reached as to how much of each kind of data *not to record*. Consider the following unit-costs which the engineers assigned to the shortage row and surplus column:

$$c_{01} = 10, \ c_{02} = 10, \ \ c_{03} = 4, \ c_{04} = 100,$$
$$c_{10} = 0, \ \ c_{20} = -1, \ c_{30} = 0, \ c_{40} = 0, \text{ and } c_{00} = 0$$

For example, it is 25 times more costly to neglect thrust data ($c_{04} = 100$) than to neglect acceleration data ($c_{03} = 4$). In general, however, it is less costly to *record* data than to *neglect* it.

The *negativity* of c_{20} is an expression of the fact that unused oscilloscopes may be profitably employed outside the model; how profitably, may be difficult at times to determine. As noted in § 14-4, Problem 7, the optimal solution is unaffected when we increase all the c_{ij} in a row or column of the equivalent transportation array by a constant. Accordingly, in experimenting on the effect of changes in the c_{ij}, it is advisable to hold at least one cost factor at a fixed value in a row and some column.

This problem may be treated by means of the standard transportation array, (19), with a shortage row and a surplus column. *Alternatively*, it may

(19)

Recording Instrument i	Surplus 0	Measuring Instrument				a_i	
		Temp. 1	Pressure 2	Accel. 3	Thrust 4		u_i
Shortage 0	340					340	
	0	10	10	4	100		.5
1	10	190				200	
	0	1	3	∞	1		.5
2		10	50	50	40	150	
	−1	.5	.5	.5	.5		0
3	256					256	
	0	2	2	10	2		.5
4	50					50	
	0	1.5	1.5	1.5	1.5		.5
b_j	656	200	50	50	40		
v_j	−.5	.5	.5	.5	.5		

be set up as in (7). From a computational viewpoint, the two methods are almost identical, as may be seen by perusal of (20) and (21).

Phase II—Cycle 0

(20)

	10	10	4	100	
10 − θ	**190 + θ**				**200**
0	1	3	∞	1	0
θ*	**10 − θ**	**50**	**50**	**40**	**150**
−1	0.5	0.5	0.5	0.5	−0.5
256					**256**
0	2	2	10	2	0
50					**50**
0	1.5	1.5	1.5	1.5	0
	200	**50**	**50**	**40**	
	1	1	1	1	

* Indicates position of incoming variable.

Phase II—Cycle 1—(Optimal)

(21)

	10	10	4	100	
200					**200**
0	1	3	∞	1	−5
10	**0**	**50**	**50**	**40**	**150**
−1	0.5	0.5	0.5	0.5	−1.0
256					**256**
0	2	2	10	2	0
50					**50**
0	1.5	1.5	1.5	1.5	0
	200	**50**	**50**	**40**	
	1.5	1.5	1.5	1.5	

15-3. FIXED VALUES AND INADMISSIBLE SQUARES

In solving transportation problems, it quite often happens that some of the variables must assume predetermined values. In the preceding section, for example, it was not possible to assign cameras to record acceleration data, so that x_{13} had to be zero. Similarly, if there exists no route from an origin i to a destination j in a network, then the variable x_{ij} must be zero. In the problem of assigning people to jobs, certain assignments may be mandatory; for example, assigning a physician to a medical position. Note, however, that *a fixed variable can always be replaced by a zero-restricted variable after subtracting its predetermined value from the corresponding row and column totals.* We will designate the squares associated with zero-restricted variables as *inadmissible* and will shade such squares when they appear in a tableau.

If only a few squares are inadmissible, the best practical procedure is to attempt an initial basic feasible solution by using the *least-cost rule* discussed earlier, § 14-3-(3), but there are a great many problems in which inadmissible squares can be avoided only at the expense of selecting basic variables having higher unit-costs than would be suggested by this rule. Moreover, if too many squares are inadmissible, there may be no solution, or no readily discernible basic solution, using a set of variables selected from the admissible squares.

If there appears to be no way of avoiding inadmissible squares, they can be used to furnish artificial variables for a simplex Phase I, in which a basic feasible solution will be constructed if possible. For this purpose, the infeasibility form, $w = \sum_{i=1}^{m} \sum_{j=1}^{n} d_{ij} x_{ij}$, is used, so that the c_{ij} entries in the array are replaced by

$$d_{ij} = \begin{cases} 1 & \text{if } (i, j) \text{ is inadmissible} \\ 0 & \text{if } (i, j) \text{ is admissible} \end{cases}$$

If a feasible solution exists, then Min w is zero, but if Min w is positive, then the problem is infeasible.

Even if the problem is feasible, it may happen that some inadmissible variables remain in the basic set at the end of Phase I. If so, they will be zero in value, and they must remain so throughout the remaining procedure. Before initiation of Phase II, any non-basic x_{ij} will be dropped from further consideration if its relative infeasibility factor d_{ij} is positive, i.e., if

$$d_{ij} - u_i - v_j > 0$$

where u_i and v_j are the implicit prices associated with the infeasibility form at the end of Phase I.

[330]

EXAMPLE: Find an optimal feasible solution to the transportation problem (1). The algorithm is initiated with any basic solution such as the one shown in (2). The latter has two inadmissible basic variables x_{42}, x_{34} indicated by heavy-bordered squares.

(1)

////	$c_{12} = 3$	$c_{13} = 3$	////	$7 = a_1$
$c_{21} = 2$	////	$c_{23} = 9$	$c_{24} = 6$	$25 = a_2$
$c_{31} = 7$	////	$c_{33} = 4$	////	$8 = a_3$
$c_{41} = 8$	////	////	$c_{44} = 5$	$3 = a_4$
$14 = b_1$	$7 = b_2$	$5 = b_3$	$17 = b_4$	

(2)

Phase I—Cycle 0
Starting Solution
(c_{ij} replaced by d_{ij})

//// ·, 0	7, 0	·, 0	////	7, −1
$14 - \theta$, 0	////	·, 0	$11 + \theta$, 0	25, 0
$\theta*$, 0	////	5, 0	**[$3 - \theta$, 1]**	8, 1
·, 0	**[0, 1]**	////	3, 0	3, 0
14, 0	7, 1	5, −1	17, 0	

(3)

Phase I—Cycle 1 (Feasible)

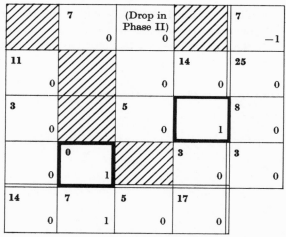

	7 / 0	(Drop in Phase II) / 0		7 / −1
11 / 0		/ 0	14 / 0	25 / 0
3 / 0		5 / 0	**[/ 1]**	8 / 0
/ 0	**[0 / 1]**		3 / 0	3 / 0
14 / 0	7 / 1	5 / 0	17 / 0	

(4)

Phase II—Cycle 1 (Optimal)
(d_{ij} replaced by c_{ij})

	7 / 3	(Drop in Phase II) / 3		7 / 3
11 / 2		/ 9	14 / 6	25 / 1
3 / 7		5 / 4		8 / 6
/ 8	**[0 / 0]**		3 / 5	3 / 0
14 / 1	7 / 0	5 / −2	17 / 5	

Note: In Phase II, all x_{ij} with $d_{ij} > 0$ are made inadmissible by shading their squares; e.g., square $(1, 3)$ is shaded because $\bar{d}_{13} > 0$. The values of c_{ij} for artificials are arbitrary; e.g., $\bar{c}_{42} = 0$.

15-4. PROBLEMS

1. Find the optimal assignment of 12 tasks to 12 machines if the time, c_{ij}, needed to set up the ith task on the jth machine is that given by the first table on page 333. (See § 15-1.)

2. Find an assignment which gives the greatest total "happiness," where the rating of the jth bachelor by the ith bride is that given in the second table on page 333 [Halmos and Vaughan, 1950-1]. (See § 15-1.)

The Machine-Task Problem

Machines	Tasks											
	(1)	(2)	(3)	(4)	(5)	(6)	(7)	(8)	(9)	(10)	(11)	(12)
(1)	79	24	13	53	47	66	85	17	92	47	46	13
(2)	43	59	33	95	55	97	34	55	84	94	26	56
(3)	29	52	26	27	13	33	70	11	71	86	6	76
(4)	88	83	64	72	90	67	27	47	83	62	35	38
(5)	65	90	56	62	53	91	48	23	6	89	49	33
(6)	44	79	86	93	71	7	86	59	17	56	45	59
(7)	35	51	9	91	39	32	3	12	79	25	79	81
(8)	50	12	59	32	23	64	20	94	97	14	11	97
(9)	25	17	39	0	38	63	87	14	4	18	11	45
(10)	68	45	99	0	94	44	99	59	37	18	38	74
(11)	93	36	91	30	44	69	68	67	81	62	66	37
(12)	19	36	5	50	49	94	95	17	63	41	84	1

The Marriage Problem

	Bill	John	Egbert	Cuthbert	Joe	Gaston	Chauncey	Clyde	Newt	Waldo
Jane	9	6	3	×	2	8	7	4	1	5
Mary	3	7	8	2	1	×	5	4	×	6
Chloe	4	2	1	6	×	8	3	9	7	5
Beulah	6	3	5	7	9	×	1	4	2	8
Phoebe	7	5	6	9	1	8	3	×	2	4
Octavia	1	10	8	4	5	3	6	9	2	7
Juliet	6	8	10	9	4	3	5	1	7	2
Myrtle	7	8	4	3	2	6	1	9	5	×
Olga	3	9	4	2	5	6	7	×	8	1
Mabel	9	3	1	8	×	4	2	7	6	5

[333]

Note: According to the description in the text, each bride is given a list of 10 names on which she is to list her preferences in a scale of 10, e.g., she may assign her first choice the number 10, her second choice the number 9, etc. She may also cross out names unacceptable to her. Thus, it should be safe to assume that all of the brides will have a number 10 (for first choice), which they do not, according to this problem. It seems that instead they have assigned the number 9 to first choice if one name is crossed off, 8 if two names are crossed off. Is this the same problem?

3. Prove that, for the alternative procedure of § 15-2, the $m + n$ multipliers, u_i and v_j, are determined uniquely by $m + n$ of the equations (14) and (15).

4. (Review.) Show that the system of equations (14), (15) of § 15-2 is triangular.

5 In § 15-2, show that the u_i and v_j are integers if the c_{ij} are integers.

6. In a transportation problem with one price set at zero, say $u_m = 0$, or in a surplus-shortage problem treated by the alternative procedure of § 15-2, prove that, if all the cost factors are zero in value except one which is unity, the implicit prices are always $+1$, or 0, or -1.

7. Why is x_{13} dropped on the first cycle of Phase II for the example in § 15-3? (See the rules of Phase I-Phase II transition of the simplex method in § 5-2.)

8. (a) Show that an extra row (or column) of slack variables with arbitrary unit costs may be introduced into a classical transportation problem without changing the optimal solution.

   (b) Also, show that the solution is unaffected when both an extra surplus row and an extra "over-supply" column of slack variables with arbitrary unit costs are introduced.

   (c) Show in this form there are no redundant equations in the system or multipliers with arbitrary values associated with a basic solution.

REFERENCES

Assignment Problem

Berge, 1962-1	Hoffman and Kuhn, 1956-1
Birkhoff, 1946-1	Hoffman and Markowitz, 1963-1
Briggs, 1962-1	Kendall, 1960-1
Dantzig and Ramser, 1959-1	Kuhn, 1955-1
Dennis, 1959-1	Kuhn and Tucker, 1958-1
Easterfield, 1946-1	Land, 1963-1
Egerváry, 1931-1	Lawler, 1963-1
Ford and Fulkerson, 1960-1	Marcus, 1960-1
Gale, 1960-1	Motzkin, 1956-1
Gass, 1964-1	Munkres, 1957-1
Gross, 1959-1	Vajda, 1961-1
Hadley, 1961-2	von Neumann, 1953-1
Halmos and Vaughan, 1950-1	Votaw and Orden, 1952-1
Hoffman, 1956-1, 1960-1	(See also references Chapter 14)

CHAPTER 16

THE TRANSSHIPMENT PROBLEM

16-1. EQUIVALENT FORMULATION OF THE MODEL

In the Hitchcock transportation problem, cities where goods are produced (origins) ship only to cities where goods are consumed (destinations); shipments do not take place between origins or between destinations, nor from destinations to origins. However, while only shipments from origin to final destination appeared in the Hitchcock model, actual shipments might in practice be routed through many intermediate cities.

It is tacitly assumed that shipments between any two cities are always transported via the least-cost routes where cost, c_{ij}, may be in terms of distance, time, or money. In some instances, the amount that can be shipped on a link between two cities may be limited, in which case it may not always be possible to fulfill our tacit assumption of a shortest route. Another point worth noting is that the determination of a shortest route from each origin to every destination, as is necessary for the Hitchcock formulation, might in itself be quite a chore. It would be desirable to have an algorithm which develops this information automatically.

A. Orden [1956-1] proposed a generalized transportation model in which *transshipment* through intermediate cities is permitted. For every city, there is a material-balance equation stating that the amount shipped out minus that shipped in is equal to the net amount produced there (if positive), or net amount consumed there (if negative).

We shall consider therefore a generalized transportation model in which transshipment through intermediate cities is permitted. For every city, there will be a material-balance equation stating:

$$\text{Gross Supply} = \text{Amount Shipped In} + \text{Produced}$$
$$= \text{Amount Shipped Out} + \text{Consumed},$$

or, in equation form,

(1) $$\sum_{i \neq j} x_{ij} + a_j^* = \sum_{k \neq j} x_{jk} + b_j^* = x_{jj}^* \quad (j = 1, 2, \ldots, n)$$

where

x_{ij} = total quantity shipped from i to j for $i \neq j$,

x_{jj}^* = gross supply at j,

a_j^* = the production at city j, and

b_j^* = the consumption at city j

If local production for local consumption is excluded from the model, so that either a_j^* or b_j^* is zero, we shall use the symbols a_j, b_j without the star. In general, the net production a_j and consumption b_j are related to a_j^* and b_j^* by

$$(2) \qquad a_j = a_j^* - \mathrm{Min}\,(a_j^*, b_j^*); \qquad\qquad b_j = b_j^* - \mathrm{Min}\,(a_j^*, b_j^*)$$

We shall refer to a_j and b_j as the (net) amounts available and required.

The transshipment problem consists in finding $x_{ij} \geq 0$ and Min z satisfying (1) and the objective equation

$$3) \qquad\qquad \sum_{i=1}^{n} \sum_{j=1}^{n} c_{ij} x_{ij} = z \qquad\qquad \text{where } i \neq j$$

Upon equating the expressions for gross supply given in (1), we obtain a complete transshipment model for n cities. The array of detached coefficients is shown in Table 16-1-I. Excluding the cost factor, each column contains only two non-zero coefficients, $+1$ and -1; more generally, if we allow surplus or shortage, then the rows include slack variables whose corresponding columns contain only one non-zero coefficient $+1$ or -1. (In Chapter 21, systems are considered that have at most two non-zero coefficients in a column but not necessarily equal and opposite in sign.)

TABLE 16-1-I

TRANSSHIPMENT MODEL—NETWORK FORMULATION
(Detached Coefficients)

Amounts Shipped	x_{12} x_{13} $\cdots$ x_{1n} x_{21} x_{23} $\cdots$ x_{2n} $\cdots$ x_{n1} x_{n2} $\cdots$ $x_{n,n-1}$	Net Produced or Consumed
City 1	1 1 $\cdots$ 1 -1 -1	$a_1^* - b_1^*$
City 2	-1 1 1 $\cdots$ 1 -1	$a_2^* - b_2^*$
	-1 -1	.
City n	-1 -1 1 1 $\cdots$ 1	$a_n^* - b_n^*$
Cost	c_{12} c_{13} $\cdots$ c_{1n} c_{21} c_{23} $\cdots$ c_{2n} $\cdots$ c_{n1} c_{n2} $\cdots$ $c_{n,n-1}$	z

The general transshipment model is characterized by a cost function and a system of equations in nonnegative variables, each column of which contains at most two non-zero coefficients ($+1$ or -1 or both). The standard transportation model is clearly a special case of this formulation. However, under mildly restrictive assumptions to be discussed in § 16-2, the general transshipment problem will be proved equivalent to the classical transportation problem.

The Network Representation.

The array in Table 16-1-I contains $n(n - 1)$ columns corresponding to the number of ways to ship from each city to any other city. If, however, all shipments are routed from one city to another by means of a *chain* of links between neighboring cities, then we need consider only the network composed of such local links. All the variables dealing with shipments to non-neighboring cities can be ignored.

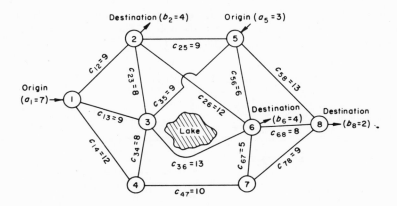

Figure 16-1-I. An example of the transshipment problem.

In the network shown in Fig. 16-1-I, the cost, c_{ij}, of shipping a ton of goods from i to a neighboring point, j, is shown on the relevant link: thus c_{36}, the cost from *3* to *6* is 13. We have not shown c_{63}, the cost from *6* to *3*, because in this example each c_{ij} happens to equal c_{ji}. *The theory we will develop, however, is valid even when $c_{ij} \neq c_{ji}$.*

Indeed, although freight rates between two cities are often the same regardless of the direction of shipment, there might be a good economic reason why they should be different. A situation in which c_{ij} is not equal to c_{ji} might actually arise in a pipeline system if i is at the top of a mountain and j is in a valley, for it costs less to pump downhill than up. As a stabilizing influence in certain economic applications, Koopmans [1947-1] and Koopmans and Reiter [1951-1], have suggested that it would be in the public interest to have differing rates to encourage demands in the direction of least use between two cities.

We will show that, with minor modification, the simplex technique developed for solving the classical transportation problem may be used in the transshipment case as well. In Chapter 17, we shall present a computationally convenient procedure, using the network diagram itself, to exhibit, in an elegant way, the underlying geometrical structure.

Reduction to the Classical Case by the Direct Shipment Procedure.

In formulating the transshipment model, we assumed no knowledge of costs except between neighboring cities, but we do presume that the shipping costs between any pair of non-neighboring cities can be obtained by finding the minimum sum-of-costs along chains of local links which connect the two cities through all possible intermediate points (actual freight rates often do not satisfy this additivity assumption). For small problems, it may not be too difficult to determine all the minimum costs merely by inspecting the network. The cheapest ways to ship from origins *1* and *5* to the three desti-nations, *2*, *6*, and *8*, in the network example of Fig. 16-1-I, are given by the classical transportation array, Table 16-1-II.

TABLE 16-1-II

Origins	Destinations			Available (a_i)
	2	*6*	*8*	
1	x_{12} $c_{12} = 9$	x_{16} $c_{16} = 21$	x_{18} $c_{18} = 29$	7
5	x_{52} $c_{52} = 9$	x_{56} $c_{56} = 6$	x_{58} $c_{58} = 13$	3
Required (b_j)	4	4	2	10

For instance, the cheapest way to ship from *1* to *6* is along the link from *1* to *2* and then to *6*. Hence, we set $c_{16} = c_{12} + c_{26} = 9 + 12 = 21$.

Although one can in this way solve the transshipment problem by the classical transportation technique, our present purpose is to show an alterna-tive approach which has certain advantages:

(a) It avoids the necessity of determining a least-cost route for every origin-destination pair.
(b) It permits treatment of problems in which certain arcs of the network have fixed capacities bounding the flows over these arcs.
(c) It may involve fewer variables, since the number of arcs of a network often is considerably less than the number of origin-destination pairs.

Reduction to the Classical Case by the Transshipment Procedure.

In Table 16-1-III, an array analogous to the classical transportation tableau is shown for the transshipment network shown in Fig. 16-1-I. Applying equations (1), the row equations are obtained by equating the gross supply to the amount consumed plus the amount shipped out; the

TABLE 16-1-III
Transshipment Model with Diagonal Supply Variables

Origin i	Destination j								Row Sum (required) $-b_j^*$
	(1)	(2)	(3)	(4)	(5)	(6)	(7)	(8)	
(1)	$-x_{11}^*$ 0	x_{12} c_{12}	x_{13} c_{13}	x_{14} c_{14}					0
(2)	x_{21} c_{21}	$-x_{22}^*$ 0	x_{23} c_{23}		x_{25} c_{25}	x_{26} c_{26}			-4
(3)	x_{31} c_{31}	x_{32} c_{32}	$-x_{33}^*$ 0	x_{34} c_{34}	x_{35} c_{35}	x_{36} c_{36}			0
(4)	x_{41} c_{41}		x_{43} c_{43}	$-x_{44}^*$ 0			x_{47} c_{47}		0
(5)		x_{52} c_{52}	x_{53} c_{53}		$-x_{55}^*$ 0	x_{56} c_{56}		x_{58} c_{58}	0
(6)		x_{62} c_{62}	x_{63} c_{63}		x_{65} c_{65}	$-x_{66}^*$ 0	x_{67} c_{67}	x_{68} c_{68}	-4
(7)				x_{74} c_{74}		x_{76} c_{76}	$-x_{77}^*$ 0	x_{78} c_{78}	0
(8)					x_{85} c_{85}	x_{86} c_{86}	x_{87} c_{87}	$-x_{88}^*$ 0	-2
Col. Sum (available) $-a_j^*$	-7	0	0	0	-3	0	0	0	-10

column equations by equating the gross supply to the amount shipped in plus produced.

Standard Tableau for the Transshipment Model.

In continuing our analysis, it will be convenient to replace the gross-supply variables, x_{jj}^*, by a new set of diagonal variables, x_{jj}, representing the net amount transshipped *through* point j. These are related to the gross supply by

$$(4) \qquad x_{jj}^* = x_{jj} + [a_j^* + b_j^* - \text{Min}\,(a_j^*, b_j^*)]$$

[339]

To justify the use of the term *transshipment variable* for x_{jj}, we rewrite (4)

(5) $x_{jj} = [x_{jj}^* - \text{Min} (a_j^*, b_j^*)] - [a_j^* - \text{Min} (a_j^*, b_j^*)] - [b_j^* - \text{Min} (a_j^*, b_j^*)]$

The subtraction of Min (a_j^*, b_j^*) from each term eliminates the local production for local consumption from the problem. If $a_j^* \geq b_j^*$, the last term drops, and $x_{jj} = x_{jj}^* - a_j^*$ is that part of the gross supply which originated elsewhere and is being transshipped. If $a_j^* < b_j^*$, the second term drops and $x_{jj} = x_{jj}^* - b_j^*$ is that part of the gross supply not locally consumed, hence transshipped. From (1) it also follows that $x_{jj}^* - a_j^* \geq 0$, $x_{jj}^* - b_j^* \geq 0$ and therefore $x_{jj} \geq 0$.

If x_{jj}^* is replaced by (4), and if we let a_j, b_j be the net production and consumption as defined by (2), the transshipment problem can be restated in the following standard diagonal form:

Transshipment Problem.   Determine nonnegative numbers, x_{ij}, and the minimum z satisfying (6), (7), and (8);

(6) Column Equations: $\sum_{i \neq j} x_{ij} - x_{jj} = b_j$ $(j = 1, 2, \ldots, n)$

(Total shipped into j minus amount transshipped = Net Consumption)

(7) Row Equations: $\sum_{k \neq j} x_{jk} - x_{jj} = a_j$ $(i = 1, 2, \ldots, n)$

(Total shipped from j minus amount transshipped = Net Production)

and the

(8) Cost Form: $\sum_{i=1}^{n} \sum_{j=1}^{n} c_{ij} x_{ij} = z$ with $c_{jj} = 0$ for all j

A general array for this standard form is displayed in Table 16-1-IV.

THEOREM 1: *Any basis for the transshipment problem is triangular.*

PROOF: If the variables, x_{ij} with $i \neq j$, are replaced by $x_{ij}' = -x_{ij}$, then equations (1) and (3) are the same as for a standard transportation problem. Because the proof of triangularity for that problem, as given in § 14-2, did not depend on the signs of the variables, it applies to the transshipment case as well. A similar argument applies to the system (6), (7), and (8) if x_{jj} is replaced by $-x_{jj}'$.

THEOREM 2: *The diagonal variables, x_{jj} or x_{jj}^*, can be made to form part of every basic feasible set.*

PROOF: Consider a new transshipment problem for which each a_i and b_j in (1) is replaced by $a_i + \varepsilon$ and $b_j + \varepsilon$, respectively, where ε is an arbitrary positive number, and x_{ij}'' are the new variables. It is clear that, in every feasible solution, $x_{jj}'' \geq \varepsilon$, so that the diagonal variables are positive and therefore must form part of every basic set. Any feasible solution of the

[340]

TABLE 16-1-IV

STANDARD TABLEAU FOR A TRANSSHIPMENT PROBLEM

Origin i	Destination j								a_i: Avail.
	(1)	(2)	(3)	(4)	(5)	(6)	(7)	(8)	Price:
(1)	$-x_{11}$ 0	x_{12} c_{12}	x_{13} c_{13}	x_{14} c_{14}	▨	▨	▨	▨	7 $-\pi_1$
(2)	x_{21} c_{21}	$-x_{22}$ 0	x_{23} c_{23}	▨	x_{25} c_{25}	x_{26} c_{26}	▨	▨	0 $-\pi_2$
(3)	x_{31} c_{31}	x_{32} c_{32}	$-x_{33}$ 0	x_{34} c_{34}	x_{35} c_{35}	x_{36} c_{36}	▨	▨	0 $-\pi_3$
(4)	x_{41} c_{41}	▨	x_{43} c_{43}	$-x_{44}$ 0	▨	▨	x_{47} c_{47}	▨	0 $-\pi_4$
(5)	▨	x_{52} c_{52}	x_{53} c_{53}	▨	$-x_{55}$ 0	x_{56} c_{56}	▨	x_{58} c_{58}	3 $-\pi_5$
(6)	▨	x_{62} c_{62}	x_{63} c_{63}	▨	x_{65} c_{65}	$-x_{66}$ 0	x_{67} c_{67}	x_{68} c_{68}	0 $-\pi_6$
(7)	▨	▨	▨	x_{74} c_{74}	▨	x_{76} c_{76}	$-x_{77}$ 0	x_{78} c_{78}	0 $-\pi_7$
(8)	▨	▨	▨	▨	x_{85} c_{85}	x_{86} c_{86}	x_{87} c_{87}	$-x_{88}$ 0	0 $-\pi_8$
b_j: Req.	0	4	0	0	0	4	0	2	
Price:	$+\pi_1$	$+\pi_2$	$+\pi_3$	$+\pi_4$	$+\pi_5$	$+\pi_6$	$+\pi_7$	$+\pi_8$	

original problem determines a feasible solution of the new one (and conversely). In fact, if one sets

(9) $$x''_{jj} = x^*_{jj} + \varepsilon, \text{ and } x''_{ij} = x_{ij} \qquad \text{for } i \neq j$$

then optimal solutions must correspond, since the value of z is invariant under the transformation.

From a procedural point of view, it is not desirable to transform the problem explicitly, since we can accomplish the same end simply by allowing the supply variables, x^*_{jj}, an *unrestricted range* of values. They will then be retained in the basic set, once they have entered it, even though their values may be zero. (See Chapter 18.) The same applies to the transshipment

[341]

variables since they are in one-to-one correspondence, and we have shown that $x_{jj} \geq 0$ is implied by $x_{ij} \geq 0$ for $i \neq j$ (refer to discussion following (4)).

THEOREM 3: *The implicit prices, u_i and v_j, for the transshipment problem can be made to satisfy the relation,*

$$(10) \qquad\qquad -u_j = v_j \qquad\qquad \text{for } j = 1, 2, \ldots, m$$

PROOF: Since $c_{ij} = u_i + v_j$ for all basic variables, x_{ij}, and since, according to Theorem 2, x_{jj} may be assumed to be in every basic feasible set, imposing the condition, $c_{jj} = 0$, will establish the desired relation.

Let us denote the value common to v_j and $-u_j$ by the symbol, π_j. Koopmans and Reiter [1951-1] call π_j the "potential" of point i in the network, in analogy with the electrostatic potential of an electrical network. (In particular, both kinds of "potential" are such that,

$$(11) \qquad \text{if } x_{ij} > 0, \text{ then } c_{ij} = \pi_j - \pi_i, \text{ and}$$
$$\text{if } c_{ij} > \pi_j - \pi_i, \text{ then } x_{ij} = 0$$

at equilibrium. In other words, positive flow from i to j can occur if and only if the voltage drop, c_{ij}, is equal and opposite to the potential difference from i to j.)

16-2. THE EQUIVALENCE OF TRANSPORTATION AND TRANSSHIPMENT PROBLEMS

There is a fundamental difference between transportation and transshipment problems: In the transportation case, each variable is bounded by the smaller of the row and column totals, whereas transshipment allows the values in a 2×2 diagonal submatrix (x_{ij}, x_{ji}, x_{ii}, x_{jj}) to be increased by an arbitrary constant, k, since the row and column sums of the resulting subarray remain unchanged, as in

$$(1) \qquad \begin{bmatrix} -x_{ii} & x_{ij} \\ x_{ji} & -x_{jj} \end{bmatrix} \rightarrow \begin{bmatrix} -(x_{ii} + k) & (x_{ij} + k) \\ (x_{ji} + k) & -(x_{jj} + k) \end{bmatrix}$$

In the case where all costs are positive, it clearly never pays to transship an amount greater than the total available from all sources. However, if some of the c_{ij} were negative, it might be that no lower bound for z would exist. For example, if $c_{ij} + c_{ji} < 0$, then $z \rightarrow -\infty$ for the class of solutions generated by $k \rightarrow +\infty$ in (1). More generally, it would pay to have such a *circulation* in the flow of the network whenever the sum of the c_{ij} around some loop is negative.[1] For a formal proof of these intuitive statements, see the Chain-Decomposition Theorem, § 19-1, Theorem 2. (Also see Problem 7 in the present chapter.) The latter theorem implies

---

[1] There are times, it is said, when the exchange rates between various currencies of the world are such that there is a net gain in exchanging between $A, B, C, D, \ldots$, and back to A again. In theory, one could make a fortune by recycling again and again. In practice some people have amassed a considerable profit before the exchange rates changed.

THEOREM 1: *If the sum of c_{ij} around every loop in the network is positive, then in any optimal solution, if one exists, the amount transshipped, x_{jj}, is bounded, and*

$$(2) \qquad x_{jj} \leq \sum a_i = \sum b_j = L$$

Defining transshipment *slack*,

$$(3) \qquad \bar{x}_{jj} = L - x_{jj}$$

we can reduce the transshipment problem to a standard transportation problem. For our example, $L = \sum a_i = \sum b_j = 10$, so that the transshipment problem given in Table 16-1-IV can be reduced to the one in Table 16-2-I.

TABLE 16-2-I

THE TRANSPORTATION EQUIVALENT OF A TRANSSHIPMENT PROBLEM

Origin i	Destination j (1)	(2)	(3)	(4)	(5)	(6)	(7)	(8)	$L + a_i$ $-\pi_i$
(1)	$\bar{x}_{11}$ $\quad 0$	x_{12} $\quad c_{12}$	x_{13} $\quad c_{13}$	x_{14} $\quad c_{14}$	/////	/////	/////	/////	17 $-\pi_1$
(2)	x_{21} $\quad c_{21}$	$\bar{x}_{22}$ $\quad 0$	x_{23} $\quad c_{23}$	/////	x_{25} $\quad c_{25}$	x_{26} $\quad c_{26}$	/////	/////	10 $-\pi_2$
(3)	x_{31} $\quad c_{31}$	x_{32} $\quad c_{32}$	$\bar{x}_{33}$ $\quad 0$	x_{34} $\quad c_{34}$	x_{35} $\quad c_{35}$	x_{36} $\quad c_{36}$	/////	/////	10 $-\pi_3$
(4)	x_{41} $\quad c_{41}$	/////	x_{43} $\quad c_{43}$	$\bar{x}_{44}$ $\quad 0$	/////	/////	x_{47} $\quad c_{47}$	/////	10 $-\pi_4$
(5)	/////	x_{52} $\quad c_{52}$	x_{53} $\quad c_{53}$	/////	$\bar{x}_{55}$ $\quad 0$	x_{56} $\quad c_{56}$	/////	x_{58} $\quad c_{58}$	13 $-\pi_5$
(6)	/////	x_{62} $\quad c_{62}$	x_{63} $\quad c_{63}$	/////	x_{65} $\quad c_{65}$	$\bar{x}_{66}$ $\quad 0$	x_{67} $\quad c_{67}$	x_{68} $\quad c_{68}$	10 $-\pi_6$
(7)	/////	/////	/////	x_{74} $\quad c_{74}$	/////	x_{76} $\quad c_{76}$	$\bar{x}_{77}$ $\quad 0$	x_{78} $\quad c_{78}$	10 $-\pi_7$
(8)	/////	/////	/////	/////	x_{85} $\quad c_{85}$	x_{86} $\quad c_{86}$	x_{87} $\quad c_{87}$	$\bar{x}_{88}$ $\quad 0$	10 $-\pi_8$
$L + b_j$ π_j	10 π_1	14 π_2	10 π_3	10 π_4	10 π_5	14 π_6	10 π_7	12 π_8	

Conversely, a classical transportation problem can readily be converted to the transshipment format. Let us consider the 3×4 transportation problem, Table 16-2-II, where destinations have been distinguished from origins by assigning them the numerically larger indices.

TABLE 16-2-II

Origins	Destinations				Available
	(4)	(5)	(6)	(7)	
(1)	x_{14} c_{14}	x_{15} c_{15}	x_{16} c_{16}	x_{17} c_{17}	a_1
(2)	x_{24} c_{24}	x_{25} c_{25}	x_{26} c_{26}	x_{27} c_{27}	a_2
(3)	x_{34} c_{34}	x_{35} c_{35}	x_{36} c_{36}	x_{37} c_{37}	a_3
Required	b_4	b_5	b_6	b_7	Totals

The original tableau may be rewritten in standard row-column form,

$$(4) \qquad \sum_{j=4}^{7} x_{ij} = a_i \qquad \text{for } i = 1, 2, 3$$

$$(5) \qquad \sum_{i=1}^{3} x_{ij} = b_j \qquad \text{for } j = 4, 5, 6, 7$$

and then reinterpreted as in (1) and (6), § 16-1; more conveniently, it may be displayed in the transshipment tableau, Table 16-2-III, where the possibility of shipping over links between origins or between destinations is to be excluded.

TABLE 16-2-III

Origins	Destinations							Available
	(1)	(2)	(3)	(4)	(5)	(6)	(7)	
(1)	$-x_{11}$			x_{14}	x_{15}	x_{16}	x_{17}	a_1
(2)		$-x_{22}$		x_{24}	x_{25}	x_{26}	x_{27}	a_2
(3)			$-x_{33}$	x_{34}	x_{35}	x_{36}	x_{37}	a_3
(4)				$-x_{44}$				0
(5)					$-x_{55}$			0
(6)						$-x_{66}$		0
(7)							$-x_{77}$	0
Required	0	0	0	b_4	b_5	b_6	b_7	Totals

16-3. SOLVING A TRANSSHIPMENT PROBLEM BY THE SIMPLEX METHOD

Finding an Initial Basic Feasible Solution.

In any connected network,[2] such as the one diagrammed in Fig. 16-1-I, it is possible to find a starting solution by inspection.

Begin by selecting a route along the network from any origin to any destination, and specify the largest flow which does not exceed the total production or consumption. Next, either by a direct path or by branching off from a previous path, connect any origin whose gross supply is not yet exhausted to destinations whose gross demand is not yet satisfied, and increase the flow along the path to the maximum possible. (If two paths intersect, as in Fig. 16-3-I, there may sometimes be a *reversal of flow* in the

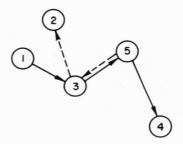

Figure 16-3-I.

common arc.) Repeat this procedure until all the demands have been satisfied.

In forming a basic solution, it is important to do the branching without forming loops and to have each point joined to every other over the constructed paths. For the latter purpose, it may be necessary to include some extra paths having *zero flow*. (The proof that these steps are always possible, and the more precise meaning of such network terms as "loop," will form part of the discussion in the next chapter and hence are omitted here.) For example, one feasible way to perform the required shipping in network Fig. 16-1-I is shown by Fig. 16-3-II below. Another feasible way is given by Fig. 16-3-III, but it would not qualify as a basic solution since it contains the loop corresponding to arcs and nodes of Fig. 16-3-IV.

---

[2] A network is connected if, given any pair of nodes, i and j, it is possible to find a *chain* of arcs, joining i to j_1, j_1 to j_2, j_2 to j_3, . . ., j_k to j. When the network consists of several separate parts and each part is a connected subnetwork, it is clear that the problem may be decomposed into independent sub-problems that can be solved in the same way.

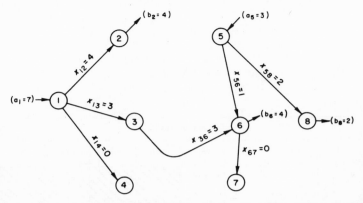

Figure 16-3-II. Graph of a basic feasible solution (see Table 16-3-I, Cycle 0).

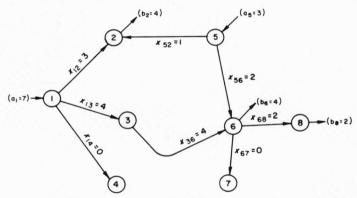

Figure 16-3-III. Graph of a feasible but not basic solution.

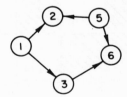

Figure 16-3-IV.

Iterative Procedure.

The basic solution depicted in Fig. 16-3-II is used as a starting solution in Table 16-3-I, cycle 0. The steps of a solution by the simplex method are shown in the tables for subsequent cycles. Since the technique is practically the same as the classical transportation algorithm given in Chapter 14, detailed discussion of the steps will not be given.

TABLE 16-3-I

Transshipment Tableau

Cycle 0

Origins	Destinations								a_i
	(1)	(2)	(3)	(4)	(5)	(6)	(7)	(8)	$-\pi_i$
(1)	**0** 0	**4** 9	**3 − θ** 9	**0 + θ** 12	▨	▨	▨	▨	**7** 0
(2)	9	**0** 0	8	▨	9	12	▨	▨	**0** −9
(3)	9	8	**−3 + θ** 0	8	9	**3 − θ** 13	▨	▨	**0** −9
(4)	12	▨	8	**0 − θ** 0	▨	▨	**θ*** (enter) 10	▨	**0** −12
(5)	▨	9	9	▨	**0** 0	**1** 6	▨	**2** 13	**3** −16
(6)	▨	12	13	▨	6	**0 + θ** 0	**0 − θ** (drop) 5	8	**0** −22
(7)	▨	▨	▨	10	▨	5	**0** 0	9	**0** −27
(8)	▨	▨	▨	▨	▨	13	8	**0** 0	**0** −29
b_j	**0** 0	**4** 9	**0** 9	**0** 12	**0** 16	**4** 22	**0** 27	**2** 29	
π_j									

Variable entering basic set is x_{47} because Min $\bar{c}_{ij} = \bar{c}_{47} = c_{47} - (\pi_7 - \pi_4) = -5$.
Variable leaving basic set is x_{67} because Max $\theta = 0$ for $x_{67} = 0 - \theta$.

TABLE 16-3-I (continued)

Cycle 1

Origins	Destinations								a_i
	(1)	(2)	(3)	(4)	(5)	(6)	(7)	(8)	$-\pi_i$
(1)	0 ; 0	4 + θ ; 9	3 − θ ; 9	0 ; 12	///	///	///	///	7 ; 0
(2)	; 9	0 − θ ; 0	; 8	///	; 9	θ* (enter) ; 12	///	///	0 ; −9
(3)	; 9	; 8	−3 + θ ; 0	; 8	; 9	3 − θ (drop) ; 13	///	///	0 ; −9
(4)	; 12	///	; 8	0 ; 0	///	///	0 ; 10	///	0 ; −12
(5)	///	; 9	; 9	///	0 ; 0	1 ; 6	///	2 ; 13	3 ; −16
(6)	///	; 12	; 13	///	; 6	0 ; 0	; 5	; 8	0 ; −22
(7)	///	///	///	; 10	///	; 5	0 ; 0	; 9	0 ; −22
(8)	///	///	///	///	; 13	; 8	; 9	0 ; 0	0 ; −29
b_j	0	4	0	0	0	4	0	2	
π_j	0	9	9	12	16	22	22	29	

Variable entering basic set is x_{26} because Min $\bar c_{ij} = \bar c_{26} = c_{26} - (\pi_6 - \pi_2) = -1$.
Variable leaving basic set is x_{36} because Max $\theta = 3$ for $x_{36} = 3 - \theta$.

TABLE 16-3-I (continued)

Cycle 2 (Optimal)

Origins	Destinations (1)	(2)	(3)	(4)	(5)	(6)	(7)	(8)	a_i / $-\pi$
(1)	**0** / 0	**7** / 9	**0** / 9	**0** / 12	▨	▨	▨	▨	**7** / 0
(2)	/ 9	**−3** / 0	/ 8	▨	/ 9	**3** / 12	▨	▨	**0** / −9
(3)	/ 9	/ 8	**0** / 0	/ 8	/ 9	/ 13	▨	▨	**0** / −9
(4)	/ 12	▨	/ 8	**0** / 0	▨	▨	**0** / 10	▨	**0** / −12
(5)	▨	/ 9	/ 9	▨	**0** / 0	**1** / 6	▨	**2** / 13	**3** / −15
(6)	▨	/ 12	/ 13	▨	/ 6	**0** / 0	/ 5	/ 8	**0** / −21
(7)	▨	▨	▨	/ 10	▨	/ 5	**0** / 0	/ 9	**0** / −22
(8)	▨	▨	▨	▨	/ 13	/ 8	/ 9	**0** / 0	**0** / −28
b_j / π_j	**0** / 0	**4** / 9	**0** / 9	**0** / 12	**0** / 15	**4** / 21	**0** / 22	**2** / 28	

16-4. PROBLEMS

1. Show that no feasible solutions exist for the transshipment model shown in Table 16-1-I unless the total production equals the total consumption.
2. Generalize the equation model to allow for the storing of excesses at a city when the total of amounts shipped-in plus produced may possibly exceed the total of amounts shipped-out plus consumed.
3. Show that, in this generalized model, no feasible solution exists if $\Sigma a_i^* < \Sigma b_j^*$, and interpret the result.
4. Formulate the transshipment model in network form (Table 16-1-I) for the example given by Fig. 16-1-I, omitting all variables x_{ij} such that the network has no arc connecting city i to city j.
5. If cities are allowed to consume and produce simultaneously (so that a_i^* and b_i^* may both be positive), review the proof that the amount transshipped is

$$x_{ii} = x_{ii}^* - a_i - b_i$$

Show that the standard form for transshipment model (Table 16-1-IV) results from the original when we define new constants and variables as follows:

$$a_i = a_i^* - \text{Min}\,(a_i^*, b_i^*)$$
$$b_i = b_i^* - \text{Min}\,(a_i^*, b_i^*)$$
$$x_{ii} = x_{ii}^* - \text{Min}\,(a_i^*, b_i^*)$$

6. Why is $x_{ii} \geq 0$ implied by the standard transshipment form, Table 16-1-IV?
7. In any transshipment problem, prove that if x_{jj} exceeds Σa_i, then there is a circularity in the flow pattern, and show that such a solution cannot be optimal if all c_{ij} are positive.
8. Solve the problem given in Fig. 16-1-I by setting up its transportation equivalent (Table 16-2-I) and applying the methods of Chapters 14 and 15.
9. The post office wishes to send a package from Los Angeles to Boston via the least-cost route. The cost of shipment between neighboring points of the transportation network are proportional to the numbers shown on connecting links of the map shown in Fig. 17-3-I. Find the route.

REFERENCES

Berge, 1962-1

Briggs, 1962-1

Dantig and Ramser, 1959-1

Dennis, 1959-1

Dilworth, 1950-1

Ford and Fulkerson 1960-1

Gale, 1960-1

Hoffman and Markowitz, 1963-1

Kantorovich and Gavurin, 1949-1

Koopmans, 1947-1

Koopmans and Reiter, 1951-1

Orden, 1956-1

(See also references Chapter 14)

CHAPTER 17

NETWORKS AND THE TRANSSHIPMENT PROBLEM

17-1. GRAPHS AND TREES

T. C. Koopmans, in his pioneering work on transportation problems, was the first to interpret properties of optimal and non-optimal solutions with respect to the linear graph associated with a network of routes [1947-1].

A *linear graph* or *network* consists of a number of *nodes* or junction points, each joined to some or all of the others by *arcs* or links. The diagrammed circles containing the labels 1, 2, . . ., 6 in Fig. 17-1-I are the

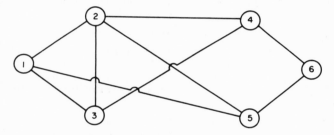

Figure 17-1-I. Example of a linear graph (network).

nodes. The arcs are indicated by straight or curved line segments, each of which links just two nodes, e.g. (1, 2), (1, 3), (1, 5), (2, 3), (2, 4), (2, 5), (3, 4), (4, 6), (5, 6). The crossing of two of these lines does not indicate intersection of the corresponding arcs except at nodes. We shall sometimes use the symbol ⌒ commonly seen in electrical diagrams to indicate a non-nodal crossing.

In transportation problems, the nodes often represent cities and the arcs represent routes between them. The unidirectional nature of flows in goods or traffic over routes leads to consideration of a directed graph (a network made up of directed arcs). The symbol $i \rightarrow j$ is used to denote a directed arc and represents an allowable precedence between i and j. Suppose, for example, in a given situation, we are allowed to proceed, if at 1, to 2 or 3; if at 2, to 3, 4, or 5; if at 4, to 3 or 6; if at 5, to 1 or 6; if at 6, to 5. This can be represented by the directed arcs, $1 \rightarrow 2$, $1 \rightarrow 3$, $2 \rightarrow 3$, $2 \rightarrow 4$, $2 \rightarrow 5$, $4 \rightarrow 3$, $4 \rightarrow 6$, $5 \rightarrow 1$, $5 \rightarrow 6$, and $6 \rightarrow 5$, as shown in Fig. 17-1-II.

There may be several distinct directed arcs joining the same two nodes, i and j; for our present discussion, however, we need consider only two: one associated with a possible shipping activity from i to j, and the other

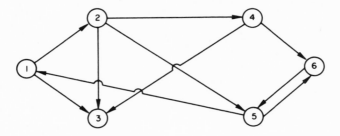

Figure 17-1-II. Example of a directed network.

j to i. We shall treat them as distinct arcs, although they may be diagrammed by a single line.

A sequence of arcs (i, i_1), (i_1, i_2), (i_2, i_3), . . ., (i_k, j), connecting the nodes, i and j, is called a *chain*, regardless of the particular ways in which these arcs may be directed (see Fig. 17-1-IIIa).

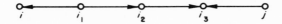

Figure 17-1-IIIa. Example of a chain.

A chain of arcs connecting i to itself is called a loop (a simple loop if the arcs are distinct) (see Fig. 17-1-IIIb).

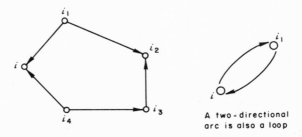

A two-directional arc is also a loop

Figure 17-1-IIIb. Examples of chains that are loops.

A graph containing no loops in which every point is connected to every other point through a chain of arcs is called a *tree*. For example, dropping several of the arcs in Fig. 17-1-II, we are left, as in Fig. 17-1-IIIc, with a subnetwork which is a directed tree. Each point, such as 3, 4, or 6, joined to a network by a single link is known as an *end*.

Our eventual objective will be to show that the $(n - 1)$ basic, non-diagonal variables of a transshipment problem correspond to $(n - 1)$ arcs

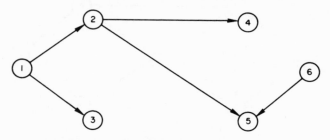

Figure 17-1-IIIc.   Example of a tree.

which form a directed tree. The following theorem will be useful for this purpose.

THEOREM 1: *A network having n nodes is a tree if it has $(n - 1)$ arcs and no loops.*

In other words, such a graph is always connected; it cannot break up into *several* trees as in Fig. 17-1-IV.

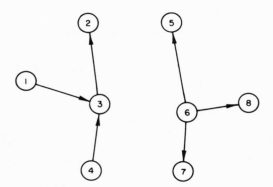

Figure 17-1-IV.   Network of disconnected trees.

The theorem being clearly true for two nodes, assume it is true for 2, 3, . . ., $n - 1$.

For the case of n nodes, it will be convenient to establish the following:

LEMMA: *Under the hypotheses of Theorem 1 there exists at least one node which is an end, that is, a point p with only one arc (p, q) connecting it to the rest of the network.*

PROOF: To find a node which is an end, begin by selecting any node, say p_1; it is joined to at least one other node, say p_2, by an arc. (If this were not the case, deleting any arc (i, j) joining a pair of the $n - 1$ remaining nodes would leave $n - 2$ arcs containing no loop. By our inductive assumption, this forms a tree and there exists a chain of arcs joining p_i to p_j. Adjoining arc (p_i, p_j) to this chain would form a loop contrary to assumption.) Because there is an arc from p_1 to some p_2, move to p_2 along the arc (p_1, p_2). Leave p_2 on another arc (if possible) and move to p_3. Because the number of points is finite and there are no loops, by proceeding in this manner, a point p will be found which is an *end* point, with only one arc (p, q) linking it to the rest of the network.

PROOF OF THEOREM 1: If the end and its single arc are deleted, then the remaining network has $(n - 1)$ points, $(n - 2)$ arcs, and since it contains no loops, it is connected by the inductive assumption. If the deleted point, p, and its arc (p, q) are reinserted, it will be possible to connect p to any other point via q, which proves that a network having n points, $(n - 1)$ arcs, and no loops is connected, hence forms a tree.

We have shown that a tree contains at least one end. As an exercise, prove

THEOREM 2: *A tree contains at least two ends.*

The Graph Associated with a Transshipment Problem.

Let us consider the transshipment problem in the form

$$(1) \qquad \sum_i x_{ik} - \sum_j x_{kj} = a_k - b_k \qquad (k = 1, 2, \ldots, n)$$

where the first summation is restricted to (i, k) corresponding to admissible arcs (i, k) and the second, to admissible arcs (k, j). The objective is to determine $x_{ij} \geq 0$ and Min z satisfying (1) and

$$(2) \qquad \sum_i \sum_j c_{ij}x_{ij} = z$$

We set up our one-to-one correspondence ($\leftrightarrow$) with a network, as follows:

(3)   Each equation $k \leftrightarrow$ node k of the graph

Each admissible $x_{ij} \leftrightarrow$ directed arc joining i to j

In the network of Fig. 17-1-V, the availabilities a_1 and a_5 at origins 1 and 5 are shown for convenience on the one-node arrows pointing into these points. By definition, these are not arcs of the network since they do not join pairs of nodes. Similarly, the requirements at destinations 2, 6, and 8 are shown on arrows pointing outward. Such arrows are omitted from points where $a_i = b_i = 0$. The arcs (i, j) of the network which correspond to basic variables, x_{ij}, are shown with heavy lines. The particular values of x_{ij} shown are those of the initial basic solution given in Table 16-3-I for the network problem shown in Fig. 16-1-I.

[355]

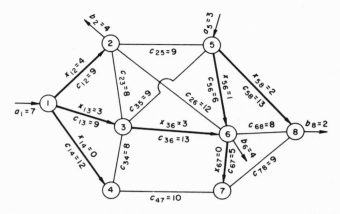

Figure 17-1-V.   The tree of heavy arcs corresponds to a basic set of variables.

All solutions to the system of equations for this problem, both feasible and infeasible, can be represented on the corresponding directed arcs of the network. Consequently, at each node k it is necessary that the sum of values of x_{ik} and a_k on arrows pointing into the node equals the sum of values of x_{kj} and b_k on arrows pointing out of it (as in Table 16-1-IV, the common value of these two sums is assigned to the diagonal variable x_{ii}). Conversely, any set of values assigned to directed arcs of a network with this property may be extended to a (feasible or infeasible) solution of the equations, by determining the omitted diagonal variables by the common values of the sums described above.

Relationships Between Bases and Trees.

THEOREM 3:   *The subnetwork corresponding to a basic set of variables is a tree.*

If the subnetwork of $(n - 1)$ arcs corresponding to the $(n - 1)$ basic, non-diagonal variables contains no loops, it is a tree by Theorem 1. It

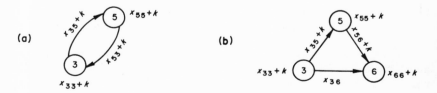

Figure 17-1-VIa, b.   Why loops do not correspond to extreme points.

remains to be shown that no basic set can give rise to a loop. Suppose, for example, that x_{35} and x_{53} are both in the basic set as in Fig. 17-1-VIa or x_{35}, x_{56}, and x_{36}, as in Fig. 17-1-VIb. If this were the case, the values of the basic variables around the loop could be altered as indicated in Fig. 17-1-VIa, while the values of all other variables would remain the same, yielding a second solution of the transshipment equations. This, however, contradicts the uniqueness property of the basic solutions; therefore, the basic set cannot include loops.

EXERCISE: Formalize this proof for a general loop.

THEOREM 4: *Any subnetwork of a graph, which is a tree, corresponds to a basic set of variables.*

To prove that a tree corresponds to a basic set of variables, it will be sufficient to show that the $(n - 1)$ variables corresponding to the directed arcs of the tree, which we will call *tree variables*, can be uniquely evaluated for any choice of a_i and b_j, provided that $\Sigma a_i = \Sigma b_j$. To find these values, set all non-tree variables equal to zero. Starting with any end k, and the single point, i, to which it links, we see that there is only one non-zero tree variable in equation k, namely x_{ik} or x_{ki}. Hence, its value is $x_{ik} = (a_i - b_i)$ or $x_{ki} = (b_i - a_i)$.

Thus the triangularity property which makes possible the finding of an equation (say k) with one unknown, evaluating the variable and dropping of the kth equation, corresponds to the tree property which makes possible the finding of an end (say node k) and its arc, evaluating the variable associated with the arc, and dropping the kth node and its arc. What remains is also a tree and the procedure may be repeated, until (on the last step) two nodes and a connecting arc remain, corresponding to a single variable and two equations. Since $\Sigma a_i = \Sigma b_j$, the sum of the constants of (1) vanishes initially *and* after each deletion; this permits a consistent evaluation of the last step. From these observations, it is clear that the tree variables comprise a basic set.

17-2. INTERPRETING THE SIMPLEX METHOD ON THE NETWORK

Phase I, Finding an Initial Basic Feasible Solution.

In this section we shall discuss a simplex procedure for finding a starting solution if one is not readily available by inspection of the graph.

Step 1. Join each origin to other nodes j of the network using only admissible arcs directed away from origins i. Similarly, join various destinations i' to other nodes j' of the network using only admissible directed arcs pointing into final destinations i'. Repeat the process iteratively using nodes j and j' in place of i and i' *being sure at all times not to form loops.* Once a chain of arcs out of an origin joins with a chain of arcs from a destination, nodes along the chain may be joined to nodes not on the chain using arcs in either direction. If there still remain nodes not connected to others, use the arcs in either direction to make the connections. If, finally, there still remain sets of points isolated from other sets of points in the graph, this means that the original problem breaks up into two or more independent problems.

EXERCISE: Show that if the original network is connected, the procedure always yields a tree.

Step 2. Evaluate the basic variables corresponding to arcs of the tree. Since the tree does not necessarily correspond to a feasible set, some variables x_{ij} may be negative. Reverse the direction of the arrow on the arc and replace x_{ij} by x_{ji} of each negative variable, which will be positive in value. Some variables x_{ji} may now correspond to inadmissible arcs.

Step 3. If all directed arcs (i, j) of the tree *are* admissible, then the tree corresponds to a basic feasible solution. If not, then try to drive out the inadmissible arcs (i, j) by the usual Phase I, consisting, in this case, of an auxiliary transshipment problem in which the infeasibility form

$$(1) \qquad w = \sum_{i, j} d_{ij} x_{ij}$$

(summed over both admissible and inadmissible arcs) has

$$(2) \qquad d_{ij} = \begin{cases} 0 & \text{if } (i, j) \text{ is an admissible arc,} \\ 1 & \text{if } (i, j) \text{ is an inadmissible arc} \end{cases}$$

This is now in the proper format for applying the tree method which will be discussed in the next section.

Step 4. If it turns out that Min $w > 0$, then of course no feasible solution exists. If, on the other hand, feasibility is achieved at any stage with no inadmissible variables x_{ij} remaining, then a basic feasible solution and its corresponding tree have been constructed. Finally, if $w = 0$, but inadmissible x_{ij} still remain, there are two roads open:

(a) Drop all arcs (i, j) whose relative cost factors $\bar{d}_{ij}$ in the infeasibility form are positive, and continue with Phase II on the subnetwork of arcs for which $\bar{d}_{ij} = 0$; or

(b) Reverse the direction of the inadmissible arc (i, j), thus making it admissible, and replace the corresponding basic variable, x_{ij}, by x_{ji}, whose value in the basic solution is zero.

In either case, follow with Phase II, using the original c_{ij} in place of d_{ij}. We have thus shown

THEOREM 1: *If a connected network possesses a feasible solution, then there exists a tree corresponding to a basic feasible solution.*

Consider as an example, the transshipment problem treated in Chapter 16. A starting solution such as the one given in Fig. 17-1-V may be used to start Phase II. We could also construct another such solution using the procedure described in the preceding section. From origins 1 and 5 we can ship directly only to nodes 2, 3, 4; 6, 8. From (2, 3, 4, 6, 8), only one new point can be reached, namely 7. Hence, the tree diagram immediately takes the form of Fig. 17-2-I. The values of the variables on branches of the tree are

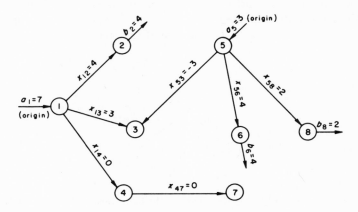

Figure 17-2-I. Starting tree and infeasible basic solution obtained by fanning out from the origins.

such that the algebraic sum at each point is zero (where the sign is determined by the arrows). Thus, the value of $x_{12} = 4$ is determined by the equation associated with end point 2 of the tree. End points 6, 7, 8 determine variables x_{56}, x_{47}, and x_{58}, respectively. This, in turn, permits evaluation of variables associated with arcs leading into ends of the subtree whose x_{ij} have not been evaluated. These are x_{53} and x_{14}. Finally, x_{13} is evaluated. The solution is not feasible, since $x_{53} = -3$. Reversing the arrow and replacing x_{53} by x_{35} produces the required basic feasible solution as shown in Fig. 17-2-II.

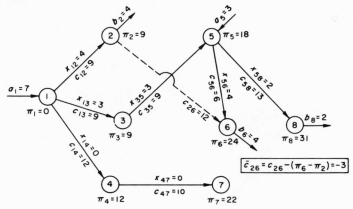

Figure 17-2-II. Graphically improving a basic feasible solution (cycle 0).

[359]

Phase II, Finding an Optimal Solution.

Compute the implicit price π_i satisfying the network Fig. 17-1-V with $\pi_j - \pi_i = c_{ij}$, for arcs (i, j) of the tree. For this purpose choose any point i and give it an arbitrary price, π_i. For example, in Fig. 17-2-II choose node 1 which is the focus of a large number of radiating arcs, and set $\pi_1 = 0$. The π_i such that $(1, i)$ or $(i, 1)$ is an arc of the tree can be evaluated next

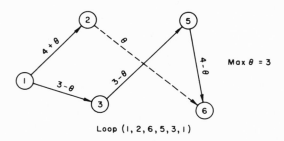

Loop $(1, 2, 6, 5, 3, 1)$

Figure 17-2-III.   Adjusting the values of the basic variables around the loop.

from Fig. 17-1-V. In this case, the arcs are $(1, 2)$, $(1, 3)$, and $(1, 4)$ leading to evaluation of π_2, π_3, π_4. From arcs $(3, 5)$ and $(4, 7)$, π_5 and π_7 can be evaluated. Finally, from $(5.\ 6)$ and $(5, 8)$, π_6 and π_8 can be evaluated.

To determine whether the basic solution shown in Fig. 17-2-II is optimal, compare $\pi_j - \pi_i$ with c_{ij}. This comparison can be made easily on the graph of the network Fig. 17-1-V by systematically scanning each arc (i, j) and forming

$$(3) \qquad \bar{c}_{ij} = c_{ij} - (\pi_j - \pi_i)$$

If this is nonnegative for all arcs, then the solution is optimal. In Fig. 17-2-II the criterion is not met since $\bar{c}_{26} = c_{26} - (\pi_6 - \pi_2) = 12 - (24 - 9) = -3$. Hence, it pays to increase the flow along the arc $(2, 6)$, indicated by

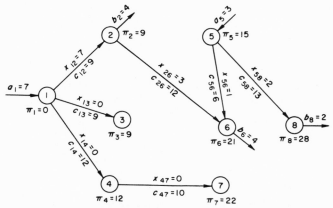

Figure 17-2-IV.   Graph of the improved basic feasible solution (cycle 1, optimal).

the dotted arrow in Fig. 17-2-II. With arc (2, 6), the subnetwork is no longer a tree, since it contains the loop shown in Fig. 17-2-III. Only the values of the variables around the loop are affected by increasing the value of x_{26} to $\theta > 0$. It is clear from Fig. 17-2-III that $\theta = 3$ is the largest value that maintains feasibility. At this value, either arc (1, 3) or (3, 5) is dropped from the tree and is replaced by (2, 6). In Fig. 17-2-IV, arc (3, 5) has been dropped. The values of π_i are recomputed, but now all $\bar{c}_{ij} \geq 0$, and the solution is optimal and is the same as that given in Table 16-3-I, cycle 2.

17-3. THE SHORTEST ROUTE PROBLEM

A. An Iterative Solution. Let us suppose that there is a package originating in Los Angeles which can be delivered to Boston along any of several different routes, shown in Fig. 17-3-I. We are interested in having the package transshipped over the shortest route.

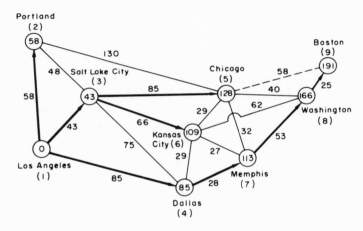

Figure 17-3-I. Starting tree for the initial guess of the shortest route from Los Angeles to Boston.

Now $x_{ij} = 1$ means that the package is shipped from city i to city j; $x_{ij} = 0$ means it is not (where $i \neq j$). Let x_{ii}^* $(i = 2, \ldots, 8)$ be the total quantity transshipped through city i. The numbers appearing in the circles are the distances from Los Angeles along heavy arrow routes. This gives rise to a system of constraints

Shipped out

(1)
$$x_{12} + x_{13} + x_{14} \qquad\qquad\qquad = 1$$
$$x_{21} - x_{22}^* + x_{23} \qquad + x_{25} \qquad = 0$$
$$x_{31} + x_{32} - x_{33}^* + x_{34} + x_{35} + x_{36} = 0$$
$$\cdots\cdots\cdots\cdots\cdots\cdots\cdots\cdots\cdots\cdots\cdots\cdots$$
$$x_{85} + x_{86} + x_{87} - x_{88}^* + x_{89} = 0$$

[361]

Shipped in

(2)
$$x_{12} - x_{22}^* + x_{32} \qquad + x_{52} \qquad\qquad\qquad = 0$$
$$x_{13} + x_{23} - x_{33}^* + x_{43} + x_{53} + x_{63} \qquad\qquad = 0$$
$$x_{14} \qquad + x_{34} - x_{44}^* \qquad\quad + x_{64} + x_{74} = 0$$
$$\cdots\cdots\cdots\cdots\cdots\cdots\cdots\cdots\cdots\cdots\cdots\cdots\cdots\cdots\cdots$$
$$x_{59} \qquad\qquad\quad + x_{89} = 1$$

(3)
$$\sum_{i=1}^{9} \sum_{j=1}^{9} d_{ij} x_{ij} = z \text{ (to be minimized)}$$

where d_{ij}, in this case, is the distance between city i and city j.

The first equation states that the amount shipped *out* of Los Angeles is unity. The last equation states that the amount shipped *into* Boston is unity. Equating the x_{ii} in the ith equation of (1) with the x_{ii} in the $(i-1)^{\text{st}}$ equation of (2) makes the amount shipped out equal to the amount shipped in for each city.

If we replace the condition $(x_{ij} = 0 \text{ or } 1)$ by $(x_{ij} \geq 0)$ (see Theorem 1, Chapter 15-1), the problem can of course be solved by the transshipment method, using either a tableau, or a graph, as explained in the last section. However, there is a closely related, but even simpler graphical procedure: starting from Los Angeles, draw some route conjectured to be optimal. For example, ship along the southern route and then up along the east coast to Boston, indicating the route with arrows. In a similar manner, draw conjectured shortest routes and arrows from Los Angeles to all other cities, making sure that the arrows do not form loops. Note that the result must be a tree since the origin is connected to every other node. Note also that the chain from the origin to any node has only directed arcs of the form:

(4)
$$\text{origin} \quad \underset{i}{\cdot}\longrightarrow \cdot \longrightarrow \cdot \longrightarrow \cdot \underset{j}{\longrightarrow} \cdot$$

An example of such a tree is shown by the heavy arrows in Fig. 17-3-I. Each such tree corresponds to a basis and it is easy to verify that the corresponding basic solution is feasible. Because of (4), the prices, π_i, are computed in the following manner: set $\pi_1 = 0$ for the origin. At each city, put a number in the node circle that is its distance from the origin via the (unique) path of the tree, e.g. from Los Angeles to Memphis via the tree is 85 plus 28, or 113. The next step is to test whether the tree represents a solution to the shortest route problem. To do this, we are interested in whether the circled numbers are actually the shortest distances from Los Angeles, when we allow other possible paths. If not, the solution can be improved in the sense that a shorter route can be found from terminal to node. The test of whether these are minimum distances goes like this. Notice that the total distance to Boston is 191; however, if the route went via Chicago, and then to Boston, it would be $128 + 58 = 186$, a decrease of 5 units, so that this particular tree is not an optimal solution. We can better the solution by inserting an arrow between Chicago and Boston, recording 186 at Boston and removing the arrow between Washington and Boston. Again we test whether a shorter route could be obtained via Portland-Chicago, say. However, $58 + 130 \geq 128$, so we try Kansas City-Chicago. But again, $109 + 29 \geq 128$. By continuing in this manner, we eventually arrive at a situation where it is not possible to improve the distance shown in any circle. Accordingly, we have arrived at the optimal solution. For the example at hand, the tree shown is optimal where the Washington-Boston arrow is dropped and the Chicago-Boston arrow inserted, changing the 191 at Boston to 186. The values of x_{ij} are unity along the path in the final tree from Los Angeles to Boston and zero elsewhere. Hence the optimal path is Los Angeles-Salt Lake-Chicago-Boston. The proof of these statements depends on the following observations:

(1) The method of scanning other cities to see if there is a shorter alternative route is the same as the test for optimality, $\pi_j - \pi_i \leq d_{ij}$.

(2) A tree in which all arcs are directed along the chains joining the origin to any node has the properties that (a) the corresponding basic solution is always feasible and (b) only one of the arcs having a given node as end-point points toward the node; the others point outward (Fig. 17-3-II).

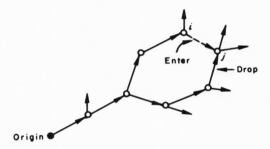

Figure 17-3-II. The special adjustment around a loop for the shortest route problem.

Observe that, if the arc (i, j) is entered into the tree to form an improved new tree, then the arc dropped (assuming non-degeneracy) must be the arc of the old tree pointing *into* j. Each new tree has the same properties.

B. A Direct Solution. Assuming all arc distances are positive, we have another procedure for obtaining the shortest route from a given origin to all other nodes in the network or to a particular destination point. The method [Dantzig, 1960-1] can be interpreted as a slight refinement of the method given in A above, those reported by Bellman [1958-1], Moore [1957-1], Dantzig [1957-2], and those proposed informally by Gale and Fulkerson to the author. It is similar to Moore's method of "fanning out" from the origin. However, its special feature is that *the fanning out is done one point at a time and the distance assigned is final.*

[363]

It is assumed that (a) one can write without effort for each node the arcs leading to other nodes in increasing order of length and (b) it is no effort to ignore an arc of the list, if it leads to a node whose distance has been assigned earlier. It will be shown that no more than $n(n-1)/2$ comparisons are needed in an n-node network to determine the shortest routes from a given origin to all other nodes.

Suppose that, at some stage k in the computing process, the shortest paths to k of the nodes from some origin are known. Call this set of k points S. (See Fig. 17-3-III.)

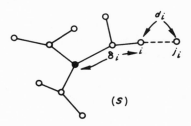

Figure 17-3-III.   Finding the shortest route in at most $n(n-1)/2$ comparisons; all arcs selected in the spanning subtree are final.

(a) Let i be a node in S,
(b) let δ_i be its least distance to the origin ●,
(c) let j_i be the closest node to i not in S, if any, and
(d) let d_i be its distance from i.

Choose j_s as the $(k+1)^{\text{st}}$ point where

$$(5) \qquad\qquad \delta_s + d_s = \operatorname{Min}\,(\delta_i + d_i) \qquad\qquad (i = 1, 2, \ldots, k)$$

(In case of ties for minimum, the process could be made more efficient by determining several new nodes j at a time.) This choice implies that the minimum path to j_s from the origin, having a length of $\delta_s + d_s$, is via s. To see this, consider any other path from j_s to the origin. Eventually, the path must reach some node i of S from some node j not in S (where j may be j_s). We now assume that the distances along the path from j_s to j are nonnegative (see Problem 5) so that the total distance to the origin along the path is not less than $\delta_i + d_i$; by (5), however, $\delta_i + d_i \geq \delta_s + d_s$.

Note that the minimum requires only k comparisons for a decision as to the $(k+1)^{\text{st}}$ point; hence in an n-node network no more than $1 + 2 + \cdots + (n-1) = n(n-1)/2$ comparisons are needed.

In practice, the number of comparisons can be considerably less than this because, after several stages, one or more of the nodes in S only have arcs leading to points already in S. The 8-node graph shown in Fig. 17-3-IV, for instance, required only 16 comparisons instead of $(8 \times 7)/2 = 28$ comparisons.

If the problem is to determine the shortest path from a given origin to a given terminal, the number of comparisons can often be reduced in practice by fanning out from both the origin and the terminal simultaneously, adding one point at a time to sets about the origin·and the terminal, as if they were two separate independent problems.

However, once the shortest path between a node and the origin or the terminal is found in one problem, the path is conceptually replaced by a single arc in the other problem. The algorithm terminates whenever the fan of one of the problems reaches its terminal in the other.

Example: Distances on links of the network are as in Fig. 17-3-IV.

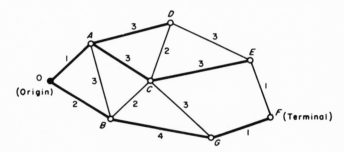

Figure 17-3-IV. An example of a shortest route problem
(optimal solution shown by heavy arcs).

For each node, list arcs branching *out* of the node by ascending arc distances:

(O)	(A)	(B)	(C)	(D)	(E)	(F)	(G)
OA-1	AB-3	BC-2	CB-2	DC-2	EF-1	FE-1	GF-1
OB-2	AC-3	BA-3	CD-2	DA-3	EC-3	FG-1	GC-3
	AD-3	BG-4	CA-3	DE-3	ED-3		GB-4
			CG-3				
			CE-3				

Step 0. The set S consists of O initially.

Step 1. Choose arc OA; write its length, 1, above column A, deleting all arcs *into* A. (Delete OA, BA, CA, DA; add A to the set S.) ("Length" means least distance from O.)

Step 2. Compare OB-2 and AB $(1 + 3)$; choose path via OB and write its length, 2, above column B, deleting all arcs *into* B. (Delete OB, AB, CB, GB; add B to the set S.)

Step 3. Compare AC $(1 + 3)$, AD $(1 + 3)$, and BC $(2 + 2)$; and, because of ties, choose paths via AC (or BC) and AD and write their length, 4, above columns C and D, deleting all arcs *into* C and D. (Delete AC, AD, BC, DC, EC, ED, GC; add C and D to the set S.)

[365]

Step 4. Compare *BG* $(2 + 4)$, *CG* $(4 + 3)$, and *DE* $(4 + 3)$; choose path via *BG*, and write its length, 6, above column *G*, deleting all arcs into *G*. (Delete *BG*, *CG*, *FG*; add *G* to the set *S*.)

Step 5. Compare *CE* $(4 + 3)$, *DE* $(4 + 3)$, and *GF* $(6 + 1)$; choose path via *CE* (or *DE*) and *GF* and write its length, 7, above columns *E* and *F*, deleting all arcs into *E* and *F*. (Delete *CE*, *DE*, *FE*, *GF*; add *E* and *F* to the set *S*.)

Because of ties, many of the steps were performed simultaneously.

The shortest paths from the origin to other nodes are along paths *OA*, *OB*, *AC*, *AD*, *BG*, *CE*, *GF* (see heavy arcs, Fig. 17-3-IV) with alternative *BC* for *AC*, and *DE* for *CE*.

17-4. PROBLEMS

1. Consider a transshipment problem consisting of k independent networks, each feasible. Connect these k networks together by introducing $k - 1$ new arcs (i_s, j_s), where i_s is a point in the sth network and j_s is a point in the $(s + 1)^{\text{st}}$ network $(s = 1, 2, \ldots, k - 1)$. Prove that $x_{i_s j_s} = 0$ in any feasible solution for the augmented network.

2. Show how the shortest route problem of Fig. 17-3-I can be solved by the transshipment method; show that the tree corresponding to a basis need not have the property that the arrows point away from the origin (Los Angeles).

3. Show that the technique simultaneously works out the shortest routes from Los Angeles to all cities. What are the shortest routes?

4. What are the best routes for distributing a_1 packages from the origin to $(n - 1)$ cities in the quantities $b_2, b_3, \ldots, b_n$, where $\sum_2^n b_i = a_1$.

5. Show for the shortest route problem of § 17-3 that, if it is permissible for d_{ij} to be negative as well as positive, and if the sum of d_{ij} values around any loop is positive, then the iterative method only is valid and that both methods fail if this is not true.

6. Solve the shortest route example of § 17-3, used to illustrate the direct method, by the iterative procedure and the method of Chapter 16.

7. *The Caterer Problem* [Jacobs, 1954-1]. A caterer has booked his services for the next T days. He requires r_t fresh napkins on the tth day, $t = 1, 2, \ldots, T$. He sends his soiled napkins to the laundry which has three speeds of service, $f = 1$, 2, or 3 days. The faster the service, the higher the cost, c_f, of laundering a napkin. He can also purchase new napkins at a cost c_0. He has an initial stock of s napkins. The caterer wishes to minimize his total outlay. Formulate as a network problem. Define the caterer at time t as a "source point" in an abstract network for soiled napkins that are connected to "laundry points" $t + 1$, $t + 2$, $t + 3$. The reverse arc is not possible. The laundry point t is connected to a fresh napkin "destination point t" which in turn is connected to the

same type point for $t + 1$. Assign values to the various parameters and solve the numerical problem.

REFERENCES

Bellman, 1958-1
Berge, 1962-1
Dantzig, 1957-2, 1960-1
Dantzig and Ramser, 1959-1
Dennis, 1959-1
Ford and Fulkerson, 1960-1
Gale, 1960-1
Hoffman, 1960-1
Hoffman and Markowitz, 1963-1
Iri, 1960-1
Kelley, 1961-1
Klee, 1964-1
König, 1936-1
Koopmans, 1947-1

Koopmans and Reiter, 1951-1
Kruskal, 1956-1
Minty, 1962-1
Moore, 1957-1
Orden, 1956-1
Pollack, 1961-1
Prager, 1963-1
Shapley, 1961-1
Tornqvist, 1961-1
Tucker, 1950-1
Vajda, 1961-1
Van Slyke, 1963-1
Veinott, Jr. and Wagner, 1962-1
Wollmer, 1964-1

(See also references Chapter 14)

The Caterer Problem

Gaddum, Hoffman, and Sokolowsky, 1954-1
Garvin, 1960-1
Gass, 1964-1

Hadley, 1961-2
Jacobs, 1954-1
Prager, 1956-1

CHAPTER 18

VARIABLES WITH UPPER BOUNDS

18-1. THE GENERAL CASE

Our purpose will be to develop short-cut computational methods for solving an important class of systems involving upper bound restraints on the variables.

In this connection it should be noted that with the growing use of linear programming models for both dynamic and static problems, the main obstacle to full application is the inability of current computational methods to cope with the magnitude of the matrices for even the simplest technological situations. However, in certain cases, such as the now classical Hitchcock-Koopmans transportation model (see Chapter 14), it has been possible to solve this linear inequality system in spite of size because of simple regularities of the system. This suggests that research be undertaken to exploit the properties of other special matrix structures in order to facilitate ready solution of larger systems.

The method described here [Dantzig, 1954-3] was first developed at The RAND Corporation to provide a short-cut computing routine for the following problem: The research personnel were dissatisfied with the long delays generally incurred between the time their request for computation was initiated and the time their work was completed. The main cause of dissatisfaction was quite clear, for there was one project that was both *top-priority* and *so large* in volume that it completely absorbed the entire computing capacity for many weeks. The research people, being human, were no longer interested in the computed answers to their problems when the computing lab finally got around to them. In this example we have a case where the priority method of scheduling was not necessarily the best.[1]

To develop a more flexible decision method than priority scheduling, a model was devised in which the value of a job decreased as its completion date was delayed. The final determination of the optimum schedule depended on solving the distribution problem defined below.

---

[1] "A Model for Optimum Scheduling of Projects on Punched Card Equipment" was developed by Clifford Shaw of RAND and the author, and reported jointly before the RAND-U.C.L.A. Seminar on Industrial Scheduling in the winter of 1952 (the latter, incidentally, being one of the forerunners of The Institute of Management Sciences).

Type Job	1st week	2nd week	3rd week	. . .	nth week	Total hours required
Job 1	x_{11}	x_{12}	x_{13}	. . .	x_{1n}	$= r_1$
Job 2	x_{21}	x_{22}	x_{23}	. . .	x_{2n}	$= r_2$
.	.	.	.		.	.
.	.	.	.		.	.
Job m	x_{m1}	x_{m2}	x_{m3}	. . .	x_{mn}	$= r_m$
Total hours available	$\leq h_1$	$\leq h_2$	$\leq h_3$	. . .	$\leq h_n$	

The variable x_{ij} is the number of hours to be assigned the ith job in the jth week. Thus, nonnegative x_{ij} and Min z are to be chosen such that the total hours assigned to the ith job equals the hours assigned, (1); the total hours assigned in the jth week must not exceed the availability, (2); and the total cost (3) is minimum.

(1)
$$\sum_{j=1}^{n} x_{ij} = r_i$$

(2)
$$\sum_{i=1}^{m} x_{ij} \leq h_j$$

(3)
$$\sum_{i=1}^{m} \sum_{j=1}^{n} c_{ij} x_{ij} = z \text{ (Min)}$$

where $(-c_{ij})$, the value to the customer of one hour expended on his project in the jth week, satisfies

(3a)
$$(-c_{i1}) \geq (-c_{i2}) \geq \ldots \geq (-c_{in})$$

In addition to these restrictions, this problem has the added wrinkle that for some i and j,

(3b)
$$x_{ij} \leq \alpha_{ij}$$

or equivalently,

(3c)
$$x_{ij} + y_{ij} = \alpha_{ij} \qquad (y_{ij} \geq 0)$$

In other words, the hours assigned the ith project in the jth week cannot exceed α_{ij}. If we were to proceed in the usual manner of adding equations and slack variables for the upper bound restraints, this could greatly enlarge the size of the problem. To illustrate, a problem with a schedule for 18 projects in 10 weeks has 28 equations in 180 unknowns without upper bounds;

[369]

with upper bound conditions, it would require an additional 180 equations like (3c), as well as 180 slack variables, y_{ij}.

General Case: Find x_j and Min z satisfying

(4)
$$\sum_{j=1}^{n} a_{ij}x_j = b_i \qquad (x_j \geq 0; \; i = 1, 2, \ldots, m)$$

$$\sum_{j=1}^{n} c_j \, x_j = z \text{ (Min)}$$

and, if x_j must also satisfy the inequality, $x_j \leq \alpha_j$, use a slack variable, y_j, and the new equation,

(5)
$$x_j + y_j = \alpha_j \qquad (x_j \geq 0; \; y_j \geq 0)$$

to account for each such restriction. We shall refer to (4) and (5) as a *capacitated* system.

The Technique Illustrated.

An idea which permits the solution of a capacitated system with little additional computational effort is based on a slight generalization of the simplex procedure. While the simplex algorithm ordinarily fixes the values of non-basic variables at zero, a little reflection makes it clear that they could be at any fixed value. The simplex criterion indicates that it pays to increase the value of a variable, x_s, if its corresponding relative cost factor, $\bar{c}_s$, is negative, and to decrease x_s, if its corresponding relative cost factor, $\bar{c}_s$, is positive. With the added lower and upper bound restraints on x_s, it will only pay to increase its value, if $\bar{c}_s < 0$ and x_s is not at its upper bound, or to decrease its value if $\bar{c}_s > 0$ and x_s is not at its lower bound.

The following example shows how the enlarged system may be solved by applying the simplex algorithm to the format of the original uncapacitated system, with very simple conventions to insure that the values assigned a variable remain in the range between its upper and lower bounds.

Example 1: Find numbers

(6)
$$0 \leq x_1 \leq 4, \quad 0 \leq x_2 \leq 5, \quad 0 \leq x_3 \leq 1,$$
$$0 \leq x_4 \leq 2, \quad 0 \leq x_5 \leq 3$$

and Min z, satisfying

(7)
$$
\begin{aligned}
x_1 \quad\;\; + x_3 - 2x_4 \qquad\qquad &= 3 \\
x_2 - \;\; x_3 + \;\; x_4 + 2x_5 \quad\;\; &= 4 \\
-2x_3 - \;\; x_4 + \;\; x_5 - z &= 0
\end{aligned}
$$

Using x_1, x_2, and $(-z)$ as basic variables, the basic feasible solution is

(8)
$$[3, \quad 4, \quad 0, \quad 0, \quad 0, \quad 0]$$

The values of the basic variables are dotted. Note that no variable is at its upper bound.

Since $\bar{c}_3$ is negative, it pays to increase the value of x_3. Holding the other non-basic variables fixed, the solution becomes,

(9) $$[3 - x_3, \quad 4 + x_3, \quad x_3, \quad 0, \quad 0, \quad -2x_3]$$

indicating that x_3 can increase to 3. However, due to the upper bound restraint specified in (6), x_3 cannot be greater than 1. Therefore, we increase x_3 only to its upper bound and hold it fixed at this value, keeping the *same basic set*. The solution becomes

(10) $$[2, \quad 5, \quad 1, \quad 0, \quad 0, \quad -2]$$

Because the basic set is unchanged, the values of $\bar{c}_j$ given in the z-equation of (7) are still applicable. Because $\bar{c}_4 = -1$, we proceed to increase x_4 first, obtaining

(11) $$[2 + 2x_4, \quad 5 - x_4, \quad 1, \quad x_4, \quad 0, \quad -2 - x_4]$$

Now x_4 cannot increase to 5, since its upper bound is 2, nor can it reach its upper bound value, because we would then have $x_1 = 2 + 2(2) = 6$, violating the upper bound of $x_1 \le 4$. The largest value permissible to x_4 is thus $x_4 = 1$. Because adopting this value causes the basic variable x_1 to assume its upper bound value, we drop x_1 from the basic set, replacing it by x_4. The canonical form relative to the new basis is obtained by using as pivot, $-2x_4$, the bold faced term in (7), obtaining

(12)
$$
\begin{aligned}
-\tfrac{1}{2}x_1 \quad\quad - \tfrac{1}{2}x_3 + x_4 \quad\quad\quad\quad &= -\tfrac{3}{2} \\
\tfrac{1}{2}x_1 + x_2 - \tfrac{1}{2}x_3 \quad\quad + 2x_5 \quad\quad &= \tfrac{11}{2} \\
-\tfrac{1}{2}x_1 \quad\quad - \tfrac{5}{2}x_3 \quad\quad + x_5 - z &= -\tfrac{3}{2}
\end{aligned}
$$

associated with the solution,

(13) $$[4, \quad 4, \quad 1, \quad 1, \quad 0, \quad -3]$$

The variable, x_1, enters the non-basic set at its upper bound value, $x_1 = 4$. It will be noted that the basic variables, x_2 and x_4, are *between* their upper and lower bounds while the non-basic variables, x_1, x_3, and x_5, are *at* their upper or lower bounds. Note that x_5, at its lower bound (zero), has a positive cost factor, while all the variables at their upper bound value have negative cost factors: $\bar{c}_1 = -\tfrac{1}{2}$ and $\bar{c}_3 = -\tfrac{5}{2}$. As we shall show in a moment, this satisfies our criterion of optimality for the bounded variable problem, and no further iterations are required.

To prove optimality in this case, substitute for those non-basic variables which are at their upper bounds in (12), the expressions

(14) $$x_1 = 4 - x_1' \quad\quad\quad x_3 = 1 - x_3'$$

thus, deriving the system,

(15)
$$\begin{aligned}
\tfrac{1}{2}x_1' \quad &+ \tfrac{1}{2}x_3' + x_4 &&= 1 \\
-\tfrac{1}{2}x_1' + x_2 &+ \tfrac{1}{2}x_3' \quad &&+ 2x_5 &&= 4 \\
\tfrac{1}{2}x_1' \quad &+ \tfrac{5}{2}x_3' \quad &&+ x_5 - z &&= 3
\end{aligned}$$

whose corresponding basic feasible solution

(16)
$$[0, \quad 4, \quad 0, \quad 1, \quad 0, \quad -3]$$

is clearly optimal, ignoring the capacity constraints $x_1' \leq 4$, $x_2 \leq 5$, $x_3' \leq 1$, $x_4 \leq 2$, $x_5 \leq 3$. Moreover, substituting $x_1' = 0$, $x_3' = 0$ into (14) yields a set of nonnegative values that satisfies all constraints (14) and (15). Since, in general, the addition of constraints like (14) can only increase or leave unchanged the minimum value that z can attain, the value $z = -3$ is minimum for the full system (14) and (15) or the equivalent system (6) and (7).

Theory of the Upper Bounding Technique.

A basic solution of the uncapacitated system (4) is defined in earlier chapters as a solution obtained by setting $(n - m)$ non-basic variables equal to zero and solving for the consequent values of the basic variables, $x_{j_1}, \ldots, x_{j_m}$. A solution is said to be feasible, if it assigns nonnegative values to all the variables. In each simplex iteration, a new basic feasible solution is derived in which one of the basic variables, x_{j_r} $(1 \leq r \leq m)$, is given a zero value and replaced in the basic set by a non-basic variable x_s.

For this chapter only, we shall use these terms in a slightly altered sense. A *feasible* solution will be one which assigns to each variable, x_j, a nonnegative value not exceeding its upper bound α_j. By a *basic feasible* solution we shall mean one in which the non-basic variables have values either zero or α_j.

Now we note that the original system (4) and (5) may be replaced by an equivalent, *uncapacitated* system in which all non-basic variables are zero. This is done by substituting $\alpha_j - x_j'$ for any non-basic variable, x_j, at its upper bound. After rearrangement, the canonical form relative to some set of basic variables, say $x_1, x_2, \ldots, x_m$, takes the form,

(17)
$$\begin{aligned}
x_1 \quad &+ \bar{a}_{1,m+1}[x_{m+1} \text{ or } (\alpha_{m+1} - x_{m+1}')] + \ldots \\
&\qquad\qquad + \bar{a}_{1n}[x_n \text{ or } (\alpha_n - x_n')] = \bar{b}_1 \\
x_2 \quad &+ \bar{a}_{2,m+1}[x_{m+1} \text{ or } (\alpha_{m+1} - x_{m+1}')] + \ldots \\
&\qquad\qquad + \bar{a}_{2n}[x_n \text{ or } (\alpha_n - x_n')] = \bar{b}_2 \\
&\cdots\cdots\cdots\cdots\cdots\cdots\cdots\cdots\cdots\cdots\cdots\cdots\cdots \\
x_m &+ \bar{a}_{m,m+1}[x_{m+1} \text{ or } (\alpha_{m+1} - x_{m+1}')] + \ldots \\
&\qquad\qquad + \bar{a}_{mn}[x_n \text{ or } (\alpha_n - x_n')] = \bar{b}_m \\
&+ \bar{c}_{m+1} \ [x_{m+1} \text{ or } (\alpha_{m+1} - x_{m+1}')] + \ldots \\
&\qquad\qquad + \bar{c}_n \ [x_n \text{ or } (\alpha_n - x_n')] = z - \bar{z}_0
\end{aligned}$$

Upon transposing the constants, $(\bar{a}_{ij}\alpha_j)$ and $\bar{c}_j\alpha_j$, to the right member, we get

$$(18) \quad x_1 \qquad + \bar{a}_{1,m+1}[x_{m+1} \text{ or } -x'_{m+1}] + \ldots + \bar{a}_{1s}[x_s \text{ or } -x'_s]$$
$$+ \ldots + \bar{a}_{1n}[x_n \text{ or } -x'_n] = b'_1$$

$$\qquad x_m + \bar{a}_{m,m+1}[x_{m+1} \text{ or } -x'_{m+1}] + \ldots + \bar{a}_{ms}[x_s \text{ or } -x'_s]$$
$$+ \ldots + \bar{a}_{mn}[x_n \text{ or } -x'_n] = b'_m$$
$$\bar{c}_{m+1} \ [x_{m+1} \text{ or } -x'_{m+1}] + \ldots + \bar{c}_s \ [x_s \text{ or } -x'_s]$$
$$+ \ldots + \bar{c}_n \ [x_n \text{ or } -x'_n] = z - \bar{z}'_0$$

where

(i) $\bar{a}_{ij}$ are the coefficients of the original canonical form;

(ii) x_{j_i}, with $i = 1, 2, \ldots, m$, is a basic variable ($j_i = i$ above);

(iii) a non-basic variable appears in (17) as either x_j or $(-x'_j)$ depending upon whether its assigned value was zero or α_j in the original solution;

(iv) $b'_i \geq 0$ and $(-\bar{z}'_0)$ are, respectively, the values of the basic variables, x_{j_i} and $(-z)$, in the basic feasible solution resulting from this assignment.

Since the basic variables and their coefficients are unaffected by the transformation, the simplex multipliers remain unchanged.

Test for Optimality.

The basic feasible solution for the equivalent problem (18) is optimal if

$$(19) \quad \begin{cases} x_j = 0 \text{ implies } \bar{c}_j = c_j - \sum_{i=1}^{m} \pi_i a_{ij} \geq 0 \\ \qquad\qquad \text{and} \\ x'_j = 0 \text{ implies } \bar{c}_j = c_j - \sum_{i=1}^{m} \pi_i a_{ij} \leq 0 \end{cases}$$

where *the primed variables must satisfy the reverse inequality* because their coefficients are of the opposite sign from those of the unprimed variables.

THEOREM 1: *A basic feasible solution of* (18) *which satisfies* (19) *is equivalent to an optimal solution of* (4) *and* (5).

The proof is immediate.

Improving a Basic Feasible Solution.

If the solution is not optimal, then the variable to be selected for increase is the non-basic variable, x_s (or x'_s), such that

$$(20) \quad \bar{c}'_s = \text{Min } \bar{c}'_j < 0 \qquad \text{where } \bar{c}'_j = \begin{cases} \bar{c}_j \text{ for non-basic } x_j \\ -\bar{c}_j \text{ for non-basic } x'_j \end{cases}$$

Let θ represent the change (plus or minus) in the value of x_s.

Case I: The non-basic candidate is unprimed. The new value of x_s is θ, where $0 \leq \theta \leq \alpha_s$.

Case II: Here x_s' is the non-basic variable to be increased; the new value of x_s is $(\alpha_s + \theta)$, where $-\alpha_s \leq \theta \leq 0$ (since, in this case, the value of x_s must be decreased from its upper bound value, α_s).

In either case, if we fix the values of all other non-basic variables, then the adjusted values of the basic variables x_{j_i}, z, and x_s in terms of the change, θ, are

(21)
$$
\begin{aligned}
x_{j_1} &= \bar{b}_1' - \bar{a}_{1s}\,\theta \\
x_{j_2} &= \bar{b}_2' - \bar{a}_{2s}\,\theta \\
&\cdots\cdots\cdots\cdots \\
x_{j_m} &= \bar{b}_m' - \bar{a}_{ms}\theta \\
z &= \bar{z}_0' + \bar{c}_s\theta
\end{aligned}
\qquad (0 \leq x_{j_i} \leq \alpha_{j_i})
$$

where

Case I: $\qquad\qquad x_s = \theta$ and $\bar{c}_s < 0$ $\qquad\qquad (0 \leq \theta \leq \alpha_s)$

Case II: $\qquad\qquad x_s = \alpha_s + \theta$ and $\bar{c}_s > 0$ $\qquad\qquad (-\alpha_s \leq \theta \leq 0)$

Case I: The greatest nonnegative *increase*, θ^*, that maintains feasibility is given by

(22)
$$
\theta^* = \mathrm{Min} \begin{cases} \alpha_s & \\ \bar{b}_i'/\bar{a}_{is} & (\bar{a}_{is} > 0) \\ (\bar{b}_i' - \alpha_{j_i})/\bar{a}_{is} & (\bar{a}_{is} < 0) \end{cases}
$$

Case II: The maximum nonnegative *decrease*, θ^*, that maintains feasibility is

(23)
$$
-\theta^* = \mathrm{Min} \begin{cases} \alpha_s & \\ \bar{b}_i'/(-\bar{a}_{is}) & (-\bar{a}_{is} > 0) \\ (\bar{b}_i' - \alpha_{j_i})/(-\bar{a}_{is}) & (-\bar{a}_{is} < 0) \end{cases}
$$

(a) If $\theta^* = \alpha_s$ in (22), then non-basic variable x_s appears as x_s' in the next iteration, or if $-\theta^* = \alpha_s$ in (23), then the non-basic variable x_s' appears as x_s in the next iteration. In either event, the basic set remains unchanged, but the variables acquire new values as determined by setting $\theta = \theta^*$ in (21).

(b) If, on the other hand, α_s is not the minimum in (22) or in (23), then x_s *replaces* some x_{j_r} as a basic variable. The new value of x_s is θ^* in Case I with x_{j_r} becoming zero or α_s, according as $\bar{a}_{rs} > 0$ or $\bar{a}_{rs} < 0$. In Case II, the new value of x_s is $(\alpha_s + \theta^*)$, with x_{j_r} becoming non-basic at zero or at α_s according as $-\bar{a}_{is} > 0$ or $-\bar{a}_{is} < 0$. The new values for the other basic variables $j_i \neq j_r$ are found by setting $\theta = \theta^*$ in (21).

Example 2: Find numbers

(24) $0 \leq x_1 \leq 1, \quad 0 \leq x_2 \leq 2, \quad 0 \leq x_3 \leq 3, \quad 0 \leq x_4 \leq 4,$

and Min z satisfying

(25)
$$
\begin{aligned}
x_1 + x_2 + x_3 + x_4 &= 6 \\
2x_1 + x_2 - 4x_3 - 5x_4 + (-z) &= 0
\end{aligned}
$$

Starting with the feasible solution $x_1 = 1$, $x_2 = 2$, $x_3 = 3$, $x_4 = 0$, and $(-z) = 8$, using x_1 as a basic variable, the initial canonical form is

(26)   Cycle 0
$$
\begin{cases}
x_1 + x_2 + x_3 + x_4 & = 6 \\
\quad - x_2 - 6x_3 - 7x_4 + (-z) & = -12
\end{cases}
$$
$$[1 - \theta_0, \quad 2, \quad 3, \quad 0 + \theta_0, \quad 8 + 7\theta_0]$$

Max $\theta_0 = 1$; x_4 replaces x_1 as a basic variable.

(27)   Cycle 1
$$
\begin{cases}
x_1 + x_2 + x_3 + x_4 & = 6 \\
7x_1 + 6x_2 + x_3 \quad\quad + (-z) & = 30
\end{cases}
$$
$$[0, \quad 2 - \theta_1, \quad 3, \quad 1 + \theta_1, \quad 15 + 6\theta_1]$$

Max $\theta_1 = 2$; x_4 is still basic and x_2, non-basic, shifts from its upper to its lower bound.

(28)   Cycle 2
$$
\begin{cases}
x_1 + x_2 + x_3 + x_4 & = 6 \\
7x_1 + 6x_2 + x_3 \quad\quad + (-z) & = 30
\end{cases}
$$
$$[0, \quad 0, \quad 3 - \theta_2, \quad 3 + \theta_2, \quad 27 + \theta_2]$$

Max $\theta_2 = 1$; x_3 replaces x_4 as a basic variable, which drops out at its upper bound.

(29)   Cycle 3 (Optimal)
$$
\begin{cases}
x_1 + x_2 + x_3 + x_4 & = 6 \\
6x_1 + 5x_2 \quad\quad - x_4 + (-z) & = 24
\end{cases}
$$
$$[0, \quad 0, \quad 2, \quad 4, \quad 28]$$

The Revised Simplex Tableau.

Only minor changes in the simplex method using multipliers are necessary to account for upper bounds (see Chapter 9). These are discussed under headings (1), (2), (3) below.

(1) In Table 9-3-Ia, add an extra row and record in it the upper bound values of the variables.

(2) In Table 18-1-I, it is advisable not only to record the relative cost

[375]

factors for $\bar{d}_j$ or $\bar{c}_j$, but also to indicate which non-basic variables are at their upper bounds. In the table below, the following notation is used:

(a) A bar above a numerical cost factor is used to indicate that the corresponding variable is at its upper bound.

(b) Brackets [ ] are used to indicate that the corresponding variable is basic.

(c) An asterisk * indicates that corresponding x_j is to enter the basic set in the next iteration.

Referring to Example 1 (see (6), (7)), we have

TABLE 18-1-I

	Relative Cost Factors $\bar{c}_j$ or d_j				
$j =$	(1)	(2)	(3)	(4)	(5)
Cycle 0	[0]	[0]	-2^*	-1	1
1	[0]	[0]	$-\overline{2}$	-1^*	1
2	$-\frac{1}{2}$	[0]	$-\frac{5}{2}$	[0]	1

(3) There is no change in the layout of Table 9-3-IIa of § 9-3. The choice of pivot element $\bar{a}_{rs}$, however, is in accordance with (22) or (23) and sequel. If x_s replaces x_{j_r}, Table 9-3-IIb is replaced by Table 18-1-II where θ^* or $(\alpha_s + \theta^*)$ is the new value of x_s accordingly as $x_s = 0$ or $x_s = \alpha_s$ in this cycle. If there is no change in the basic set, then all β_{ij}, π_i, and σ_i remain unchanged; the new values for the basic variables, z and w are as shown in the next to last column of Table 18-1-II, except that row r becomes $x_{j_r} = (\bar{b}'_r - \bar{a}_{rs}\theta^*)$.

TABLE 18-1-II

Tableau at Start of Cycle $\ell + 1$ (if x_s Replaces x_{j_r} as Basic Variable)

Basic Variables	Columns of the Canonical Form					Values of Basic Variables	x_s
	x_{n+1} $\cdots$		x_{n+m}	$-z$	$-w$		
x_{j_1}	$\overleftarrow{\quad}$ Inverse of basis $\overrightarrow{\quad}$ $\beta_{11} - \bar{a}_{1s}\beta^*_{r1}$ $\cdots$		$\beta_{1m} - \bar{a}_{1s}\beta^*_{rm}$			$\bar{b}'_1 - \bar{a}_{1s}\theta^*$	
$\cdot$	$\cdot$		$\cdot$			$\cdot$	
x_s	β^*_{r1} $\cdots$		β^*_{rm}			θ^* or $\alpha_s + \theta^*$	
$\cdot$	$\cdot$		$\cdot$			$\cdot$	
x_{j_m}	$\beta_{m1} - \bar{a}_{ms}\beta^*_{r1}$ $\cdots$		$\beta_{mm} - \bar{a}_{ms}\beta^*_{rm}$			$\bar{b}'_m - \bar{a}_{ms}\theta^*$	
$-z$	$-\pi_1 - \bar{c}_s\beta^*_{r1}$ $\cdots$		$-\pi_m - \bar{c}_s\beta^*_{rm}$	1		$-\bar{z}'_0 - \bar{c}_s\theta^*$	
$-w$	$-\sigma_1 - d_s\beta^*_{r1}$ $\cdots$		$-\sigma_m - d_s\beta^*_{rm}$		1	$-\bar{w}'_0 - d_s\theta^*$	

$\beta^*_{ri} = \beta_{ri}/\bar{a}_{rs}$ $(i = 1, 2, \ldots, m)$

θ^* determined by formula (22) or (23).

x_s column blank at start of cycle.

[376]

18-2. THE BOUNDED VARIABLE TRANSPORTATION PROBLEM AND GENERALIZATIONS

Solving a Bounded Variable Transportation Problem.

The theory of upper bounding will be applied to a capacitated transportation problem. In general form, the problem is that of finding nonnegative x_{ij} and minimum z satisfying

(1) The Row Equations: $\qquad \sum\limits_{j=1}^{n} x_{ij} = a_i$
  $(i = 1, 2, \ldots, m)$

(2) The Column Equations: $\qquad \sum\limits_{i=1}^{m} x_{ij} = b_j$
  $(j = 1, 2, \ldots, n)$

(3) The Upper Bounds: $\qquad\qquad x_{ij} \leq \alpha_{ij}$, and
  (for all i and j)

(4) The Objective Function: $\qquad \sum\limits_{i=1}^{m}\sum\limits_{j=1}^{n} c_{ij}x_{ij} = z$

Referring to (5) as the *standard, 3×4 transportation array for bounded variables*, we observe that Theorem 1 below is a direct translation of the optimality criteria given in the preceding section.

(5)

x_{11}	α_{11}	x_{12}	α_{12}	x_{13}	α_{13}	x_{14}	α_{14}	a_1
	c_{11}		c_{12}		c_{13}		c_{14}	u_1
x_{21}	α_{21}	x_{22}	α_{22}	x_{23}	α_{23}	x_{24}	α_{24}	a_2
	c_{21}		c_{22}		c_{23}		c_{24}	u_2
x_{31}	α_{31}	x_{32}	α_{32}	x_{33}	α_{33}	x_{34}	α_{34}	a_3
	c_{31}		c_{32}		c_{33}		c_{34}	u_3
b_1		b_2		b_3		b_4		
	v_1		v_2		v_3		v_4	Implicit $\uparrow$ $\leftarrow$ Prices

THEOREM 1: *A feasible solution, $x_{ij} = x_{ij}^o$, for the capacitated transportation problem is optimal, if there is a set of implicit prices u_i and v_j and relative cost factors $\bar{c}_{ij} = c_{ij} - u_i - v_j$, such that*

$$
\begin{aligned}
0 < x_{ij}^o < \alpha_{ij} &\Rightarrow \bar{c}_{ij} = 0 \\
x_{ij}^o = 0 &\Rightarrow \bar{c}_{ij} \geq 0 \\
x_{ij}^o = \alpha_{ij} &\Rightarrow \bar{c}_{ij} \leq 0
\end{aligned}
$$

(6)

We will show how the methods of § 18-1 may be adapted efficiently to

[377]

this class by solving a simple numerical example given in (7) below. Later in this section, we will show that the class of capacitated transportation problems is actually equivalent to the class of ordinary transportation problems, and also consider various generalizations of the capacity concept.

(7)

$x_{11} \leq 12$	$x_{12} \leq 13$	$x_{13} \leq 5$	$x_{14} \leq 20$	25
$c_{11} = 10$	5	6	7	
$x_{21} \leq 14$	$x_{22} \leq 20$	$x_{23} \leq 10$	$x_{24} \leq 9$	25
8	2	7	6	
$x_{31} \leq 18$	$x_{32} \leq 4$	$x_{33} \leq 25$	$x_{34} \leq 7$	50
9	3	4	8	
15	20	30	35	

Finding an Initial Basic Feasible Solution.

While simple rules have been devised for finding an initial solution in an uncapacitated transportation problem, it does not appear possible to construct such a rule in the capacitated case. If one were able to do this, one would thereby also have found a simple solution to the problem: find an assignment of m men to m jobs where certain men are excluded from certain jobs. Formulated in mathematical terms, the problem is: given an $m \times m$ incidence matrix (elements 0 or 1), pick out a permutation of ones or show none exists. So far; no one has been able to give a *non-iterative procedure* for solving this problem.

In attempting to find an initial solution for (7), it is generally useful to begin by selecting a box with the minimum c_{ij}, which in (7) is c_{22} with a value of 2, and to assign as high a value as possible to the corresponding variable without forcing any variable to exceed its upper bound. Here we set $x_{22} = 20$. If the size of this entry is finally limited by a row or column equation, consider it a basic variable and make no more entries in that row or column. If, on the other hand, the value of the variable is limited by its upper bound restriction, then consider the variable non-basic at its upper bound and place a bar above the entry. In case of a tie between the two types of limitations, always consider the row or column as limiting and the variable as basic. Repeat the procedure with the remaining boxes.

Applied to (7), this routine yields in order, the assignments: $x_{22} = 20$ (basic), $x_{33} = 25$ (bounded), $x_{13} = 5$ (basic), $x_{24} = 5$ (basic), $x_{14} = 20$ (basic), $x_{34} = 7$ (bounded), $x_{31} = 15$ (basic). Since the third row and fourth column still have 3 units unassigned, the solution is not feasible. Extra "short" boxes are added to the array: an $i = 0$ row and $j = 0$ column, and $d_{ij} = 0$

[378]

replaces the original c_{ij}, and $d_{ij} = 1$ in the shortage boxes. This is summarized in (8).

(8)

				Short	$3 - \theta_0$		
						1	0
	12		13	5	5	20	20	25
	$d_{11} = 0$		0		0		0	-1
	14	$20 - \theta_0$	20		10	$5 + \theta_0$	9	25
Short	0		0	, 0			0	-1
$3 - \theta_0$	15	18	θ_0^*	4	$\overline{25}$	25	$\overline{7}$	7	50
	1		0		0		0	1
	15		20	30		35		u_i
	0	-1		1		1	1	v_j

Note that $d_{30} = d_{04} = 1$ must equal u_3 and v_4 respectively, since we have shown in § 15-2-(14), that slack rows and columns can be regarded as having prices u_0 and v_0 equal to zero.

Proceeding now with Phase I, minimizing the sum of the artificial variables, in particular, $x_{04} + x_{30}$, we find that a single iteration furnishes a feasible solution as given by (9). The original cost factors, c_{ij}, are now restored.

(9)

	12		13	5	5	20	20	25
	10		5		6		7	0
	14	$17 - \theta$	20		10	$8 + \theta$	9	25
	8		2		7		6	-1
15	18	$3 + \theta$	4	$\overline{25}$	25	$\overline{7} - \theta^*$	7	50
	9		3		4		8	0
15		20		30		35		u_i
	9		3		6		7	v_j

However, this solution is not optimal, because x_{34} is a non-basic variable at its upper bound, whose relative cost factor should be nonpositive, while in reality, $\bar{c}_{34} = c_{34} - u_3 - v_4 = 8 - 0 - 7 = +1$. Thus, it pays to decrease x_{34} from its upper bound value, keeping the other non-basic variables fixed and adjusting the basic variables. The greatest decrease, θ, that maintains

[379]

feasibility is $\theta = 1$, and at this value it is stopped by the upper bounding restriction, $x_{24} = 8 + \theta \leq 9$.

The new array, given in (10), is optimal.

(10)

	12		13	**5**	5	**20**	20	**25**	
	10		5		6		7		-1
	14	**16**	20		10	$\overline{9}$	9	**25**	
	8		2		7		6		-1
15	18	**4**	4	$\overline{25}$	25	**6**	7	**50**	
	9		3		4		8		0
15		**20**		**30**		**35**			u_i
	9		3		7		8	v_j	

The foregoing method implies the following theorem whose proof for the general bounded transportation problem is left as an exercise.

THEOREM 2: *If the upper bounds, the quantities available, and the quantities required are all integers, every basic solution will be integral in a bounded transportation problem.*

On the Equivalence of a Bounded Transportation Problem and the Classical Transportation Problem.

It will be noted that each variable x_{ij} appears in *three* equations with non-zero coefficients; not only in (1) and (2), the row and column equations used in the classical problem, but in addition the upper bounding inequality (3), which may be rewritten

$$(11) \qquad\qquad x_{ij} + y_{ij} = \alpha_{ij} \qquad\qquad (y_{ij} \geq 0)$$

where variable, y_{ij}, represents slack. The system can, however, be replaced by an obviously equivalent one in which each variable enters only two equations just as in the classical transportation form. Consider the problem of finding $x_{ij} \geq 0$ and Min z satisfying

$$(12) \qquad \text{Row:} \qquad \sum_{j=1}^{n} x_{ij} \qquad\quad = a_i$$
$$\quad (i = 1, \ldots, m)$$

$$\qquad\qquad \text{Column:} \qquad -x_{ij} - y_{ij} \qquad = -\alpha_{ij}$$
$$\qquad\qquad \text{(all } i, j)$$

$$\qquad\qquad \text{Row:} \qquad\qquad\qquad y_{ij} + x'_{ij} = \alpha_{ij}$$
$$\qquad\qquad \text{(all } i, j)$$

[380]

Column:
$(j = 1, \ldots, n)$

$$-\sum_{i=1}^{m} x'_{ij} = -b_j$$

$$\sum_{i=1}^{m} \sum_{j=1}^{n} c_{ij} x_{ij} \qquad = z \text{ (Min)}$$

An illuminating interpretation of this result is in terms of networks. The conventional graph for a capacitated transportation problem may be represented as in Fig. 18-2-I. The numbers α_{ij} on the directed arc joining

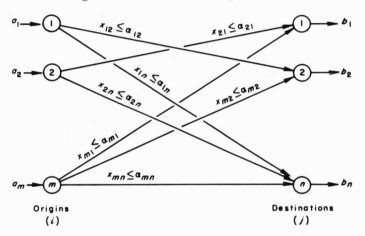

Figure 18-2-I. Bi-partite graph of a capacitated transportation problem.

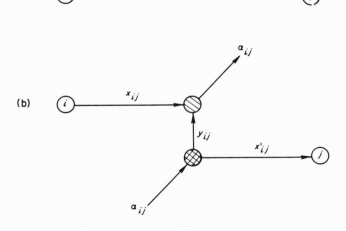

Figures 18-2-IIa, b. How to replace a capacitated arc by unrestricted arcs.

[381]

origin i and destination j are the *arc capacities*. The device used in (12) replaces each *capacitated* arc of Fig. 18-2-IIa by the *set* of *unrestricted* arcs of Fig. 18-2-IIb.

Transportation Problems with Bounded Partial Sums of Variables.

An idea formalized by A. S. Manne deals with bounding, not only variables, but also partial sums of variables. For simplicity, let us consider a case with only one such partial sum. In the scheduling of jobs on computing machinery discussed earlier, the condition $x_{11} \leq 40$ might be interpreted to mean that no more than one man can be assigned to job 1 in week 1. In some problems a more involved condition might be desired, such as $x_{11} + x_{31} + x_{61} \leq 40$, expressing the circumstance that jobs 1, 3, and 6 can be assigned only to a certain individual. Similarly, a condition like $x_{11} + x_{12} + x_{13} \geq k$ might mean that at least k hours must be worked on job 1 during the first three weeks. Just as with the variables themselves, a transportation problem with a bounded partial sum of variables in either a row or a column can be reduced to a standard transportation problem. To see this, consider the system (1), (2) and the added condition

$$(13) \qquad x_{11} + x_{12} + \ldots + x_{1k} \leq \alpha$$

This may be written in row-column format as in Table 18-2-I.

TABLE 18-2-I

x_{10}	x_{11}	$\cdots$	x_{1k}				α
y_{10}				$x_{1,k+1}$	$\cdots$	x_{1n}	a_1
	x_{21}	$\cdots$	x_{2k}	$x_{2,k+1}$	$\cdots$	x_{2n}	a_2
	$\cdot$		$\cdot$	$\cdot$		$\cdot$	$\cdot$
	x_{m1}	$\cdots$	x_{mk}	$x_{m,k+1}$	$\cdots$	x_{mn}	a_m
α	b_1	$\cdots$	b_k	b_{k+1}	$\cdots$	b_n	Totals

(The inadmissible boxes are shaded.) It is clear that any number of conditions like (13) can be added to the system by similarly treating each in turn. For example, the added condition on column 2

$$(14) \qquad x_{12} + x_{32} + x_{62} \leq \beta$$

may be taken care of by splitting column 2 and using a second slack variable. Moreover, there may be other conditions on column 2, such as

(15) $$x_{22} + x_{42} + x_{52} \leq \gamma$$

that do not involve the same variables. Also, there can be more than one condition on the same variables in the same column, for example, condition (14) and

(16) $$x_{12} + x_{62} \leq \delta$$

could be taken care of by further splitting the column associated with the variables x_{12}, x_{32}, x_{62}.

THEOREM 3: *A transportation problem with added partial sum conditions in rows and columns can be reduced to a standard transportation problem, if any two conditions in a column (or row) either have no variables in common, or the variables of one of the conditions are a subset of the variables of the other condition.*

THEOREM 4: *If a bounded partial sum of variables includes variables in different columns or rows, the basis need not be triangular, so that non-integral basic solutions can be obtained.*

EXERCISE: Prove these last two theorems.

18-3. PROBLEMS

The General Case. (Refer to § 18-1.)

1. (a) Review the rules for determining the candidate for entering the basic set or shifting to upper or lower bound and the variable leaving the basic set.

   (b) Modify the procedure to improve a general feasible solution.

   (c) Modify the procedure to cover a problem where variables have lower bounds other than zero.

   (d) Does the lexicographic scheme for getting around degeneracy still apply to the bounded variable method; if not, what modifications are necessary?

The Bounded Transportation Problem and Generalization. (Refer to § 18-2.)

2. Give a direct proof of Theorem 1 of § 18-2.

3. Show for capacitated transportation problem of § 18-2-(1), (2), (3), and (4) that no feasible solution exists if there is a row p, such that $\sum_{j=1}^{n} \alpha_{pj} < a_p$ or a column q such that $\sum_{i=1}^{m} \alpha_{iq} < b_q$.

4. Construct an example to show that a feasible solution satisfying (1), (2), and (3) need not exist even if, for *all i* = 1, 2, . . ., *m* and *j* = 1, 2, ... *n*,

$$\sum_{j=1}^{n} \alpha_{ij} \geq a_i, \ \sum_{i=1}^{m} \alpha_{ij} \geq b_j$$

5. Consider the example shown in § 18-2-(7); restate in the form § 18-2-(1), (2), (3), and (4).

6. In the 5 × 5 array below, the exclusion of men from certain jobs is indicated by shaded boxes. Show why this is a bounded variable problem. Use the methods of § 18-2 to find a feasible solution.

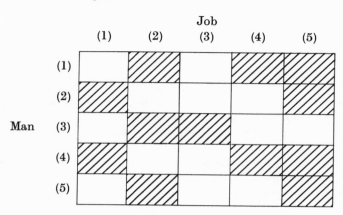

7. Construct an example where artificial variables x_{0j}, x_{i0} are required as part of every basis during Phase II. Amplify the discussion of the text to cover situations in which artificial variables form a part of the basis during Phase II.

8. Prove that the solution shown in § 18-2-(10) is optimal. Is it unique? If not, construct all other optimal solutions.

9. Given a capacitated transportation problem with $m = 5$ rows and $n = 7$ columns and the additional partial row sum condition $x_{32} + x_{35} + x_{37} \leq \alpha$, find an equivalent capacitated transportation problem with no side conditions.

10. Construct examples to show that if the sets of variables used in the partial sums are not *nested* or mutually exclusive in a row or column, then the basis need not be triangular.

11. If a bounded partial sum of variables includes variables in different rows or columns, show that the basis need not be triangular; in other words, it is not equivalent to a transportation problem.

REFERENCES

Berge, 1962-1
Cahn, 1948-1
Charnes and Cooper, 1955-1, 1959-1
Dantzig, 1949-1, 1954-3, 1956-2, 1957-3
Dantzig and Ramser, 1959-1
Dantzig and Van Slyke, 1964-1
Eiseman, 1964-1

Ford and Fulkerson, 1957-1, 1960-1
Hoffman and Markowitz, 1963-1
Hu and Prager, 1958-1
Prager, 1957-1
Vajda, 1958-1, 1961-1
Wagner, 1958-1, 1959-1
(See also references Chapter 14)

CHAPTER 19

MAXIMAL FLOWS IN NETWORKS

19-1. FORD-FULKERSON THEORY

Consider a network connecting two nodes, a *source* and a *destination*, by way of several intermediate nodes. Each arc of the network is assigned two numbers, representing the flow *capacity* along the arc in each direction. Assuming a steady state condition, *find a maximal flow from the source to the destination*. In this section we shall follow the theory developed by Ford and Fulkerson [1954-1; 1960-1].

In network Fig. 19-1-I, the source and destination are distinguished from the other nodes by double circles. The flow capacities, α_{ij}, in each direction

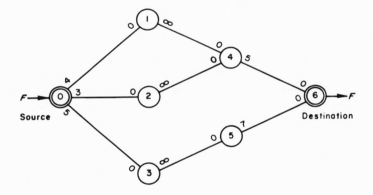

Figure 19-1-I.   A maximal flow problem with directed arc capacities.

are shown by numbers along each arc near the node at which the flow might originate.

If $x_{ij} \geq 0$ denotes the quantity of flow from i to j, then the following *constraints on capacity* hold:

(1) $$0 \leq x_{ij} \leq \alpha_{ij}$$

(2) $$0 \leq x_{ji} \leq \alpha_{ji}$$

Thus in Fig. 19-1-I, for example, $0 \leq x_{01} \leq 4$, $0 \leq x_{10} \leq 0$; $0 \leq x_{14} \leq \infty$, $0 \leq x_{41} \leq 0$, etc. In addition, the following *conservation-of-flow* equations hold: except for the source where $k = 0$, and the destination where $k = n$,

[385]

the sum of flows into node k balances the sum of flows out of it, so that

$$(3) \qquad \sum_i x_{ik} - \sum_j x_{kj} = 0 \qquad (k = 1, 2, \ldots, n - 1)$$

where all terms x_{ik} and x_{kj} are omitted from these sums, except those corresponding to arcs of the network. We denote by F the flow into the source from outside the network; then, by definition,

$$(4) \qquad F + \sum_i x_{i0} - \sum_j x_{0j} = 0$$

It is not difficult to show, in view of (3), that the flow out of the system at the destination also equals F for, if we sum the $n - 1$ relations appearing in (3) and (4), each variable, x_{ij}, appears in two equations with opposite signs (hence cancels), except for those representing flows into the destination. Reversing signs, one obtains

$$(5) \qquad \sum_i x_{in} - \sum_j x_{nj} - F = 0$$

The Maximal Flow Problem is to choose $x_{ij} \geq 0$ and Max F satisfying (1), (2), (3), (4), and (5).

Finding Feasible Solutions to Transportation and Transshipment Problems.

It is interesting to note that the problem of finding a feasible solution to an assignment problem or, more generally, to a transportation problem in which not all x_{ij} are admissible, is equivalent (as we shall see in a moment) to solving a maximal flow problem. Recall that the primal-dual algorithm (§ 11-4) seeks feasible solutions to a sequence of restricted primal problems. This implies that transportation problems could be solved by means of a sequence of maximal flow problems. This idea is developed into an efficient algorithm in the next chapter. The following transportation ·problem (actually not solvable) can be reduced to a network flow problem like Fig. 19-1-I.

(6)

Origins	Destinations		Row Total
	(4)	(5)	
(1)	x_{14}	/////	4
(2)	x_{24}	/////	3
(3)	/////	x_{35}	5
Column Total	5	7	

It is clear that a feasible solution to (6), if it exists, corresponds to finding $x_{ij} \geq 0$ in the array (7) that sum to unknown row and column totals x_{0i} and x_{j0} such that the sum, z, of these marginal totals is maximum and *equal* to the sum of column or row capacities.

(7)

Origins	Destinations		Row Total
	(4)	(5)	
(1)	x_{14}	//////	x_{01}
(2)	x_{24}	//////	x_{02}
(3)	//////	x_{35}	x_{03}
Column Total	x_{46}	x_{56}	

$(x_{01} \leq 4)$

$(x_{02} \leq 3)$

$(x_{03} \leq 5)$

$$(x_{46} \leq 5)\,(x_{56} \leq 7)$$

$$x_{01} + x_{02} + x_{03} = x_{46} + x_{56} = z \text{ (Max)}$$

On the other hand, if the maximum value of z is less than the specified capacities, as is the case here, no feasible solution to (6) exists. It is now obvious that Fig. 19-1-I is the network representation of (7).

In the case of a transshipment problem, a modified network is formed by joining all nodes with surplus available to a fictitious common source node by arcs with capacities equal to the surpluses available, and by joining all nodes with unsatisfied needs to a common fictitious destination by arcs with capacities equal to the deficit. A feasible solution to the transshipment problem will then correspond to a maximal flow solution to the modified network problem, which equals the sum of the capacities of the arcs from the source node (or into the destination node).

Properties of Network Flow Problems.

The following theorem is easily seen:

THEOREM 1: *A set of $x_{ij} \geq 0$ satisfying the capacity constraints and the conservation equations can be replaced by another set x'_{ij} with the same total flow F in which either x'_{ij} or x'_{ji} is zero by setting*

(8)
$$x'_{ij} = x_{ij} - \text{Min}\,(x_{ij}, x_{ji})$$

We shall only consider flows where this is always the case. For example, if

[387]

on a *directed arc* joining i to j a number 6 appears, this will mean $x_{ij} = 6$ and $x_{ji} = 0$.

$$\underset{3}{\overset{7 \qquad 6}{(i) \longrightarrow (j)}} \qquad (x_{ij} \leq 7, x_{ji} \leq 3)$$

It is now possible to replace all variables x_{ij} and x_{ji} by their difference

$$(9) \qquad \bar{x}_{ij} = x_{ij} - x_{ji}$$

in which case $\begin{cases} \bar{x}_{ij} > 0 \text{ corresponds to } \quad \bar{x}_{ij} = x'_{ij} \text{ and } x'_{ji} = 0 \\ \bar{x}_{ij} < 0 \text{ corresponds to } -\bar{x}_{ij} = x'_{ji} \text{ and } x'_{ij} = 0 \end{cases}$

The capacity constraints and conservation equations become

$$(10) \qquad -\alpha_{ji} \leq \bar{x}_{ij} \leq \alpha_{ij}$$

$$\sum_i \bar{x}_{ik} = 0 \qquad (k = 1, 2, \ldots, n-1)$$

$$F + \sum_i \bar{x}_{i0} = 0$$

$$-F + \sum_i \bar{x}_{in} = 0$$

THEOREM 2: *A set of $\bar{x}_{ij}$ and $F > 0$ satisfying the capacity constraints and the conservation equations can be decomposed into a sum of positive chain flows from the source to the destination and a set of circular flows such that the direction of positive flows in any common arc is the same for all chains.*

DEFINITION: A *chain flow*, K, is a constant flow value $\bar{x}_{ij} = K$ for every arc $(i \rightarrow j)$ along a chain and $\bar{x}_{ij} = 0$ elsewhere. This theorem is an interesting one because it means that a solution to a flow problem or a transshipment problem corresponds to our intuitive notion that items start from nodes of surplus and move (flow) from one node to the next without losing their identity until arriving finally at some node of deficit.

The proof is straightforward. Assume $F > 0$. Choose a chain starting at 0 with initial arc $(0 \rightarrow i_1)$, where

$$(11) \qquad \bar{x}_{0i_1} = \underset{i}{\text{Max}} \ \bar{x}_{0i} > 0$$

That $\bar{x}_{0i_1} > 0$ follows from $F > 0$ and the conservation relation $F = \Sigma \bar{x}_{0i}$. We now repeat our procedure at node i, choosing the second arc $(i_1 \rightarrow i_2)$ of the chain by

$$(12) \qquad \bar{x}_{i_1,i_2} = \underset{i}{\text{Max}} \ \bar{x}_{i_1,i} > 0$$

Again by the conservation equation at i_1 and the fact that $\bar{x}_{0i_1} > 0$, it follows that $\bar{x}_{i_1,i_2} > 0$.

Upon iteration, we either (a) generate a chain that returns to a node

[388]

arrived at earlier, thus forming a "loop," or (b) we complete a chain to the destination. If a loop is generated, subtract a constant $K > 0$ from each $\bar{x}_{ij}$ for arcs (i, j) of the loop where, letting $\in$ denote "belongs to,"

$$(13) \qquad\qquad K = \text{Min } \bar{x}_{ij} \qquad\qquad [(i, j) \in \text{loop}]$$

It is clear that the new values of $\bar{x}_{ij}$ satisfy the capacity and conservation relations. Starting again at the node where the chain first formed a loop, the chain generation procedure is continued. Only a finite number of loops can be removed from the solution by the above procedure, since each new solution generated by a loop removal has at least one more $\bar{x}_{ij}$ that is zero.

Hence, after a finite number of steps, a chain from origin to destination can be constructed with positive flow along it. A value K is then assigned to the chain by setting

$$(14) \qquad\qquad K = \text{Min } \bar{x}_{ij} > 0 \qquad\qquad \text{for all } (i, j) \in \text{chain}$$

A new solution to the flow problem is now constructed with flow value, $F - K$, by subtracting K from each $\bar{x}_{ij}$ value corresponding to arcs (i, j) along the chain. The entire procedure can now be repeated with the new problem if $F - K > 0$. Again we note that there can only be a finite number of chain removals because each new solution has at least one more $\bar{x}_{ij}$ that is zero.

Finally, if $F = 0$ and some $\bar{x}_{ij} > 0$, starting with node i and arc $(i \to j)$, the above procedure can be followed to construct a loop which can be removed. In a finite number of steps all residual loops can be removed. This completes the constructive proof of the theorem.

THEOREM 3: *If there exists no chain of arcs, each with positive capacity, joining the source to the destination, then the maximal flow is zero.*

PROOF: Assume, on the contrary, that it is possible to have the maximal flow positive. By the previous theorem it is then possible to decompose it into *chains* of positive flows. Along any such chain with flow value $K > 0$, we must have $0 < K \le \bar{x}_{ij} \le \alpha_{ij}$, because the method of decomposition is such that each $\bar{x}_{ij} > 0$ is represented as a sum of nonnegative chain flows along the directed arc joining i to j. It follows that the selected chain has arcs of positive capacity.

We can argue, conversely, that if there exists a chain with arcs of positive capacity, we may choose $K = \text{Min } \alpha_{ij} > 0$ for arcs along the chain and thereby obtain a flow $F = K > 0$ along the chain; hence

THEOREM 4: *The maximal flow is positive if there exists a chain of arcs, each with positive capacity, joining the source to the destination.*

The following theorem permits us constructively to obtain a maximal flow in a network by seeking in associated networks a chain of arcs each with positive capacity joining the source to the destination.

THEOREM 5: *A solution $F = F_0$, $\bar{x}_{ij} = \bar{x}_{ij}^o$ is maximal if and only if the*

[389]

maximal flow F' is zero in a second network formed by replacing α_{ij} by $\alpha'_{ij} = \alpha_{ij} - \bar{x}^o_{ij}$.

PROOF: Suppose, on the contrary, that there exists a solution, $F' = F'_0 > 0$, $-\alpha'_{ji} \le \bar{y}^o_{ij} \le \alpha'_{ij}$ to the associated problem. Then

$$(15) \qquad -(\alpha_{ji} + \bar{x}^o_{ij}) \le \bar{y}_{ij} \le \alpha_{ij} - \bar{x}^o_{ij},$$
$$-\alpha_{ji} \le \bar{y}_{ij} + \bar{x}^o_{ij} \le \alpha_{ij}$$

It follows that $\bar{x}_{ij} = \bar{y}^o_{ij} + \bar{x}^o_{ij}$ is an admissible solution to the original network with flow $F = (F'_0 + F_0) > F_0$, contradicting the hypothesis of

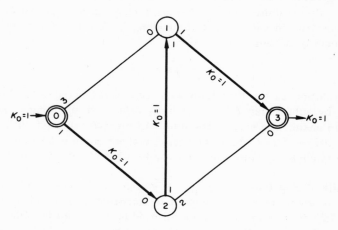

Figure 19-1-IIa.   A maximal flow example with an initiating chain flow (cycle 0).

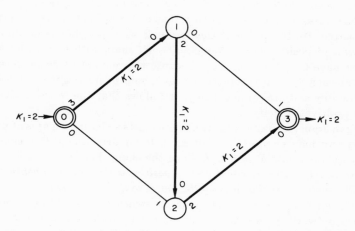

Figure 19-1-IIb.   Adjusted arc capacities and an augmenting chain flow (cycle 1).

maximal flow. Thus, if $F = F_0$ is not maximal, an improved solution to the original system can be constructed.

EXERCISE: Show the necessity as well as the sufficiency of the hypothesis of Theorem 5.

A simple example, Fig. 19-1-IIa, illustrates this. To initiate the computation, seek a chain joining 0 to 3 with arcs of positive capacity. (Later we shall describe how to do this systematically.) One such is the chain $(0 \rightarrow 2)$, $(2 \rightarrow 1)$, $(1 \rightarrow 3)$ with capacities $(1, 1, 1)$; along it, initiate the flow $K_0 = 1$.

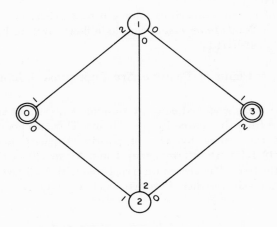

Figure 19-1-IIc. Final adjusted arc capacities, no additional chain flow possible (cycle 2).

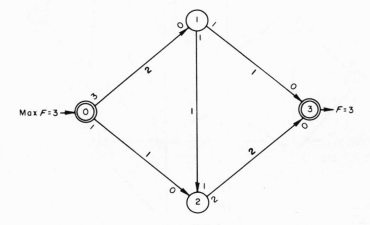

Figure 19-1-IId. This maximal flow is the algebraic sum of the previous chain flows.

This is represented by the numbers at the middle of the arcs, the arrows indicating the direction of flow along the chain. Adjust the capacity of each arc by subtracting $K_0 = 1$ from the capacity at the *base* of the arrow and adding it to the capacity at the *point* of the arrow. This results in Fig. 19-1-IIb.

In the new network there is only one chain of arcs with positive capacity; namely $(0 \rightarrow 1)$, $(1 \rightarrow 2)$, $(2 \rightarrow 3)$, with capacities $(3, 2, 2)$. Hence a flow of $K_1 = 2$ can be set up along this chain. Again adjusting the capacities of the network, we have Fig. 19-1-IIc.

No chain of positive capacities joining 0 to 3 exists. We now form our maximal flow as *the algebraic sum* of the chain flows given in Fig. 19-1-IIa, b as shown in Fig. 19-1-IId.

Constructing a Chain of Positive Arc Capacities Joining Source to Destination.

This can be done systematically by forming a tree of all the nodes that can be reached from the source by such chains. Thus, all nodes that can be reached from the source by arcs of positive capacity are determined first. In Fig. 19-1-III, these are nodes 1 and 5; arcs $(0 \rightarrow 1)$ and $(0 \rightarrow 5)$ form part of the tree. The procedure is repeated with each new node in turn, omitting nodes reached earlier. It is easy to show that, if a chain of positive

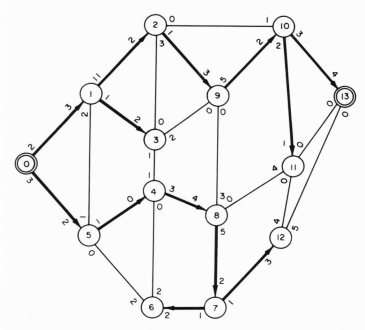

Figure 19-1-III.   Fanning-out procedure for finding a positive chain flow.

arc capacities exists joining the source to any node, this procedure will construct at least one such chain.

EXERCISE: Show that the above procedure will always construct a chain of positive capacities from origin to destination, if one exists.

THEOREM 6: *If a maximal flow exists and the capacities are integers, the procedure will construct only a finite number of positive chain-flows, whose algebraic sum is the maximal flow.*

PROOF: Note that if α_{ij} are integers, then the chain flow, K, is also an integer, and the same is true of the successive adjusted arc-capacities, α'_{ij}. But each flow being positive implies that F must increase by at least unity on each iteration. Hence, only a finite number of iterations is possible since F is finite.

Properties of Cuts in Networks.

When the flow $F = F_0$ is maximal for $x_{ij} = x^o_{ij}$, it will be observed that certain of the directed arcs of the network are used to full capacity, or *saturated*, i.e., $x_{ii} = \alpha_{ii}$. It is easy to see that, if for this set all the saturated arcs are removed from the network, or more precisely, if their α_{ij} values are set equal to zero, no flow is possible. Indeed, if a positive flow over some chain of unsaturated arcs existed, the same chain would have *positive arc capacity* for the adjusted network, $\alpha'_{ij} = \alpha_{ij} - x^o_{ij}$, and by Theorem 5, $x_{ij} = x^o_{ij}$ would not be a maximal flow solution.

DEFINITION: A *cut* is any set of directed arcs containing at least one arc from every chain of positive capacity joining the source to the destination.

DEFINITION: The *cut value* is the sum of the capacities of the arcs of the cut.

From our remarks it is clear that the collection of saturated arcs in a maximal solution constitutes a cut. Thus, in Fig. 19-1-IId, the set of directed arcs, $(1 \to 2)$, $(1 \to 3)$, $(0 \to 2)$, $(2 \to 3)$, with capacities, $(1, 1, 1, 2)$, constitutes a cut. The cut value, in this case, is $1 + 1 + 1 + 2 = 5$. It will be noted that this cut has two subsets which are also cuts. These are marked in Figs. 19-1-IVa and IVb with the bullet symbol indicating the direction of the arc belonging to the cut.

The cut value in both of these cases is less than before, namely, $1 + 1 + 1 = 3$ and $1 + 2 = 3$. Notice, however, that this is the same value as the maximum flow value. It is also the smallest value that can be obtained for any cut. Fulkerson first conjectured that the minimum cut value was always equal to the maximal flow value. This was first established for so-called "planar networks" (RAND Seminar, 1954). Later Ford and Fulkerson established this as true in general [Ford and Fulkerson, 1954-1].

THEOREM 7: *The Max-flow value equals the Min-cut value.*

PROOF: We first establish that, if $\{F, \bar{x}_{ij}\}$ is any flow and C is any cut value for some arbitrary cut, then $C \geq F$. Decompose the flow into a sum of r positive chain flows. Suppose that arc $(i_1 \to j_1)$ of the cut is shared with a

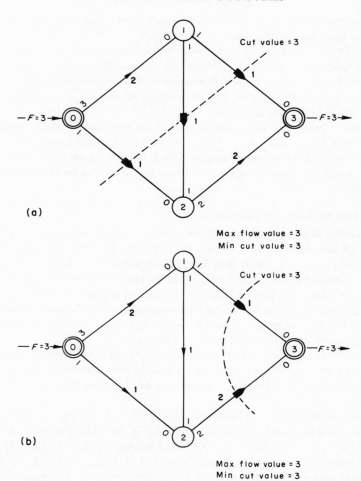

Figures 19-1-IVa, b.   An example of the max flow-min cut theorem.

set S_1 of chains p_1 with flow values K_{p_1}; suppose that arc $(i_2 \to j_2)$ of the cut is shared with a set, S_2, of the chains where S_2 may have chains in common with S_1, etc. We may write

(16)
$$c_{i_1, j_1} \geq \bar{x}_{i_1, j_1} = \sum_{p_1 \varepsilon S_1} K_{p_1}$$

$$c_{i_2, j_2} \geq \bar{x}_{i_2, j_2} = \sum_{p_2 \varepsilon S_2} K_{p_2}$$

. . . .

Because every chain $p = 1, 2, \ldots, r$ of the decomposition must have at least one arc belonging to the cut, K_p must appear in at least one of the sums above. Hence, summing the entire set of inequalities,

$$(17) \qquad C = c_{i_1, j_1} + c_{i_2, j_2} + \ldots \geq K_1 + K_2 + \ldots + K_r = F$$

We shall now show that, if $F = F_0$ is the maximal flow for $\bar{x}_{ij} = \bar{x}_{ij}^o$, a subset of the saturated arcs constitutes a cut with value $C_0 = F_0$. Since in general $C \geq F$, the theorem follows. Divide the nodes of the network into two classes. In the *first* class, place all nodes that can be reached from the source node by one or more chains composed of unsaturated arcs. In the *second* class, place all the remaining nodes (if any). All directed arcs $(i \rightarrow j)$, joining a node i of the first class to a node j of the second must be saturated. (Otherwise, j could be reached from the origin via some unsaturated chain through i.) First, we will show that the set of these arcs forms a cut and, second, that its cut value is minimal.

Call the set of these saturated arcs S, and suppose there exists some chain joining source to destination that avoids all the saturated arcs of S. Since the entire set of saturated arcs, S^*, forms a cut, *let a chain, p, be chosen that shares the least number of arcs with S^* and none with S.* Let arc $(i \rightarrow j)$ be the first such saturated arc along the chain, p. It follows that node i is in the first class. Hence, j is also in the first class. (Otherwise, arc $(i \rightarrow j)$ would belong to S.) But in this case, j can be reached from the source by a chain of unsaturated arcs. This chain can then be joined to the remainder of the chain from j to the destination; the new chain now has one less saturated arc of S^* than p, contrary to the assumption that p had the least number.

We wish now to show that the cut value of S is $C_0 = F_0$. Sum the conservation relations (3) over all nodes of the first class. Variables $\bar{x}_{ij}$ and $\bar{x}_{ji}$ cancel, if both i and j are in the first class. What remains is only the sum,

$$(18) \qquad\qquad F_0 = \sum \bar{x}_{ij}^o \qquad\qquad \text{for } (i \rightarrow j) \in S$$

where the i belongs to the first class and the j to the second. Since the $(i \rightarrow j)$ are all the arcs of the cut S, and since these are all saturated, we have

$$(19) \qquad\qquad F_0 = \sum \bar{x}_{ij}^o = \sum \alpha_{ij} = C_0 \qquad\qquad [(i \rightarrow j) \in S]$$

and the theorem follows. It is now easy to prove:

THEOREM 8: *Given any partition of the nodes into two classes, where the first class includes the source and the second class the destination, then a feasible solution $(F = F_0, \bar{x}_{ij} = \bar{x}_{ij}^o)$ is maximal, if every arc $(i \rightarrow j)$ is saturated that joins a node of the first class to a node of the second class.*

Observe that, if we sum the conservation equations corresponding to nodes of the first class, we obtain for *any* feasible solution,

$$(20) \qquad\qquad F = \sum \bar{x}_{ij}$$

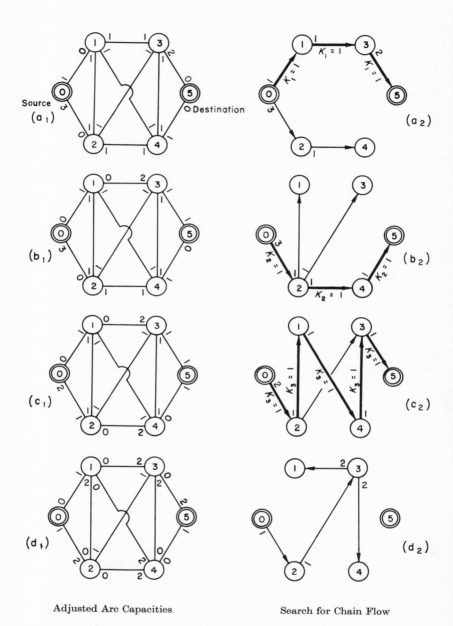

Adjusted Arc Capacities   Search for Chain Flow

Figure 19-1-V. A second example of the Ford-Fulkerson max-flow algorithm.

where the summation extends over all arcs $(i \to j)$ such that i is in the first class and j is in the second. Because the solution is feasible, $\bar{x}_{ij} \leq \alpha_{ij}$. However, our particular solution has the property that $\bar{x}^o_{ij} = \alpha_{ij}$. It follows that

$$(21) \qquad F = \sum \bar{x}_{ij} \leq \sum \alpha_{ij} = \sum \bar{x}^o_{ij} = F_0$$

EXERCISE: Show that the set of arcs $(i \to j)$, defined above, forms a cut and its cut value is minimum.

To illustrate the method with a second example, consider Fig. 19-1-Va$_1$, where the capacities on the arcs in each direction are indicated. Thus the capacity on the arc $(0 \to 1)$, is 1, and in the reverse direction, 0, etc. Assume a starting flow, $x_{ij} = 0$, then Fig. 19-1-Va$_2$ represents a possible tree of positive arc capacities fanning out from the source. The flow can now be increased along the chain $(0, 1, 3, 5)$ to $K_1 = 1$, at which point the arcs, $(0, 1)$ and $(1, 3)$, are saturated. The modified network, Fig. 19-1-Vb$_1$, is formed by setting $\alpha'_{ij} = \alpha_{ij} - K_1$ and $\alpha'_{ji} = \alpha_{ji} + K_1$ for arcs $(i \to j)$ of the chain. In Fig. 19-1-Vb$_2$ is a new tree of positive arc capacities fanning out from (0), resulting in the chain $(0, 2, 4, 5)$. The successive solutions are shown in Fig. 19-1-Vb$_1$, Vc$_1$, and Vd$_1$, the various trees in Fig. 19-1-Vb$_2$, Vc$_2$, and Vd$_2$. Since it is not possible in the final Fig. 19-1-Vd$_2$ to reach the destination, the procedure is terminated. The sum of the chain flows found in Fig. 19-1-Va$_2$, Vb$_2$, and Vc$_2$ constitutes a maximal flow. This is shown on network Fig. 19-1-VI. Saturated arcs are marked with the symbol pointing

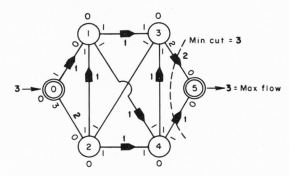

Figure 19-1-VI. Max flow-min cut solution for the second example.

in the direction of saturation. To find the cut with minimum value, choose saturated arcs leading from nodes of the first class to nodes of the second. The nodes in the first class can all be reached from the source along unsaturated chains. This set was determined by the nodes in the subtree of positive arc capacities Fig. 19-1-Vd$_2$. Hence, the nodes of the first class are 0, 2, 3, 1, 4 and the cut is made up of arcs $(3 \to 5)$ and $(4 \to 5)$ as shown in Fig. 19-1-VI.

[397]

19-2. THE TREE METHOD FOR SOLVING MAXIMAL FLOW PROBLEMS

This technique [Dantzig and Fulkerson, 1956-1; Fulkerson and Dantzig, 1955-1] is identical in principle with the one used earlier for solving capacitated transportation problems. We shall, however, illustrate a variation of it again giving a network interpretation for the maximal flow problem. Suppose we have the network in Fig. 19-2-Ia, with source A, destination B, and arc

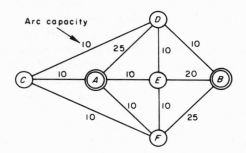

Figure 19-2-Ia.   A max-flow example: The flow at start of cycle 0 is zero.

capacities as indicated; these are assumed equal in both directions. To start, select two subtrees[1] of arcs—one, T_A, branching out from the source A, the other, T_B, branching out from the destination, B, so that every intermediate node is reached by just one of the trees. For example, T_B might contain no arcs, and T_A might be made up of AC, CD, DE, EF (see Fig. 19-2-Ib). Notice

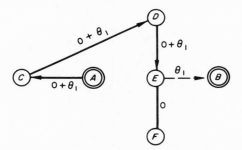

Figure 19-2-Ib.   Heavy arcs form cycle 0 basis: The incremental chain
flow is $\theta_1 = 10$.

that, since the network is connected, it is always possible to select two such trees. Next, introduce any arc which leads from T_A to T_B. There will be

---

[1] It is clear that, in a connected network with equal arc capacities in either direction, arcs may be removed until a tree is left. There is then a unique chain joining A and B. Elimination of any arc of this chain gives two trees of the kind described.

just one chain from A to B; flow as much as possible along this chain. In the example EB, is such an arc, and we have then the flow diagram of Fig. 19-2-IIa with the arcs AC, CD, DE saturated. Select any one of these

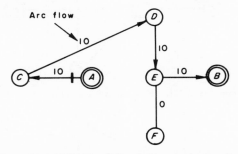

Figure 19-2-IIa.   Feasible solution start of cycle 1.

saturated arcs, say AC, and place some identifying mark on it. In Fig. 19-2-IIa we have used a bar (**|**); this symbol will be used throughout to designate a subset of the saturated arcs. Now observe that, if the barred arc is dropped from the picture (Fig. 19-2-IIb), we again have two trees,

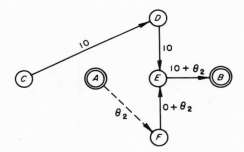

Figure 19-2-IIb.   Cycle 1 basis: The incremental chain flow is $\theta_2 = 10$.

T_A consisting of no arcs and $T_B = \{EB, ED, DC, EF\}$. If the underlying basic solutions were nondegenerate, T_A and T_B would always consist of unsaturated arcs, i.e., we would always have $\alpha_{ji} < \bar{x}_{ij} < \alpha_{ij}$. Again introduce any unbarred arc leading from T_A to T_B, say AF. This creates a flow of 10 units along the chain AF, FE, EB, and saturates each arc of this chain. Select one of these, say AF and "bar" it. We now have the diagram given in Fig. 19-2-III, and we have achieved a flow of 20. Dropping barred arcs gives the same tree as in Fig. 19-2-IIb. Introduce arc AE from T_A to T_B. This leads to a situation we have not met previously, in that the chain thus constructed, namely AE, EB, cannot take any more flow because EB, though unbarred, is at its upper limit (the degenerate case). Bar EB and

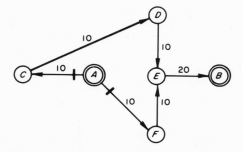

Figure 19-2-III.   Feasible solution start of cycle 2.

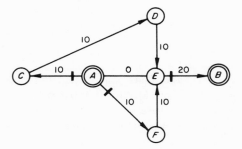

Figure 19-2-IVa.   Feasible solution start of cycle 3.

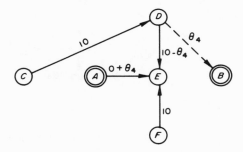

Figure 19-2-IVb.   Cycle 3 basis: The incremental chain flow is $\theta_4 = 10$.

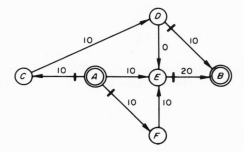

Figure 19-2-Va.   Feasible solution start of cycle 4.

leave AE in with a flow of zero, obtaining Fig. 19-2-IVa, with new trees as shown in Fig. 19-2-IVb. Introduce DB to get the chain AE, ED, DB. This time we can get an increase even though DE is saturated, since the flow in Fig. 19-2-IVa is from D to E. Thus, if the flow from A to E is increased by $\theta_4 \geq 0$, the flow from D to E must be decreased by θ_4, and the flow from D to B increased by θ_4, in order to preserve the conservation equations at E and D (see Fig. 19-2-IVb). The largest possible value of θ_4 is 10, since the capacity of DB (and of AE) is 10. This cancels the flow from D to E. Bar DB and proceed.

Repeated application of this procedure produces the sequence of flows depicted in Figs. 19-2-Va, b and 19-2-VIa, b.

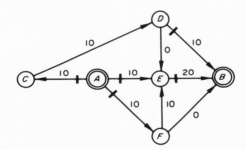

Figure 19-2-Vb.   Feasible solution start of cycle 5.

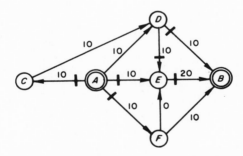

Figure 19-2-VIa.   Feasible solution start of cycle 6.

Now in Fig. 19-2-VIb the trees are $T_A = \{AD, DC\}$, $T_B = \{FB, EF\}$, and there are no more arcs to introduce from T_A to T_B. At this stage examine the barred arcs connecting nodes of T_A to those of T_B. If the flow in each of these is in the right direction, that is, from T_A to T_B, an optimum has been reached, as we shall prove. If, on the other hand, the flow in one of the barred arcs which join T_A to T_B is in the wrong direction, an increase in total flow may possibly be obtained by decreasing the flow in this arc. To see this, notice that the arc in question, together with arcs of T_A and T_B,

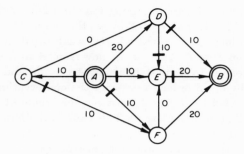

Figure 19-2-VIb.   Feasible solution start of cycle 7.

will form a (unique) chain joining A and B which might look, for example, like Fig. 19-2-VII. In this case, the iterative process is continued.

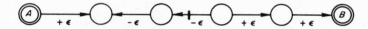

Figure 19-2-VII.

Proof of the Tree Method: Let us assume, for a general network, that the iterative process is finite and that the final subtrees, T_0 and T_n, are as shown in Fig. 19-2-VIII. Join the destination n to the source by a fictitious

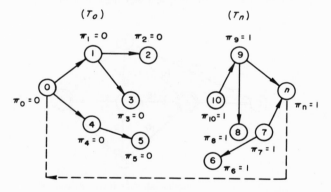

Figure 19-2-VIII.   With a back flow arc, the graph of the basis forms a single tree.

back flow arc $(n, 0)$ so that now *the subtrees, T_0 and T_n, and the arc $(n, 0)$ form a single tree* in the network. The direction of the arrows on all arcs corresponds to the direction of positive flow. If the flow is zero, this direction is undefined and may be arbitrarily chosen. The capacitated transshipment problem is to maximize the flow, F, along the arc $(n, 0)$. The conditions of the problem are

[402]

$$\sum_j \bar{x}_{ij} = 0 \qquad\qquad (i = 1, 2, \ldots, n)$$

$$-\alpha_{ji} \le x_{ij} \le \alpha_{ij}$$

$$-x_{n,0} = -F \text{ (Min)}$$

Thus, in this case, $c_{n0} = -1$, while all the other c_{ij} are zero.

As shown in § 17-1, the $\bar{x}_{ij}$ corresponding to arcs (i, j) of a tree form a basic set. The simplex multipliers satisfy the equation, $\pi_j - \pi_i = c_{ij}$, for arcs (i, j), corresponding to basic variables. Since one multiplier may be arbitrarily chosen, we set $\pi_0 = 0$. Each node, i, in the subtree, T_0, will then have a multiplier, π_i, of zero, and each node in T_n will have a multiplier of unity. It is now easy to see that the final solution, $x_{ij} = x_{ij}^o$, is optimal, because all arcs (i, j) connecting T_0 to T_n, are saturated, i.e., all the corresponding non-basic variables are at their upper bound $[x_{ij} = \alpha_{ij}]$ and have nonpositive cost factors $[c_{ij} - (\pi_j - \pi_i) = -1]$, while, for all the basic variables, $c_{ij} - (\pi_j - \pi_i) = 0$. The conditions for optimality of a bounded variable problem are fulfilled. (See § 18-2-(6).)

We have assumed a finite number of iterations. It will be noted that each iteration generates two subtrees which, if joined by the arc $(n, 0)$ form a single tree. Hence, each successive solution corresponds to a basic solution. Assuming nondegeneracy, there would be a positive increase in flow on each iteration, hence it would not be possible to repeat a basis. In the case of degeneracy (which occurred frequently in the example), a randomized rule of rejection from the basis will insure with probability one against circling in the algorithm. (See Chapter 10; see also Problem 1 and § 6-1.)

19-3. PROBLEMS

1. Determine a perturbation scheme for avoiding degeneracy. Using Orden's approach (§ 14-4, Problems 14, 15), find a fixed value for ε in advance. Note that it will be necessary to use the equivalence of the capacitated flow problem with the transportation problem.
2. Solve the problem shown in Fig. 19-1-III by the Ford-Fulkerson Method, and the Simplex Method. Compare relative efficiencies.

REFERENCES

Berge, 1962-1
Boldyreff, 1955-1
Dantzig and Fulkerson, 1956-1
Egerváry, 1931-1
Flood, 1960-1
Ford and Fulkerson, 1954-1, 1955-1, 1956-1, 2, 1957-1, 1958-1, 1960-1
Fulkerson, 1956-1, 1961-1, 1964-1
Fulkerson and Dantzig, 1955-1

Gale, 1960-1
Gomory and Hu, 1960-1, 2, 1964-1
Hadley, 1961-2
Hoffman, 1960-1
Iri, 1960-1
Kuhn, 1955-1
Munkres, 1957-1
Ryser, 1961-1
Shapley, 1959-1, 1961-1

(See also references Chapter 14)

CHAPTER 20

THE PRIMAL–DUAL METHOD FOR TRANSPORTATION PROBLEMS

20-1. INTRODUCTION

Although the simplex method, as adapted to the transportation array by the techniques of Chapter 14, has been used successfully to solve large problems involving hundreds of equations in thousands of unknowns, the *primal-dual transportation method* presented in this chapter appears to have certain advantages. In an informal experiment by Ford, Fulkerson, and the author, this method has been compared with the simplex procedure in a number of small problems and was found to take roughly half the effort. For example, one 20 × 20 optimal assignment for which the simplex method required well over an hour of hand computation, was accomplished by the present method in about thirty minutes. With larger problems the advantage may be greater. However, the experience reported informally to the author has not been conclusive.

As in § 11-4, the technique keeps the relative cost factors nonnegative while it works toward feasibility, so that when a feasible solution is obtained it will *already* be optimal. Historically, the technique evolved from a combinatorial procedure called the "Hungarian Method," which was designed by H. Kuhn [1955-1] for solving a specialized assignment problem and is based on a proof, by a Hungarian mathematician, Egerváry [1931-1], for a linear graph theorem of König.

Ford and Fulkerson [1955-1] subsequently discovered a simplified algorithm for solving maximal flow problems in networks (see Chapter 19). This algorithm, when applied to the Hitchcock transportation network, serves as a substitute for part of Kuhn's procedure, enabling an analogous solution of the transportation problem and the least cost capacitated transshipment problem. A number of other authors have also developed methods for solving such problems based on Kuhn's algorithm; notably Munkres [1957-1] and Flood [1960-1].

The *out-of-kilter* method of Fulkerson [1961-2] for minimal cost flow problems generalizes the primal-dual method so that it may be initiated with an infeasible dual solution as well as an infeasible primal solution. Computer codes based on this algorithm (developed by Jack D. Little and Richard J. Clasen of RAND) are being successfully applied in several industries.

20-2. THE FORD-FULKERSON ALGORITHM

The Hitchcock problem is to find an $m \times n$ array, $x = (x_{ij})$, of nonnegative numbers, x_{ij}, which minimizes the objective function, $\sum_{i=1}^{m} \sum_{j=1}^{n} c_{ij} x_{ij}$, subject to the constraints,

$$(1) \qquad \sum_{j=1}^{n} x_{ij} = a_i \qquad (i = 1, 2, \ldots, m)$$

$$\sum_{i=1}^{m} x_{ij} = b_j \qquad (j = 1, 2, \ldots, n)$$

where a_i and b_j, specified nonnegative integers, satisfy $\sum_{i=1}^{m} a_i = \sum_{j=1}^{n} b_j$. (If $m = n$ and all the a_i and b_j are equal to 1, this reduces to an optimal assignment problem.)

To describe the process, we will work through an example due to Ford and Fulkerson [1956-1]:

Unit Shipping Costs c_{ij}

	Surpluses	Shortages				(j)			
(2)	$a_1 = 3$	$b_1 = 3$		(1)	(2)	(3)	(4)	(5)	(6)
	$a_2 = 4$	$b_2 = 3$							
	$a_3 = 2$	$b_3 = 6$	(1)	5	3	7	3	8	5
	$a_4 = 8$	$b_4 = 2$	(2)	5	6	12	5	7	11
		$b_5 = 1$	(i) (3)	2	8	3	4	8	2
		$b_6 = 2$	(4)	9	6	10	5	10	9

The computational procedure carries along the original unit-cost matrix, (c_{ij}), and also an auxiliary array of the same size, which is the *restricted primal* array. Associated with each element, c_{ij}, of the cost matrix will be prices, u_i and v_j, such that $c_{ij} - u_i - v_j$ is nonnegative.

Associated with each row of the restricted primal array, at any stage of the procedure, will be a "surplus," and with each column a "shortage." These are the portions of the a_i and b_j still not allocated to routes.

Determining Nonnegative Values of the Relative Cost Factors, $\bar{c}_{ij}$, for Initial Selection of a Restricted Primal Array.

For each row i, assign the value, $u_i = \min_j c_{ij}$. Subtract this value from each entry in the row to form the ith row of the $(c_{ij} - u_i)$ array. Then, for each column j, assign the value, $v_j = \min_i (c_{ij} - u_i)$. Subtract this value from each element, $c_{ij} - u_i$, in the column to form the jth column of $(\bar{c}_{ij})$ (which equals $(c_{ij} - u_i - v_j)$), the relative-cost array. For our example, this produces (3), (4), and (5) in turn.

(3)

$$c_{ij} \qquad\qquad u_i = \operatorname*{Min}_j c_{ij}$$

5	3	7	3	8	5	3
5	6	12	5	7	11	5
2	8	3	4	8	2	2
9	6	10	5	10	9	5

(4)

$$c'_{ij} = c_{ij} - u_i$$

2	0	4	0	5	2
0	1	7	0	2	6
0	6	1	2	6	0
4	1	5	0	5	4

$$\operatorname*{Min}_i c'_{ij} = v_j \rightarrow \quad 0 \qquad 0 \qquad 1 \qquad 0 \qquad 2 \qquad 0$$

(5)

$$\bar{c}_{ij} = c_{ij} - u_i - v_j$$

2	0	3	0	3	2
0	1	6	0	0	6
0	6	0	2	4	0
4	1	4	0	3	4

For the restricted primal problem, we seek to reduce the shortages by assigning positive values only to those x_{ij} for which $\bar{c}_{ij}$ is zero. Thus, for our example, entries must be made only in the squares with inscribed boxes of (6), since these correspond to the $\bar{c}_{ij}$ which are zero in (5).

Step 0: Initiate the Labeling

Start by labeling each row for which a surplus occurs, appending a minus sign (label) next to the surplus value.

(6)

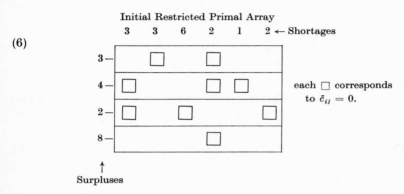

Initial Restricted Primal Array

each □ corresponds to $\bar{c}_{ij} = 0$.

Step 1: Searching for a Chain

In each row containing a minus "label," append a plus "label" to each unlabeled inscribed box. If a row contains two or more minus labels, change all but one to plus, affixing minus to the box whose entry is largest. In each column containing a plus label, append a minus label to each unlabeled box containing a non-zero entry. Continue until either (a) a plus label is entered in a shortage column, in which case proceed to Step 2, or (b) it becomes impossible, under the rules, to enter any more labels—in which case proceed to Step 3.

Step 2: Allocating Shortage Along the Chain

Let k represent an amount to be determined, and begin by indicating that k is to be *subtracted from the deficit* in the column containing the plus label which terminated Step 1 according to rule 1(a). The procedure now consists of either (a) selecting a column where k has previously been subtracted from some entry or from the current shortage, and adding k to just one of the plus-labeled entries in the column (there is always at least one such entry), or (b) selecting the row where k has just been added to some entry, and subtracting k from the minus-labeled entry or from the minus-labeled surplus (there is only one minus label in a labeled row).

Continue until k is shown subtracted from some entry in a surplus row. Now substitute for k the value of the smallest entry which must be reduced by k and perform the indicated additions and subtractions of k. If a surplus remains in any row, erase all the plus and minus labels and return to Step 0. If no surplus remains, terminate, for feasibility has thus been achieved, and *the set of entries now constitutes an optimal solution* since all the relative cost factors have been kept nonnegative.

Step 3:   Finding a New Restricted Primal

Let $(i, j) \in S$ mean that square (i, j) is in a *labeled row and an unlabeled column*. Similarly, let $(i, j) \in S'$ mean that square (i, j) is in an *unlabeled row and a labeled column*. (Note that neither S nor S' contains any labeled squares.)

Determine a constant, Δ, and a square (r, s) in S, such that

$$(7) \qquad\qquad \Delta = \bar{c}_{rs} = \operatorname*{Min}_{(i,\,j)\varepsilon S} \ \bar{c}_{ij}$$

and new $\bar{c}_{ij}$ values,

$$\bar{c}_{ij}^* = \begin{cases} \bar{c}_{ij} - \Delta \text{ if } (i, j) \in S & \text{(Labeled row, unlabeled column)} \\ \bar{c}_{ij} + \Delta \text{ if } (i, j) \in S' & \text{(Unlabeled row, labeled column)} \\ \bar{c}_{ij} & \text{otherwise} \end{cases}$$

As an alternative method of effecting these changes, we may first adjust the values of u_i to $u_i^* = u_i + \Delta$ for rows i with labels and v_j to $v_j^* = v_j - \Delta$ in columns with labels. The values of c_{ij}^* may then be determined as

$$\bar{c}_{ij}^* = c_{ij} - u_i^* - v_j^*$$

In the restricted-primal array, correct the positions of the inscribed boxes to correspond to $\bar{c}_{ij}^* = 0$. There will be at least one new box in S, for $\Delta = \bar{c}_{rs}$. All the boxes in S' will drop (their entries are zero) and the others will remain unchanged. Leaving the labels intact, return to Step 1 and continue the labeling process by scanning those rows where new boxes were inscribed.

Illustration.   In our example, having appended a minus label to the surpluses, we begin by scanning row 1 for inscribed boxes and by plus-labeling the x_{12} square of (6). Because the second column has surplus, rule 1(a) directs us to Step 2. This results in (8).

(8)

Setting $k = 3$, and adjusting the entries decreases the shortage by 3 units and completes Step 2. We now repeat Step 1 since the problem is still

[408]

infeasible. After several repetitions of the Step 1-Step 2 cycle, the array appears as in (9) and then as in (10a).

(9)

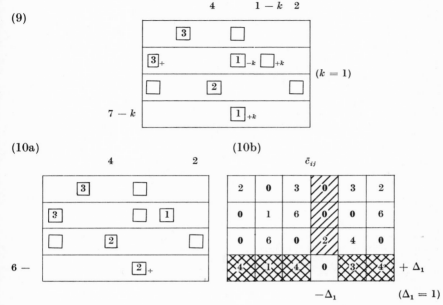

(10a)   (10b)

(11a)   (11b)

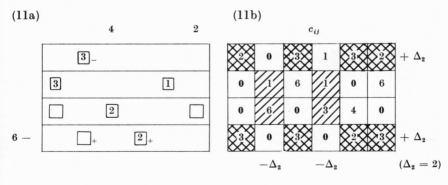

As specified by rule 1(b), because no more plus or minus labels may be entered, we now proceed to Step 3, again using the array in (5) (which is repeated as (10b) above). The only labeled entry is in the fourth row and fourth column; S consists of the double-hatched squares and S' the single-hatched squares. Now, since the smallest element in the squares of S is 1, we subtract $\Delta = 1$ from the $\bar{c}_{ij}$ values of S and add $\Delta = 1$ to the $\bar{c}_{ij}$ values of S'. This has the effect of keeping $\bar{c}_{44}$ fixed at zero while reducing the cost factor, $\bar{c}_{42}$, to zero, as shown in (11b).

The new restricted primal problem appears in (11a), and the remainder of the procedure is shown by the subsequent displays.

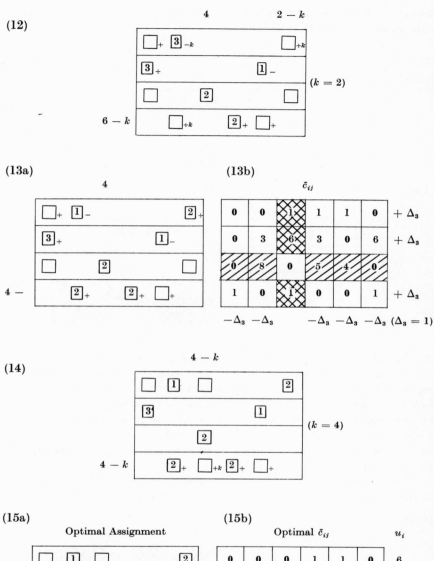

The optimal set of prices, given in (15b), is formed by successively adjusting the initial values of u_i and v_j, as given in (3) and (4), by the corresponding values of $\pm \Delta$ (if any) given in (10b), (11b), (13b), and (15b).

Finiteness of the Primal-Dual Transportation Method.

Each application of Step 1 must make either Step 2 or Step 3 possible. There can be, at most, $N = \Sigma a_i = \Sigma b_j$ applications of Step 2 if a_i and b_j are integers, for, in that case, the successive k-parameters are all positive integers, and the surpluses and shortages are decreased by at least unity at each application of Step 2.

THEOREM 1: *The algorithm will not lead to Step 3 unless shortage columns (and possibly others) are unlabeled.*

This must certainly be true if any column still has shortage, since, if such a column contained a plus sign, Step 2 (and not Step 3) would have followed after Step 1, in accordance with rule 1(a); and if such a column contained a minus sign, this label would always have been preceded by a plus sign in the same column.

THEOREM 2: *There can be, at most, $n - 2$ applications of Step 3 between applications of Step 2* (where n is the number of columns).

To see this, note that a boxed entry having a label at the end of Step 1 will remain boxed after Step 3, since the only $\bar{c}_{ij}$ values modified are those situated in unlabeled rows or columns. In addition, *there will be at least one new label entered in a previously unlabeled column, s,* corresponding to $(r, s) \in S$, such that $\bar{c}_{rs} = \Delta$. Since rows of S are labeled (by definition) and every labeled row contains one minus label, we follow Step 3 by re-applying Step 1. The rules will, therefore, ascribe a plus label to the x_{rs} square. There can thus be no more than $n - 2$ successive returns to Step 3 after Step 1 before a labeling occurs in a shortage column (invoking Step 2).

THEOREM 3: *A transportation array will be optimized by this Primal-Dual Method in not more than $N(n - 2)$ cycles, where $N = \Sigma a_i = \Sigma b_j$, and n is the number of columns.*

20-3. PROBLEMS

1. Complete the proof of Theorem 3.
2. Modify the Primal-Dual Method for transportation problems to account for the inadmissibility of some x_{ij}.
3. How does the Primal-Dual Transportation Method relate to the more general primal-dual algorithm of § 11-4?
4. Show that Steps 1 and 2 constitute special application of the Ford-Fulkerson Method for achieving maximal flow in a network (see Chapter 19).
5. Explain the Primal-Dual Transportation Method by diagramming the procedure of Steps 1, 2, and 3 as a flow-chart.

[411]

6. How does the magnitude of Δ affect the amount by which the value of the dual objective function is changed during an iteration?

7. Show that, instead of starting our process of labeling by appending minus labels to surplus row, we could start by attaching minus labels to shortage columns, etc.

8. Show that the progress of the algorithm will be accelerated by double-labeling, using both of the possible labeling methods, as mentioned in the last problem, one after the other during a single application of Step 1.

9. *Warehouse problem:* Suppose a number of commodities i can be purchased (or sold) at prices p_{it} at the start of period t; it costs s_{it} to store it for one period. If the capacity, S, of a storage warehouse is fixed, what is the optimal storage, purchase, sales program? Show that an item is either used to completely stock a warehouse or, if in stock, is either completely held or sold out. References: Cahn [1948-1], Charnes and Cooper [1955-1], Dantzig [1949-1; 1957-3], Prager [1957-1].

REFERENCES

Cahn, 1948-1
Charnes and Cooper, 1955-1
Dantzig, 1949-1, 1957-3
Egerváry, 1931-1
Flood, 1960-1
Ford and Fulkerson, 1955-1, 1956-1, 1960-1
Fulkerson, 1961-2

Garvin, 1960-1
Hadley, 1961-2
Hoffman, 1960-1
Jewell, 1957-1
Kuhn, 1955-1
Munkres, 1957-1
Prager, 1957-1
(See also references Chapter 14)

CHAPTER 21

THE WEIGHTED DISTRIBUTION PROBLEM

21-1. THE NEAR-TRIANGULARITY OF THE BASIS

The standard transportation model uses a particularly simple constraint matrix in which each variable has at most two non-zero coefficients whose values are $+1$ and -1. We propose to examine a model which is similar in form, for it allows at most two non-zero coefficients for each variable.

Problem 1. The Row-Column Weighted Distribution Problem.

Find nonnegative y_{ij} and Min z satisfying

(1) The Row Equations:
$(i = 1, 2, \ldots, m)$
$$\sum_{j=1}^{n} a_{ij} y_{ij} = a_i$$

(2) The Column Equations:
$(j = 1, 2, \ldots, n)$
$$\sum_{i=1}^{m} b_{ij} y_{ij} = b_j$$

(3) The Objective Function:
$$\sum_{i=1}^{m} \sum_{j=1}^{n} c'_{ij} y_{ij} = z$$

where a_i and b_j are nonnegative, and a_{ij} is positive. Before proceeding, we will transform the variables so that all row coefficients become unity. Thus, when we replace the y_{ij} by new variables, defined as $x_{ij} = a_{ij} y_{ij}$, the row equations take on unit coefficients in place of the a_{ij}, while the coefficients of the column equations become $p_{ij} = b_{ij}/a_{ij}$ and the cost equation becomes $c_{ij} = c'_{ij}/a_{ij}$. In this way we arrive at

The Standard Form of the Weighted Distribution Problem.

(4)
$$\sum_{j=1}^{n} x_{ij} = a_i \qquad \text{(Row equations, } i = 1, 2, \ldots, m)$$

(5)
$$\sum_{i=1}^{m} p_{ij} x_{ij} = b_j \qquad \text{(Column equations, } j = 1, 2, \ldots, n)$$

(6)
$$\sum_{i=1}^{n} \sum_{j=1}^{n} c_{ij} x_{ij} = z$$

where $x_{ij} \geq 0$, and z is to be minimized.

[413]

In a typical application, the a_i represent availabilities which must not be exceeded (as in the machine-task example to be discussed). In this case (4) is replaced by (7).

$$(7) \qquad \sum_{j=1}^{m} x_{ij} \leq a_i \qquad \text{for } i = 1, 2, \ldots, m$$

The theory and technique of solution are virtually the same for the system, {(5), (6), and (7)} as for {(4), (5), and (6)}.

The Dual of the Standard Weighted Distribution Problem is: Find u_i, v_j, and the Maximum q, such that

$$(8) \qquad u_i + p_{ij}v_j \leq c_{ij} \qquad \text{for } i = 1, 2, \ldots, m$$
$$\text{and } j = 1, 2, \ldots, n$$

where

$$(9) \qquad \sum_{i=1}^{m} u_i a_i + \sum_{j=1}^{n} v_j b_j = q \text{ (Max)}$$

Criterion of Optimality: A set of x_{ij} satisfying the primal problem is an optimal solution if there are u_i and v_j satisfying the dual, such that

$$(10) \qquad x_{ij} > 0 \Rightarrow u_i + p_{ij}v_j = c_{ij}$$
$$u_i + p_{ij}v_j < c_{ij} \Rightarrow x_{ij} = 0$$

Illustrative Applications.

1. A number of different tasks can be accomplished on one of several types of available machines, some more efficiently than others. The tasks are to be assigned to machines in such a way that all tasks are completed within the machine-time available and at a minimum over-all cost.

To set up the mathematical model, let

a_i = number of hours availa..le on i^{th} type machine,

b_j = number of units of jth type task to be performed,

c_{ij} = cost to do one unit of the jth type task on the ith type machine,

p_{ij} = number of units of the jth type task that can be processed per hour on the ith type machine,

x_{ij} = number of hours machine i is to work on task j.

2. A fleet, consisting of various types of aircraft, is to be assigned to airline routes in order to satisfy the passenger demand at the least operating costs. In this case, for some period, let

a_i = number of aircraft of type i in the fleet,

b_j = number of passengers requiring passage on the jth route,

c_{ij} = operating costs per aircraft of type i assigned to route j in the period,

[414]

$p_{ij} = $ the total number of passengers that can be accommodated by one aircraft of type i if assigned to route j during the period,

$x_{ij} = $ number of aircraft of type i assigned to the jth route.

Tableau and Implicit Prices for the Weighted Distribution Problem.

The tableau for a 2×3 problem takes the form (11)

(11)

x_{11} p_{11} c_{11}	x_{12} p_{12} c_{12}	x_{13} p_{13} c_{13}	a_1 u_1
x_{21} p_{21} c_{21}	x_{22} p_{22} c_{22}	x_{23} p_{23} c_{23}	a_2 u_2
b_1 v_1	b_2 v_2	b_3 v_3	

One practical observation is in order: since the entries, x_{ij}, u_i, and v_j, are numerical and must be changed from one iteration to the next, it is important for hand computation that the chart be arranged in some convenient manner, as above, to facilitate the manual labor.

Finding a Starting Basic Solution.

The weighted distribution problem differs from the standard transportation problem in that no simple rule for directly obtaining an initial basic feasible solution has been found as yet. However, for the case in which all the p_{ij} are *nonnegative*, we shall describe and illustrate a method analogous to the rule of solution given in § 15-3, using the simple numerical problem which appears below.

(12)

x_{11} $p_{11} = 1$ $c_{11} = 4$	x_{12} $p_{12} = 2$ $c_{12} = -8$	x_{13} $p_{13} = 1$ $c_{13} = 3$	$a_1 = 4$
x_{21} $p_{21} = 2$ $c_{21} = 6$	x_{22} $p_{22} = 1$ $c_{22} = 4$	x_{23} $p_{23} = 1$ $c_{23} = 7$	$a_2 = 5$
$b_1 = 5$	$b_2 = 2$	$b_3 = 3$	

Step 1. Select a basic variable by choosing a square arbitrarily (a good choice would be one having a smallest c_{ij}), and increasing the corresponding x_{ij} to the largest value consistent with its row and column totals. Delete the row or the column that becomes *saturated*, i.e., the one whose total has

[415]

just been attained (should a row and a column be saturated simultaneously, delete one or the other, but not both). Now repeat this cycle as necessary. For the example (12), squares were chosen as follows:

Square	Value of the Variable	Saturated Row or Column
(1, 3)	$x_{13} = 3$	col. 3
(1, 1)	$x_{11} = 1$	row 1
(2, 2)	$x_{22} = 2$	col. 2
(2, 1)	$x_{21} = 2$	col. 1

Step 2. One column or row total, in general, will remain unsaturated. We then introduce an artificial variable by adding a "deficit" square, (r, s), either $(0, s)$ or $(r, 0)$, to the unsaturated row or column. Next, we minimize the infeasibility form, $\Sigma\Sigma d_{ij}x_{ij}$, where $d_{ij} = 0$ for all i and j, with one exception, for the supplementary square $d_{rs} = 1$. If the deficit occurs in a column, we arbitrarily set $p_{rs} = 1$, while for a row, we need not define p_{rs} at all (since there is no column equation corresponding to the deficit).

EXERCISE: Modify this rule to cover the case where some p_{ij} may be negative.

The Phase I multipliers, u_i and v_j, must be such that $u_i + p_{ij}v_j = 0$ for x_{ij} a basic variable, except that $u_r = 1$, if the rth row is left unsaturated, and $v_j = 1$ if the jth column is left unsaturated. In our example, row 2 is not saturated; the initial tableau for Phase I, therefore, takes the form (13).

(13)

	$(j = 1)$	$(j = 2)$	$(j = 3)$	a_i	u_i
Deficit	1 1 0	2 0	3 1 0	4	$\frac{1}{2}$
1 ● 1	2 2 0	2 1 0	1 0	5	1
b_j	5	2	3		
v_j	$-\frac{1}{2}$	-1	$-\frac{1}{2}$		

Implicit prices ←———

The dot in square $(2, 0)$ is to indicate that p_{ij} is undefined (i.e., there is no equation for column 0). Because of the deficit the price of $u_2 = 1$; the remainder of the prices, u_i and v_j, are computed using equation (10) with c_{ij} replaced by d_{ij}. Since $d_{23} - (u_2 + p_{23}v_3) = 0 - [1 + 1 \cdot (-1/2)] = -(1/2)$, the infeasibility can be diminished by increasing x_{23} and adjusting the basic variables to compensate for this increase ; see (14).

(14)

	$1 + \theta$ 1 0	2 0	$3 - \theta$ 1 0	4
Deficit				
$1 - (1/2)\theta$ ● 1	$2 - (1/2)\theta$ 2 0	2 1 0	θ^* 1 0	5
	5	2	3	

It is clear that Max $\theta = 2$, and that the infeasibility vanishes at this value. Thus, x_{23} becomes a new basic variable replacing the deficit variable, x_{20}, and Phase I is already complete; we drop the deficit box. The starting tableau for Phase II, showing the u_i and v_j as well as θ entries, both of which we shall explain in a moment, is (15).

(15)

$3 + 2\theta$ 1 4	θ^* 2 -8	$1 - 3\theta$ 1 3	4 6
$1 - \theta$ 2 6	$2 - 2\theta$ 1 4	$2 + 3\theta$ 1 7	5 10

5
     -2
	2
	     -6
		3
		     $-3 \; \leftarrow v_j$
			$\uparrow$
			 u_i

Computing Implicit Prices (Simplex Multipliers).

The values of u_i and v_j from (10), must satisfy a system of five equations in the five unknowns, u_1, u_2, v_1, v_2, and v_3:

(16)

$$
\begin{aligned}
u_1 \quad &+ v_1 \qquad\qquad = 4 \\
u_1 \quad &\qquad\quad\, + v_3 = 3 \\
u_2 + 2v_1 \quad &\qquad\qquad = 6 \\
u_2 \quad &+ v_2 \qquad\quad = 4 \\
u_2 \quad &\qquad\quad\, + v_3 = 7
\end{aligned}
$$

In contradistinction to the standard transportation model, there need not be a redundancy in the system of equations $\{(1), (2)\}$. *In general, therefore, it is not possible to choose one of the prices arbitrarily.* Similarly, the bases of system $\{(1), (2)\}$ need not be triangular. Nevertheless, the system is nearly triangular in the following sense: Choose any variable, say u_2, and treat it as a parameter in terms of which the other variables are to be evaluated.

[417]

This leads to equations in a single variable, which can be immediately evaluated in terms of the parameter. From (16), we get

(17) $v_1 = 3 - \frac{1}{2}u_2,$ $v_2 = 4 - u_2,$ $v_3 = 7 - u_2$

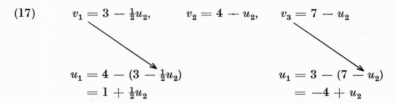

$$u_1 = 4 - (3 - \tfrac{1}{2}u_2) \qquad\qquad u_1 = 3 - (7 - u_2)$$
$$= 1 + \tfrac{1}{2}u_2 \qquad\qquad\qquad = -4 + u_2$$

We have arrived at two expressions for u_1 in terms of the parameter u_2. Equating them leads to a numerical evaluation of u_2 and, hence, of all the variables it defines. Thus, since $1 + \frac{1}{2}u_2 = -4 + u_2$, we have $u_2 = 10$ whence $v_1 = -2$, $v_2 = -6$, $v_3 = -3$, and $u_1 = 6$.

A complete set of prices for our example has now been brought to hand. However, in certain other cases, some implicit prices might still remain unevaluated after such a procedure. In that event, any unevaluated price may, as before, be treated as a parameter and additional variables evaluated in terms of it by successive substitution until two equations in two variables appear which allow its evaluation. We now generalize these remarks.

THEOREM 1: *Assuming a basis of rank $n + m$, implicit prices can be evaluated by treating any one of them as a parameter, and solving a sequence of equations in one unknown, repeating the procedure as necessary for any residual set of unevaluated prices.*

PROOF: Each equation of (10) contains two prices. If one of them is selected as a parameter, several others can be expressed in terms of it. By successive substitutions this leads to a set of variables evaluable in terms of this parameter, which have no variable in common with any equation still containing an unevaluated variable (for this in turn could be immediately evaluated in terms of the parameter and added to the set). We shall show in this set that there is just one variable that is linearly expressed in exactly two different ways. By equating the two expressions, we can determine the value of the parameter. If more than one price in the set were doubly expressed (i.e., if one variable could be evaluated in more than two ways), this would mean that the equations contain either a redundancy or an inconsistency. On the other hand, if no variable were doubly evaluable, then the value of the parameter could be chosen arbitrarily. If the basis is of rank $n + m$, however, neither one of these situations is possible, for the set of equations associated with the transpose of a basis must always lead to a unique solution.

Improving the Basic Solution.

The implicit prices, computed as above, are used to determine whether the current solution is minimal, according to condition (10), and to compute an improved solution if it is not. The solution we have computed for our example is not yet optimal, since

$$c_{12} - u_1 - p_{12}v_2 = -8 - 6 - 2(-6) = -2$$

Accordingly, set $x_{12} = \theta$, and adjust the basic variables. In our example, we compute the values of the basic variables, which result by changing the constant terms to

$$a_1' = 4 - \theta,\ a_2' = 5,\ b_1' = 5,\ b_2' = 2 - 2\theta,\ \text{and}\ b_3' = 3$$

The new values of the basic variables are expressed linearly, in the form $\alpha + \beta\theta$, where α is the old value and $\beta\theta$ is the compensatory change necessitated by the increase of θ in the value of the non-basic variable coming into the basic set. The old values, α, are known, and therefore only the amount by which basic variables change, Δx_{ij}, need be computed. They must satisfy five equations in five unknowns:

$$(18) \quad \begin{cases} \Delta x_{11} + \Delta x_{13} & = -\theta \\ \qquad\qquad + \Delta x_{21} + \Delta x_{22} + \Delta x_{23} = 0 \\ \Delta x_{11} \qquad + 2\Delta x_{21} & = 0 \\ \qquad\qquad\qquad + \Delta x_{22} & = -2\theta \\ \Delta x_{13} \qquad\qquad\qquad + \Delta x_{23} = 0 \end{cases}$$

This, of course, is the transpose of the system used earlier for evaluating the implicit prices. After we evaluate Δx_{22} from the fourth equation and substitute its value in the others, each of the remaining equations has precisely two variables that are still unknown. Moreover, it is clear that if one unknown is introduced parametrically, the others may be evaluated in terms of it. Thus, if Δx_{11} is chosen as a parameter, it can be used in turn to express Δx_{13}, Δx_{23}, Δx_{21} and then back to Δx_{11}. This gives an equation in Δx_{11} alone, and the latter can therefore be numerically evaluated. The cycle of dashes in (18) indicates this order of expression. Explicitly,

$$(19) \qquad \Delta x_{22} = -2\theta$$
$$\Delta x_{13} = -\theta - \Delta x_{11}$$
$$\Delta x_{23} = -\Delta x_{13} = \theta + \Delta x_{11}$$
$$\Delta x_{21} = -\Delta x_{22} - \Delta x_{23} = +\theta - \Delta x_{11}$$
$$\Delta x_{11} = -2\Delta x_{21} = -2\theta + 2\Delta x_{11}\ \text{or}\ \Delta x_{11} = 2\theta.$$

Substituting the value $\Delta x_{11} = 2\theta$ in the remaining equations yields $\Delta x_{13} = -3\theta$, $\Delta x_{23} = 3\theta$, and $\Delta x_{21} = -\theta$.

This method of evaluating changes in the basic variables is perfectly general. Indeed, the procedure applied here to nearly triangular bases is an analogue of the process by which one exploits the basic triangularity which occurs in transportation problems.

THEOREM 2: *Given any basis of rank $n + m$ for a weighted distribution* *problem, either (a) there exists a row or column with just one basic variable, or (b) each row and column has precisely two basic variables and $m = n$. If (a) is true, then the sub-basis, resulting by deletion of the row or column which contains only this basic variable, has the same properties.*

PROOF: Each row and column has at least one basic variable. If none of them have precisely one, then every row and column has two or more. In the latter case, the number of basic variables, $n + m$, cannot be less than twice the number of rows or twice the number of columns; hence,

(20)
$$n + m \geq 2m \quad \text{and} \quad n + m \geq 2n$$

or, by adding,

$$2(n + m) \geq 2m + 2n$$

where equality holds only if equality holds in both expressions (20), i.e., if each row and each column has precisely two basic variables, and $m = n$. But the equality *must* hold. This argument can be repeated for the sub-basis if there is one equation having a single variable and if the row and column in which it occurs have been deleted.

21-2. LINEAR GRAPH STRUCTURE OF THE BASIS

When the weighted distribution problem is interpreted in the context of a linear network, the linear graph whose arcs correspond to the variables of a basic set possesses a characteristic structure.

The discussion will be facilitated if we consider the model simply as a set of equations having certain well-defined properties, and for this purpose it will be convenient to make use of single-subscripted letters to represent the variables involved. It will be recalled that the classical transportation model, § 14-2, had a system of constraints composed of two subsystems, one of which (with row equations) referred to *exports from* each source to the various destinations, while the second subsystem (with column equations) dealt with *imports to* each destination from the various sources. In the transshipment model, § 16-1, each variable had at most two non-zero coefficients ± 1. In the weighted model, we remove the restriction ± 1 and consider a class of problems in which at most two coefficients of each variable x_j are non-zero, one in equation $i = g(j)$ and the other in $i = h(j)$. When x_j has only one non-zero coefficient $g(j) = h(j)$.

Problem 2. The General Weighted Distribution Problem.

Choose a set of nonnegative numbers, x_j, and the Minimum z, such that

(1)
$$\sum_{j=1}^{n} a_{ij} x_j = b_i \qquad (i = 1, 2, \ldots, m)$$

$$\sum_{j=1}^{n} c_j x_j = z \text{ (Min)}$$

where $a_{ij} = 0$ unless $i = g(j)$ or $i = h(j)$. We will refer to any x_j having either a_{gj} or a_{hj} zero (but not both) as a *slack variable*.

Each equation of (1) corresponds to a node in the network form of the model, while each non-slack variable, x_i, corresponds to an undirected arc joining node $g(j)$ to node $h(j)$. Slack arcs may be considered (as pointed out by F. Harary) as arcs which connect two nodes that are identical.

In drawing a linear graph, the nodes may be placed in any convenient position. Thus Fig. 21-2-I and Fig. 21-2-II are pictures of the same network, but the nodes in Fig. 21-2-II have been repositioned, so as to illustrate more clearly its essential structure. If slack variables are to be admissible, then the network must also include *slack arcs*, associated with these variables, each having only a single node.

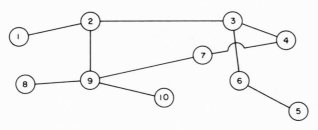

Figure 21-2 I.   Graph of a weighted distribution problem.

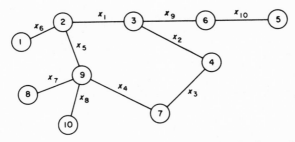

Figure 21-2-II.   Rearranged graph of a weighted distribution problem.

In Fig. 21-2-III is depicted a linear graph whose arcs correspond to the variables of a basis. This graph is composed of four isolated, connected subgraphs.

THEOREM 1: *Each connected subgraph of a basic graph for system* (1) *has precisely one loop.*

PROOF: It is clear that each connected part consists of an equal number of nodes and arcs, for the variables associated with the arcs appear only in the equations associated with the nodes of the subgraph, and these equations could not, in general, be satisfied by fewer variables than equations. On the other hand, the total number of basic variables equals the total number

[421]

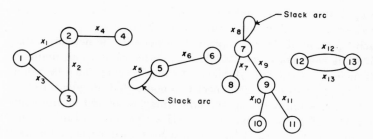

Figure 21-2-III. The basis graph has one or more connected parts each consisting of a tree and one added arc.

of equations, so equality must hold for each isolated subgraph in the network.

Now a connected subgraph having no slack arc(s) must contain at least one loop, since it would otherwise have fewer arcs than nodes. If we were to delete an arc belonging to a loop in this part, we would be left with a connected subgraph in which the number of arcs would be one less than the number of nodes, which therefore [Theorem 1, § 17-1] constitutes a tree. But a tree contains no loops; hence, the subgraph must initially have had exactly one loop.

On the other hand, if a connected subgraph has one or more slack arcs, then the graph formed by deleting them has a smaller number of arcs than nodes, the difference being equal to the number of arcs deleted. But since only the slack arcs (i.e., arcs having one node) were deleted, the resulting subgraph is still connected, and this is possible only if the number of slack arcs was one and the remaining subgraph, a tree. The proof is completed by defining an arc as a one-arc loop.

Computing an Associated Solution.

To evaluate the variables of a basis, one may begin with nodes having exactly one arc. Thus, for Fig. 21-2-II, we have

(2)
$$a_{1,6}x_6 = b_1$$
$$a_{8,7}x_7 = b_8$$
$$a_{10,8}x_8 = b_{10}$$
$$a_{5,10}x_{10} = b_5$$

If a node has several arcs, all but one of whose variables have been evaluated, then the excepted variable can be evaluated immediately. Thus, after x_{10} is determined as above, x_9 can be evaluated at node 6 from the equation,

(3)
$$a_{6,9}x_9 + a_{6,10}x_{10} = b_6$$

By this means, all variables, except those corresponding to arcs of the loop, can successively be evaluated. The evaluation of such loop variables may proceed by the method we shall now illustrate.

$$
\begin{aligned}
a_{31}x_1 + a_{32}x_2 &\phantom{+ a_{43}x_3 + a_{95}x_5} = \bar{b}_3 \\
a_{42}x_2 + a_{43}x_3 &\phantom{+ a_{95}x_5} = \bar{b}_4 \\
a_{73}x_3 + a_{74}x_4 &\phantom{+ a_{95}x_5} = \bar{b}_7 \\
a_{94}x_4 + a_{95}x_5 &= \bar{b}_9 \\
a_{21}x_1 \phantom{+ a_{32}x_2} + a_{25}x_5 &= \bar{b}_2
\end{aligned}
$$

(4)

The number $\bar{b}_i$ is the value of b_i adjusted by subtraction of such terms in the original array as are missing from (4). These missing terms belong to arcs, whose numerical values have already been determined by the foregoing procedure. Because of the nearly triangular structure of system (4), we may treat one variable of the loop as the parameter and then evaluate all the others in terms of it as we proceed around the loop. Upon completion of this circuit, a second expression for the parameter will result, and by equating the two expressions we may evaluate it numerically.

Thus, by proceeding clockwise about the loop in network Fig. 21-2-II, one arrives at the following explicit formula for x_1:

(5)
$$
x_1 = \frac{\dfrac{1}{a_{21}}\left[\bar{b}_2 - \dfrac{a_{25}}{a_{95}}\left(\bar{b}_9 - \dfrac{a_{94}}{a_{74}}\left[\bar{b}_7 - \dfrac{a_{73}}{a_{43}}\left(\bar{b}_4 - \dfrac{a_{42}}{a_{32}}\bar{b}_3\right)\right]\right)\right]}{1 - \dfrac{-a_{25}}{a_{95}}\cdot\dfrac{-a_{94}}{a_{74}}\cdot\dfrac{-a_{73}}{a_{43}}\cdot\dfrac{-a_{42}}{a_{32}}\cdot\dfrac{-a_{31}}{a_{21}}}
$$

EXERCISE: Derive an equivalent expression by proceeding counterclockwise about the loop, and then show algebraically that the two formulas are identical.

Evaluation of the Implicit Prices Associated with a Basis.

If the basis includes slack variables, then the implicit price for any equation associated with the single node of a slack arc can, of course, be immediately evaluated, and, from this, all the prices for the entire subgraph.

If, on the other hand, an isolated subgraph contains a loop, then the prices may first be determined at nodes sequenced around the loop, and the remainder evaluated by successively proceeding to nodes which have an arc in common with nodes whose prices have already been determined. If x_j is a basic variable and π_i is the price associated with the ith equation, then

(6)
$$
a_{gj}\pi_g + a_{hj}\pi_h = c_j
$$

where $g = g(j)$ and $h = h(j)$ are the node designations of the equations corresponding to the non-zero coefficients of x_j.

For Fig. 21-2-II the arcs around the loop give rise to the system:

(7)
$$
\begin{aligned}
a_{31}\pi_3 \qquad\qquad\qquad &+ a_{21}\pi_2 = c_1 \\
a_{32}\pi_3 + a_{42}\pi_4 \qquad\qquad\qquad &= c_2 \\
a_{43}\pi_4 + a_{73}\pi_7 \qquad\qquad &= c_3 \\
a_{74}\pi_7 + a_{94}\pi_9 \qquad &= c_4 \\
a_{95}\pi_9 + a_{25}\pi_2 &= c_5
\end{aligned}
$$

Moreover, since the coefficient matrix in (7) is the transpose of the one in (4), the systems have analogous structures, and the same technique of evaluation may be used for the implicit pricing as for the basic solution itself.

21-3. A SUBCLASS WITH TRIANGULAR OPTIMUM BASES

The technique we have described for exploiting near-triangularity of the basis structure is a little more complex than the methods we have applied to the standard transportation problem. This is partly because the equations of the weighted distribution can have non-triangular bases.

However, even though non-optimal bases need not be triangular, H. Markowitz [1954-2] found that, for an important class of these problems, any basis corresponding to an optimal solution *is* triangular, regardless of the values of the constant terms [Theorem 1, below]. Unfortunately, if the usual simplex process is employed, no computational advantage results from the fact that the final basis is triangular. Markowitz's idea was to vary the procedure, so that each basis occurring in the course of the algorithm would be made triangular. He noted that, for certain values of the constant terms, an optimal basic solution is immediately available, and, by *parametrizing* these terms, one could subsequently adjust them to any desired values. Since the bases are, in this way, kept both feasible and optimal throughout the process, they must remain triangular. This is the idea we will develop in the present section.

Two forms of the problem were considered by Markowitz; the first appears below and the second will be discussed later under (5).

Determine nonnegative numbers and the minimum z satisfying

(1)
$$
\begin{cases}
\displaystyle\sum_{j=1}^{n} a_{ij}x_{ij} + x_i = a_i & \text{for } i = 1, 2, \ldots, m \\[2ex]
\displaystyle\sum_{i=1}^{m} b_{ij}x_{ij} = b_j & \text{for } j = m+1, m+2, \ldots, m+n
\end{cases}
$$

(2)
$$
-\sum_{i=1}^{m} c_i x_i = z \qquad\qquad (c_i > 0)
$$

where a_{ij} and b_{ij} are nonnegative, while a_i and b_j are positive. The n column equations have been numbered $j = m + 1$, $m + 2$, . . ., $m + n$, to bring out the one-to-one correspondence between the $m + n$ nodes and the $m + n$ equations. Problems of this kind first came to light in attempts to assign machines to a fixed set of tasks in such a way as to minimize the use of machine time by maximizing the total value of the machine time left unused after the tasks have been completed; that is, by building up certain of the slack variables, x_i. (See illustrative applications in § 21-1.)

THEOREM 1: *Every optimal basis for {(1), (2)} is triangular.*

PROOF: If, on the contrary, a basis is not triangular, there is a subset of the equations whose linear subgraph is connected, contains one loop, and has no slack variable arcs, by Theorem 1 of § 21-2. The prices corresponding to nodes about the loop may be evaluated by means of equations, such as § 21-2-(7). However, since there are no slack variables, the coefficients in the objective form are all zero for the subset of the basic variables contained in these equations. Hence, the implicit prices must all vanish for this subset of equations. In particular, if x_{rs} is one of the basic variables in the subset, then $u_r = 0$. However, the conditions for an optimal basis are that

(3)
$$a_{ij}u_i + b_{ij}v_j \leq 0$$
$$-u_i \geq c_i > 0 \qquad \text{for } i = 1, 2, \ldots, m$$
$$\text{and } j = m + 1, m + 2, \ldots, m + n$$

which contradicts the assertion that $u_r = 0$. Hence, loops are not possible (except slack-arc loops) and the basis must be triangular.

Finding an Initial Feasible Dual Solution.

If the a_i are replaced by sufficiently large values a_i^*, a starting solution with a triangular basis is immediately available. As basic variables, choose the slacks and one variable, x_{rj}, from each column j, such that

(4)
$$\underset{i}{\text{Min}} \frac{a_{ij}c_i}{-b_{ij}} = \frac{a_{rj}c_r}{-b_{rj}} = v_j \qquad (b_{ij}, b_{rj} \neq 0)$$

Then (assuming that all b_{ij} are nonnegative), it is easy to see that the prices $u_i = c_i$ and v_j above satisfy (3), so that the basic solution is both feasible and optimal.

EXERCISE: Determine explicitly how large to make a_i^* in order to guarantee feasibility.

The next step is to replace the constants a_i by $a_i + \lambda(a_i^* - a_i)$ and determine the values of the basic variables as a function of λ. The solution is feasible and optimal when $\lambda = 1$. Finally, the parametric linear programming algorithm (§ 11-3) can be applied to reduce λ to zero. At the end of this section we will describe an adaptation of the algorithm to this problem.

The second form of the problem, considered by Markowitz, is as follows: Determine numbers $x_j \geq 0$ and maximum λ, such that

(5)
$$\sum_j a_{ij}x_{ij} + x_i = a_i \qquad (i = 1, 2, \ldots, m)$$

$$\sum_i b_{ij}x_{ij} = \lambda b_j \qquad (j = m+1, m+2, \ldots, m+n)$$

In the previous formulation we sought to maximize the unused machine time after performing a fixed set of tasks, but here we seek that allocation which will turn out the most work when the *proportion* b_j of each type task is fixed. This type of problem arises naturally if the different type tasks are combined in fixed proportions to form completed assemblies (e.g., parts of a calculator to be used for completed machines).

THEOREM 2: *For any fixed λ, a basis can be determined that is triangular.*

PROOF: Let λ be any fixed value in (5). Maximize $\Sigma c_i x_i$. By Theorem 1, the final basis is triangular, completing the proof. To solve (5), one can proceed as follows: for $\lambda = 0$, use the same basic set as found by (4). The corresponding basic solution, $x_{ij} = 0$, $x_i = a_i$ for all i, j is feasible and optimal for (5). Apply the parametric linear programming algorithm to increase λ to a maximum. The successive bases will be triangular.

Iterative Procedure. To simplify the calculations, we assume $a_{ij} > 0$; it is convenient to consider system $\{(1), (2)\}$ in the form:

Find $x' \geq 0$, $x_i' \geq 0$, Max z' satisfying

(6)
$$\left\{ \begin{array}{ll} \sum_{j=1}^{n} x_{ij}' + x_i' = a_i', & \\ -\sum_{i=1}^{m} \beta_{ij}x_{ij}' = -b_j, & (\beta_{ij} \geq 0) \\ \sum_{i=1}^{m} x_i' = z' \text{ (Max)} & \end{array} \right.$$

where we have chosen to maximize instead of minimize. This can be done by a simple transformation of variables $x_{ij}' = c_i a_{ij} x_{ij}$ ($x_{ij} = x_{ij}'$, if $a_{ij} = 0$) and $c_i x_i = x_i'$, and by setting $\beta_{ij} = b_{ij}/c_i a_{ij}$ ($\beta_{ij} = b_{ij}$, if $a_{ij} = 0$) and $c_i a_i = a_i'$. We have assumed $a_{ij} \neq 0$ in (6).

EXERCISE: Explain why in practice $a_{ij} = 0$ usually implies $b_{ij} = 0$.

The *dual* of (6) is: Find u_i, v_j, Min $\bar{z}'$ satisfying:

(7)
$$u_i - \beta_{ij}v_j \geq 0$$
$$u_i \geq 1$$
$$a_i'u_i - b_jv_j = \bar{z}' \text{ (Min)}$$

where $i = 1, 2, \ldots, m$; $j = 1, 2, \ldots, n$.

[426]

Replacing a_i' by $\theta a_i'$: Let us suppose that the $a_i' > 0$ have been replaced by $\theta a_i'$ for $i = 1, 2, \ldots, m$ and that for θ sufficiently large, we have at hand an optimal basic solution to (6). Then the basis is triangular and consists of a number of trees each connected to a slack arc, as shown in Fig. 21-3-I, which we will refer to as an sl+tree where *sl* is short for *slack arc*.

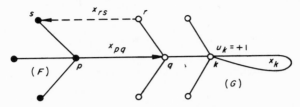

Figure 21-3-I.   Improving a basic solution.

However, if θ is reduced, the value of some basic variable associated with an arc of some sl+tree may become negative. By the rules of the parametric programming algorithm (§ 11-3), the first basic variable to change sign below a critical value $\theta = \theta^*$ will be dropped from the basic set in the next iteration. In case the variable to be dropped is not a slack, say x_{pq} as in Fig. 21-3-I, then the removal of the arc (p, q) from the sl+tree separates it into parts (F) and (G). We assume for convenience that node $p \in F$ and that nodes $k, q \in G$. Now (F), containing no slack variables, must join in the graph of the new basis with either (G) or some other sl+tree by an arc (r, s) associated with the new basic variable. In case x_k, the slack variable, is dropped, then, of course, (G) is vacuous and (F) must join up with some other sl+tree.

We shall now determine which basic variable to introduce into the basic set. We note that the prices on all nodes on all other sl+trees do not change with the change in basis, nor is there any change on the nodes of (G). Hence, the only changes are the prices on the nodes of (F). However, the prices on the nodes of (F) were determined before a change of basis by a set of relations:

$$(8) \qquad\qquad u_i - \beta_{ij} v_j = 0 \qquad\qquad (i, j \in F)$$

where (i, j) is an arc of (F) and the price u_p on the node p where u_p was determined via similar relations on (G) and $u_k = 1$. Relations (8) still hold after a change of basis, but the price on p can change from u_p^o to, say, μu_p^o. Since relations (8) are *homogeneous*, it follows that the prices on all nodes i of (F) will all change proportionally from u_i^o to μu_i^o. We have assumed $p \in F$ and $q, k \in G$; similar remarks hold if $q \in F$ and $p, k \in G$.

EXERCISE: Show that all implicit prices are nonnegative.

From these observations it is easy to put together the following rules for deciding the factor, μ, of proportionality and the variable, x_{rs} or x_r, to introduce into the basic set:

Case I: If x_{pq} is dropped, where p is in F and q is not in F, or if a slack variable x_k is dropped, then $\mu > 1$. If it exists, choose x_{rs} to enter where r is not in F and s is in F, such that

$$(9) \qquad \mu = \frac{u_r}{\beta_{rs}v_s} = \text{Min } \frac{u_i}{\beta_{ij}v_j} > 1 \qquad (j \text{ in } F, i \text{ not in } F).$$

If no such (r, s) exists, terminate.

Case II: If x_{pq} is dropped, where p is not in F and q is, then $\mu < 1$. If it exists, choose x_{rs} to enter where r is in F and s is not in F, such that

$$(10) \qquad \mu' = \frac{\beta_{rs}v_s}{u_r} = \text{Max } \frac{\beta_{ij}v_j}{u_i} < 1 \qquad (i \text{ in } F, j \text{ not in } F)$$

or choose slack variable x_r to enter, where r is in F

$$(11) \qquad \mu'' = \frac{1}{u_r} = \text{Max } \frac{1}{u_i} < 1 \qquad (i \text{ in } F)$$

depending on which ratio, $\mu = \mu'$ or $\mu = \mu''$, is the larger. If no such (r, s) exists, terminate.

The following can easily be shown:

EXERCISE: If the x_{rs} or x_r chosen above is introduced into the basic set in the place of x_{pq} or x_p, show that the new solution (if non-degenerate) will be feasible in some range of values $\theta < \theta^*$.

EXERCISE: If it is not possible to find an i not in F, j in F for Case I or an i in F, j not in F for Case II, show that there can be no feasible solution for $\theta < \theta^*$.

Example: Consider the array:

		$(j = 3)$	$(j = 4)$	$(j = 5)$	(slack)	a_i
(12)	$(i = 1)$	x_{13} $\beta_{13} = 1$	x_{14} $\beta_{14} = 2$	x_{15} $\beta_{15} = 3$	x_1	8
	$(i = 2)$	x_{23} $\beta_{23} = 4$	x_{24} $\beta_{24} = 3$	x_{25} $\beta_{25} = 6$	x_2	2
	b_j	8	6	12		

which represents the equations

(13) Row Equations: $x_{13} + x_{14} + x_{15} + x_1 = 8$ $(= 8\theta$ when right-hand side is parametrized)

$$x_{23} + x_{24} + x_{25} + x_2 = 2 \quad (= 2\theta \text{ when right-hand side is parametrized})$$

(14) Column Equations:

$$x_{13} + 4x_{23} = 8$$
$$2x_{14} + 3x_{24} = 6$$
$$3x_{15} + 6x_{25} = 12$$
$$x_1 + x_2 = z \text{ (Max)}$$

To construct a starting solution choose for basic variables the variable in each column j corresponding to Max β_{ij} and the slack variables. For the example the basic variables are x_{23}, x_{24}, x_{25}, x_1, x_2. The graph of the basis, the prices, and the values of the basic variables are shown in Fig. 21-3-II.

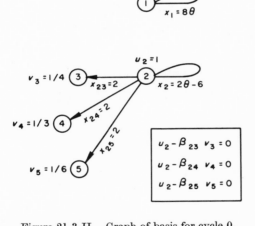

Figure 21-3-II.   Graph of basis for cycle 0.

It is easy to verify $u_1 - \beta_{1j}v_j \geq 0$ for $j = 3$, 4, 5, so that the solution is optimal and feasible for $\theta \geq 3$. Reducing θ below the critical value $\theta^* = 3$, x_2 changes sign; hence x_2 is to be dropped as basic variable. To do this, prices are modified as shown in Fig. 21-3-III. By the calculation shown at the right of the figure, x_{14} becomes the new basic variable to replace x_2. The graph of the new basis, the prices, and the values of basic variables are given in Fig. 21-3-IV.

When θ is reduced below the critical value $\theta^* = 2$, x_{24} changes sign and accordingly will be dropped on the next iteration. Hence, prices are modified as shown in Fig. 21-3-V, and by the calculation shown at the right, x_{15} will be the new basic variable.

[429]

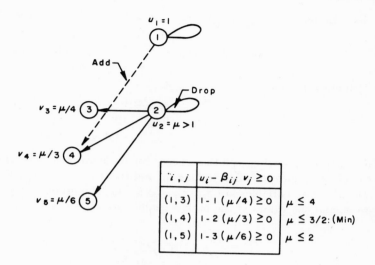

Figure 21-3-III.   Graph of basis for cycle 1.

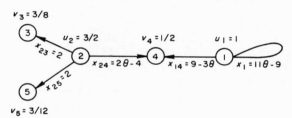

Figure 21-3-IV.   Graph of basis for cycle 2 (start).

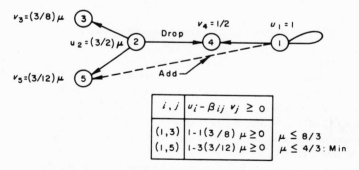

Figure 21-3-V.   Graph of basis for cycle 2 (end).

[430]

The graph of the new basis is given by Fig. 21-3-VI.

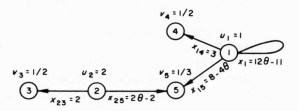

Figure 21-3-VI.   Graph of basis for cycle 3 (optimum).

The value of θ can be reduced to 1 without affecting feasibility. At $\theta = 1$ the parametrized right-hand side of (1) attains the desired a_i values, hence the optimal solution is given by (15) for $\theta = 1$. This solution is recapped below (boxes indicate position of basic variables).

(15) $x_{13} = 0$ $x_{14} = \boxed{3}$ $x_{15} = \boxed{4}$ $x_1 = \boxed{1}$

$\qquad\quad x_{23} = \boxed{2}$ $x_{24} = 0$ $x_{25} = \boxed{0}$ $x_2 = 0$

21-4. PROBLEMS

1. (Review.)   What is the change of variables referred to in the second paragraph of § 21-1? Why does it fail if a coefficient is negative in a row equation? How would you work the simplex method if some variables were allowed to be negative? How is p_{ij} related to the previous coefficients?

2. What is the dual for the system of equations (4), (5), and (6) of § 21-1?

3. Change the constants a_i and b_j in such a way that more than one iteration is needed in Phase I of the example in § 21-1.

4. (Review.)   In § 21-3, show how to choose a_i^* sufficiently large so that the basic solution will also be feasible. Interpret the meaning of the optimal solution in this case.

5. How is the selection made if some β_{ij} is negative?

6. Apply the procedure and solve a 3×4 example. Use linear graphs to guide computation of prices and adjustments in the values of basic variables.

7. Solve the 3×4 example as in Example 1, § 21-1, where b_i are replaced by λb_i. Choose λ initially sufficiently small so that feasibility is attained, and then parametrically increase λ to 1.

8. Set up a machine-task model in the standard form of the weighted distribution problem, § 21-1-(4), (5), (6). Assume the cost per hour, c_{ij}, for the ith machine is the same, regardless of the task, and c_i is the revenue per hour derived from other uses of the left-over machine time. If the

[431]

objective is to minimize net costs, show for such a model that system (6) of § 21-3 can be obtained from system {(1), (2)} of § 21-3.

9. If u_i and v_j are the prices associated with the ith row equation and the jth column equation of § 21-3-(6) respectively, show that the prices of an optimal solution satisfy $u_i \geq 0$, $v_j > 0$.

10. Starting from (15) of § 21-3, continue to reduce θ and find the value of θ below which there is no feasible solution. Show that, in this case, it is not possible to determine which variable is to enter the basic set.

11. Review problems and illustrative examples in Chapters 3, 4, 5 and determine which ones are weighted distribution problems. Solve those which are numerical.

12. (Unsolved.) Does there exist a transformation of variables and constants that will convert the first type of system considered by Markowitz § 21-3-(1), (2) to his second type § 21-3-(5)?

REFERENCES

Eisemann, 1964-2
Eisemann and Lourie, 1959-1
Ferguson and Dantzig, 1954-1, 1956-1
Hadley, 1962-2

Jewell, 1960-1
Kantorovich, 1939-1
Markowitz, 1954-2
(See also references Chapter 14)

CHAPTER 22

PROGRAMS WITH VARIABLE COEFFICIENTS

22-1. WOLFE'S GENERALIZED PROGRAM[1]

In this chapter, we will consider problems in which there is some freedom in the choice of coefficients of an activity. Such problems arise when a system is being designed or when the input and output characteristics of a process depend on one or more parameters, such as temperature, which can be regulated.

First, a matter of notation; it will be convenient to consider the linear programming problem in vector form: Find $x_j \geq 0$ for $j \neq 0$ and Max x_0 satisfying

$$(1) \qquad P_0 x_0 + P_1 x_1 + P_2 x_2 + \ldots + P_n x_n = Q$$

For example, if we had to find $x_j \geq 0$ and Min z satisfying

$$
(2) \qquad
\begin{aligned}
x_1 + x_2 - 4x_3 + 2x_4 &= 5 \\
-x_1 + x_2 - x_3 + 3x_4 &= 1 \\
6x_1 + 4x_2 + x_3 - 2x_4 &= z
\end{aligned}
$$

we would set $z = -x_0$, obtaining

$$(3) \qquad \begin{bmatrix} 0 \\ 0 \\ 1 \end{bmatrix} x_0 + \begin{bmatrix} 1 \\ -1 \\ 6 \end{bmatrix} x_1 + \begin{bmatrix} 1 \\ 1 \\ 4 \end{bmatrix} x_2 + \begin{bmatrix} -4 \\ -1 \\ +1 \end{bmatrix} x_3 + \begin{bmatrix} 2 \\ 3 \\ -2 \end{bmatrix} x_4 = \begin{bmatrix} 5 \\ 1 \\ 0 \end{bmatrix}$$

It will also be convenient to redefine the simplex multipliers $\pi = (\pi_1, \pi_2, \ldots, \pi_m, \pi_{m+1})$, so that

$$(4) \qquad \begin{aligned} \pi P_j &= 0 \qquad \text{if } x_j \neq x_0 \text{ is a basic variable} \\ \pi P_0 &= 1 \end{aligned}$$

The last of these multipliers, π_{m+1}, is always 1 because $P_0 = U_{m+1}$ is a unit

---

[1] The approach to this class of problems was first developed in the joint work of Philip Wolfe and the author on a *decomposition principle* for large-scale programs (discussed in Chapter 23); because it was Wolfe who suggested that the procedure developed there could be formalized as a special case of a "Generalized Linear Program," we associate his name with it here [Dantzig and Wolfe, 1960-1; Gomory and Hu, 1960-1].

vector and x_0 is unrestricted in sign. Hence these multipliers would generate a modified cost equation $\Sigma \bar{c}_j x_j$, where (referring to a standard linear program)

$$\bar{c}_j = \pi P_j = \sum_{i=1}^{m} \pi_i a_{ij} + 1 \cdot c_j$$

It is now evident, since we are adding the sum term to c_j instead of subtracting, that the multipliers $\pi_1, \pi_2, \ldots, \pi_m$ will have the opposite sign to those defined in § 9-2. As usual, in order for a basic feasible solution to be optimal $\bar{c}_j = \pi P_j \geq 0$ for all j.

DEFINITION: A *Generalized Linear Program* is a linear programming problem with variable coefficients as follows: *Find $x_j \geq 0$ for $j \neq 0$ and* Max x_0 *satisfying*

(5) $$P_0 x_0 + P_1 x_1 + \ldots + P_n x_n = Q$$

where each P_j for $j \neq 0$ may be freely chosen to be any $P_j \in C_j$, where each C_j is a convex set. By simple extension the fixed vectors in (5), P_0 and Q, may be replaced by any vectors P_0, Q drawn from convex sets C_0 and C_q. This is further discussed in the subsection on "Equivalent Formulations" at the end of this section. The convex sets we shall consider here are defined by systems of linear inequalities. However, the methods of Chapter 24 can be used to extend the results to general convex sets.

For example, (3) becomes a program with variable coefficients if we generalize it to the following form: Find $x_j \geq 0$ for $j \neq 0$, Max x_0 *satisfying*

(6) $$\begin{bmatrix} 0 \\ 0 \\ 1 \end{bmatrix} x_0 + \begin{bmatrix} 1 \\ -1 \\ 6 \end{bmatrix} x_1 + \begin{bmatrix} 1 \\ 1 \\ 4 \end{bmatrix} x_2 + \begin{bmatrix} -4 \\ -1 \\ 1 \end{bmatrix} x_3 + \begin{bmatrix} y_1 \\ y_2 \\ y_3 \end{bmatrix} x_4 = \begin{bmatrix} 5 \\ 1 \\ 0 \end{bmatrix}$$

where y_i may be chosen as any values satisfying

(7) $$y_1 + 2y_2 + 3y_3 = 2 \qquad\qquad (y_i \geq 0)$$

One may wonder whether a system such as (6), (7) is formally a linear programming system. However, if we set $y_1 x_4 = u_1$, $y_2 x_4 = u_2$, $y_3 x_4 = u_3$ and multiply (7) by x_4, it is easily seen that the system may be re-expressed linearly in x_j and u_i (see Problem 2). In general we have:

COMMENT: *A system* (5) *in which some column $P_t = (y_1, y_2, \ldots, y_m)$ must satisfy a system S_t of linear inequalities in variables y_i for $i = 1, 2, \ldots, m$, and auxiliary variables $y_{m+1}, \ldots, y_{m+k}$ independent of the rest of the system, can be replaced by a linear inequality system by multiplying the relations of S_t by $x_t \geq 0$ and substituting new variables $u_{it} = y_i x_t$.*

While the above remark permits us formally to expand the system to make it linear, this expansion does not necessarily lead to a linear program which is equivalent to the original system because it is possible for the linear program to have a solution such that $x_t = 0$ and $u_{it} \neq 0$ at the same time. For further discussion of this point, see Problem 2. Great advantage accrues by *not* using this approach. Using instead the variable coefficient concept, the general program is solved by a series of adjustments of the values of y_i obtained by solving an auxiliary program or *subprograms* in the y_i above. In effect, a large linear program is decomposed into smaller linear programs.

The Method Illustrated.

The working out of example {(6), (7)} will illustrate clearly the general procedure. Suppose we initiate the computation with the basic set of variables x_0, x_1, x_2. We wish to ascertain whether or not the basic feasible solution $x_0 = -24$, $x_1 = 2$, $x_2 = 3$, $x_3 = x_4 = 0$ is optimal for (6), which we will refer to as *a master program*. The simplex multipliers

$$(8) \qquad \pi = [-5, 1, 1]$$

are defined so that $\pi P_0 = 1$, $\pi P_1 = 0$, $\pi P_2 = 0$. Multiplying equations (6) on the left by π, we obtain

$$(9) \qquad x_0 + (\pi P_3)x_3 + (\pi P_4)x_4 = (\pi Q)$$

where

$$(10) \qquad \pi P_3 = 20, \qquad \pi Q = -24$$

$$(11) \qquad \pi P_4 = -5y_1 + y_2 + y_3$$

It is clear that the test for maximum x_0 is $\pi P_j \geq 0$ for all j. On the other hand, if $\pi P_4 < 0$, it is possible to find a better solution by increasing the value of x_4. Therefore, let us set $z_4 = \pi P_4$ and consider the auxiliary linear programming problem of finding $y_i \geq 0$, and Min z_4 satisfying

$$(12) \qquad y_1 + 2y_2 + 3y_3 = 2 \qquad\qquad (y_i \geq 0)$$

$$(13) \qquad -5y_1 + y_2 + y_3 = z_4 \,(\text{Min}) \qquad\qquad (z_4 = \pi P_4)$$

What we are doing is in keeping with the usual simplex procedure of bringing into the basis that column which prices out the least. The solution yielding minimal πP_4 is immediate, namely, $y_1 = 2$, $y_2 = 0$, $y_3 = 0$; $\pi P_4 = -10$.

We can now obtain an improved solution by introducing the column $(y_1' = 2, y_2' = 0, y_3' = 0)$ into the basis of the master program. However, we must allow for the possibility of revising later the values of y_i. We can do both by rewriting the problem in the form

$$(14) \qquad \begin{bmatrix} 0 \\ 0 \\ 1 \end{bmatrix} x_0 + \begin{bmatrix} 1 \\ -1 \\ 6 \end{bmatrix} x_1 + \begin{bmatrix} 1 \\ 1 \\ 4 \end{bmatrix} x_2 + \begin{bmatrix} -4 \\ -1 \\ 1 \end{bmatrix} x_3 + \begin{bmatrix} 2 \\ 0 \\ 0 \end{bmatrix} x_4' + \begin{bmatrix} y_1'' \\ y_2'' \\ y_3'' \end{bmatrix} x_4'' = \begin{bmatrix} 5 \\ 1 \\ 0 \end{bmatrix}$$

$$\qquad\qquad\qquad \text{(drop)}$$

$$\qquad\quad \bullet \qquad\quad \bullet \qquad\quad \bullet \qquad\qquad\qquad \star$$

where the y_i'' satisfy the same relations as the y_i:

$$（15） \qquad y_1'' + 2y_2'' + 3y_3'' = 2 \qquad\qquad (y_i'' \geq 0)$$

We shall refer to the column $\langle y_1'', y_2'', y_3'' \rangle$ as the *generic column*. It appears we have changed our original problem; they are equivalent, however. To see this we rewrite any solution to (14) back in the form (6) by setting $x_4 = x_4' + x_4''$ and letting the coefficients of x_4 be given by

$$（16） \qquad \begin{bmatrix} y_1 \\ y_2 \\ y_3 \end{bmatrix} = \begin{bmatrix} 2 \\ 0 \\ 0 \end{bmatrix} \frac{x_4'}{x_4' + x_4''} + \begin{bmatrix} y_1'' \\ y_2'' \\ y_3'' \end{bmatrix} \frac{x_4''}{x_4' + x_4''} \qquad (x_4' + x_4'' > 0)$$

The right-hand side is clearly a convex combination of two points lying in a convex set defined by (12); as a consequence the point (y_1, y_2, y_3) must lie in the convex set also. Conversely, to any solution of (12) we can associate a solution of (16), for example, set $x_4' = 0$; in this case $x_4 = x_4''$, $y_i = y_i''$.

When x_4' is introduced into the basic set of the master program, x_1 will be found to drop out. The new basic solution is $x_0 = -4$, $x_2 = 1$, $x_4' = 2$; $x_1 = x_3 = x_4'' = 0$. The corresponding simplex multipliers are

$$（17） \qquad \pi = [0, -4, 1]$$

where π is defined by (4), so that $\pi P_0 = 1$, $\pi P_2 = 0$, $\pi P_4' = 0$. To test for maximum x_0 we form

$$（18） \qquad \begin{aligned} \pi P_1 &= 10 \\ \pi P_3 &= 5 \\ \pi P_4'' &= -4y_2'' + y_3'' \end{aligned}$$

The only possibility for increasing values of x_0 is to find values of y_i'' so that $\pi P_4'' < 0$. Accordingly, we consider the new subprogram

$$（19） \qquad \begin{aligned} y_1'' + 2y_2'' + 3y_3'' &= 2 \qquad\qquad (y_i'' \geq 0) \\ -4y_2'' + y_3'' &= \pi P_4'' \ (\text{Min}) \end{aligned}$$

This yields $y_1'' = 0$, $y_2'' = 1$, $y_3'' = 0$ and $\pi P_4 = -4$.

Our augmented master problem now becomes

(20)

$$\begin{bmatrix} 0 \\ 0 \\ 1 \end{bmatrix} x_0 + \begin{bmatrix} 1 \\ -1 \\ 6 \end{bmatrix} x_1 + \begin{bmatrix} 1 \\ 1 \\ 4 \end{bmatrix} x_2 + \begin{bmatrix} -4 \\ -1 \\ 1 \end{bmatrix} x_3 + \begin{bmatrix} 2 \\ 0 \\ 0 \end{bmatrix} x_4' + \begin{bmatrix} 0 \\ 1 \\ 0 \end{bmatrix} x_4'' + \begin{bmatrix} y_1''' \\ y_2''' \\ y_3''' \end{bmatrix} x_4''' = \begin{bmatrix} 5 \\ 1 \\ 0 \end{bmatrix}$$

$\bullet \qquad\qquad \underset{\text{drop}}{\bullet} \qquad\qquad\qquad \bullet \qquad \star$

where again we have allowed for the possibility that we may again revise the values of y_i by the introduction of the "generic" column y_i''' and variable x_4'''.

Introducing x_4'' into the basic set, x_2 drops out and the new basic solution is $x_0 = 0$, $x_4' = \frac{5}{2}$, $x_4'' = 1$; $x_1 = x_2 = x_3 = 0$; the new simplex multipliers

$$(21) \qquad\qquad \pi = [0,\, 0,\, 1]$$

are defined by $\pi P_0 = 1$, $\pi P_4' = 0$, $\pi P_4'' = 0$. We now have

$$\pi P_1 = 6$$
$$(22) \qquad\qquad \pi P_2 = 4$$
$$\pi P_3 = 1$$
$$\pi P_4''' = y_3'''$$

The auxiliary linear program is: Find y_i''' and Min $\pi P_4'''$ satisfying

$$(23) \qquad\qquad y_1''' + 2y_2''' + 3y_3''' = 2 \qquad\qquad (y_i''' \geq 0)$$
$$y_3''' = \pi P_4''' \text{ (Min)}$$

But this yields as one optimal solution $y_1''' = 2$, $y_2''' = 0$, and $y_3''' = \text{Min } \pi P_4''' = 0$. Thus, at this stage, no improved solution to (20) can be found modifying the values of y_i. Since all other $\pi P_j \geq 0$ the basic solution is optimal.

EXERCISE: From the optimal solution to (20), (23) derive the optimal solution to (6), (7).

It would appear that this process, iterated many times, could expand the problem by an indefinite number of columns. Such is not the case, however, since no more of these added columns need be retained than are currently used in the basis. We shall show that any column which drops out of the basis may be "dropped" because it is included in the convex sets defining the generic columns associated with the master program and these convex sets are each defined by a system of linear inequalities. We now formalize some of the terms and concepts used so far.

DEFINITION: *A restricted master program* (at the kth stage of the algorithm) consists of variables $x_j^{(k)}$ with specified columns of coefficients $P_j^{(k)}$ drawn from the convex sets C_j. Its optimal solution determines values for the simplex multipliers, $\pi = \pi^0$, for use in the subprograms.

DEFINITION: The jth *subprogram* is: Find $P_j \in C_j$ which minimizes the linear form, $\pi^0 P_j$ (in the unknown components of P_j), where $\pi = \pi^0$ is known. Its optimal solution $P_j = P_j^*$ generates an additional specified column of coefficients P_j^* for the next restricted master program.

THEOREM 1: *If terms $\sum_1^n P_j x_j$ are added to a restricted master program, where the "generic columns," P_j, are general elements of convex sets C_j, the new problem is equivalent to the original generalized linear program.*

The General Theory for Polyhedral C_j.

We assume here that each convex set C_j is polyhedral, i.e., defined by a system of linear inequalities. In this case a general P_j can be represented by a convex linear combination of a *finite set of extreme points* of C_j plus a nonnegative linear combination of a *finite set of homogeneous solutions* (in case C_j is unbounded).

DEFINITION: By a *homogeneous solution* $\bar{P}_j$ is meant one with the property that if $P_j \in C_j$, then $P_j + k\bar{P}_j \in C_j$ for all $k \geq 0$.

THEOREM 2: *A solution* (x_j^*, P_j^*) *for* $j = 0, 1, 2, \ldots, n$, *is optimal if there exists a* π, *such that* $\pi P_0 = 1$, $\pi P_j \geq 0$ *for all* $P_j \in C_j$ *and* $\pi P_j^* = 0$ *for all* j *for which* $x_j^* > 0$, $j \neq 0$.

THEOREM 3: *Only a finite number of iterations of the simplex algorithm is required if each basic feasible solution is improved by introducing into the basis either an extreme point* $P_j^* \in C_j$ *chosen so that*

$$(24) \qquad \pi P_j^* = \operatorname*{Min}_{P_j \in C_j} \pi P_j < 0 \qquad\qquad (j = 1, 2, \ldots, n)$$

where π *are the simplex multipliers of the basis or by introducing into the basis any homogeneous solution* $\bar{P}_j^*$ *from a finite set such that* $\pi \bar{P}_j^* < 0$.

PROOF: From our earlier remarks, Theorem 2 is obvious. With regard to Theorem 3, finiteness of the algorithm is also obvious if we can show that columns of any basis must be drawn from a finite class. Since C_j is a convex set defined by a set of inequalities, each P_j^* is obtained by solving a linear program which minimizes the linear form πP_j where π is fixed and the components of P_j are unknown.

If C_j is bounded, P_j^* will be *one of a finite number of basic solutions*. If C_j is unbounded, then it may happen that πP_j has no lower bound. In this case, on some iteration of the simplex method a homogeneous solution will be obtained (see Chapter 6, Problem 19). In the notation of the standard simplex method as applied to the canonical form for the subproblem for C_j, on some iteration a column will be found such that all coefficients, say $\bar{a}_{is}$, will be nonpositive and the relative cost factor $\bar{c}_s < 0$. In this case, letting y_{j_i} represent the ith basic variable of the subproblem, the set of values $y_{j_i} = -\bar{a}_{is} \geq 0$, $y_s = 1$, and all other $y_i = 0$ forms a homogeneous solution $\bar{P}_j$ for C_j with the requisite property; namely $\bar{c}_s = \pi \bar{P}_j \leq 0$, where π is the set of simplex multipliers for the basis of the master program. Since the number of canonical forms for the various subprograms (omitting the objective equation) is finite, the number of columns with the property $\bar{a}_{is} \leq 0$ for all i is finite. Hence the set of $\bar{P}_j$ is also finite.

Equivalent Formulations.

It was assumed in (5) that P_0 and Q were fixed vectors. However, if it is desired to have Q freely chosen from a convex set C_q, it is possible to do so by considering the system

$$(25) \qquad P_0 x_0 + P_1 x_1 + \ldots + P_n x_n - Q x_{n+1} = 0$$
$$x_{n+1} = 1$$

EXERCISE: Extend the results so that P_0 can be drawn from a convex set C_0.

EXERCISE: Reduce the following problem to a generalized linear program: Find vectors $P_j \in C_j$, $Q \in C_q$ such that

$$(26) \qquad P_1 + P_2 + \ldots + P_n = Q$$

EXERCISE: Suppose in place of condition (7), we have $y_1^2 + y_2^2 + y_3^2 \leq 1$. Show that this is a generalized linear program. Apply methods of this section and contrast with the polyhedral case.

Convex Programs. (See Chapter 24.)

Kuhn and Tucker [1950-2] considered a broad class of problems of the form: Find $x = (x_1, x_2, \ldots, x_n)$ and Min z satisfying

$$(27) \qquad G_i(x) \leq 0 \qquad\qquad (i = 1, 2, \ldots, m)$$
$$G_0(x) = z \text{ (Min)}$$

where $G_i(x)$ are convex functions and x is restricted to a convex set R.

We replace this by the equivalent problem: Find λ, λ_i, y_i satisfying

$$(28) \qquad
\begin{aligned}
\lambda &= 1 \qquad (\lambda_1 \geq 0, \lambda_2 \geq 0, \ldots, \lambda_m \geq 0) \\
y_1 \lambda + \lambda_1 &= 0 \\
y_2 \lambda + \lambda_2 &= 0 \\
&\vdots \\
y_m \lambda + \lambda_m &= 0 \\
y_0 \lambda &= z \text{ (Min)}
\end{aligned}$$

where $y_i \geq G_i(x)$ for some $x \in R$. To show that the set of possible $y = (y_0, y_1, \ldots, y_m)$ forms a convex set, C_y, suppose $y_i' \geq G_i(x')$, $y_i'' \geq G_i(x'')$, and let $\lambda + \mu = 1$ and $\lambda \geq 0$, $\mu \geq 0$. Then

$$(29) \qquad y_i = \lambda y_i' + \mu y_i'' \geq \lambda G_i(x') + \mu G_i(x'') \geq G_i(\lambda x' + \mu x'')$$

where $(\lambda x' + \mu x'') \in R$ because R is convex. The methods of Chapter 24 can be used to extend the results to solve in general this essentially *one variable* linear program with coefficients generated by a set of general convex functions of a point x in n dimensions.

EXERCISE: Prove that if $y_i^o \geq G_i(x^o)$ solves the linear program with $\lambda = \lambda^o$, $\lambda_i = \lambda_i^o$, then $y_i^* = G_i(x^o)$ also solves the program and $G_0(x^o) \leq y_0^o$.

EXERCISE: Suppose a feasible solution to (28) exists with $y = y^o$, where y^o is a convex combination of several y^k such that for each k, $y_i^k \geq G_i(x^k)$, and suppose that feasible solutions may or may not exist for these y^k, prove there exists an x^o such that $y_i^o \geq G_i(x^o)$ where $y^o = (1, y_1^o, \ldots, y_m^o, y_0^o)$.

EXERCISE: Prove that the simplex multipliers π_i^0 of the optimal solution of each master program for (28) are nonnegative. Show that the subprogram can be stated: Find $x \in R$ such that $F(x)$ is minimum where

$$F(x) = \sum \pi_i^0 G_i(x)$$

Prove that $F(x)$ is convex. Relate this to the method of Lagrange multipliers, § 6-5.

22-2. NOTES ON SPECIAL CASES

The Case of One Control Parameter T.

Many industrial processes have a continuous spectrum of alternative activities depending on the settings of certain controls such as temperature (T), pressure (P), recycle ratio (R), etc. This is particularly true in refinery applications where, to keep things simple, only one standard way to operate the equipment is often assumed in any one problem; or sometimes a few typical sets of values are selected that "span" the range of possibilities.

Suppose there is one *control* T, whose range of settings is $T_1 \leq T \leq T_2$; let $j = 1$ be a single *activity* whose technological coefficients depend on T.

Its coefficients for $T = T_1$ and $T = T_2$ and general T are

(1)

T_1	T_2	T
$a_{11}^{(1)}$	$a_{11}^{(2)}$	y_1
$a_{21}^{(1)}$	$a_{21}^{(2)}$	y_2
.	.	.
.	.	.
.	.	.
$a_{m1}^{(1)}$	$a_{m1}^{(2)}$	y_m
$c_1^{(1)}$	$c_1^{(2)}$	y_{m+1}

where $y_i = y_i(T)$ for $i = 1, 2, \ldots, m, m + 1$ are functions of T.

In many applications a linear interpolation between the first two columns of coefficients is a satisfactory approximation for a general T. If this is the case, the equivalent linear programming problem becomes:

(2)
$$a_{11}^{(1)}x_{11} + a_{11}^{(2)}x_{21} + a_{12}x_2 + \ldots + a_{1n}x_n = b_1$$
$$a_{21}^{(1)}x_{11} + a_{21}^{(2)}x_{21} + a_{22}x_2 + \ldots + a_{2n}x_n = b_2$$
$$\cdots\cdots\cdots\cdots\cdots\cdots\cdots\cdots\cdots\cdots\cdots\cdots\cdots$$
$$a_{m1}^{(1)}x_{11} + a_{m1}^{(2)}x_{21} + a_{m2}x_2 + \ldots + a_{mn}x_n = b_m$$
$$c_1^{(1)}x_{11} + c_1^{(2)}x_{21} + c_2x_2 + \ldots + c_nx_n = z$$

where $x_1 = x_{11} + x_{21}$ is the level of the first activity. It is clear we are assuming that the variable coefficients y_i are given by the linear interpolation (3), where $\lambda_1 = x_{11}/x_1$ corresponds to some temperature setting T.

$$\begin{aligned}
\lambda_1 + \lambda_2 &= 1, \\
\lambda_1 a_{i1}^{(1)} + \lambda_2 a_{i1}^{(2)} &= y_i \qquad (\lambda_i \geq 0\,;\, i = 1, 2, \ldots, m) \\
\lambda_1 c_1^{(1)} + \lambda_2 c_1^{(2)} &= y_{m+1}
\end{aligned}$$

(3)

In particular, if the temperature setting T has also the same linear interpolation, then

(4)
$$\frac{x_{11} T_1 + x_{21} T_2}{x_{11} + x_{21}} = T$$

The set of relations (3) defines a convex set of possible values for $(y_1, y_2, \ldots, y_m)$. The method of § 22-1 is therefore applicable. If π is the set of multipliers associated with a basis and $\bar{c}_1^{(1)} = c_1^{(1)} - \Sigma \pi_i a_{i1}^{(1)}$ and $\bar{c}_1^{(2)} = c_1^{(2)} - \Sigma \pi_i a_{i1}^{(2)}$, then the subprogram reduces to

$$\begin{aligned}
\lambda_1 + \lambda_2 &= 1 \qquad\qquad\qquad (\lambda_i \geq 0) \\
\bar{c}_1^{(1)} \lambda_1 + \bar{c}_1^{(2)} \lambda_2 &= \pi P_1 \;(\text{Min})
\end{aligned}$$

The extreme point solutions for (λ_1, λ_2) are either $(1, 0)$ or $(0, 1)$. Thus either the first or the second column of (2) would be introduced into the basis. Because of this small number of possible extreme points of the subprogram (two in this case), it does not pay to use the method of § 22-1.

In order to interpolate between several possible values of T, say $T = T_1$, $T_2, \ldots, T_k$, let us consider the linear program

(5)
$$a_{11}^{(1)} x_{11} + a_{11}^{(2)} x_{21} + \ldots + a_{11}^{(k)} x_{k1} + \sum_{2}^{n} a_{1j} x_j = b_1$$

$$a_{21}^{(1)} x_{11} + a_{21}^{(2)} x_{21} + \ldots + a_{21}^{(k)} x_{k1} + \sum_{2}^{n} a_{2j} x_j = b_2$$

$$\cdots\cdots\cdots\cdots\cdots\cdots\cdots\cdots\cdots\cdots\cdots\cdots\cdots\cdots$$

$$a_{m1}^{(1)} x_{11} + a_{m1}^{(2)} x_{21} + \ldots + a_{m1}^{(k)} x_{k1} + \sum_{2}^{n} a_{mj} x_j = b_m$$

$$c_1^{(1)} x_{11} + c_1^{(2)} x_{21} + \ldots + c_1^{(k)} x_{k1} + \sum_{2}^{n} c_j x_j = z$$

where $a_{i1}^{(r)}$ is the value of $y_i = y_i(T)$ for $T = T_r$, $r = 1, 2, \ldots, k$. In general, letting

(6)
$$x_1 = x_{11} + x_{21} + \ldots + x_{k1}$$

it is clear that we are *assuming* the linear interpolations

(7)
$$\frac{x_{11}}{x_1} a_{i1}^{(1)} + \frac{x_{21}}{x_1} a_{i1}^{(2)} + \ldots + \frac{x_{k1}}{x_1} a_{i1}^{(k)} = y_i$$

and a similar expression for c_1.

[441]

However, in some applications *a linear interpolation between two columns of coefficients is satisfactory, providing the range of their T values is sufficiently small. If not, then it is necessary to break up the range into several parts* $T_1 \leq T_2 \ldots \leq T_r \leq \ldots \leq T_k$, so that a linear interpolation between the vectors $[y_1(T), y_2(T), \ldots, y_{m+1}(T)]$ for adjacent pairs $T = T_i$ and $T = T_{i+1}$ is an acceptable approximation. For this situation, an optimal solution to system (5) is acceptable only if the positive x_{ri} occur in adjacent pairs as underlined in (8):

$$(8) \quad \text{either} \quad (a) \quad x_{11} \geq 0, \ x_{21} \geq 0, \ x_{31} = 0, \ x_{41} = 0, \ldots$$

$$\text{or} \quad (b) \quad x_{11} = 0, \ x_{21} \geq 0, \ x_{31} \geq 0, \ x_{41} = 0, \ldots$$

$$\text{or} \quad (c) \quad x_{11} = 0, \ x_{21} = 0, \ x_{31} \geq 0, \ x_{41} \geq 0, \ldots$$

$$\cdot \ \cdot$$

The following results can be established: (a) If the coefficients y_i except y_{m+1} are linear in T and y_{m+1} is a strictly convex function of T, then (8) will hold. (b) Let T' be some strictly monotonic function of the control parameter T; if the coefficients y_i, $i \neq m + 1$, are linear functions of T' and y_{m+1} is a strictly convex function of T', then (8) must hold. (c) If y_{m+1} is just a convex (but not necessarily strictly convex) function of T', then (8) need not hold, but if not, then the *average* values a_{i1} and c_{i1} obtained at the minimum are the coefficients y_i corresponding to some fixed T' and the optimum solution to (5) is exact—not an approximation to the original nonlinear problem. (d) Suppose the system has the property that the optimal prices $\pi_i \leq 0$ for some subset of the items (where π_i are defined so that $\Sigma a_{ij}\pi_i = c_i$ for basic x_i); suppose that y_i depend on T' only for these items and these are convex functions of T', then either property (8) holds for an optimum solution or the average solution is exact for some fixed T'.

Interpreting a Mixed Solution.

An interesting question arises if (8) does not hold and moreover any adjustment of the solution so that it does hold only increases the value of z. In this situation we have no physical interpretation of the solution in the sense there are values x_1 given by (6) and a_{i1}, c_1 given by (7) which correspond to some value of T. This may or may not be acceptable. If the activity is such that T is not an adjustable control, but rather a design characteristic that once settled for some value cannot be changed, then the answer is, of course, not acceptable. (We shall discuss what to do in this case in a moment.)

If T is easily adjustable, there may be an "out." Let us suppose the optimal solution yields $x_{11} > 0$, $x_{12} = x_{13} = 0$, $x_{14} > 0$. We may interpret this to mean that it pays to use more than one setting for T. Thus, if the activity is actually performed with several pieces of equipment, some can be set for the value $T = T_1$ and the others for $T = T_4$. Or, if only one piece of equipment is used, it may be set part of the time at T_1 and the rest of the time at T_4.

If Only One Value of T Is Acceptable.

This case can be treated by limiting the number of alternative T values. For example, suppose a basic solution is at hand using a fixed value $T = T_r$. There are no alternative columns for the moment corresponding to other values of T. It is now desired to see if the solution can be improved by changing the value of T. Accordingly, new columns are introduced corresponding to adjacent values of T, say T_{r-1} and T_{r+1}, these being selected sufficiently close that linear interpolation of their a_{i1} values is acceptable. These columns are then priced out; and, if it pays to do so, one of the alternative T columns is introduced. If, as a result, T_r is replaced in the basis by, say T_{r+1}, then, T_{r+2} is added as a possible alternative column and T_{r-1} is dropped from consideration in the next iteration. The new solution is then priced out on the added column and on all $P_j, j = 2, \ldots, n$, since the shift in T may make it profitable to make other choices for the basic variables. On the other hand if the introduction of the alternative column T_{r+1} causes not the T_r column, but some other column to drop, then a T_{r+2} column is added as a possible alternative and the T_{r-1} column is retained and both are priced out along with the other columns; if T_{r+2} becomes a candidate by the pricing out procedure, it is allowed to enter the basis only if it replaces T_r, if not it is dropped as a candidate in the next iteration; similarly T_{r-1} is allowed to be a candidate only if it replaces T_{r+1}.

This procedure will eventually arrive at a value of $T = T_r^*$, such that the alternatives T_{r-1}^* or T_{r+1}^* result in no admissible improvement, or it will eventually arrive at an interpolation between two T values T_r, T_{r+1}. This does not mean that this T is best; all that has been found is a T that is *locally* best. If there is any suspicion that there may be other local optima that are superior, it is necessary to revise the procedure so as to drive T in turn through all values $T = T_1$, T_2, $\ldots$, T_k. If there are other local optima superior to $T = T_r$, their z values must lie between the z value for $T = T_r$ and the z value obtained by allowing free choice among all alternative T_r columns. From a practical point of view, it might be best to allow unrestricted choice initially. If the solution satisfies (8), then of course the solution admits physical interpretation and is optimal. If not, it is often feasible to use the average T value

$$(9) \qquad T = \sum_r x_{r1} T_r / x_1$$

as a starting value for the above procedure. For example, in gasoline blending problems there is a nonlinear "octane change" as a function of the amount

T of tetraethyl lead added to a mixture of blending stocks whose proportions are also to be determined. While the structure of such a problem is more complex than that described here, a linear programming solution can arise for which there is no physical interpretation. This is due to a lack of convexity of a certain octane "response surface." However, it is so slight that the approximation (9) gives excellent results and no further iterations are used in practice [Kawaratani, Ullman, and Dantzig, 1960-1].

The Case of Several Independent Control Parameters, Each Affecting a Different Activity.

While the discussion so far has centered about one control T and one activity $j = 1$, it should be noted that, if there were several independent control parameters, each affecting a different activity, the values of all the parameters could be determined *simultaneously* by splitting up each such activity column into parts corresponding to the different control settings.

The Case of Several Control Parameters Applying to the Same Activity.

For the case of only two control parameters whose range is $T_1 \leq T \leq T_2$ and $S_1 \leq S \leq S_2$, one can introduce the four extreme cases (T_1, S_1), (T_1, S_2), (T_2, S_1) and (T_2, S_2) as four alternative columns. Thus in (5) the coefficients of x_{11} could be interpreted as those obtained by setting $(T, S) = (T_1, S_1)$, etc. Again, if the resulting linear interpolations given by (6) and (7) are acceptable, the problem may be solved in this manner. Nothing prevents the introduction of any number of alternative columns corresponding to a grid of (T_i, S_j) values in order to obtain a more accurate approximation.

(10)

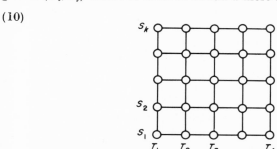

Again the only difficulty that can arise is one of physical interpretation if the optimal solution chooses non-adjacent grid points with positive weights.

When there are more than two control parameters associated with an activity, it is recommended that variables be used that measure the *change in the value of the parameters*. To illustrate, let the coordinates of P_1, the first activity, be some function of the three control parameters, R, S, T (for each component of the vector P_1) which we denote by $P_1 = P_1(R, S, T)$. Let us suppose that for $(R, S, T) = (R_0, S_0, T_0)$ a solution to the linear programming problem is known, and that the linear approximation,

(11) $P_1(R_0 + \Delta R, S_0 + \Delta S, T_0 + \Delta T)$
$$\doteq P_1^o + \Delta R \cdot E^o + \Delta S \cdot F^o + \Delta T \cdot G^o$$

where P_1^o, E^o, F^o, G^o are fixed vectors, is acceptable within the ranges

(12) $-\alpha_1' \leq \Delta R \leq \alpha_1, \quad -\alpha_2' \leq \Delta S \leq \alpha_2, \quad -\alpha_3' \leq \Delta T \leq \alpha_3$

This formulation permits immediate and easy solution via the methods of § 22-1 and the upper bounding methods of § 18-1.

Let π be the simplex multipliers associated with the known basis of the master program. By Theorem 3, § 22-1, we set up the subprogram: Minimize $\pi P_1 = \pi P_1^o + \Delta R \pi E^o + \Delta S \pi F^o + \Delta T \pi G^o$ subject to the constraints (12). This subprogram divides into three independent linear programs:

$$-\alpha_1' \leq \Delta R \leq \alpha_1 \qquad (\pi E^o)\Delta R = z_R(\text{Min})$$
$$-\alpha_2' \leq \Delta S \leq \alpha_2 \qquad (\pi F^o)\Delta S = z_S (\text{Min})$$
$$-\alpha_3' \leq \Delta T \leq \alpha_3 \qquad (\pi G^o)\Delta T = z_T (\text{Min})$$

These are readily solved; for example, setting $\bar{e} = \pi E^0$, the solution for ΔR is $\Delta R = -\alpha_1'$, 0, or α_1 according as $\bar{e} > 0$, $\bar{e} = 0$, or $\bar{e} < 0$. Substituting these values into (11) yields a new column, P_1', to be introduced into the basis in the next iteration. After that iteration, expression (11) may be retained for further iterations, or it may be replaced by a new linear approximation about the new values of R, S, and T determined by the iteration. If, however, expression (11) is changed while P_1^o vector is still in the basis, we may encounter difficulties in physical interpretation of the results.

As an alternative to the subprogram of § 22-1, an equivalent linear program can be obtained by multiplying all expressions in (11) and (12) through by x_1 and introducing new variables $x_1\Delta R = x_{11}$, $x_1\Delta S = x_{21}$, $x_{11}\Delta S = x_{31}$. This yields, setting $P_1 = \langle a_{11}, a_{12}, \ldots, a_{1m}, c_1 \rangle$,

(13) $a_{i1}x_1 = a_{i1}^o x_1 + e_{i1}x_{11} + f_{i1}x_{21} + g_{i1}x_{31}$
$$-\alpha_1'x_1 \leq x_{11} \leq \alpha_1 x_1, \quad -\alpha_2'x_1 \leq x_{21} \leq \alpha_2 x_1, \quad -\alpha_3'x_1 \leq x_{31} \leq \alpha_3 x_1$$

Thus the final linear programming problem requiring solution becomes

(14) $a_{11}^o x_1 + e_{11} x_{11} + f_{11} x_{21} + g_{11} x_{31} + (a_{12} x_2 + \ldots + a_{1n} x_n) = b_1$
$a_{21}^o x_1 + e_{21} x_{11} + f_{21} x_{21} + g_{21} x_{31} + (a_{22} x_2 + \ldots + a_{2n} x_n) = b_2$
$$\cdots \cdots \cdots \cdots \cdots \cdots \cdots \cdots \cdots$$
$a_{m1}^o x_1 + e_{m1} x_{11} + f_{m1} x_{21} + g_{m1} x_{31} + (a_{m2} x_2 + \ldots + a_{mn} x_n) = b_m$
$c_1^o x_1 + e x_{11} + f x_{21} + g x_{31} + (c_2 x_2 + \ldots + c_n x_n) = z \text{ (Min)}$

where $x_j \geq 0$, and x_{r1} and x_1 are subject to (13).

22-3. PROBLEMS

1. *Review:* Extend the theory of § 22-1 to cover the case where C_0 and C_q are general convex sets instead of convex sets each consisting of one fixed vector.

2. (a) In system § 22-1-(6) and (7), replace each $y_i x_4$ by u_i and reduce to a linear inequality system and solve numerically. Can this solution be used to solve the original system?

   (b) Review § 22-1, Comment, in general. Suppose a solution is obtained for the new system with $x_t = 0$; show that $y_i x_t \neq 0$ may be possible. Construct an example where this is the case.

   (c) Show that the linear program is equivalent to the original generalized program for the system (6) and (7).

   (d) Show in general that the linear program is equivalent to the original generalized program if the linear program implies a relation $\Sigma a_i u_i \leq a_0 x_t$ with positive a_i, where $u_i = y_i x_t$.

   (e) Consider the general problem of the existence of $a_i > 0$ such that $\Sigma a_i u_i \leq a_0 x_t$ for all $x_t \geq 0$ and $u_i \geq 0$ satisfying a linear inequality system $(x, u)D \geq d$. Set up a linear program for finding such a_i if they exist.

   Hint: Because of homogeneity, let $a_i = v_i + 1$ where $v_i \geq 0$. Then the problem is equivalent to finding u_i, x_j, and v_i such that

$$
\begin{array}{c|c}
x \geq 0, \ u \geq 0 & v_i \geq 0 \\
(x, u)D \geq d & v_t = 1 \\
\Sigma u_i - x_t = \bar{x}_t &
\end{array}
$$

$$
\theta = \min_v \max_{x|v} \left[\sum v_i u_i - v_0 x_t + v_t \bar{x}_t \right]
$$

   If $\theta \leq 0$, then $a_i > 0$ exists. Use Problem 2 of Chapter 13 to complete this discussion.

3. Complete the exercises given in § 22-1.

4. Simplify (13) of § 22-2 by substituting $\bar{x}$:

$$
\bar{x}_{r1} = x_{r1} + \alpha'_r x_1 \qquad\qquad (r = 1, 2, 3)
$$

5. (Unsolved.) Develop a theory for the case of one control parameter affecting simultaneously several activities.

6. (Unsolved.) In connection with (d) following § 22-2-(8), devise a procedure for converting k given functions, $F_i(T)$, to convex functions of a parameter T' where T' is a monotonic function of T, providing such a conversion is possible. (See Problem 7.)

7. Formulate Problem 6 as a linear program if the k given functions are defined for discrete T_i and it is desired to find increasing T'_i corresponding

to increasing T_i such that the broken line fit through the discrete points $[T_i', F(T_i)]$ is a convex function of T'.

8. Establish the assertions (a), (b), (c), (d) following § 22-2-(8).

REFERENCES

Dantzig, 1957-3, 1960-1, 1963-1, 1964-2
Dantzig and Van Slyke, 1964-1
Dantzig and Wolfe, 1961-1
Ford and Fulkerson, 1958-1

Hu, 1964-1, 1963-1
Gomory and Hu, 1960-1, 2
Kawaratani, Ullman and Dantzig, 1960-1
Kuhn and Tucker, 1950-2

CHAPTER 23

A DECOMPOSITION PRINCIPLE FOR LINEAR PROGRAMS

23-1. THE GENERAL PRINCIPLE

To introduce a typical situation that suggests the application of the decomposition principle, consider the problem facing a manager of a plant with two almost independent shops. Within each shop, there are many constraints which are unaffected by the activities of the other shop, but there are a few constraints and a common objective that tie the two shops together. The manager's problem may be formulated in linear programming terms as follows: Find $X \geq 0$, $Y \geq 0$, and Max x_0 satisfying

$$(1) \qquad \begin{aligned} A_1 X &= b_1 \\ A_2 Y &= b_2 \\ P_0 x_0 + \bar{A}_1 X + \bar{A}_2 Y &= \bar{b} \end{aligned}$$

We are using an extension of the notation set up at the beginning of Chapter 22. X is the vector of activity levels in the first shop; Y, that in the second. The first line of (1) expresses the constraints which involve directly only the first shop; the second line does the same for the second shop; the last line expresses the objective function and those constraints which bind together the shops.

On looking at (1), the manager feels that the size of the problem has gotten out of hand. Both A_1 and A_2 are moderately large, and together they make a problem that exceeds the capacity of available computers. "But what I really have," reflects the manager, "is not this *one* big problem but *two* moderate sized ones, one for each shop. All I need is a way to break the problem into two parts and still take account of their interconnections."

In this chapter we will follow through on the manager's hunch by developing a technique which decomposes linear programs similar to (1) into

(a) *subprograms corresponding to its almost independent parts, and*
(b) *a master program which ties together the subprograms.*

The price paid for this decomposition is that the master program and the subprogram may have to be solved several times. First the master program is solved, and from its solution, objective functions are generated for each of the subprograms. Then these are solved, and from their solution new columns are generated to be added to the master program. The process is

[448]

then repeated until, after a finite number of cycles, an optimality test is passed.[1] In the next section we will show how this technique can be applied to certain problems arising in dynamic systems, and in the last section it will be used to show how central planning can be accomplished without complete information at the center.

For our discussion it will be convenient to think of problem (1) in the following form: Solve the linear program

$$(2) \qquad P_0 x_0 + \bar{A}_1 X + \bar{A}_2 Y = \bar{b}$$

subject to the additional constraints

$$(3) \qquad \begin{aligned} \mathscr{L}_1 &: \quad A_1 X = b_1 & (X \geq 0) \\ \mathscr{L}_2 &: \quad A_2 Y = b_2 & (Y \geq 0) \end{aligned}$$

The A_i, $\bar{A}_i$ are, of course, matrices; P_0, $\bar{b}$, and b_i are vectors.

It will simplify the discussion to assume the feasible sets for $\mathscr{L}_1$ and $\mathscr{L}_2$ to be bounded convexes and to indicate later the minor modifications in the formulas needed to take care of the unbounded case. *Under this assumption,* any $X \geq 0$ solving $A_1 X = b_1$ can be represented by a convex combination of the *extreme points* of the set of feasible solutions of $\mathscr{L}_1$. Since the set of different basic feasible solutions $X = X_1$, $X = X_2$, . . ., $X = X_K$ defines the *finite* set of extreme points, we can represent any solution X by

$$(4) \qquad X = \sum_1^K \lambda_i X_i \qquad \left(\sum_1^K \lambda_i = 1; \lambda_i \geq 0 \right)$$

Conversely, any X represented by (4) is feasible for $\mathscr{L}_1$. Similarly, any $Y \geq 0$ solving $A_2 Y = b_2$ can be represented by

$$(5) \qquad Y = \sum_1^L \mu_j Y_j \qquad \left(\sum_1^L \mu_j = 1; \mu_j \geq 0 \right)$$

where Y_1, Y_2, . . ., Y_L are the finite set of basic feasible solutions of $\mathscr{L}_2$. Hence, any solution X and Y solving (1) can be re-expressed in terms of λ_i, μ_j; thus

$$(6) \qquad \left\lbrace \begin{aligned} & P_0 x_0 + \sum_1^K \lambda_i (\bar{A}_1 X_i) + \sum_1^L \mu_j (\bar{A}_2 Y_j) = \bar{b} \quad (\lambda_i \geq 0; \mu_j \geq 0) \\ & \sum_1^K \lambda_i \qquad\qquad\qquad\qquad\qquad = 1 \\ & \qquad\qquad \sum_1^L \mu_j \qquad\qquad\qquad = 1 \end{aligned} \right.$$

[1] Historically, it was this special case that first gave rise to the more general concept of a generalized linear program developed in § 22-1 [Dantzig and Wolfe, 1960-1]. The decomposition principle approach was inspired by the proposals of Ford and Fulkerson [1958-1] for solving multistage commodity network problems. W. S. Jewell [1958-1] should also be credited with using a similar approach for the latter.

and, conversely, any λ and μ satisfying (6), determine an X and Y by (4) and (5), and give a feasible solution to (1). Denoting, in general, the linear transforms of X and Y,

$$(7) \qquad\qquad S = \bar{A}_1 X, \quad T = \bar{A}_2 Y$$

and, in particular,

$$(8) \qquad S_i = \bar{A}_1 X_i, \quad T_j = \bar{A}_2 Y_j \quad (i = 1, 2, \ldots, K; j = 1, 2, \ldots, L)$$

the original linear program is *equivalent* to the problem:

Find $\lambda_1 \geq 0, \ldots, \lambda_K \geq 0; \mu_1 \geq 0, \ldots, \mu_L \geq 0$ and Max x_0 satisfying

$$(9) \qquad P_0 x_0 + \sum_1^K S_i \lambda_i + \sum_1^L T_j \mu_j = b \qquad (\lambda_i \geq 0; \mu_i \geq 0)$$

$$\sum_1^K \lambda_i \qquad\qquad = 1$$

$$\sum_1^L \mu_j \quad = 1$$

DEFINITION: The linear program (9) generated from the extreme point solutions of $\mathscr{L}_i$ by (8) is called the equivalent *extremal problem*, or the *full master program*.

The basic solutions of $\mathscr{L}_1$ and $\mathscr{L}_2$ are probably far too numerous for us ever to express this extremal problem explicitly; rather, we propose to solve it by generating only those columns S_i and T_j which the simplex method brings into the successive bases.

Let us suppose that we have at hand an *initial, basic feasible solution* $\lambda_i = \lambda_i^o$ and $\mu_j = \mu_j^o$ to the extremal problem. If b has m components, then there will be $m + 2$ columns, say $S_1, S_2, \ldots, S_k; T_1, T_2, \ldots, T_l$ in the corresponding basis, where $k + l = m + 2$. Corresponding to this basic feasible solution to the extremal problem, is the solution $X = X^o$, $Y = Y^o$, $x_0 = x_0^o$ to (1) given by

$$(10) \qquad X^o = \lambda_1^o X_1 + \lambda_2^o X_2 + \ldots + \lambda_k^o X_k \quad (\Sigma \lambda_i^o = 1; \lambda_i^o \geq 0)$$
$$Y^o = \mu_1^o Y_1 + \mu_2^o Y_2 + \ldots + \mu_l^o Y_l \quad (\Sigma \mu_i^o = 1; \mu_i^o \geq 0)$$

At the end of this section we will give a Phase I procedure by which such a starting solution and representation may be found.

In order to test optimality of the basic solution or to generate a better solution to the master program, let the row vector $(\pi^o; -s^o, -t^o)$ denote the simplex multipliers associated with starting basis

$$
(11) \qquad B = \begin{bmatrix} P_0 & S_1 & S_2 & \ldots & S_k & T_1 & T_2 & \ldots & T_l \\ 0 & 1 & 1 & & 1 & 0 & 0 & & 0 \\ 0 & 0 & 0 & & 0 & 1 & 1 & & 1 \end{bmatrix}
\begin{matrix} \text{Multipliers} \\ : \ (\pi^o) \\ : \ (-s^o) \\ : \ (-t^o) \end{matrix}
$$

where s^o, t^o correspond to the last two rows of B. As discussed in § 22-1, $(\pi^o; -s^o, -t^o)$ is determined such that

$$(12) \qquad \pi^o P_0 = 1, \quad \pi^o S_i = s^o, \quad \pi^o T_j = t^o$$

for $i = 1, 2, \ldots, k$; $j = 1, 2, \ldots, l$.

The standard simplex method now requires us to bring into the basis that column of (9) which has the lowest relative cost, $\pi^o S_i - s^o < 0$ or $\pi^o T_j - t^o < 0$, if any. That is, we must determine S_* and T_* such that

$$(13) \qquad \pi^o S_* = \operatorname*{Min}_i \pi^o S_i$$
$$\pi^o T_* = \operatorname*{Min}_j \pi^o T_j$$

But

$$(14) \qquad \operatorname{Min} \pi^o S_i = \operatorname{Min} (\pi^o \bar{A}_1) X_i = \operatorname*{Min}_{\left\{ \begin{smallmatrix} X \geq 0 \\ A_1 X = b_1 \end{smallmatrix} \right.} \gamma_i^o X$$

where $\gamma_1^o = \pi^o \bar{A}_1$. That is, we determine S_* by finding the solution, X_*, to

The Subprogram $\mathscr{L}_1$:

$$(15) \qquad A_1 X = b_1 \qquad\qquad\qquad (X \geq 0)$$
$$\gamma_1^o X = z_1 \text{ (Min)} \qquad\qquad (\gamma_1^o = \pi^o \bar{A}_1)$$

If the simplex method is used on the subprogram, X_* will always be one of the $X_1, \ldots, X_K$. We can then form $S_* = \bar{A}_1 X_*$ and bring it into the basis. If

$$(16) \qquad \operatorname{Min} z_1 = \gamma_1^o X_* < s^o$$

then the relative cost factor for S_*, $\pi^o S_* - s^o = \gamma_1^o X_* - s^o$, is negative and the introduction of S_* into the basis will (assuming nondegeneracy) bring about a finite increase in x_0.

Likewise, we can determine T_* from the Y_* which solves

The Subprogram $\mathscr{L}_2$:

$$(17) \qquad A_2 Y = b_2 \qquad\qquad\qquad (Y \geq 0)$$
$$\gamma_2^o Y = z_2 \text{ (Min)} \qquad\qquad (\gamma_2^o = \pi^o \bar{A}_2)$$

If $\operatorname{Min} z_2 < t^o$, then introducing $T_* = \bar{A}_2 Y_*$ into the basis will (assuming nondegeneracy) increase x_0 by a finite amount. We introduce S_* or T_*, whichever has the lower relative cost factor.

On the other hand, if $\operatorname{Min} z_1 = s^o$ and $\operatorname{Min} z_2 = t^o$, then all the relative cost factors for (9) are nonnegative. Consequently, we are at the optimal solution of the equivalent extremal problem, and therefore, X^o and Y^o given by (10) constitute an optimal solution to (1).

DEFINITION: The program obtained from the full master program (9) by dropping all the columns except those in the basis and the new S_* (or T_*)

about to be introduced, is known as *The Restricted Master Program*:
Find $\lambda_i \geq 0$, $\mu_j \geq 0$, and Max x_0 such that

$$
\begin{aligned}
(18) \quad P_0 x_0 + S_1 \lambda_1 + \ldots + S_k \lambda_k + S_* \lambda_* + T_1 \mu_1 + \ldots + T_l \mu_l &= b \\
\lambda_1 + \ldots + \lambda_k + \lambda_* &= 1 \\
\mu_1 + \ldots + \mu_l &= 1
\end{aligned}
$$

Iterative Process and Final Solution.

We now proceed to solve the restricted master program. The resulting optimal solution yields a new (π, s, t); these, in turn, determine new γ_1 and γ_2, which constitute new objective forms for $\mathscr{L}_1$ and $\mathscr{L}_2$. The subprograms are then solved with the new objective forms, and the optimality test above is applied. If the test fails, a new column is added to the restricted master program, corresponding to the subprogram failing the test. The whole process is then repeated, and the cycle continued until the optimality test is passed. The optimal solution is then given by $X = \sum_i \lambda_i X_i$ and $Y = \sum_j \mu_j Y_j$, where the λ_i and μ_j are the solution to the final restricted master program and the X_i and Y_j are the solutions of $\mathscr{L}_1$ and $\mathscr{L}_2$ corresponding to columns in the final basis of the last restricted master program. If the restricted master programs are nondegenerate (or ε-perturbed), the introduction of each S_* or T_* will, as we remarked, increase x_0 by a finite amount. Hence, none of the finite number of bases of (9) can reappear, so the iterative procedure is finite. We have established

THEOREM 1: *The solution $X = X^o$, $Y = Y^o$ corresponding to a basic solution of the master program is optimal if there exist no solutions to the subprograms with z_1, z_2 values less than those of the solutions which were used to generate the basis of the master program, i.e., it is optimal if*

$$
(19) \qquad \text{Min } z_1 = s^o, \quad \text{Min } z_2 = t^o
$$

If the restricted master programs are nondegenerate (or ε-perturbed) such an optimum will be reached in a finite number of iterations.

THEOREM 2: *An upper bound for the values x_0 is*

$$
\begin{aligned}
(20) \qquad \text{Max } x_0 &\leq x_0^o + (s^o - \text{Min } z_1) + (t^o - \text{Min } z_2) \\
&\leq x_0^o + (s^o - \pi^o S_*) + (t^o - \pi^o T_*)
\end{aligned}
$$

PROOF: Multiply (9) by the multipliers, $(\pi^o; -s^o, -t^o)$, and sum. The constant term is x_0^o, which is the value of x_0 for the basic solution. We have, therefore,

$$
(21) \qquad x_0 + \sum_1^K (\pi^o S_i - s^o)\lambda_i + \sum_1^L (\pi^o T_j - t^o)\mu_j = x_0^o
$$

$$
(22) \qquad x_0 + \sum_1^K (\text{Min } z_1 - s^o)\lambda_i + \sum_1^L (\text{Min } z_2 - t^o)\mu_j \leq x_0^o
$$

and the result follows.

Computational Remarks.

The change of basis in the restricted master program is performed, of course, by the simplex method using multipliers (Chapter 9). In this format, the *lexicographic ordering rule* may be used to resolve degeneracy and assure that no basis is repeated (Chapter 10). As various columns of the master program are generated during the iterative process, one of the following three variants is customarily used:

(1) The restricted master program is augmented by each new column, but each column that drops out of the basis is dropped from the current restricted master.

(2) The restricted master program is augmented by more and more columns and those dropping out of the basis are retained as supplementary columns.

(3) The restricted master program is augmented by more and more columns, and those dropping out of the basis are retained up to the available memory capacity within the electronic computer; at this point columns that price out most positive are dropped.

Observe also that on each cycle after the first we can start the solution of a subprogram or the master program from the basic solution which was optimal on the preceding cycle. Thus, no Phase I procedures are necessary except before the first cycle, and there is a good chance that only a few pivot operations will be necessary for the re-solution of the subprograms and master program.

Modifications Necessary for Unbounded $\mathscr{L}_i$.

Even though the set of feasible solutions to the entire problem (1) is bounded, it is quite possible that the sets of solutions for some $\mathscr{L}_i$ are unbounded. In this case, there may be no lower bound for z_i, and the minimization of z_i via the simplex procedure will result in a *homogeneous* solution X_*, Y_*, satisfying

$$(23) \qquad \begin{aligned} A_1 X_* &= 0 \ \text{or} \ A_2 Y_* = 0 \\ \gamma_1 X_* &< 0 \ \text{or} \ \gamma_2 Y_* < 0 \end{aligned}$$

These X_*, Y_* as pointed out in a similar discussion at the end of § 22-1, belong to a finite class (extreme rays, Chapter 7). In this case *we can generate the full class of solutions to $\mathscr{L}_i$ by considering solutions that are convex combinations of the nonhomogeneous solutions and nonnegative combinations of the homogeneous solutions.* Thus, in place of (4) and (5)

$$(24) \qquad \begin{aligned} X' &= X_1 \bar{\lambda}_1 + X_2 \bar{\lambda}_2 + \ldots + X_K \bar{\lambda}_K \\ Y' &= Y_1 \bar{\mu}_1 + Y_2 \bar{\mu}_2 + \ldots + Y_L \bar{\mu}_L \end{aligned}$$

where $\bar{\lambda}_i \geq 0$, $\bar{\mu}_i \geq 0$, satisfy a condition that the $\bar{\lambda}_i$ and $\bar{\mu}_j$ must each sum

[453]

to unity when restricted to those i and j corresponding to nonhomogeneous solutions, i.e.,

(25)
$$\delta_1 \bar{\lambda}_1 + \delta_2 \bar{\lambda}_2 + \ldots + \delta_K \bar{\lambda}_K = 1$$
$$\delta_1' \bar{u}_1 + \delta_2' \bar{u}_2 + \ldots + \delta_L' \bar{u}_L = 1$$

where

(26)
$$\begin{cases} \delta_i = 1 \text{ if } X_i \text{ is a basic feasible solution,} \\ \delta_i = 0 \text{ if } X_i \text{ is a homogeneous solution,} \end{cases}$$
$$\begin{cases} \delta_i' = 1 \text{ if } Y_i \text{ is a basic feasible solution,} \\ \delta_i' = 0 \text{ if } Y_i \text{ is a homogeneous solution} \end{cases}$$

This means that the basis B is redefined to be

(27)
$$B = \begin{bmatrix} P_0 & S_1 \ldots S_k & T_1 \ldots T_l \\ 0 & \delta_1 \ldots \delta_k & 0 \ldots 0 \\ 0 & 0 \ldots 0 & \delta_1' \ldots \delta_l' \end{bmatrix}$$

In the event $b_1 = 0$ or $b_2 = 0$, only homogeneous solutions are of interest. In this case the corresponding restrictions (25) can be dropped from the master program.

Since there is only a finite number of homogeneous solutions generated by the simplex process, the proof of the finiteness of the iterative procedure remains valid.

Initiating the Algorithm.

We assumed in (10) an initial solution X^o, Y^o represented in terms of basic feasible solutions X_i, Y_j and—we may now add—homogeneous solutions of $\mathscr{L}_1$ and $\mathscr{L}_2$, respectively. Such an initial solution can be obtained by a Phase I procedure.

Let X_1 and Y_1 be any arbitrary solution to $\mathscr{L}_1$ and $\mathscr{L}_2$, and S_1, T_1 their transforms under (7). Let the starting basis of the master program of Phase I be

(28)
$$P_0 x_0 + \lambda_1 S_1 + \mu_1 T_1 \pm U_1 \varepsilon_1 \pm U_2 \varepsilon_2 \pm \ldots \pm U_m \varepsilon_m = \bar{b}$$
$$\lambda_1 = 1$$
$$\mu_1 = 1$$
$$\varepsilon_1 + \varepsilon_2 + \ldots + \varepsilon_m - w = 0$$

where U_i is an $m + 1$ component unit vector with 1 in row i, where $m + 1$ is the number of rows in $[\bar{A}_1, \bar{A}_2]$. The variables $\varepsilon_1, \varepsilon_2, \ldots, \varepsilon_m$; x_0, λ_1, μ_1, and w form a basic set. The signs of the U_i are chosen so that the artificial variables ε_i are nonnegative in the basic solution. During Phase I, the objective is to minimize w. Accordingly, the simplex multipliers are defined so that all columns price out to zero except the $(-w)$ column, which prices out to unity. From the Phase I-Phase II process, we deduce:

THEOREM 3: *An optimal basic feasible solution to the original system can be represented as the sum of at most $m + 2$ basic feasible solutions of the two* *parts where m is the number of equations in the interconnecting part* (2) *exclusive of the objective form.*

23-2. DECOMPOSITION PRINCIPLE, ANIMATED

PROLOGUE

The coordinator, "Staff," of the Central Agency must procure tankers to assist his distributor, "Sub," in the shipping of their product from two plants to four terminals. Staff hates details and has asked Sub to furnish him with only two numbers, the cost, c, of the proposed shipping plan, and the number of tankers, t, required to support it.

Distributor, Sub, has two arrays, a unit cost matrix $[c_{ij}]$, and a unit tanker requirement matrix $[t_{ij}]$ (tankers required per unit shipped):

$$[c_{ij}] = \begin{bmatrix} 3 & 6 & 6 & 5 \\ 8 & 1 & 3 & 6 \end{bmatrix}; \ [t_{ij}] = \begin{bmatrix} 0 & 0 & 2 & 0 \\ 0 & 2 & 0 & 0 \end{bmatrix}$$

(The zeros in the $[t_{ij}]$ array indicate shipments by pipeline instead of by boat.) Since the general objective is to minimize costs, Sub sets out to solve the transportation problem, below, where a_i are the known availabilities at the plants and b_j are the known requirements at the terminals.

Available

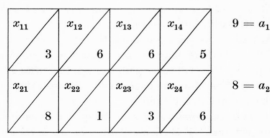

$9 = a_1$

$8 = a_2$

Required: $2 = b_1$ $\quad 7 = b_2$ $\quad 3 = b_3$ $\quad 5 = b_4$

Having taken a ten-day operations research course where he learned how to solve small transportation problems, Sub soon discovers the *minimum cost* solution to this problem to be

$$[x_{ij}]_1 = \begin{bmatrix} 2 & 0 & 2 & 5 \\ 0 & 7 & 1 & 0 \end{bmatrix}$$

In this case $c = \Sigma\Sigma c_{ij}x_{ij} = 53$, $t = \Sigma\Sigma t_{ij}x_{ij} = 18$. Hence, the two numbers that Sub furnishes Staff, in his proposed plan, are

$$P_1 = \begin{bmatrix} c_1 \\ t_1 \end{bmatrix} = \begin{bmatrix} 53 \\ 18 \end{bmatrix}$$

where P_1 represents the vector made up of the components of his first plan.

[455]

Staff discovers, however, that a sudden shortage of tankers has developed, and the most he can muster for Sub is 9 tankers. Noting that two out of Sub's eight possible shipping activities have to use tankers, Staff requests Sub to find a solution that "goes easy on the use of tankers." Sub, being literal, forgets costs and immediately comes up with the following solution that minimizes the use of tankers

$$[x_{ij}]_2 = \begin{bmatrix} 0 & 7 & 0 & 2 \\ 2 & 0 & 3 & 3 \end{bmatrix}$$

In this case $\Sigma\Sigma c_{ij}x_{ij} = 95 = c_2$, $\Sigma\Sigma t_{ij}x_{ij} = 0 = t_2$. Hence, Sub's new proposed plan is

$$P_2 = \begin{bmatrix} c_2 \\ t_2 \end{bmatrix} = \begin{bmatrix} 95 \\ 0 \end{bmatrix}$$

ACT I.

STAFF: Well, whatever else one might say about Sub's new plan, it certainly has gone easy on the use of tankers; in fact, none are used. But look what has happened to costs—they have nearly doubled! I just can't tell Sub that he can have only 9 tankers and let him find his own least-cost solution; I tried that the last time there was a tanker shortage, and costs soared. Somehow I wish I had sent Sub to that six-week operations research course, instead of the ten-day one. It would probably have been a lot cheaper in the long run. Note: *At this point, Staff has decided to call in his economist friend, F. M. Dalks,[2] as a consultant.*

DALKS: According to good economic theory, what you should do is to tell Sub that there may be an extra premium charge for the use of tankers. This will teach Sub to keep the costs down and at the same time not use tankers excessively, because they are now part of the charges in the total bill.

STAFF (*Enthusiastic and not above a bit of subterfuge if it gets results*): Let's do just that. (F.M. *is crestfallen; theory is theory, but putting it into practice is another matter.*)

DALKS: Let's go a little more slowly. It is not always easy to calculate what the prices should be on scarce commodities. It depends on many factors. But let me assure you it has been rigorously established, beyond any doubt, that such prices always exist. (*Seeing distrust creep into Staff's eyes,* F.M. *begins to toy with the idea of coming down out of the "ivory tower."*) In this case, however, we have only one scarce commodity, tankers, and we could try various premium charges for tankers and see what happens to Sub's use of them. This way we could eventually get Sub to come up with a plan that offers both feasibility and least-cost.

[2] F. M. Dalks, like the letters of his name, is a composite of leading mathematical economists of his time, who have applied linear programming to economic theory.

STAFF: Sounds like a good approach.

DALKS: According to theory, if tankers are in surplus, the price on tankers should be zero. Since Sub's latest plan, P_2, doesn't use any tankers at all, this is certainly the case. As a start, we can tell Sub the price, $\pi = 0$, on tankers. How's that?

STAFF (*Sarcastically*): Terrific! The only trouble with it is that we have already tried placing no value on tankers, and Sub came up with some plan or other which we couldn't use. I threw it away, but maybe Marge saved a copy. . . . Ah! See how valuable a secretary can be; here is a copy. See Sub's old plan: $P_1 = \langle 53, 18 \rangle$. It isn't feasible, so what good is it?

DALKS: I have another idea. I was reading an O.R. journal the other day. Of course, I don't usually read that kind of journal, but when I do, I find it is not so peripheral to econometrics as some people think. Anyway, a friend wanted my opinion about an article on a "decomposition principle." He thought it might throw some light on how to handle price problems when there are breakpoints due to discontinuity in the derivatives of the underlying production functions. But this is beside the point. The article suggests that we should take a weighted average of the two plans (*he moves to the blackboard*) like this:

$$P_1\lambda_1 + P_2\lambda_2 = \begin{bmatrix} 53 \\ 18 \end{bmatrix} \lambda_1 + \begin{bmatrix} 95 \\ 0 \end{bmatrix} \lambda_2$$

where $\lambda_1 + \lambda_2 = 1$, and, of course, $0 \leq \lambda_1 \leq 1$. For example, we could try $\lambda_1 = \frac{1}{2}$, $\lambda_2 = \frac{1}{2}$. Say, this gives

$$\frac{1}{2}(53 + 95) = 74$$
$$\frac{1}{2}(18 + 0) = 9$$

which is a lot cheaper than 95 and happens to use up the available tankers. How's that?

STAFF: That's splendid, simply splendid! But how do we know that we can average Sub's proposals in this way? How will Sub know what to do? I don't want to get into the details of Sub's shipping schedule, you know.

DALKS: Oh! Don't worry about that. Just tell Sub to average the detailed schedules he used for generating plans P_1 and P_2, and he has the answer.

STAFF: That is a neat trick—averaging the old and new plans—and to think I was smart enough not to throw away that old plan. The boss is going to be very pleased when I tell him how we figured this one out. Before doing so, let's study this average plan of yours a little to make sure it's okay. Let's see, 9 tankers and an over-all transportation cost of 74. Isn't 74 rather high, considering that the least-cost solution might have been 53, if it were not for the tanker shortage?

DALKS: Well, according to the article, this does not necessarily give the best solution. What we are supposed to do is set up a little linear program that tells us how to "blend" old and new plans in the best way. Here it is.

$$53\lambda_1 + 95\lambda_2 + (-z) = 0 \qquad\qquad (\lambda_i \geq 0)$$
$$\lambda_0 + 18\lambda_1 + 0\lambda_2 \qquad\quad = 9$$
$$\lambda_1 + \quad \lambda_2 \quad \bullet \quad = 1$$
$$\bullet \qquad\quad \bullet \qquad\quad \bullet$$

where λ_0 is the slack (if any) in the use of tankers. It's fairly obvious, in this case, that $\lambda_0 = 0$, $\lambda_1 = \frac{1}{2}$, $\lambda_2 = \frac{1}{2}$, with a cost $z^1 = 74$ so that we don't learn anything we don't already know. The important thing is that it gives us an idea of what price we should tell Sub to set on tankers. We do this by solving the dual linear program.

STAFF: I'm afraid you are in over my head. What's the solution?

DALKS: Well, the dual solution is very interesting. It works out this way. You see, the basic variables associated with the optimal primal solution are indicated by the three dots ● ● ● under the λ_1, λ_2, and $-z$ columns. It means we should choose multipliers $(1, \pi^1, -s^1)$ for the three equations in such a way that when we multiply and sum, the λ_1 and λ_2 terms vanish. It is easy to see that the following conditions must hold:

$$53 + 18\pi^1 - s^1 = 0 \text{ (coefficient of } \lambda_1)$$
$$95 + \quad 0\pi^1 - s^1 = 0 \text{ (coefficient of } \lambda_2)$$

or $s^1 = +95$ and $\pi^1 = +\frac{42}{18} = 2\frac{1}{3}$.

STAFF: I don't understand why $\pi^1 = 2\frac{1}{3}$ is positive. As I understand linear programming price-conventions, this means Sub is paid to use tankers, instead of having to pay a premium for their use (§ 12-3).

DALKS: Yes, but not in this case. For once, for this kind of problem, the linear programmers have set up their sign conventions sensibly, just as we economists do. So, in this case, π means what it says. In other words, we tell Sub that the premium charge on tankers might be $2\frac{1}{3}$ units per tanker. Let's try this and see what happens.

STAFF: Quite an interesting game we are playing with Sub. What is this $s^1 = +95$?

DALKS: Oh, that is to see whether or not we should try to blend Sub's proposal number three (when it comes in) with P_1 and P_2. But we can talk more about this later (§ 23-1, Theorem 1).

STAFF: But I don't understand. Does that mean that Sub is going to send

[458]

us another "infeasible" proposal, and we will have to do some more combining of proposals?

DALKS: Yes, I am afraid it does, unless we are awfully lucky!

Note: *At this point Sub is instructed to set up a new unit cost matrix,*

$$[c_{ij}] + 2\tfrac{1}{3}[t_{ij}] = \begin{bmatrix} 3 & 6 & 6 + 4\tfrac{2}{3} & 5 \\ 8 & 1 + 4\tfrac{2}{3} & 3 & 6 \end{bmatrix}$$

In due course, Sub arrives at the following optimal solution to his transportation problem:

$$[x_{ij}]_3 = \begin{bmatrix} 2 & 2 & 0 & 5 \\ 0 & 5 & 3 & 0 \end{bmatrix}$$

In this case, $\Sigma\Sigma c_{ij}x_{ij} = 57$, and $\Sigma\Sigma t_{ij}x_{ij} = 10$. Therefore, the third plan he submits, is

$$P_3 = \begin{bmatrix} c_3 \\ t_3 \end{bmatrix} = \begin{bmatrix} 57 \\ 10 \end{bmatrix}$$

ACT II.

STAFF: I begin to understand it now. What we do is set up a new little linear program. Is there some special name by which we can refer to it?

DALKS: It is called a "restricted master." But first, we want to test to see if P_3 is worth considering. Remember $s^1 = 95$? What we do is "price out" the new proposal and compare it with 95, the "break-even value." Since the new plan has a transportation cost of 57 and there will be a charge of $2\tfrac{1}{3}$ units for each of the 10 tankers used, we have $57 + 23\tfrac{1}{3} = 80\tfrac{1}{3}$. This is *less* than $s^1 = 95$, so we can now go ahead with the restricted master. Here it is:

$$53\lambda_1 + 95\lambda_2 + 57\lambda_3 + (-z) = 0$$
$$\lambda_0 + 18 \cdot \lambda_1 + 0\lambda_2 + 10\lambda_3 \qquad = 9$$
$$\lambda_1 + \lambda_2 + \lambda_3 \qquad = 1$$

STAFF: Does it take very long to solve? I'm curious to see what the answer is.

DALKS: Well, in this case, no! According to linear programming theory, only two of the three plans that Sub submitted are going to be used. Since no average of plans No. 1 and 3 will have less than 10 tankers, this leaves only one new possibility, a combination of P_2 and P_3. The new solution is easy. It is obviously $\lambda_2 = \tfrac{1}{10}$, $\lambda_3 = \tfrac{9}{10}$. This gives a cost of $z^2 = 95(\tfrac{1}{10}) + 57(\tfrac{9}{10}) = 60.8$.

STAFF: That's a big improvement! We have cut the cost from $z^0 = 95$ to $z^1 = 74$ and now to $z^2 = 60.8$. How much more do you think we can reduce it if we keep this up?

[459]

DALKS: Well, not too much. It can't go any lower than 53, because we know that the value of z for the cheapest cost solution is 53 when there is no restriction on tankers. But perhaps we can do a little better. According to decomposition theory, we can always get an estimate of a lower bound by going back to the previous basic solution. Here is the formula (§ 23-1, Theorem 2):

$$\text{Min } z \geq z^1 \; - s^1 \; + c_3 \; + \pi^1 t_3 = 74 - 95 + 57 + 23\tfrac{1}{3} = 59\tfrac{1}{3}$$

STAFF: Fantastic! If you are right, very little saving below $z^2 = 60.8$ is possible. I would like to see what the true minimum is and see how good your guess really is.

DALKS: Okay, but it is not really a guess. Let us determine a new price on tankers. Since λ_2 and λ_3 are new basic variables, we have

$$95 + \; 0\pi^2 - s^2 = 0$$
$$57 + 10\pi^2 - s^2 = 0$$

or $s^2 = 95$ and $\pi^2 = \tfrac{38}{10} = 3.8$. It shows we should raise the ante on tankers from $\pi^1 = 2\tfrac{1}{3}$ to $\pi^2 = 3.8$.

STAFF: I hope Sub won't become too unhappy with our changing our minds so often. He might start complaining to the big boss before this noble experiment is finished.

Note: *In due course, Sub sets up his new array*

$$[c_{ij}] + 3.8[t_{ij}] = \begin{bmatrix} 3 & 6 & 6+7.6 & 5 \\ 8 & 1+7.6 & 3 & 6 \end{bmatrix}$$

and derives a new optimal solution

$$[x_{ij}]_4 = \begin{bmatrix} 2 & 7 & 0 & 0 \\ 0 & 0 & 3 & 5 \end{bmatrix}$$

Here $\Sigma\Sigma c_{ij}x_{ij} = 87$ and $\Sigma\Sigma t_{ij}x_{ij} = 0$. So this, Sub's fourth plan, becomes

$$P_4 = \begin{bmatrix} c_4 \\ t_4 \end{bmatrix} = \begin{bmatrix} 87 \\ 0 \end{bmatrix}$$

ACT III.

STAFF: This gets better and better. Obviously we can substitute $\tfrac{1}{10}$ of P_4 for the $\tfrac{1}{10}P_2$ that we used earlier and get a better solution. So, let's go ahead with the restricted master. Here it is.

$$53\lambda_1 + \; 95\lambda_2 + 57\lambda_3 + \; 87\lambda_4 + (-z) = 0$$
$$\lambda_0 + 18\lambda_1 + 0 \cdot \lambda_2 + 10\lambda_3 + 0 \cdot \lambda_4 \qquad = 9$$
$$\lambda_1 + \quad \lambda_2 + \quad \lambda_3 + \quad \lambda_4 \qquad = 1$$

Let us see what the new value of z is. Not much improvement, $z^3 = 57(\tfrac{9}{10}) + 87(\tfrac{1}{10}) = 60$. Maybe your lower bound of $59\tfrac{1}{3}$ is not so bad after all. Let's try your formula again for the lower bound.

For this purpose, we go back to the previous basic solution. Is that not so? That's funny! This time don't we get

$$\text{Min } z \geq z^2 - s^2 + c_4 + \pi^2 t_4 = 60.8 - 95 + 87.0 = 52.8?$$

DALKS: It appears that our previous estimate of $59\frac{1}{3}$ was just a very lucky one. I guess we should make the lower bound estimate each cycle, because some are better than others.

STAFF: I suppose now we will have to get a new price

$$57 + 10\pi^3 - s^3 = 0$$
$$87 + 0\pi^3 - s^3 = 0$$

or $s^3 = 87$ and $\pi^3 = 3$. This time we tell Sub the price on tankers has dropped to 3.

Note: *Sub's new problem becomes*

$$[c_{ij} + 3t_{ij}] = \begin{bmatrix} 3 & 6 & 6+6 & 5 \\ 8 & 1+6 & 3 & 6 \end{bmatrix}$$

which he quickly solves because his last solution, $[x_{ij}]_4$, is still optimal. Also he finds that his previous one, $[x_{ij}]_3$, is also optimal.

ACT IV.

STAFF: What does this mean? Sub has come up with the same solution as last time.

DALKS: It means that there is no improvement. Let us try our lower bound estimate and see what it says. If we use $c_4 = 87$, $t_4 = 0$ in the formula, then

$$\text{Min } z \geq z^3 - s^3 + c_4 + \pi^3 t_4 = 60 - 87 + 87 + 0 = 60$$

If we use $c_3 = 57$, $t_3 = 10$, instead of c_4, t_4, which is Sub's other optimum solution, we also get

$$z \geq 60 - 87 + 57 + 3(10) = 60$$

Since our lower bound 60 is the same as our value of z, this proves we are done.

STAFF: I must tell the boss about our new decentralized decision process and send out orders to Sub to form the weighted average of his plans, namely, $.9P_3 + .1P_4$.

Note: *When Sub carries out his orders he finds his optimal plan to be*

$$.9[x_{ij}]_3 + .1[x_{ij}]_4 = \begin{bmatrix} 2 & 2\frac{1}{2} & 0 & 4\frac{1}{2} \\ 0 & 4\frac{1}{2} & 3 & \frac{1}{2} \end{bmatrix}$$

DALKS: Technically, this is not exactly what we economists mean when we say "decentralized planning." A better term would be "central planning without full information at the center." A very interesting experiment! I may write a paper on how for the first time prices were used to control, in a precisely defined way, a real life situation.

The End

[461]

23-3. CENTRAL PLANNING WITHOUT COMPLETE INFORMATION AT THE CENTER[3]

The theory developed in § 23-1 makes it possible to plan the over-all operation of an organization without the central staff having full knowledge of the technology of each part. We shall deal with the case in which the technology matrix is constant over time and there is no capital expansion except for current needs.

Consider, then, an economy or industrial complex with T plants and m items which are traded between plants. Plant p has a technological matrix, A_p, of m_p rows expressing constraints on intermediate products, plant capacity, and local demands. In addition to A_p, each plant has a trade matrix, $\bar{A}_p$, which has m rows that correspond to m commodities traded between plants or supplied to the consumption sector of the economy. Plant p also has a vector of constraint constants, b_p. The constraints for plant p are then

$$(1) \qquad A_p X_p = b_p, \qquad X_p \geq 0 \qquad (p = 1, 2, \ldots, T)$$

where X_p is the vector of its activity levels.

The Central Trade Agency has constraints specifying that the amounts of item j procured from various plants minus the amounts supplied to them be greater than or equal to the amount it turns over to final *minimum basic demand* (consumption, defense, exports, and the like). Using I to denote the identity matrix, these constraints may be written

$$(2) \qquad \bar{A}_1 X_1 + \bar{A}_2 X_2 + \ldots + \bar{A}_T X_T + IY = \bar{b} \qquad (Y \geq 0)$$

Y being the vector of final incremental demands in excess of the minimum basic demand $\bar{b}$. (With our sign conventions the components of $\bar{b}$ are all negative.)

The planners attach a certain set of values, specified by the row vector $-c$, to final incremental demands so that $-cY$ represents the value of the plan to them. The total problem facing the economy may then be written

$$(3) \qquad \begin{aligned} A_1 X_1 \qquad\qquad\qquad\qquad &= b_1 \\ A_2 X_2 \qquad\qquad\qquad &= b_2 \\ \vdots \qquad\qquad &\quad \vdots \\ A_T X_T \qquad &= b_T \\ \bar{A}_1 X_1 + \bar{A}_2 X_2 + \ldots + \bar{A}_T X_T + IY &= \bar{b} \\ cY &= z \; (\text{Min}) \end{aligned}$$

---

[3] This section was also contributed by C. Almon to bring out some of the potentialities of the decomposition principle for decentralized planning.

This is an angular system which the theory of § 23-1 will decompose into T subprograms and one master program. If the A_p matrices were all available they could be sent to the Central Planning Agency where a large computer, programmed to use our decomposition principle, would soon produce the optimal solution.

In reality, however, the A_p matrices are hard to compose. It may require substantial engineering time to specify each new activity even though no real technological change, or basic innovation is involved. There may be many things which no one doubts could be done, but which it would require much valuable time to specify in detail. For instance, no engineer would, just for the sake of adding an activity to the A_p matrix, spend a week to carefully specify the characteristics of a transformer using copper wire instead of aluminum if a few rough calculations showed that the resulting product would cost about twice what the present one does and offer no compensating advantages.

For such reasons, the complete A_p are probably not explicitly known; rather we may regard them as potentially known to the plants, with some effort being required to make them explicit. Since potential knowledge can hardly be sent to the Central Planning Agency, this Agency lacks complete information. It does not, however, completely lack information, for it has available the records of Central Trade which show how much each plant used and supplied of each common item for several preceding years, say *two* for simplicity. Thus it knows the values of $S_p = \bar{A}_p X_p$ determined by two feasible solutions to the entire program and hence to each subprogram:

(4)
$$\begin{aligned} A_p X_p^o = b_p; & \quad S_p^o = \bar{A}_p X_p^o \\ A_p X_p^1 = b_p; & \quad S_p^1 = \bar{A}_p X_p^1 \end{aligned} \qquad (p = 1, \ldots, T)$$

(If there was no capital expansion, the b_p are the same in the two years. If there was capital expansion, the first year's plan could be converted into a feasible plan for the second year and used in (4).)

The Central Planning Agency uses this data to make up a *master program* with $m + T$ constraints as follows:

(5)
$$\begin{aligned} S_1^o \lambda_1^o + S_1^1 \lambda_1^1 + S_2^o \lambda_2^o + S_2^1 \lambda_2^1 + \ldots + S_T^o \lambda_T^o + S_T^1 \lambda_T^1 + I Y &= b \\ \lambda_1^o + \lambda_1^1 &= 1 \\ \lambda_2^o + \lambda_2^1 &= 1 \\ & \quad \vdots \\ \lambda_T^o + \lambda_T^1 &= 1 \\ c Y &= z \text{ (Min)} \end{aligned}$$

The planners then solve this master program and come up with simplex multipliers $(\pi; -s)$, π having m elements, and s having T. Economically

[463]

speaking, π is, of course, a vector of prices. For each plant we can then make an objective form

$$\text{Minimize } z_p = \pi S_p = (\pi \bar{A}_p) X_p$$

In words, this objective form states: Minimize the excess of the cost of purchases over the value of sales, i.e., minimize losses or, what comes to the same thing, *maximize profits*.

The planners then announce these prices, π, and instruct all plant managers to propose plans for the operation of their plant in the next year. Specifically, the plan is to state how much of each item they will buy and sell to Central Trade. In making these proposals, they are to assume that they can buy, at the announced prices, all they need of any of the m items and likewise sell all they produce. They are further instructed to propose the plan which will maximize their profits.

On receipt of these instructions, the managers call in their engineers, give them the prices, and tell them to leave no stone unturned in looking for ways to cut costs and increase profits *at these prices*. The engineers now have the guidance they need to set about making explicit a portion of their potential knowledge. In a month or so they produce what they believe to be their optimal plans, and the managers give the plans to Central Planning.

It would be extraordinary good luck if these plans will satisfy (2) and constitute a feasible program for the whole economy; usually Central Planning will have to coordinate them. For each plant p for which the proposed profits exceed s_p, the Agency adds an activity, S_p^2, to the master program (5). Then it re-solves this program, obtaining a new $(\pi; -s)$, say $(\pi'; -s')$ and also a λ solution. The λ are used to combine the new proposals with the previous solutions to get what we may call the optimal feasible plan, given the information possessed by the Central Planning Agency.

In principle, the planners could then announce π', get new proposals, and repeat the process until the optimal is found. In practice, planning takes time, production must go on, and the planners reason that consistent plans that get better and better are to be preferred over no plans. Hence, they announce *in quantitative terms* their feasible plan. They tell each plant manager how much of each traded commodity he must produce and how much he is allowed to purchase; this information is summarized for plant p in the column vector $S_p = \sum_i \lambda_p^i S_p^i$ where the values of λ_p^i are those of the optimum solution of the restricted master. They also announce the prices $(\pi'; -s')$ and direct that trade be conducted at these prices. They may also instruct the managers that, subject to their meeting the quantitative goals S_p, they should also maximize profits. Such a rule is intended as a guide to avoid possible waste in the event that S is not precisely achieved for one reason or another. It is important to note that they cannot tell the manager simply to maximize the profits (omitting production goals, S_p) for if they did, Central Trade would almost certainly have difficulty with its constraints (2).

Toward the end of the period for which production was planned, the order again goes out to propose plans for the next period, this time using π' as a guide. The managers, knowing that this order was coming, have been at work all year looking for ways to make profits, and they soon have their proposals. From these, Central Planning makes up new activities to add to the master program and matters proceed as before, the values of the plans always increasing. The essential point to bear in mind is that the master program remembers all previous proposals, except those which it is no longer using at all.

We leave to the reader's judgment the problem of the economic significance of the finiteness proposition of § 23-1. He should also consider the related, though not identical, question of whether it will ever be possible for the planners to abandon the quota and allotment system and simply direct the managers to maximize their profits.

Concluding Remark.

Our discussion has been intended to elucidate the workings of the decomposition principle as a planning tool, rather than to explain the methods actually used by a present-day industrial complex or by a socialist economy. We have shown that there exists a special method of allocation by a central authority and a specially devised system of prices that can induce the separate plants to submit *summarized proposals*, which can be combined into better and better over-all plans. Whether or not the system of allocation, prices, and proposals used by a particular economy or complex approximate those envisaged by our method, we cannot say. Our iterative process can be diagrammed as follows:

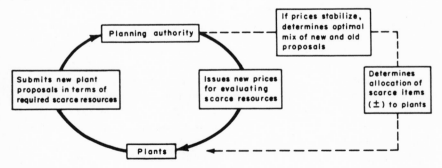

Figure 23-3-I. Decentralized planning using the decomposition principle.

Many people familiar with planning in large organizations are conscious of a flow of information similar to the above. *The difference is that the*

[465]

decomposition principle replaces the not-too-well-understood procedure by one that is rigorous and well defined.

23-4. DECOMPOSING MULTI-STAGE PROGRAMS

The methods developed in § 23-1 extend immediately to problems where there are more than two subprograms, the so-called "angular" systems of the form:

(1)
$$A_1 X_1 \qquad\qquad\qquad\qquad = b_1$$

$$A_t X_t \qquad\qquad\qquad = b_t$$

$$(X_t \geq 0)$$

$$A_T X_T = b_T$$
$$\bar{A}_1 X_1 + \ldots + \bar{A}_t X_t + \ldots + \bar{A}_T X_T = \bar{b}$$
$$C_1 X_1 + \ldots + C_t X_t + \ldots + C_T X_T = z \text{ (Min)}$$

where the A_i and $\bar{A}_i$ are matrices, and X_i and C_i are vectors.

Let us now consider another important class of structures, those of the form: Find X_t and Max x_0 satisfying

(2)
$$A_1 X_1 \qquad\qquad\qquad = e_1 \qquad (X_t \geq 0)$$
$$\bar{A}_1 X_1 + A_2 X_2 \qquad\qquad = e_2$$
$$\bar{A}_2 X_2 + A_3 X_3 \qquad = e_3$$
$$\bar{A}_3 X_3 + A_4 X_4 + P_0 x_0 = e_4$$

where X_t are vectors, A_t matrices, e_t and P_0 vectors. These are called *multistage* systems (so-called "staircase" systems) and often arise in the study of processes through time in which the activities of one period are directly connected with those of the preceding and following periods but with no others. In such cases, the several A_t may all be the same, as may be the $\bar{A}_t$. Although our results would permit computational advantage to be taken of such constancy, we shall not assume it.

Following the general lines of what we did in § 23-1, we begin by making a subprogram out of *every other* stage by rewriting (2) in the following form: Solve the program: Find $X_t \geq 0$ and Max x_0 satisfying

(3)
$$\bar{A}_1 X_1 + A_2 X_2 \qquad\qquad = e_2$$
$$\bar{A}_3 X_3 + A_4 X_4 + P_0 x_0 = e_4$$

subject to the constraints

(4) $$\mathscr{L}_1: A_1 X_1 = e_1 \qquad \mathscr{L}_2: \bar{A}_2 X_2 + A_3 X_3 = e_3$$

Thus, equations (4) have been selected to play the role of the independent parts, while equations (3) that of the binding constraints. The reader, of course, recognizes that the roles of (3) and (4) could be interchanged and that there are several other ways we could choose the subprograms.

We denote the extreme points of $\mathscr{L}_1$ by $X_1 = X_{1i}$ for $i = 1, 2, \ldots, K$ and those of $\mathscr{L}_2$ by $[X_{2j}, X_{3j}]$ for $j = 1, 2, \ldots, L$ and denote their transforms by

(4.1) $$S_i = \bar{A}_1 X_{1i}, \; [T_j = A_2 X_{2j}, \; \bar{T}_j = \bar{A}_3 X_{3j}]$$

In this case the master program takes the form: Find Max x_0, $\lambda_i \geq 0$, $\mu_j \geq 0$ satisfying

(5)
$$\sum_{i=1}^{K} S_i \lambda_i + \sum_{j=1}^{L} T_j \mu_j \qquad = e_2$$

$$\sum_{i=1}^{K} \lambda_i \qquad = 1$$

$$\sum_{j=1}^{L} \bar{T}_j \mu_j + A_4 X_4 + P_0 x_0 \qquad = e_4$$

$$\sum_{j=1}^{L} \mu_j \qquad = 1$$

Starting with some basic set of variables λ_i, μ_j and components X_{4p} of X_4 of the master program, we can solve for simplex multipliers, derive objective forms for $\mathscr{L}_1$ and $\mathscr{L}_2$, solve, use transforms of their solutions to add columns to the restricted master, re-solve, and repeat the process until the optimality test is passed.

When we set about to solve (5), however, the first thing we observe is that the master program itself is of the staircase form (2), but with half the number of stages. Hence, the logical thing to do is to *decompose this master program*. Accordingly, let us refer to (5) as the *first level master program* and proceed to its decomposition. We rewrite (5) in the form:

Find Max x_0 such that

(6) $$\sum_{j=1}^{L} \bar{T}_j \mu_j + A_4 X_4 + P_0 x_0 = e_4 \qquad (\mu_j \geq 0; \; X_4 \geq 0)$$

[467]

subject to

$$(7) \qquad \mathscr{L}_3: \quad \sum_{i=1}^{K} S_i \lambda_i + \sum_{j=1}^{L} T_j \mu_j = e_2 \qquad (\lambda_i \geq 0)$$

$$\sum_{i=1}^{K} \lambda_i = 1$$

$$\sum_{j=1}^{L} \mu_j = 1$$

We denote the extreme points of $\mathscr{L}_3$ by $\lambda_i = \lambda_i^q$, $\mu_j = \mu_j^q$ for $q = 1, 2,$ . . ., Q, and denote for the latter its transform $\sum_{j=1}^{L} T_j \mu^q = R_q$. Substituting in (6) we get the *second level master program*:

$$(8) \qquad \sum_{q=1}^{Q} R_q v_q + A_4 X_4 + P_0 x_0 = e_4 \qquad (v_q \geq 0; \; X_4 \geq 0)$$

$$\sum_{q=1}^{Q} v_q = 1, \quad \text{where } R_q = \sum_{j=1}^{L} T_j \mu_j^q$$

We have now decomposed the four-stage program into four programs, $\mathscr{L}_1$, $\mathscr{L}_2$, $\mathscr{L}_3$ and (8), whose total number of equations is three more than the corresponding number of equations of the four original stages.

Let us now outline the iterative procedure by which these programs are solved. First, we solve *a restricted second level master program* (8) and determine, in addition to v_q, the simplex multipliers $(\pi_4^o; \; -u_4^o)$ such that $\pi_4^o P_0 = 1$, the basis columns R_q price out to u_4^o, and those of A_4 price out nonnegative. (Compare with § 23-1-(12).) Next, we determine an objective form for $\mathscr{L}_3$, namely

$$(9) \qquad \text{Minimize } z_4 = \sum_{j=1}^{L} (\pi_4 \bar{T}_j) \mu_j$$

We assume we have at hand some feasible basis for $\mathscr{L}_3$. The values of simplex multipliers $(\pi_3^o; \; u_3, \; v_3^o)$ for this basis can now be determined using the values of $(\pi_4 \bar{T}_j)$ pertaining to basis columns. We now wish to test $\mathscr{L}_3$ for optimality by pricing out (using these multipliers) all columns $i = 1, 2,$ . . ., K and $j = 1, 2, \ldots, L$. However, since K and L can be large, we wish to discover the columns $i = i_0$ and $j = j_0$ that price out the least *without actually generating all the columns* in advance; we note by (4.1)

$$(10) \quad \pi_4^o \bar{T}_{j_0} - \pi_3^o T_{j_0} = \underset{j}{\text{Min}} \, [\pi_4^o \bar{T}_j - \pi_3^o T_j]$$

$$= \text{Min} \, [(-\pi_3^o A_2) X_2 + (\pi_4^o \bar{A}_3) X_3] \leq v_3^o, \quad ((X_2, X_3) \in \mathscr{L}_2)$$

[468]

and

$$(11) \qquad -\pi_3 S_{i_0} = \underset{i}{\text{Min}} \left[-\pi_3^o S_i \right] = \text{Min} \left[-(\pi_3^o \bar{A}_1) X_1 \right] \leq u_3^o \qquad (X_1 \in \mathscr{L}_1)$$

Hence, the problem reduces to minimizing the two linear objective forms; the first, (10), in variables (X_2, X_3), where $(X_2, X_3) \in \mathscr{L}_2$, and the second, (11), linear in X_1, where $X_1 \in \mathscr{L}_1$. If the solutions to these two linear subprograms yield equality, then subprogram $\mathscr{L}_3$ was optimum and the problem terminates. If not, then the transforms of the extreme point solution $X_1 = X_{1*}$ or $(X_2, X_3) = (X_{2*}, X_{3*})$ associated with the most negative one is adjoined to the restricted $\mathscr{L}_3$ problem and used, in turn, to generate a new extreme solution for the second-order master problem.

As in § 23-1, we note that it is not necessary to carry over from one cycle to the next any columns of (7) or (8) not in the basis. Non-basic columns in these programs may be dropped and forgotten; they will be generated again if needed.

Although we have been working with a four-stage program, our procedure has been perfectly general. Letting $[p]$ mean the largest integer not exceeding p, we can see the following:

THEOREM 1: *A K-stage problem can be decomposed into K-subprograms; one corresponding to each stage, the total number of equations in the set of subprograms is $K - 1$ more than the total number of equations of the original problem; the subprograms form a hierarchy with $[K/2]$ or $[K/2] + 1$ equations in the lowest rung, $[K/4]$ or $[K/4] + 1$ in the next, etc.*

It will be noted that the procedure yields the *optimal multipliers*, but it was necessary to do some side calculations to get the optimal values of the primal variables. It may be useful to consider the *dual* of a multi-stage program, for it has the same structure. The calculations carried out on the dual permit direct evaluation of the primal variables and indirect evaluation of the multipliers.

23-5. PROBLEMS

1. Consider the method used of decomposing the multi-stage system § 23-4-(2); develop the analogous method for decentralized planning in such a structure. Generalize.

2. With reference to Problem 1, develop alternative methods corresponding to other ways to decompose such a system.

3. With reference to the discussion following § 23-4, Theorem 1, dualize § 23-4-(2) and develop a method based on the decomposition principle that will evaluate directly the primal variables.

4. Establish in general the statement in § 23-4, Theorem 1, that there are $K - 1$ more equations in the set of subprograms than in the original system.

5. Analogous to § 23-1-(20), develop a lower bound for z for the simplex method for the case where one of the equations is of the form $\sum_1^n x_j = 1$.

6. Let α_j be an upper bound for x_j and let $x_0 + \sum_1^n \bar{c}_j x_j = x_0^o$; show, in general, that another upper bound for x_0 is $x_0^o - \Sigma \bar{c}_j \alpha_j$, where the summation is restricted to those j such that $\bar{c}_j < 0$.

REFERENCES

Abadie, 1963-1
Abadie and Williams, 1963-1
Curtes, 1963-1
Dantzig, 1957-3, 1960-1, 1963-1, 1964-2
Dantzig and Wolfe, 1961-1
Dzielinski and Gomory, 1963-1
Ford and Fulkerson, 1958-1
Gauthier, 1961-1
Gomory and Hu, 1960-2
Jewell, 1958-1
Kawaratani, Ullman, and Dantzig, 1960-1
Kuhn and Tucker, 1950-2
Macguire, 1963-1
Malinvaud, 1963-1
Manne, 1960-1
Marschak, 1962-1
Rosen, 1963-2
Whinston, 1962-1, 1964-1
Williams, 1962-1
Wolfe and Dantzig, 1962-1

CHAPTER 24

CONVEX PROGRAMMING

24-1. GENERAL THEORY

Kuhn and Tucker in their paper on "Nonlinear Programming" [1950-2] [Tucker, 1957-1] considered the problem of minimizing a convex function with variables x_1, x_2, . . ., x_n subject to the condition that the values assumed by a system of concave functions in these variables be nonnegative. They showed that if the concave functions were *differentiable*, the method of Lagrange multipliers could be appropriately extended to inequality restrictions on concave functions (see discussion in § 6-5). Instead of concave functions, their negative, convex functions (for definition, see § 7-1 and Fig. 7-1-VIII) will be used whose values must be nonpositive. Following Slater [1950-1] and Uzawa [1958-1], our object will be to show that their results hold even if the functions are not differentiable, provided: (a) the domain of variation is restricted to a closed bounded convex set R; (b) there exists at least one point where the convex functions are all negative; and, (c) the convex functions are continuous[1] in R. We shall also give a constructive procedure for solving such systems using the generalized programming approach. Philip Wolfe first discussed this idea at the RAND Symposium on Mathematical Programming, 1959, for convex objectives; at the same meeting, H. O. Hartley discussed the case of variable coefficients in a column of a special form. The first proof of convergence can be found in Dantzig [1960-3]; see also A. C. Williams [1960-1].

Problem A: Find a point $x = (x_1, x_2, . . ., x_n)$ in a closed bounded convex set R and the minimum value of z satisfying

$$(1) \qquad \phi_i(x) \leq 0 \qquad\qquad (i = 1, 2, . . ., m)$$
$$\phi_0(x) = z \text{ (Min)}$$

where the $\phi_i(x)$ are continuous convex functions.

THEOREM 1: *If there exists $x^o \in R$ such that $\phi_i(x^o) < 0$ for $i = 1, 2, . . ., m$, then there exist multipliers $\hat{\pi}_1 \geq 0, \hat{\pi}_2 \geq 0, . . ., \hat{\pi}_m \geq 0$ and an $\hat{x} \in R$ which solves (1) with Min z and satisfies*

$$(2a) \qquad F(\hat{x}) = \text{Min } F(x) = \underset{x \in R}{\text{Min}} \left[\phi_0(x) + \sum_1^m \hat{\pi}_i \phi_i(x) \right]$$

---

[1] Since a general convex function is always continuous in the interior of the domain of definition, R, we are essentially assuming that this continuity extends to the boundary.

or, if the $\phi_i(x)$ are differentiable, satisfies the Kuhn-Tucker condition,

(2b)
$$\sum_{j=1}^{n} (x_j - \hat{x}_j) \frac{\partial F}{\partial x_j}\Big|_{x = \hat{x}} \geq 0 \qquad \text{for all } x \in R,$$

where $F(x)$ is defined by the bracket term in (2a).

EXERCISE: Show that a convex differentiable function $F(x)$ defined over a closed bounded convex set R attains a minimum at $x = \hat{x}$ if and only if (2b) is satisfied.

EXERCISE: Show that the usual primal-dual complementary slackness for optimality is a special case of (2b).

We shall consider Problem A in a slightly more general form.

Problem B: Find a point $x = (x_1, x_2, \ldots, x_n)$ in a closed bounded convex set R and Min z satisfying

(3)
$$L_i(x) = 0 \qquad (i = 1, 2, \ldots, r)$$
$$\phi_i(x) \leq 0 \qquad (i = r + 1, \ldots, m)$$
$$\phi_0(x) = z \text{ (Min)}$$

where $\phi_i(x) = L_i(x)$, for $i = 1, 2, \ldots, r$, are *linear*, and $\phi_i(x)$, for $i = 0$ and $r + 1, \ldots, m$, *are continuous convex functions.*

As noted in § 22-1, we may rewrite (3) in the form

(4)
$$\lambda_0 = 1 \qquad (\mu_i \geq 0)$$
$$y_1 \lambda_0 = 0$$
$$\cdot \qquad \cdot$$
$$\cdot \qquad \cdot$$
$$\cdot \qquad \cdot$$
$$y_r \lambda_0 = 0$$
$$y_{r+1} \lambda_0 + \mu_{r+1} = 0$$
$$\cdot \qquad \cdot$$
$$\cdot \qquad \cdot$$
$$\cdot \qquad \cdot$$
$$y_m \lambda_0 + \mu_m = 0$$
$$y_0 \lambda_0 = z \text{ (Min)}$$

where y_i are variable coefficients that may be freely chosen subject to the conditions that $y_i = L_i(x)$ for $1 \leq i \leq r$ and $y_i \geq \phi_i(x)$ for $r + 1 \leq i \leq m$ for some $x \in R$.

EXERCISE: Show that the set of possible $P = \langle 1, y_1, y_2, \ldots, y_m, y_0 \rangle$ is a *convex set* and that (4) is a generalized program; see § 22-1-(27), (28).

Nondegeneracy Assumption. There exists at least one nondegenerate basic feasible solution to a restricted master problem, (5), generated by some p choices of admissible P:

(5)
$$\lambda_1 P_1 + \ldots + \lambda_p P_p + \mu_{r+1} U_{r+1} + \ldots + \mu_m U_m + (-z) U_{m+1} = U_0$$
$$(\lambda_j \geq 0, \ \mu_i \geq 0)$$

where U_i denotes the unit vector with its unit component in equation i of (4), where i may range from $i = 0$ to $i = m + 1$. This restricted master, which we assume for convenience to be the initial restricted master, whose columns form a *basis*, is shown explicitly in detached coefficient form and in greater detail in (6). Because the basic solution is nondegenerate, the values of λ_i and μ_{r+l} are positive.

(6)

Initial Restricted Master Program for Problem B, Cycle k (for Initial Basis set $k = 0, p = r + 1$)								Multipliers
$\lambda_1 \geq 0$ ...	$\lambda_p \geq 0$ ...	$\lambda_{p+k} \geq 0$	$\mu_{r+1} \geq 0$ ...	$\mu_m \geq 0$	$(-z)$	Constants		
1 ...	1 ...	1	0..............		0	1		(π_0)
y_1^1 ...	y_1^p ...	y_1^{p+k}	0..............		0	0		(π_1)
$\cdot$	$\cdot$	$\cdot$	$\cdot$		$\cdot$	$\cdot$		$\cdot$
$\cdot$	$\cdot$	$\cdot$	$\cdot$		$\cdot$	$\cdot$		$\cdot$
y_r^1 ...	y_r^p ...	y_r^{p+k}	0..............		0	0		$\cdot$
y_{r+1}^1 ...	y_{r+1}^p ...	y_{r+1}^{p+k}	1		0	0		$\cdot$
$\cdot$	$\cdot$	$\cdot$	$\cdot$		$\cdot$	$\cdot$		$\cdot$
$\cdot$	$\cdot$	$\cdot$	$\cdot$		$\cdot$	$\cdot$		$\cdot$
y_m^1 ...	y_m^p ...	y_m^{p+k}		1	0	0		(π_m)
y_0^1 ...	y_0^p ...	y_0^{p+k}	0 ...	0	1	0		(1)

EXERCISE: Show that the nondegeneracy assumption implies the existence of a point x^o such that $L_i(x^o) = 0$ for $i = 1, 2, \ldots, r$ and $\phi_i(x^o) < 0$ for $i = r + 1, \ldots, m$.

EXERCISE: Show that if there exists a point x^o satisfying the above conditions and a nondegenerate basis for the system of r linear equations $L_i(x) = 0$ above, then there exists a nondegenerate basis for the system as a whole.

Since we have shown that (4) is a generalized program, we are in a position to apply the methods of § 22-1 to affect a solution. This is an iterative procedure that was shown to converge in a finite number of steps when the variable coefficients associated with any column are drawn from a convex polyhedron. However, in both Problems A and B we are dealing with *general convex sets* and our purpose is to show that the process, if infinite, converges to a solution.

EXERCISE: Assuming that the iterative procedure converges, formulate a "Phase I" type problem that will yield, in a *finite* number of iterations, a nondegenerate basic feasible solution satisfying (5), if one exists. *Hint:* Make use of the two previous exercises.

[473]

Finding an Initial Nondegenerate Basic Feasible Solution to a Restricted Master Program.

Under the hypothesis of Theorem 1, where there are no linear equations $L_i(x)$ to be satisfied, there exists an $x = x^o$ such that $\phi_i(x^o) < 0$ for $i = 1, 2, \ldots, m$. The nondegeneracy condition is then satisfied by the basic solution formed by using m slack variables and the variable $\lambda_1 = 1$, where the coefficients of λ_1 are $y_i^1 = \phi_i(x^o)$ [see (7)]. Hence for Problem A, there *always exists at least one nondegenerate basic feasible solution*.

(7)

Initial Restricted Master (and Basis) for Problem A							
λ_1	μ_1	.	.	.	μ_m	$(-z)$	Constants
1							1
$\phi_1(x^o)$	1						0
.							.
.		.					.
.			.				.
$\phi_m(x^o)$				.	1		0
$\phi_0(x^o)$						1	0

For Problem B, we assume that we have at hand a nondegenerate basic feasible solution to some restricted master with which to initiate the algorithm. See the first and second exercises above.

Iterative Procedure.

We now review the iterative procedure given in Chapter 22 for a generalized program. The restricted master (5) for some cycle k is optimized, yielding a new basic feasible solution λ^k, and a new set of simplex multipliers π^k. These multipliers are used to generate a new column P_{p+k+1} for the restricted master for cycle $k + 1$ *where all columns of the master program for cycle k are retained and used in cycle $k + 1$*. (Note that retention of the columns was optional in Chapter 22, but here it is required for the proof of convergence.)

The components of λ^k, the kth basic feasible solution, will be denoted by

$$\lambda_1^k, \lambda_2^k, \ldots, \lambda_{p+k}^k, \mu_{r+1}^k, \ldots, \mu_m^k \geq 0$$

and

$$z^k = \sum_{j=1}^{p+k} \lambda_j^k y_0^j$$

In order to express conveniently the kth approximation, $\hat{x}^k$, to a minimizing solution of Problem B, we will assume that each column P_j of the master program is defined by choosing some value $x = x^j$ and setting

$$P_j = \langle 1, \phi_1(x^j), \phi_2(x^j), \ldots, \phi_m(x^j); \phi_0(x^j) \rangle \qquad (j = 1, 2, \ldots, p + k)$$

[474]

In this case the kth approximation to the minimizing solution of (3) is

$$(8) \qquad \hat{x}^k = \sum_{j=1}^{p+k} \lambda_j^k x^j; \quad \hat{z}^k = \phi_0\,(\hat{x}^k)$$

The simplex multipliers for cycle k satisfy the following conditions:

$$(9) \qquad \pi^k U_{m+1} = 1$$

$$\left.\begin{array}{l} \pi^k P_j \quad = 0 \\ \pi^k U_i \quad = 0 \end{array}\right\} \text{ if } \lambda_j \text{ or } \mu_i \text{ is a basic variable}$$

$$\left.\begin{array}{l} \pi^k P_j \quad \geq 0 \\ \pi^k U_i \quad \geq 0 \end{array}\right\} \text{ if } \lambda_j \text{ or } \mu_i \text{ is a nonbasic variable}$$

It follows that the components $i = r + 1, \ldots, m$ of $\pi^k = [\pi_0^k, \pi_1^k, \ldots, \pi_m^k; 1]$ are *nonnegative* because $\pi_i^k = \pi^k U_i \geq 0$ for these i.

To test whether or not the kth approximate solution (8) is optimal, the function

$$(10) \qquad \Delta(x|\pi^k) = \phi_0(x) + \sum_{1}^{m} \pi_i^k \phi_i(x) + \pi_0^k$$

is *minimized* over all $x \in R$.

THEOREM 2: *If Min* $\Delta(x|\pi^k) \geq 0$ *for* $x \in R$, *then* $\hat{x}^k$ *is optimal.*

PROOF: Let $x \in R$ satisfy

$$(11) \qquad \begin{array}{ll} L_i(x) = 0 & (i = 1, 2, \ldots, r) \\ \phi_i(x) \leq 0 & (i = r + 1, \ldots, m) \end{array}$$

Multiplying the ith relation by π_i^k, where $\pi_i^k \geq 0$ for $i = r + 1, \ldots, m$, and adding gives

$$(12) \qquad \sum \pi_i^k \phi_i(x) \leq 0$$

Adding $\phi_0(x) + \pi_0^k$ to both sides of this inequality yields

$$(13) \qquad \Delta(x|\pi^k) \leq \phi_0(x) + \pi_0^k$$

Setting $\lambda = \lambda^k$ in the master program (6), multiplying its rows by the corresponding components of π^k, and summing yield, by the complementary slackness conditions (9) of the optimal solutions to the primal and dual systems,

$$(14) \qquad -z^k = \pi_0^k$$

So that

$$(15) \qquad \Delta(x|\pi_0^k) + z^k \leq \phi_0(x)$$

On the other hand, for the approximate solution $\hat{x}^k = \Sigma \lambda_j^k x^j$, it follows from the convexity of $\phi_0(x)$ that

$$(16) \qquad \phi_0(\hat{x}^k) \leq \sum_{j=1}^{p+k} \lambda_j^k \phi_0(x^j) = \sum_{j=1}^{p+k} \lambda_j^k y_0^j = z^k$$

By first selecting that x which minimizes $\phi_0(x)$ in (15) and then that x which minimizes $\Delta(x|\pi_0^k)$, it is easy to see that

THEOREM 3: *Lower and upper bounds for* Min $\phi_0(x)$ *are*

$$(17) \qquad \underset{x \in R}{\text{Min}} \; \Delta(x|\pi^k) + z^k \leq \text{Min} \; \phi_0(x) \leq \phi_0(\hat{x}^k) \leq z^k$$

Continuing with the proof of Theorem 2, setting $x = \hat{x}$ in (13), noting (16),

$$(18) \qquad \text{Min} \; \Delta(x|\pi^k) \leq \Delta(\hat{x}|\pi^k) \leq \phi_0(\hat{x}^k) + \pi_0^k = \phi_0(\hat{x}^k) - z^k \leq 0$$

If now we employ the hypothesis Min $\Delta(x|\pi^k) \geq 0$, the above implies

$$(19) \qquad \text{Min} \; \Delta(x|\pi_0^k) = 0$$

and, by Theorem 3,

$$(20) \qquad -\pi_0^k = z^k = \phi_0(\hat{x}^k) = \text{Min} \; \phi_0(x)$$

which establishes Theorem 2.

EXERCISES:

(a) Prove Theorem 3 in detail.

(b) Show that a nonnegative weighted sum of convex functions is a convex function.

(c) Show that $\Delta(x|\pi^k)$ is a continuous convex function on R.

(d) Show that there exists an $\hat{x} \in R$, such that $\Delta(\hat{x}|\pi^k) = \text{Min} \; \Delta(x|\pi^k)$.

Generating a New Column for the Master Program.

If Min $\Delta(x|\pi^k) < 0$, define $x^{k+1} \in R$ and P_{p+k+1} by

$$(21) \qquad \Delta(x^{k+1}|\pi^k) = \underset{x \in R}{\text{Min}} \; \Delta(x|\pi^k) < 0$$

$$(22) \qquad P_{p+k+1} = \langle 1, \phi_1(x^{k+1}), \ldots, \phi_m(x^{k+1}); \phi_0(x^{k+1}) \rangle$$

It follows from the definitions (10), (21), and (22), that

$$(23) \qquad \pi^k P_{p+k+1} = \Delta(x^{k+1}|\pi^k) < 0$$

If we could now show that Min $\Delta(x|\pi^k)$ tends to zero as $k \to \infty$, it would be easy to show convergence of $\phi_0(x^k)$ from Theorem 3, since z^k forms a monotonically decreasing sequence bounded from below [see Exercise (d)]. However, note that convergence can also be established if Min Δ tends to zero on some subset of the k's; indeed, the latter is all we shall be able to prove. For this purpose we first show

THEOREM 4: *If a nondegenerate basic feasible solution exists for some master program, there is an infinite subset K of values of k, such that* Lim π^k *exists for $k \in K$.*
$$k \to \infty$$

PROOF: Let B be the basis of some master program associated with the nondegenerate basic feasible solution. For convenience, let this be the solution for (6), the initial master program $k = 0$, and let

$$(24) \qquad B = [P_1, P_2, \ldots, P_{m+1}, U_{m+1}]$$

where some of the P_j may be the U_i associated with the slack variables. Thus $\lambda^o = \langle \lambda_1^o, \lambda_2^o, \ldots, \lambda_{m+1}^o, -z^o \rangle$ satisfies

$$(25) \qquad B\lambda^o = U_0$$

and, by nondegeneracy, the components λ_i^o are positive. Thus

$$(26) \qquad \lambda^o = B^{-1}U_0 = [\lambda_1^o, \lambda_2^o, \ldots, \lambda_{m+1}^o, -z^o]^T \qquad \text{where } \lambda_i^o > 0$$

On the other hand, any π^k solving the dual master program for cycle k satisfies $\pi^k P_j \geq 0$, $\pi^k U_{m+1} = 1$ by (9), and therefore the components of a vector $\gamma^k = (\gamma_1^k, \gamma_2^k, \ldots, \gamma_m^k, 1)$ defined by (27) are nonnegative

$$(27) \qquad \pi^k B = \gamma^k \geq 0 \qquad\qquad (\gamma_i^k \geq 0)$$

Observe that $\pi^k = \gamma^k B^{-1}$, and in particular, that

$$\begin{aligned} \pi_0^k = \pi^k U_0 &= \gamma^k(B^{-1}U_0) = \gamma^k \lambda^o \\ &= \gamma_1^k \lambda_1^o + \gamma_2^k \lambda_2^o + \ldots + \gamma_{m+1}^k \lambda_{m+1}^o - z^o \end{aligned}$$

Hence, noting that $\pi_0^k = -z^k \leq -\phi(\hat{x}^k) \leq -\text{Min } \phi_0(x)$, we have

$$(28) \qquad z^o - \text{Min } \phi_0(x) \geq (\gamma_1^k \lambda_1^o + \gamma_2^k \lambda_2^o + \ldots + \gamma_{m+1}^k \lambda_{m+1}^o) \qquad (\lambda_i^o > 0)$$

It is now easy to see, because $\gamma_i^k \geq 0$, and $\lambda_i^o > 0$, that by reducing the right-hand side of (28) by dropping all products except the ith,

$$(29) \qquad 0 \leq \gamma_i^k \leq [z^o - \text{Min } \phi_0(x)]/\lambda_i^o$$

Therefore the components of γ^k have finite upper and lower bounds and Theorem 4 follows from the exercises below.

EXERCISE: If the components of γ^k have finite upper and lower bounds, then the same is true for any linear transform, in particular, the components of π^k, where $\pi^k = \gamma^k B^{-1}$.

EXERCISE: If the components of π^k have finite upper and lower bounds, there exists an infinite subset, K, of values k such that $\text{Lim } \pi^k$ exists for $k \in K$ as $k \to \infty$.

THEOREM 5: *For x satisfying the conditions of Problem B,*

$$\lim_{k \to \infty} \phi_0(\hat{x}^k) = \text{Min } \phi_0(x)$$

PROOF: Either the process is finite and an optimum solution is obtained or for all k we have

$$(30) \qquad \text{Min } \Delta(x|\pi^k) = \pi^k P_{k+1} < 0$$

and, since the master program for any cycle $l > k$ contains the column P_{k+1}, we have also for all k and all $l > k$,

$$(31) \qquad \pi^l P_{k+1} \geq 0 \qquad (l > k)$$

For $k \in K$ and $l \in K$ the difference, $(\pi^k - \pi^l) \to 0$ as $k \to \infty$ and $l > k$, by Theorem 4. Since R is bounded and $\phi_i(x)$ is continuous in R, $\phi_i(x)$ is bounded in R and so is the ith component, $\phi_i(x_j)$, of P_j over all j. Because the components of P_{k+1} are bounded from above and below, the difference $(\pi^k - \pi^l) P_{k+1}$ must also tend to zero. But, if the difference between the left sides of (30) and (31) goes to zero and $\pi^k P_{k+1}$ is negative and $\pi^l P_{k+1}$ is nonnegative, then $\pi^k P_{k+1}$ must come arbitrarily close to zero; that is, for any $\varepsilon > 0$, there exists a k_ε such that for any $k \in K$ and greater than k_ε,

$$(32) \qquad -\varepsilon < \operatorname*{Min}_{x \in R} \Delta(x|\pi^k) < 0 \qquad (k \geq k_\varepsilon,\ k \in K)$$

From Theorem 3 and (32), the convergence of z_k to $\operatorname{Min} \phi_0(x)$ now follows on the set $k \in K$. But the z_k are monotonically decreasing for all k. We conclude z_k tends to $\operatorname{Min} \phi_0(x)$ for any set $k \to \infty$ (not just for $k \in K$). Since z_k is an upper bound for $\phi_0(\hat{x}^k)$, the latter also must converge to this limit. This establishes Theorem 5.

THEOREM 6: *Let $\hat{\pi} = \operatorname{Lim}_{k \to \infty} \pi^k$ for $k \in K$ and let $\hat{x}$ be any optimum solution to Problem B, then*

$$(33) \qquad F(\hat{x}) = \operatorname{Min} F(x) = \operatorname*{Min}_{x \in R} \left[\phi_0(x) + \sum_{i=1}^{m} \hat{\pi}_i \phi_i(x) \right]$$

where $\hat{\pi}$ has nonnegative components for $i = r + 1, \ldots, m$.

PROOF: From (32), for $k > k_\varepsilon$ and $k \in K$

$$(34) \qquad -\varepsilon \leq \Delta(x|\pi^k) \leq \phi_0(x) + \pi_0^k$$

where the inequality on the right is from (13). In the limit, letting $k \to +\infty$, $\varepsilon \to 0$, $\operatorname{Lim} \pi^k = \hat{\pi}$ and

$$(35) \qquad 0 \leq \Delta(x|\hat{\pi}) = F(x) + \hat{\pi}_0 \leq \phi_0(x) + \hat{\pi}_0$$

where $\Delta(x|\hat{\pi})$ is defined by (10).

On the other hand, by (20)

$$(36) \qquad \hat{\pi}_0 = \operatorname{Lim} \pi_0^k = \operatorname{Lim} (-z_k) = -\operatorname*{Min}_{x \in R} \phi_0(x) = -\phi_0(\hat{x})$$

Hence, substituting $x = \hat{x}$ into (35) and noting the above, we have

$$(37) \qquad 0 = F(\hat{x}) + \hat{\pi}_0 \leq F(x) + \hat{\pi}_0$$

thus establishing Theorem 6 and, as a special case, Theorem 1.

24-2. HOMOGENEOUS OBJECTIVES AND THE CHEMICAL EQUILIBRIUM PROBLEM

Homogeneous Objective Functions of the First Degree.

In some applications, such as the chemical problem to be discussed later, we have to minimize a convex function

$$(1) \qquad G(x) = \bar{x} G\left(\frac{x_1}{\bar{x}}, \frac{x_2}{\bar{x}}, \ldots, \frac{x_n}{\bar{x}}\right)$$

where

$$(2) \qquad \bar{x} = x_1 + x_2 + \ldots + x_n$$

subject to a system of linear equations in nonnegative variables,

$$(3) \qquad \sum_{j=1}^{n} a_{ij} x_j = b_i, \qquad x_j \geq 0 \quad (i = 1, 2, \ldots, m)$$

Note that if each component of x is multiplied by t, the value of $G(x)$ is multiplied by t:

$$(4) \qquad G(tx) = tG(x)$$

That is to say, G is a *homogeneous function of first degree.*

We will assume that $G(u) > 0$ is a continuous convex function on the set of possible u satisfying

$$(5) \qquad u_1 + u_2 + \ldots + u_n = 1 \qquad\qquad (u_j \geq 0)$$

During the iterative process, we shall generate solutions $\hat{x}^1, \hat{x}^2, \ldots$ satisfying (3), such that $G(\hat{x}^k)$ is monotonically decreasing. Letting z_0 be an upper bound for $G(x)$, for $x = \hat{x}^k$ we have for such x

$$(6) \qquad G(x) = \bar{x} G(u) < z_0 \qquad\qquad (x = \hat{x}^k)$$
$$0 \leq \bar{x} < z_0/\text{Min } G(u)$$

It follows that the components of such x are bounded from above and below.

Consider the equivalent *single-variable* generalized program

$$(7) \qquad \begin{cases} \bar{x}\left[\displaystyle\sum_{j=1}^{n} a_{1j} u_j\right] = b_1 & \left(\bar{x} \geq 0, \, u_j \geq 0, \, \sum u_j = 1\right) \\[2ex] \bar{x}\left[\displaystyle\sum_{j=1}^{n} a_{2j} u_j\right] = b_2 \\[2ex] \qquad\qquad \cdots\cdots\cdots\cdots \\[2ex] \bar{x}\left[\displaystyle\sum_{j=1}^{n} a_{mj} u_j\right] = b_m \\[2ex] \bar{x} G(u) = z \; (\text{Min}) \end{cases}$$

[479]

where $\bar{x} \geq 0$ is the variable whose coefficients are linear in u_j subject to (5). This gives rise to a master program that forms a general solution out of a nonnegative linear combination of columns of coefficients generated by various solutions u^k to the subprograms. This is in contradistinction to the usual case where convex combinations are required. This greater flexibility is possible, because the set of coefficients are homogeneous functions in u. To be explicit, we start with some set of m vectors $u = u^p$ satisfying (5) and, setting $[a_{ij}] = A$, generate

$$(8) \qquad\qquad S_p = Au^p \qquad\qquad (p = 1, 2, \ldots, m)$$
$$c_p = G(u^p)$$

Assuming that the m columns form a feasible basis the first restricted master becomes

$$(9) \qquad\qquad \sum_1^m S_p \lambda_p^1 = b \qquad\qquad (\lambda_p^1 \geq 0)$$

$$\sum_1^m c_p \lambda_p^1 = z^1 \text{ (Min)}$$

This determines the simplex multipliers π^1 which satisfy

$$(10) \qquad\qquad \pi^1 S_p + c_p = 0 \qquad\qquad (p = 1, 2, \ldots, m)$$

To test optimality, the expression

$$(11) \qquad\qquad \Delta(u|\pi^1) = G(u) + (\pi^1 A)u$$

is minimized over all u satisfying (5). If Min $\Delta \geq 0$, the solution

$$(12) \qquad\qquad \hat{x} = \sum_1^m \lambda_p^1 u^p$$

is optimal. If not, choose u^{m+1} such that

$$(13) \qquad\qquad G(u^{m+1}) + (\pi^1 A)u^{m+1} = \text{Min } \Delta\ (u|\pi^1)$$

Augment the master system (9) by $S_{m+1} = Au^{m+1}$ and $c_{m+1} = G(u^{m+1})$, optimize the new restricted master with $\lambda = \lambda^2$, and repeat the cycle with new multipliers $\pi = \pi^2$, etc.

A slight variation in our earlier proof given in § 24-1 (to take account of the fact that we no longer have the $\Sigma\lambda_i = 1$ constraint or its multiplier s) yields the following

THEOREM 1: *If there exists at least one nondegenerate basic feasible solution to a master program, then the modified algorithm converges to an optimal solution.*

EXERCISE: Show that, if $G(x)$ is a linear objective form, then it is also convex and homogeneous of the first degree, and that the procedure just developed reduces to the standard simplex method.

EXERCISE: Prove Theorem 1. What role does (6) play in the proof?

The Chemical Equilibrium Problem.

For an application of the preceding theory, let us consider the problem of determining the molecular composition of the equilibrium state of a gaseous mixture containing m different types of atoms [White, Johnson, and Dantzig, 1958-1]. While in theory these will combine into all chemically possible molecular species, in practice only the standard types which occur in measurable amounts are considered.

Let

b_i = the number of atomic weights of atom type i present in the mixture,

x_j = the number of moles of molecular species j present in the mixture, where

(14) $$x_j \geq 0 \qquad (j = 1, 2, \ldots, n)$$

$\bar{x}$ = the total number of moles of gas in the mixture, i.e.,

(15) $$\bar{x} = \sum x_j$$

a_{ij} = the number of atoms of type i in a molecule of species j.

Then the mass-balance equations are

(16) $$\sum_{j=1}^{n} a_{ij} x_j = b_i \qquad \text{for} \quad i = 1, 2, \ldots, m$$

The determination of the equilibrium composition of a gaseous mixture is equivalent to the determination of the values of the mole numbers x_j that obey constraints (16) and minimize the total free energy of the mixture given by

(17) $$G(x_1, \ldots, x_n) = \sum_{1}^{n} c_j x_j + \sum_{1}^{n} x_j \log (x_j/\bar{x})$$
$$= \bar{x} \left[\sum_{1}^{n} c_j (x_j/\bar{x}) + \sum_{1}^{n} (x_j/\bar{x}) \log (x_j/\bar{x}) \right]$$
$$= \bar{x} \sum_{1}^{n} (c_j u_j + u_j \log u_j) \qquad (u_j = x_j/\bar{x} \geq 0)$$

which can be shown to be a convex function. The c_j are the values of *Gibbs free energy functions* F^o/RT of the atomic species at a given temperature plus the natural logarithm of the pressure in atmospheres.

Our problem is to minimize (17), a first degree homogeneous form, subject

[481]

to the linear equality and inequality constraints (14), (15), and (16). The function

$$(18) \qquad G(u) = \sum (c_j u_j + u_j \log u_j) \qquad (u_j \geq 0)$$

is clearly convex.

For this application, then,

$$(19) \qquad \Delta = G(u) + \sum \pi_i^k \sum a_{ij} u_j$$
$$= \sum (u_j \log u_j + \bar{c}_j^k u_j)$$

where π_i^k are the simplex multipliers of some iteration defined by relations analogous to (10). Let

$$(20) \qquad \bar{c}_j^k = c_j + \sum_{i=1}^{m} \pi_i^k a_{ij}$$

To find the Min Δ subject to

$$(21) \qquad \sum u_j = 1 \qquad (u_j \geq 0)$$

we ignore the relations $u_j \geq 0$ and find the unconditional minimum of the function

$$(22) \qquad \bar{\Delta} = \sum \left(u_j \log u_j + \bar{c}_j^k u_j \right) - \theta \left(\sum u_j - 1 \right)$$

where θ is a Lagrange multiplier (see § 6-5). We set the partial derivatives of $\bar{\Delta}$ with respect to u_j to zero; thus

$$(23) \qquad \frac{\partial \bar{\Delta}}{\partial u_j} = 1 + \log u_j + \bar{c}_j^k - \theta = 0$$

whence u_j may be written in the form

$$(24) \qquad u_j = A e^{-\bar{c}_j^k}$$

where $A = e^{\theta - 1} > 0$. Substituting into (21) determines A and

$$(25) \qquad u_j = e^{-\bar{c}_j^k} \bigg/ \sum_{i=1}^{n} e^{-\bar{c}_i^k}$$

so that the conditions $u_j \geq 0$ hold at the minimum. These, then, are the values $u_j = u_j^{k+1}$ with which to initiate the next iteration.

24-3. SEPARABLE CONVEX OBJECTIVES

DEFINITION: If the objective function to be minimized, instead of being linear, is of the form

$$(1) \qquad \sum_{j=1}^{n} \phi_j(x_j) = z \text{ (Min)} \qquad (0 \leq x_j \leq h_j)$$

[482]

where $\phi_j(x_j)$ is a convex function, it is called *convex-separable*, a term used by Charnes to describe this class of objective forms [Charnes and Lemke, 1954-1; Dantzig, 1956-2]. We shall assume that h_j is a given finite upper bound for x_j and the x_j are subject to

$$(2) \qquad \sum_{j=1}^{n} a_{ij}x_j = b_i \qquad\qquad (i = 1, 2, \ldots, m)$$

To illustrate, if the first 100 units of an activity can be performed at \$1 per unit, the next 50 units at \$1.25 per unit and the next 50 units at \$1.50 per unit, then the total cost $\phi(x)$ is convex in the range $0 \leq x \leq 200$. In general, if the first α_1 units cost s_1 per unit, the second α_2 units cost s_2 per unit, . . ., the last α_k units cost s_k per unit, then the total cost $\phi(x)$ is convex if $s_1 \leq s_2 \leq \ldots \leq s_k$, but is not convex if, for any r, $s_r > s_{r+1}$.

EXERCISE: The definition of a convex function is given in §7-1. Show that it is equivalent to the definition: a function $\phi(x)$ is convex if

$$(3) \qquad \phi\left(\sum \lambda_r x_r\right) \leq \sum \lambda_r \phi(x_r)$$

for any $\lambda_r \geq 0$, such that $\Sigma \lambda_r = 1$.

EXERCISE: Show that, if the cost of the jth activity is proportional to the square of the jth activity, $\phi_j(x_j) = c_j x_j^2$, then $\phi(x_j)$ is convex for $c_j \geq 0$ but is not convex for $c_j < 0$.

As a third example, if the total cost $\phi(x)$ consists of a fixed charge f and the remaining cost is proportional to the activity level, then $\phi(x)$ is convex. On the other hand, if there is a fixed charge f only if $x > 0$, then we can write

$$(4) \qquad \phi(x) = \begin{cases} f + hx, & \text{if } x > 0 \\ 0, & \text{if } x = 0 \end{cases}$$

In this case $\phi(x)$ is not convex, if $f > 0$.

EXERCISE: Show that if $f \leq 0$, $\phi(x)$, above, is convex.

To replace equations (1) and (2) by a standard linear programming problem, we assume that $\phi_j(x)$ is a broken-line function. Later we shall remove this restriction. (In the event that $\phi_j(x)$ has a continuous derivative, one can select $k + 1$ points on the curve such that the broken line fit through these points is a sufficiently close approximation.)

The Equivalent Linear Program.

For $r = 0, 1, 2, \ldots, k$, let (f_{rj}, g_{rj}) be the coordinates of the break points $(x_j, \phi_j(x_j))$ of the function $\phi_j(x)$ (see Fig. 24-3-I). Any x_j in the range $f_{0j} \leq x_j \leq f_{kj}$ may be represented by

$$(5) \qquad x_j = \lambda_{0j}f_{0j} + \lambda_{1j}f_{1j} + \ldots + \lambda_{kj}f_{kj} \qquad\qquad (\lambda_{rj} \geq 0)$$

[483]

where

(6)
$$1 = \lambda_{0j} + \lambda_{1j} + \ldots + \lambda_{kj}$$

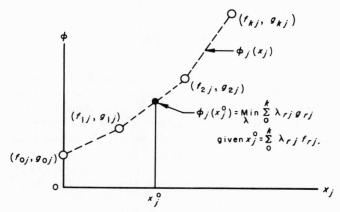

Figure 24-3-I. Converting a convex function into a linear programming format.

Since ϕ_j is a convex function, we then have, by (3),

(7)
$$\phi_j(x_j) \leq \lambda_{0j}g_{0j} + \lambda_{1j}g_{1j} + \ldots + \lambda_{kj}g_{kj}$$

To solve (1) and (2), determine $\lambda_{rj} \geq 0$, and Min z' satisfying

(8)
$$\sum_{j=1}^{n} a_{ij}[\lambda_{0j}f_{0j} + \lambda_{1j}f_{1j} + \ldots + \lambda_{kj}f_{kj}] = b_i \qquad (i = 1, 2, \ldots, m)$$

(9)
$$\lambda_{0j} + \lambda_{1j} + \ldots + \lambda_{kj} = 1 \qquad (j = 1, 2, \ldots, n)$$

(10)
$$\sum_{j=1}^{n} [\lambda_{0j}g_{0j} + \lambda_{1j}g_{1j} + \ldots + \lambda_{kj}g_{kj}] = z' \text{ (Min)}$$

and substitute the resulting λ into (5) to determine x_j. To prove that solving (8)–(10) is equivalent to solving (1) and (2), we have only to show that Min $z \geq$ Min z'. From (7), Min $z \leq$ Min z'. To show that Min $z \geq$ Min z', take the x_j yielding the minimum to (1) and (2) and represent them as combinations of the abscissas of the two breakpoints immediately to the left and right. The resulting λ satisfy (8) and (9) and satisfy (7) with *equality*, so that the z' resulting in (10) equals Min z. Hence, Min $z \geq$ Min z', as we were to show.

Bounded-Variable Method.

It will be noted that the above procedure increases the number of variables and increases the number of equations by one for each $\phi_j(x_j)$. By use of the upper bounding method, it is possible to maintain the original number of equations. The original variables will be replaced by sets of new bounded variables which (except in the cost row) will all have their several columns of coefficients identical (so that a number of short cuts are possible;

[484]

see Chapter 18). In Fig. 24-3-II the slopes of the broken line are denoted by s_i and the width of the intervals by α_i.

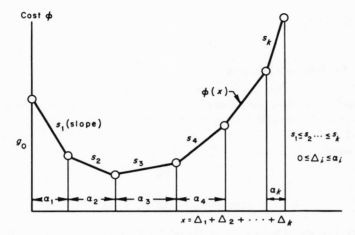

Figure 24-3-II. Converting a convex function into a linear programming format using bounded variables.

From the convexity of $\phi(x)$ follow the relations

(11)
$$s_1 \leq s_2 \leq \ldots \leq s_k$$

We now assert that

(12)
$$\phi(x) = g_0 + \text{Min} [s_1\Delta_1 + s_2\Delta_2 + \ldots + s_k\Delta_k]$$

where

(13)
$$x = \Delta_1 + \Delta_2 + \ldots + \Delta_k$$

and

(14)
$$0 \leq \Delta_i \leq \alpha_i$$

Indeed, since $s_1 \leq s_2 \leq \ldots \leq s_k$, it is obvious that the way to find the minimum is to choose Δ_1 as large as possible until it hits its upper bound α_1, then take Δ_2 in turn, etc., until a Δ_r is reached, such that setting $\Delta_r = \alpha_r$ the value of x is exceeded, in which case the value of Δ_r is reduced so that (13) holds. It is clear that this process is simply generating the curve $\phi(x)$ from 0 up to the value x.

Equivalent Linear Program.

To solve (1) and (2), determine $\Delta_{rj} \geq 0$ and Min z' satisfying

(15)
$$\sum_{j=1}^{n} a_{ij}[\Delta_{1j} + \Delta_{2j} + \ldots + \Delta_{kj}] = b_i \qquad (i = 1, 2, \ldots, m)$$

$$\sum_{j=1}^{n} [s_{1j}\Delta_{1j} + s_{2j}\Delta_{2j} + \ldots + s_{kj}\Delta_{kj}] = z' \text{ (Min)}$$

[485]

where

(16) $$0 \leq \Delta_{rj} \leq \alpha_{rj}$$

and determine x_j by

(17) $$x_j = \Delta_{1j} + \Delta_{2j} + \ldots + \Delta_{kj}$$

The Variable-Coefficient Approach.

This method has the advantage that it uses the original convex functions instead of a broken line fit. While the procedure appears to be the continuous analogue of our earlier procedure, we do require the convergence proof of § 24-1 to justify it. Referring to equations (5), (6), and (7), we may write in a purely formal way

(18)
$$x_j = \lambda_j f_j$$
$$1 = \lambda_j$$
$$\phi_j(x_j) \leq \lambda_j g_j$$

where (f_j, g_j) is a pair of variable coefficients. The set, C_j, of possible values for these coefficients consists of those points (f_j, g_j) for which $g_j \geq \phi_j(f_j)$. Since the function ϕ_j is convex, this set is convex by definition; it is therefore appropriate to use the variable coefficient method given in Chapter 22. In that chapter, however, we assumed that the C_j were defined by a finite number of linear equations. In that case the iterative process is finite. The process is an infinite one if the derivative of ϕ_j is continuous and non-constant. (See § 24-1 for convergence proof.)

Formally, the full system with variable coefficients takes the form: Find $x_j \geq 0, f_j, g_j \geq \phi_j(f_j)$, and Min z satisfying

(19)   Multipliers

$$
\begin{aligned}
a_{11}x_1 &+ a_{12}x_2 + \ldots + a_{1n}x_n &&= b_1 & \pi_1 \\
a_{21}x_1 &+ a_{22}x_2 + \ldots + a_{2n}x_n &&= b_2 & \pi_2 \\
&\cdots\cdots\cdots\cdots\cdots\cdots\cdots\cdots\cdots\cdots\cdots && \cdots & \cdots \\
a_{m1}x_1 &+ a_{m2}x_2 + \ldots + a_{mn}x_n &&= b_m & \pi_m \\
x_1 - \lambda_1 f_1 & &&= 0 & -s_1 \\
\lambda_1 & &&= 1 & t_1 \\
& x_2 - \lambda_2 f_2 &&= 0 & -s_2 \\
& \lambda_2 &&= 1 & t_2 \\
& & x_n - \lambda_n f_n &= 0 & -s_n \\
& & \lambda_n &= 1 & t_n \\
\lambda_1 g_1 &+ \lambda_2 g_2 + \ldots + \lambda_n g_n &&= z \text{ (Min)}
\end{aligned}
$$

[486]

where the multipliers associated with the system are shown on the right. In all, there are $2n + m$ constraints.

EXERCISE: Show that the set of possible coefficients (f_1, g_1) in (19) is a convex set.

According to the variable coefficient theory (Chapter 22), a basis is formed using particular values for f_j and g_j where one is allowed to form columns using more than one set of (f_j, g_j) values for a given j. Certain of the j will have associated with them just one column of values (f_{j1}, g_{j1}) in the basis, and others will have two associated values (f_{j1}, g_{j1}) and (f_{j2}, g_{j2}).

EXERCISE: Show that it is not possible to have zero or more than two different (f_{ji}, g_{ji}), $i = 1, 2, 3, \ldots$ in a basis.

We will use λ_{ji} for the variable associated with (f_{ji}, g_{ji}). It can be arranged that all the x_j are in the basic set. For example, we could initiate Phase I with x_j, λ_j, and a set of m artificial variables as a basic set. Since x_j can be assumed unrestricted in sign, they will remain in all subsequent basic sets. Assuming no artificial variables remain at the end of Phase I, it follows, because there are $2n + m$ basic variables, that n are x_j; $n - m$ are singles, λ_{j1}; and m are pairs, λ_{j1} and λ_{j2}.

Interpreted another way, m of the x_j, say x_{j_1}, x_{j_2}, $\ldots$, x_{j_m}, satisfy a relation

$$(20) \qquad f_{j1} \leq x_j \leq f_{j2} \qquad\qquad (j = j_i)$$

while the remaining x_j satisfy

$$(21) \qquad x_j = f_{j1} \qquad\qquad (j \neq j_i)$$

EXERCISE: Discuss the case where there may be artificial variables in Phase II.

THEOREM 1: *The simplex multipliers are determined by*

$$(22) \qquad s_j = (g_{j2} - g_{j1})/(f_{j2} - f_{j1}) \qquad (j = j_1, j_2, \ldots, j_m)$$

$$(23) \qquad \sum_{i=1}^{m} a_{ij}\pi_i = s_j \qquad (j = j_1, j_2, \ldots, j_m)$$

$$(24) \qquad s_j = \sum_{i=1}^{m} a_{ij}\pi_i \qquad \text{for } j \neq j_i$$

$$(25) \qquad t_j = g_{j1} - s_j f_{j1} \qquad \text{all } j$$

PROOF: From (19) we have that

$$(26) \qquad s_j f_{j1} + t_j = g_{j1} \qquad (j = j_1, j_2, \ldots, j_m)$$
$$s_j f_{j2} + t_j = g_{j2}$$

Subtracting the first from the second and solving for s_j give (22). Equations

(23)–(25) follow directly from (19). Note that in (23) the s_j are known and the π_i are to be determined, while in (24) the π_i are known and the s_j are determined. In (25), only t_j is unknown.

For optimality of a solution $x_j = x_j^o$, we require that

$$(27) \qquad\qquad g_j - (s_j f_j + t_j) \geq 0 \qquad\qquad (j = 1, 2, \ldots, n)$$

for all possible choices of (f_j, g_j).

EXERCISE: Why is this sufficient?

Since s_j and t_j are fixed, we solve the subproblem of minimizing $z_j = \phi_j(f_j) - s_j f_j$. If ϕ_j has a continuous slope, $\phi_j'(f_j)$, we seek $f_j \geq 0$ such that

$$(28) \qquad\qquad \phi_j'(f_j) = s_j$$

In Fig. 24-3-III, we graph the function $g_j = \phi_j(f_j)$, and for each point (f_j^o, g_j^o) on the curve we consider the line passing through it, $g_j - s_j f_j = g_j^o - s_j^o f_j^o$. We then seek that line with minimum g_j intercept, denoted by z_j. By (28) this occurs at the point of tangency if such a point exists.

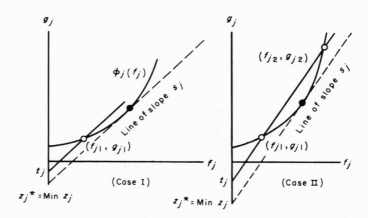

Figure 24-3-III. Solving a separable objective problem using a generalized programming approach.

It may not be possible to find such a tangency point (f_j, g_j), for it may be that the slope at $f_j = 0$ is greater than s_j; then the best choice is $f_j = 0$, $g_j = \phi_j(0)$, since convexity of $\phi_j(x)$ implies a monotone increasing slope. If $\phi_j'(f_j) \leq s_j$ for all $f_j > 0$, then the best choice is $f_j = h_j$. If j corresponds to a variable having two associated λ's in the basis, then the slope of the line joining (f_{j1}, g_{j1}) to (f_{j2}, g_{j2}) is s_j, by (22); in this case there is always somewhere between these two points, a point satisfying (28), provided the slope is a continuous function of f_j. We conclude

THEOREM 2: *A solution $(x_1^o, x_2^o, \ldots, x_n^o)$ is optimal if for each j the simplex multipliers s_j determined by Theorem 1 satisfy*

$$s_j = \phi_j'(x_j^o) \quad \text{if } 0 < x_j^o < h_j$$

$$s_j \leq \phi_j'(0) \quad \text{if } 0 = x_j^o$$

$$s_j \geq \phi_j'(h_j) \quad \text{if } x_j^o = h_j$$

or, more generally, $\phi_j^L(x_j^o) \leq s_j \leq \phi_j^R(x_j^o)$ where ϕ^L and ϕ^R, the left or right derivatives, are omitted for $\phi_j^L(0)$ or $\phi_j^R(h_j)$.

Algorithm.

The foregoing analysis suggests a variant of the simplex method in which m variables x_j are considered basic, with bounds $f_{j1} \leq x_j \leq f_{j2}$ and $n - m$ variables are non-basic at fixed values f_{j1}. It is assumed a basic feasible solution $x_j = x_j^o$ of this type is at hand to initiate the algorithm whose steps are as follows:

Step 1. Compute slopes $s_j = \phi_j'(x_j^o)$; for basic variables x_j, either decrease upper bound, f_{j2}, or increase lower bound, f_{j1}, so that the adjusted bounds are closer together and satisfy

$$(29) \qquad s_j = \phi_j'(x_j^o) = \frac{g_{j2} - g_{j1}}{f_{j2} - f_{j1}} \qquad (x_j \text{ basic})$$

(In case $\phi_j'(x_j)$ is discontinuous, replace $\phi_j'(x_j)$ by the left derivative $\phi_j^L(x_j)$ in the above discussion.)

Step 2. Compute the simplex multipliers π_i by (23).

Step 3. Compute the s_j and t_j for non-basic variables by (24) and (25).

Step 4. For non-basic j, determine f_j^* such that

(a) $f_j^* = 0$ if $s_j < \phi_j^R(0)$

(b) $f_j^* = h_j$ if $s_j \geq \phi_j^L(h_j)$

(c) $\phi_j^L(f_j^*) \leq s_j \leq \phi_j^R(f_j^*)$ otherwise

Step 5. Compute $g_j^* = \phi_j(f_j^*)$ and $z_j^* = g_j^* - s_j f_j^*$.

Step 6. Determine p, non-basic, such that

$$(z_p^* - t_p) = \underset{j \text{ non-basic}}{\text{Min}} (z_j^* - t_j) \leq 0$$

If Min $(z_j - t_j) = 0$, *terminate.* The basic solution is optimal.

Step 7. Keeping all other non-basic variables at their values f_{j1}, adjust the value of x_j and the basic variables as follows:

Decrease or increase x_p from its fixed value f_{p1} according to whether f_p^* is less than or greater than f_{p1}. Drop the basic variable which hits its upper or lower bound first or stop if x_p hits the value f_p^* first. In the latter case, f_p^* is the new fixed value of x_p which is still non-basic. In the

[489]

former case, x_p becomes a new basic variable with f_p^* and f_{p1} as its new bounds; the basic variable which hits its bound is then dropped from the basis and fixed at the value of this bound.

Convergence: It is not known whether or not the algorithm as given above converges to Min z. In order that the proof of convergence given in § 24-1 apply, some provision must also be made in the algorithm for first re-introducing into the basis any previously generated column such that $g_j - s_j f_j - t_j < 0$.

EXERCISE: Expand the algorithm to allow the re-introduction of previously generated columns. Review the proof of convergence and show why it breaks down if the latter is not done.

EXERCISE: Develop a simpler form of the algorithm by replacing the upper and lower bounds f_{j1} and f_{j2}, as defined above, by $f_{j1} = 0$ and $f_{j2} = h_j$ and setting $s_j = \phi'_j(x_j^o)$ for basic x_j.

24-4. QUADRATIC PROGRAMMING

Although a convex quadratic objective can be treated by the methods of § 24-1 and can be reduced to the convex separable case discussed in § 24-3, the linear nature of its partial derivatives has given rise to an elegant theory important in its own right. It is doubtful at this writing that the full potentiality of this theory has been realized.

Quadratic programs can arise in several ways; four listed by Wolfe in his [1959-1] paper are as follows:

Regression: To find the best least-square fit to given data, where certain parameters are known a priori to satisfy linear inequalities constraints.

Efficient Production: Maximization of profit, assuming linear production functions and linearly varying marginal costs [Dorfman, 1951-1].

Minimum Variance: To find the solution of a linear program with variable cost coefficients which will have given expected costs and minimum variance [Markowitz, 1956-1, 1959-1].

Convex Programming: To find the minimum of a general convex function under linear constraints and quadratic approximation [White, Johnson, and Dantzig, 1958-1].

Historically, it was Barankin and Dorfman [1958-1] who first pointed out that, if the linear Lagrangian conditions of optimality were combined with those of the original system, the optimum solution was a basic solution in the enlarged system with the property that only one of certain pairs of variables were in the basic set. Markowitz [1956-1, 1959-1], on the other hand, showed that it was possible to modify the enlarged system and then parametrically generate a class of basic solutions with the above special property which converged to the optimum in a finite number of iterations. Finally, Wolfe [1959-1] proved that an easy way to do this is by slightly modifying the simplex algorithm so as not to allow a variable to enter the basic set if its "complementary" variable is already in the basic set. Thus, by modifying a few instructions in a simplex code for linear programs, it was possible to solve a convex quadratic program! We shall present here a variant of Wolfe's elegant procedure. The chief difference is that ours is more nearly a strict analogue of the simplex method; it has a tighter selection rule and a monotonically decreasing objective.

Preliminaries.

Before stating the problem, let us note that every quadratic form can be conveniently expressed in terms of a *symmetric matrix* associated with its coefficients. For example, for $n = 3$ variables,

$$(1) \qquad Q(x) = c_{11}x_1^2 + c_{22}x_2^2 + c_{33}^2 x_3^2 + 2c_{12}x_1x_2 + 2c_{23}x_2x_3 + 2c_{13}x_1x_3$$

$$= [x_1, x_2, x_3] \begin{bmatrix} c_{11} & c_{12} & c_{13} \\ c_{12} & c_{22} & c_{23} \\ c_{13} & c_{23} & c_{33} \end{bmatrix} \begin{bmatrix} x_1 \\ x_2 \\ x_3 \end{bmatrix} = x^T C x$$

where T stands for *transpose*.

DEFINITION: A quadratic form is called *positive definite* if $x^T C x > 0$ for all $x \neq 0$; it is called *positive semi-definite* if $x^T C x \geq 0$ for all x.

Problem: Find $x = (x_1, x_2, \ldots, x_n) \geq 0$ and Min $Q(x)$ satisfying

$$(2) \qquad \begin{aligned} Ax &= b & A &= [a_{ij}] & (i = 1, 2, \ldots, m) \\ x^T C x &= Q(x) & C &= [c_{ij}] \end{aligned}$$

where $Q(x)$ is a convex quadratic function.

LEMMA 1: *$x^T C x$ is convex if and only if it is positive semi-definite.*

PROOF: Assume $x^T C x$ is a convex function. To prove $x^T C x \geq 0$, suppose on the contrary, $(x^o)^T C x^o < 0$ for some $x = x^o$. Then, for $x' = -x^o$, it is also true $(x')^T C x' < 0$ and for any convex combination, x^*, of x^o and x' we also have $(x^*)^T C x^* < 0$ because $x^T C x$ is convex. In particular, for $x^* = \frac{1}{2}x^o + \frac{1}{2}x'$ we have $(\frac{1}{2}x^o + \frac{1}{2}x')^T C(\frac{1}{2}x^o + \frac{1}{2}x') < 0$ or $(0)^T C(0) < 0$, a contradiction, since $\frac{1}{2}x^o + \frac{1}{2}x' = 0$.

The convexity of a positive semi-definite form follows from Lemma 2 below because a linear transform, $\bar{x}$, of the variables x reduces $Q(x)$ to a sum of convex functions in $\bar{x}$.

LEMMA 2: *If $x^T C x$ is positive semi-definite, there exists a non-singular matrix E such that a change of variables $x = E\bar{x}$ yields*

$$(3) \qquad x^T C x = \sum_1^n \lambda_j \bar{x}_j^2, \qquad (\lambda_j \geq 0)$$

where $\lambda_j \geq 0$ is the jth diagonal element of a diagonal matrix $E^T C E$.

[491]

PROOF: Select any variable, say x_1, with $c_{11} > 0$. (See first exercise below.) Express $Q(x)$ as a quadratic polynomial in x_1 and "complete the square"; thus

$$(4) \qquad x^T C x = c_{11} x_1^2 + 2 x_1 \sum_{j=2}^{n} c_{1j} x_j + \sum_{i=2}^{n} \sum_{j=2}^{n} c_{ij} x_i x_j, \qquad (c_{11} > 0)$$

$$= \frac{1}{c_{11}} \left[\sum_{j=1}^{n} c_{1j} x_j \right]^2 - \frac{1}{c_{11}} \left[\sum_{j=2}^{n} c_{1j} x_j \right]^2 + \sum_{i=2}^{n} \sum_{j=2}^{n} c_{ij} x_i x_j$$

$$= \frac{1}{c_{11}} \bar{x}_1^2 + \sum_{i=2}^{n} \sum_{j=2}^{n} c'_{ij} x_i x_j$$

where $\bar{x}_1 = \sum_{j=1}^{n} c_{1j} x_j$ and $c'_{ij} = (c_{11} c_{ij} - c_{1i} c_{1j})/c_{11}$. The process may now be repeated using the quadratic expression in $(x_2, \ldots, x_n)$ on the right. The process terminates in $k \leq n$ steps. Set $\bar{x}_j = x_j$ and $\lambda_j = 0$ for $j = k + 1$, ..., n.

EXERCISE: Show that either $c_{11} > 0$ or all $c_{11} = c_{12} \ldots = c_{1n} = 0$ in a positive semi-definite quadratic form.

EXERCISE: Show that the determinants of all the principal minors of C are positive if $Q(x)$ is positive definite, in particular $c_{11} > 0$.

EXERCISE: Show that if $k = n$, $Q(x)$ is positive definite; and that if $k < n$, it is semi-definite.

EXERCISE: Apply Lemma 2 to show that, if $x^T C x$ is positive semi-definite and if $(x^o)^T C x^o = 0$, for $x = x^o$, then $C x^o = 0$.

EXERCISE: Complete the proof of Lemma 1.

Optimality Conditions.

Let A_j, C_j denote the jth columns of A and C, respectively, and let

$$(5) \qquad\qquad y_j = C_j^T x - \pi A_j \qquad\qquad (\pi = \pi_1, \pi_2, \ldots, \pi_m)$$

THEOREM 1: *A solution $x = x^o$ is minimal if there exist $\pi = \pi^o$ and $y = y^o$ such that*

$$(6) \qquad\qquad A x^o = b, \qquad x^o \geq 0$$

$$(7) \qquad\qquad y_j^o = C_j^T x^o - \pi^o A_j \geq 0 \qquad\qquad (j = 1, 2, \ldots, n)$$

$$(8) \qquad\qquad y_j^o = 0 \text{ if } x_j^o > 0$$

PROOF: Rewrite $Q(x)$ in the form

$$(9) \quad Q(x) - Q(x^o) = 2 \sum_{j=1}^{n} \left[\sum_{i=1}^{n} c_{ij} x_i^o \right] (x_j - x_j^o) + \sum_{j=1}^{n} \sum_{i=1}^{n} c_{ij} (x_i - x_i^o)(x_j - x_j^o)$$

$$= 2 \sum_{j=1}^{n} (C_j^T x^o)(x_j - x_j^o) + (x - x^o)^T C(x - x^o)$$

[492]

Let $x \geq 0$ be any solution satisfying $Ax = b$, then

$$(10) \qquad A(x - x^o) = \sum_{j=1}^{n} A_j(x_j - x_j^o) = 0$$

Multiplying on the left by $2\pi^o$ and subtracting from (9) yield

$$(11) \quad Q(x) - Q(x^o) = 2 \sum_{j=1}^{n} (C_j^T x^o - \pi^o A_j)(x_j - x_j^o) + (x - x^o)^T C(x - x^o)$$

$$= 2 \sum_{j=1}^{n} y_j^o(x_j - x_j^o) + (x - x^o)^T C(x - x^o)$$

For the class of solutions with the property $y_j^o = 0$ for $x_j^o > 0$, (11) simplifies to

$$(12) \qquad Q(x) - Q(x^o) = 2 \sum_{y_j^o \neq 0} y_j^o x_j + (x - x^o)^T C(x - x^o)$$

Note that (12) holds by (8) and $y_j^o \geq 0$ holds by (7), thus all terms in (12) are nonnegative, therefore $Q(x) \geq Q(x^o)$.

Improving a Non-optimal Solution.

Consider the system

$$(13) \qquad \begin{aligned} Ax &= b \\ Cx - A^T \pi^T - I_n y &= 0 \end{aligned} \qquad (x \geq 0)$$

where $x^T C x$ is assumed to be positive semi-definite. Let x^o, π^o, y^o be a basic feasible solution associated with a basic set *with the complementarity property*, namely, for each j either x_j or y_j, but not both, is in the basic set. We shall assume further that the right-hand side has been perturbed to insure that all basic solutions are nondegenerate. Note that neither π nor y is sign restricted; only $x \geq 0$ is required for a feasible solution to (13); an optimal solution will have been obtained if $y_j \geq 0$ and $x_j y_j = 0$ for all j.

THEOREM 2: *If a basis is complementary and $y_s^o < 0$, then any increase of the non-basic variable x_s, with adjustment of only the basic variables, generates a class of solutions x', π', y', such that $x^T Q x$ decreases as long as $y_s' < 0$.*

PROOF: Let x be any solution in the class above, i.e., generated by increasing x_s; in particular, let x' be generated by $x_s = x_s'$. Analogous to (11), $Q(x) - Q(x') = 2y_s'(x_s - x_s') + (x - x')^T C(x - x')$ since for all $j \neq s$ either $x_j = x_j' = 0$ if x_j is non-basic or if x_j is basic $y_j = y_j' = 0$ by the complementarity assumption. The adjusted values of the basic variables are linear functions of x_s, hence it follows that $(x - x') = (x_s - x_s')v$ where v is a *constant vector*. Hence, $Q(x) - Q(x') = (x_s - x_s')[2y_s' + (x_s - x_s')(v^T Cv)]$ and it is clear that, if $y_s' < 0$, the right-hand side is negative for sufficiently small $(x_s - x_s') > 0$.

[493]

Moreover for $Q(x)$ to decrease with an increase of $x_s \geq 0$ from, say, x_s' to x_s'', it must be accompanied by $y_s' < y_s''$ because

$$Q(x'') - Q(x') = 2(x_s'' - x_s')y_s' + (x_s'' - x_s')^2 v^T C v$$

and, by interchanging the roles of x' and x'',

$$Q(x') - Q(x'') = 2(x_s' - x_s'')y_s'' + (x_s'' - x_s')^2 v^T C v$$

whence $2(y_s'' - y_s') = 2(x_s'' - x_s')v^T C v \geq 0$. But $v^T C v \neq 0$ because $v^T C v = 0$ implies $Cv = 0$ for positive semi-definite forms (see last exercise following proof of Lemma 2) and if $Cv = 0$, then from (9), $Q(x'') - Q(x') = 2(x_s'' - x_s')$ $(x')^T C v + (x_s'' - x_s')^2 v^T C v = 0$ which contradicts $Q(x'') - Q(x') < 0$; we conclude $y_s'' > y_s'$.

As in the simplex method, we require that all solutions generated by increasing x_s and adjusting the basic variables remain feasible, i.e., $x_j \geq 0$ for all j. In this process, either y_s attains the value zero first, and thus can be dropped from the basic set, or the value of some basic x_r attains the zero value first and is dropped.

THEOREM 3: *If x_r drops as basic variable, introduction of y_r either causes $x^T C x$ to decrease (and some x_{r_1} or y_s to be dropped) or causes $x^T C x$ to stay fixed and y_s to be dropped; if x_{r_1} is dropped, this theorem may be reapplied; if y_s is dropped either initially or upon increase of y_r Theorem 2 may be reapplied.*

PROOF: Our proof is completely general; however, for convenience we will illustrate it on system (14)

(14)	x_1	x_2	x_3	x_4	x_5	$-\pi_1$	$-\pi_2$	y_1	y_2	y_3	y_4	y_5	Constants
	a_{11}	a_{12}	a_{13}	a_{14}	a_{15}								b_1
	a_{21}	a_{22}	a_{23}	a_{24}	a_{25}								b_2
	c_{11}	c_{12}	c_{13}	c_{14}	c_{15}	a_{11}	a_{21}	-1					0
	c_{12}	c_{22}	c_{23}	c_{24}	c_{25}	a_{12}	a_{22}		-1				0
	c_{13}	c_{23}	c_{33}	c_{34}	c_{35}	a_{13}	a_{23}			-1			0
	c_{14}	c_{24}	c_{34}	c_{44}	c_{45}	a_{14}	a_{24}				-1		0
	c_{15}	c_{25}	c_{35}	c_{45}	c_{55}	a_{15}	a_{25}					-1	0
B:	●	●	●	●	★	●	●					●	
B':	●	●	●		●	●	●			★	●		

Let system (14) in vector form be

$$(15) \quad P_1 x_1 + P_2 x_2 + P_3 x_3 + P_4 x_4 + P_5 x_5 + (P_6 \pi_1 + P_7 \pi_2)$$
$$+ \bar{P}_1 y_1 + \bar{P}_2 y_2 + \bar{P}_3 y_3 + \bar{P}_4 y_4 + \bar{P}_5 y_5 = P_0$$

We suppose that we have on some cycle a basis B and a basic feasible complementary solution (x^o, π^o, y^o) with basic variables $x_1, x_2, x_3, x_4, \pi_1, \pi_2, y_5$

and the value of $y_5 = y_5^o < 0$. In this case, x_5 will be the new basic variable and we assume that x_4 will drop. This yields a new basis B'. In (14), the heavy dots ($\bullet$) indicate that the column is in the basis B, and the star indicates that the column P_5 associated with x_5 is replacing a vector P_4 of the basis B to form basis B'; see second row of dots. The dropping of x_4 automatically requires that y_4 become the new basic variable for the basis following B'; see $\star$ in the B' row of (14).

Let the representation of both P_5 and $\bar{P}_4$ in terms of the basis B be:

$$(16) \qquad P_5 = P_1\alpha_1 + P_2\alpha_2 + P_3\alpha_3 + P_4\alpha_4 + (P_6\alpha_6 + P_7\alpha_7) + \bar{P}_5\bar{\alpha}_5$$

$$(17) \qquad \bar{P}_4 = P_1\lambda_1 + P_2\lambda_2 + P_3\lambda_3 + P_4\lambda_4 + (P_6\lambda_6 + P_7\lambda_7) + \bar{P}_5\bar{\lambda}_5$$

We first show that $\lambda_4 \leq 0$ in (17). Setting $\lambda = (\lambda_1, \lambda_2, \lambda_3, \lambda_4)$, the first six rows of representation (17) yield (18) and (19):

$$(18) \qquad [a_{11} \ \ a_{12} \ \ a_{13} \ \ a_{14}] \lambda^T \qquad\qquad\qquad = \quad 0$$
$$\qquad\qquad [a_{21} \ \ a_{22} \ \ a_{23} \ \ a_{24}] \lambda^T \qquad\qquad\qquad = \quad 0$$

$$(19) \qquad \begin{bmatrix} c_{11} & c_{12} & c_{13} & c_{14} \\ c_{12} & c_{22} & c_{23} & c_{24} \\ c_{13} & c_{23} & c_{33} & c_{34} \\ c_{14} & c_{24} & c_{34} & c_{44} \end{bmatrix} \lambda^T + \begin{bmatrix} a_{11} \\ a_{12} \\ a_{13} \\ a_{14} \end{bmatrix} \lambda_6 + \begin{bmatrix} a_{21} \\ a_{22} \\ a_{23} \\ a_{24} \end{bmatrix} \lambda_7 = \begin{bmatrix} 0 \\ 0 \\ 0 \\ -1 \end{bmatrix}$$

Multiplying (19) by λ on the left and denoting the square matrix by C_4 yield, by (18), $\lambda C_4 \lambda^T = -\lambda_4$. Since $\lambda C_4 \lambda^T$ is positive semi-definite (C_4 is a principal minor of C), $\lambda C \lambda^T \geq 0$ and $\lambda_4 \leq 0$.

Case $\lambda_4 < 0$: Our objective is to show that, if x_4 drops out of the basic set upon introduction of x_5 into the basic set and if the non-basic complementary variable to x_4, namely y_4, is subsequently increased (with adjustment of the values of the new basic variables), then x_5 and y_5 will continue to increase and $x^T C x$ to decrease as long as y_5 remains negative. This assumes $\lambda_4 < 0$. (Later, for the case $\lambda_4 = 0$, we shall show that x_5 and $x^T C x$ will remain unchanged but y_5 will decrease to zero when y_4 is increased in value.) Let the representation of $\bar{P}_4$ in terms of the basis B' be

$$(20) \qquad \bar{P}_4 = P_1\lambda_1' + P_2\lambda_2' + P_3\lambda_3' + P_5\lambda_5' + (P_6\lambda_6' + P_7\lambda_7') + \bar{P}_5\bar{\lambda}_5'$$

and let the basic solution associated with B' be

$$(21) \qquad P_0 = P_1 x_1' + P_2 x_2' + P_3 x_3' + P_5 x_5' + (P_6\pi_1' + P_7\pi_2') + \bar{P}_5 y_5'$$

We observe that in the representation (16) of P_5 in terms of B, the weight α_4 on P_4 is positive (since x_4 decreased when x_5 increased). Since (20) is obtained by eliminating P_4 from (16) and (17) and since $\lambda_4 < 0$ and $\alpha_4 > 0$, it follows that $\lambda_5' < 0$. If $y_4 = \theta > 0$ units of $\bar{P}_4$ are introduced into the solution and the values of the basic variables are adjusted, we obtain from (20) and (21),

$$(22) \quad P_0 = P_1(x_1' - \theta\lambda_1') + \ldots + P_3(x_3' - \theta\lambda_3') + P_5(x_5' - \theta\lambda_5') + \ldots$$
$$+ \bar{P}_4\theta + \bar{P}_5(y_5' - \theta\bar{\lambda}_5')$$

Thus $x_5 = x_5' - \theta\lambda_5'$ will increase when $y_4 = \theta > 0$ is increased since $\lambda_5' < 0$. Moreover, we may adopt the point of view for the purpose of the proof, that it is the increase in x_5 that is "causing" the increase in y_4 (instead of the other way around), so that we are, in fact, repeating the situation just considered of increasing x_5 and adjusting the other "basic" variables, except here y_4 is in the basic set instead of x_4. It follows, therefore, as before, that an increase in x_5 decreases x^TCx as long as y_5 remains negative in value in the adjustment of the basic solution by the increase of x_5.

Case $\lambda_4 = 0$: On the other hand, if $\lambda_4 = 0$ in (17), then we must set $\lambda_i = \lambda_i'$ in (20) because the representation of P_4 is the same, whether in terms of B or B'; hence, $\lambda_5' = 0$. In this case $\lambda C_4 \lambda^T = -\lambda_4 = 0$ and therefore, because C is positive semi-definite, $C_4\lambda = 0$. In addition, $\lambda = 0$ must hold because $\lambda \neq 0$ implies a dependence of the first four columns of (18) and (19) which is *impossible* because then the square array of coefficients of (18) and (19), and in turn B, would be singular. Setting $\lambda_1', \ldots, \lambda_5' = 0$ in (20) and (21), we observe (and this holds in general) that $\bar{P}_4$ is dependent only on the columns of π_i and of y_j, and therefore the values of $x_j' - \theta\lambda_j'$ remain unchanged in (21) with increasing values of $y_4 = \theta$.

Because the y_j are not sign restricted, y_4 can be increased until y_5 is dropped out of the basic set at value zero (since all x_j values are unaffected). Hence, in this shift of basis there is no change in the value of x^TCx; however, the introduction of y_4 into the basic set and the dropping of y_5 give rise to a new basic set that satisfies the complementarity property. We may thus reapply Theorem 2 to reduce x^TCx.

The Quadratic Algorithm.

Step I. *Initiate:* Let x^o be a basic feasible solution for $Ax = b$, $x \geq 0$, with basic variables $x_{j_1}, x_{j_2}, \ldots, x_{j_m}$; choose for the initial set of basic variables x_j for the enlarged problem these x_{j_i}, the complements y_j of the non-basic x_j, and the set of π_i.

Step II. For the values of y_j^o of the basic solution, determine Min $y_j^o = y_s^o$. If $y_s^o \geq 0$, *terminate; the solution is optimal.* If $y_s^o < 0$ introduce into the basic set x_s; if y_s drops from the basic set, repeat Step II. Go to Step III if x_r drops.

Step III. Introduce y_r into basic set. If y_s drops, return to Step II; otherwise, if some x_{r_2} drops, repeat Step III with r_2 playing the role of r.

THEOREM 4. *The iterative process is finite.*

EXERCISE: Prove Theorem 4.

EXERCISE: Extend the results of this section to cover the case of a convex objective form consisting of mixed quadratic and linear terms.

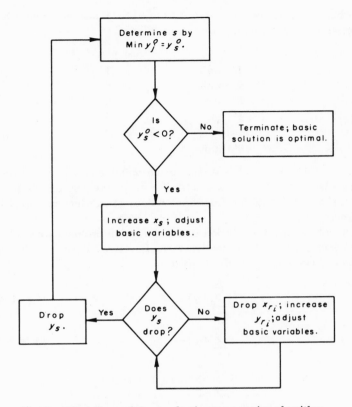

Figure 24-4-I.   Flow chart of the quadratic programming algorithm.

24-5.   PROBLEMS

1. Show that the bounded variable problem of § 24-3-(12), (13), (14) is equivalent to the original convex-separable problem.
2. Show for § 24-3-(15), (16), (17) that, if Δ_{pq} is in the basis, Δ_{tq} is not, where $t \neq p$. Show under the simplex criterion that Δ_{tq} is not a candidate to enter the basic set if Δ_{pq} is in the basic set.
3. Solve the distribution problem below by both methods of § 24-3. Which is easier ?

				Total
x_{11}	x_{12}	x_{13}	x_{14}	9
x_{21}	x_{22}	x_{23}	x_{24}	9
x_{31}	x_{32}	x_{33}	x_{34}	9
Total				
5	10	4	8	

where the cost per unit shipped from (i) to (j) has incrementally increasing costs per total amount shipped as follows:

	Cost per Unit
1st unit	1
2nd unit	2
3rd unit	3
4th unit	4
. . . .	
9th unit	9

4. Show that the total cost $\phi(x)$ of shipping $x = x_{ij}$ units from i to j in Problem 3 is $\phi(x) = x(x + 1)/2$ if x is an integer. Show that, if we set $\phi(x) = x(x + 1)/2$ for fractional values of x, the optimal solution has fractional values for x_{ij}.

5. Show how to get a solution to a distribution problem with integer-valued variables when the objective form is convex-separable. To be precise, find integers $x_{ij} \geq 0$, Min z satisfying

$$\sum_{j=1}^{n} x_{ij} = a_i \qquad (i = 1, 2, \ldots, m)$$

$$\sum_{i=1}^{m} x_{ij} = b_j \qquad (j = 1, 2, \ldots, n)$$

$$\sum_{i=1}^{m} \sum_{j=1}^{m} \phi_{ij}(x_{ij}) = z \text{ (Min)}$$

where a_i and b_j are integers and $\phi_{ij}(x_{ij})$ are convex functions (for example, $\phi_{ij}(x_{ij}) = x_{ij}^2$ or $x_{ij}(x_{ij} + 1)/2$).

REFERENCES

Arrow, Hurwicz, and Uzawa, 1958-1, 1961-1
Barankin and Dorfman, 1958-1
Beale, 1955-2, 1959-2
Beckenbach, 1948-1
Charnes and Lemke, 1954-1
Cottle, 1963-1, 1963-2, 1963-3, 1964-1 1964-2
Dantzig, 1955-1, 1956-2, 1960-3
Dorfman, 1951-1
Dorn, 1963-1
Duffin, 1956-1
Forsythe, 1955-1
Hartley and Loftsgard, 1958-1
Karlin, 1959-1
Kelley, 1960-1
Kuhn and Tucker, 1950-2
Mangasarian, 1962-1

Mangasarian and Ponstein, 1963-1
Markowitz, 1952-1, 1956-1, 1959-1
Miller, 1960-1, 1963-1
Rosen, 1960-1, 1961-1, 1963-1
Shetty, 1959-1
Simon, 1956-1
Slater, 1950-1
Stoer, 1964-1
Theil and Van de Panne, 1960-1
Thrall, 1955-1
Tucker, 1957-1
Uzawa, 1958-1
Vazsonyi, 1955-1
White, Johnson, and Dantzig, 1958-1
Wilde, 1962-1
Williams, A. C., 1960-1
Wolfe, 1957-1, 1959-1, 1960-1, 1961-1, 3, 1962-1, 1963-1

Zoutendijk, 1960-1

CHAPTER 25

UNCERTAINTY

In the final analysis, most applied programming problems involve uncertainty in either the technology matrix or the constant terms. The techniques discussed so far, however, do not take into account the uncertain nature of the coefficients of the program. In the period 1955–60, various individuals have tried to extend linear programming methods to deal with the problem of optimizing in some sense an objective function, subject to constraints whose constants are subject to random variation [Dantzig, 1955-1; Ferguson and Dantzig, 1956-1]. One of the basic difficulties is that the problem is capable of many formulations, with only fragmentary results for each of the formulations [Madansky, 1959-1]. In this chapter we shall examine some of the solved problems in this area, cautioning the reader that the treatment is incomplete and that much research remains to be done.

For the concepts of probability and statistical theory used in this chapter, the reader is referred to [Feller, 1957-1].

25-1. SCHEDULING TO MEET VARIABLE COST

By way of background let us recall that there are in common use two essentially different types of scheduling applications—one designed for the short run and one for the long run. For the latter the effect of probabilistic or chance events is reduced to a minimum by the usual technique of providing plenty of *fat* in the system. For example, consumption rates, attrition rates, and wear-out rates are all planned on the high side; times to ship, times to travel, and times to produce are always made well above actual needs. Indeed, the entire system is put together with plenty of fat with the hope that it will be a *shock absorber*, which will permit the general objective and timing of the plan to be executed in spite of unforeseen events. More precisely, the fat is introduced into the system so that, whatever be the random unforeseen event, the activities chosen will still be feasible. Activities which satisfy this proviso are called *permanently feasible*.

The effect of chance events is also reduced to a minimum by the technique of providing plenty of *slack* in the system. By this we mean that scarce exogenous inputs to the system are estimated on the low side, so that it is highly unlikely for the set of chosen activities to be infeasible because of shortages.

In the general course of things, long-range plans are revised frequently because the stochastic elements of the problem have a nasty way of intruding. For this reason the chief contribution, if any, of the long-range plan, is to effect an immediate decision—such as the appropriation of funds or the initiation of an important development contract.

For short-run scheduling, many of the *slack* and *fat* techniques of its long-range brother are employed. The principal differences are attention to detail and the short time-horizon. As long as *capabilities* are well above *requirements* (or demands) or if the *demands can be shifted in time*, this approach presents no problems, since it is feasible to implement the schedule in detail. However, where there are shortages, the projected plan based on such techniques may lead to actions far from optimal, whereas these new methods, where applicable, may result in considerable savings.

Minimum Expected Costs.

A nutrition expert wishes to advise his followers on a minimum-cost diet without prior knowledge of the prices [Stigler, 1945-1]. Because prices of food' (except for general inflationary trends) are likely to show variability due to weather conditions, supply, etc., he wants to assume a distribution of possible prices rather than a fixed price for each food, and determine a diet that meets specified nutritional requirements and minimizes the expected total cost. Let x_j be the quantity in pounds of jth food purchased, p_j its price; let a_{ij} be the quantity of the ith nutrient (e.g., Vitamin A) contained in a unit quantity of the jth food; and let b_i be the minimum quantity required by an individual for good health. Then the x_j must be chosen so that

$$(1) \qquad \sum_{j=1}^{n} a_{ij}x_j \geq b_i, \qquad x_j \geq 0 \qquad (i = 1, 2, \ldots, m)$$

The cost of the diet will be

$$(2) \qquad C = \sum_{j=1}^{n} p_j x_j$$

However, the x_j are chosen *before* the prices are known, so that for the *fixed* selected values of x_j the total cost C becomes a random variable that is a weighted sum of random variables p_j. We shall denote the *expected value* of any variable, say u, by $\mathscr{E}u$ or $\mathscr{E}(u)$. Accordingly, the expected cost E of such a diet is clearly

$$(3) \qquad E = \mathscr{E}C = \sum_{j} \bar{p}_j x_j$$

where $\bar{p}_j$ is the expected price of food j. Since the $\bar{p}_j$ are assumed known in advance, the best choices of x_j are those which satisfy (1), and minimize E. We have, therefore, in general

[500]

THEOREM 1: *If the unit costs p_j in (2) are randomly distributed independently of the x_j, then the minimum expected total cost solution is obtained by finding x_j, ≥ 0 satisfying (1) and minimizing C with p_j replaced by $\bar{p}_j = \mathcal{E}(p_j)$.*

On the other hand if each p_j depends on x_j, we write $p_j x_j = \phi_j(x_j, p_j)$; remembering the expectation of a sum is equal to the sum of the expectations:

$$(4) \qquad E = \mathcal{E}C = \sum_{j=1}^{n} \mathcal{E}\phi_j(x_j, p_j) = \sum_{j=1}^{n} \phi_j(x_j)$$

where $\phi(x_j)$ is some (not necessarily linear) function of x_j. Special methods for minimizing E for the case where $\phi(x_j, p_j)$ is convex in the x_j were given in § 24-3.

The following example illustrates a case where the expected cost is not linear in the x_j. Let x_j be the quantity of the jth good manufactured and let the constraints be manufacturing capacity restraints. Assume that costs are threefold: there are a non-random manufacturing cost c_{0j}, a non-random stockage cost c_{1j} for those items not bought by a random demand, and a non-random shortage cost c_{2j}, if the random demand exceeds the supply; then

$$E = \sum_j c_{0j} x_j + \sum_j c_{1j} \mathcal{E}(x_j - d_j | x_j > d_j) + \sum_j c_{2j} \mathcal{E}(d_j - x_j | x_j < d_j)$$

where the symbol $\mathcal{E}(A | B)$ is read *the expected value of A given that B is true.* This problem, though set up as a one-stage problem with the uncertainty appearing only in the objective function, could be set up as a two-stage problem with the uncertainty in the constraints instead. As such, it becomes a problem of the type described in § 25-2 and treated more fully in § 25-3 and in Elmaghraby's paper [1960-1].

Minimum Variance for Fixed Expected Costs.

Referring again to our nutrition problem, it may be desirable to control the variance V of the expected costs. Thus, a solution to (1) and (3) that results in a low expected cost, but one that has great variability, may not be as desirable as one which shows greater cost stability. This certainly was the case considered by H. Markowitz in his analysis of "portfolio" selections [Markowitz, 1952-1]. Stockbrokers often advise their customers to buy a variety of stocks, some of which they regard as very safe, low-yield stocks, while others (like oil exploration stocks) may have a high average yield but show great variation (depending, say, on whether or not oil is discovered). The objective of such an analysis is to produce for each of a variety of expected profit levels $-E$, portfolio selections that minimize variance (Fig. 25-1-I).

It is then left to the customer to decide what combination of "yield level" and "risk level" (Min V) he wants.

Let us now assume that the price is *independent* of x_j and that we know the *variance* (or standard error squared) σ_j^2 of p_j, the price of an individual item, and the *covariance* σ_{jk} between two prices p_j and p_k. Let $\sigma_{jk} = \sigma_j \sigma_k \rho_{jk}$ where the *correlation coefficient* between the two prices ρ_{jk} satisfies $-1 \leq \rho_{jk} \leq +1$. Since all x_j units are purchased at the *same* cost p_j, the variance of

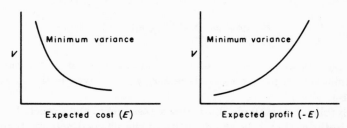

Figure 25-1-I. Minimum variance is a convex function of expected cost or profit.

$x_j p_j$ is given by $x_j^2 \sigma_j^2$ and the covariance between $x_j p_j$ and $x_k p_k$ is given by $x_j x_k \sigma_{jk}$. From this it follows that the variance V of E is given by the *quadratic expression*

$$(5) \qquad V = \mathscr{E}[C - E]^2 = \sum_{j=1}^{n} \sum_{k=1}^{n} x_j x_k \sigma_{jk} \qquad (\sigma_{jj} = \sigma_j^2)$$

If, in particular, food prices are highly correlated so that for all practical purposes $\rho_{jk} \doteq 1$ and $\sigma_{jk} \doteq \sigma_j \sigma_k$, then in this case it would be advisable to replace $V^{\frac{1}{2}}$ by the *linear expression* bounding it given in (6),

$$(6) \qquad V^{\frac{1}{2}} \leq x_1 \sigma_1 + x_2 \sigma_2 + \ldots + x_n \sigma_n$$

where equality holds if all correlation coefficients $\rho_{jk} = 1$. On the other hand, if the prices are independent so that $\rho_{jk} = 0$, then

$$(7) \qquad V = x_1^2 \sigma_1^2 + x_2^2 \sigma_2^2 + \ldots + x_n^2 \sigma_n^2 \qquad (\rho_{jk} = 0)$$

We now address ourselves to the general problem of determining the solution to (1), (3), and (5) that minimizes V for fixed E.

Case I: $V^{\frac{1}{2}}$ is Linear. If (6) holds, then we solve the problem of determining Min $V^{\frac{1}{2}}$ subject to $E \leq E^*$, where E^* is an upper bound which we wish to impose on expected costs. Since the restriction is linear, we may study the effect on V of varying E^* as a parameter. In this case we have a standard parametric programming problem (see § 11-3).

Case II: V is a Sum of Squares. If (7) holds, then V is convex-separable and the convex functions x_j^2 may be approximated by broken-line functions. This reduces the problem again to a standard parametric programming problem (combined with an upper-bounding technique, if desired). Here we are varying one of the constant terms. See § 11-3 and § 24-3. However, the following alternative is recommended. Replace V by

$$(8) \qquad \bar{V} = x_1^2 \sigma_1^2 + x_2^2 \sigma_2^2 + \ldots + x_n^2 \sigma_n^2 + k \cdot E^* \qquad (E \leq E^*)$$

Again using a broken-line fit for x_j^2, the problem is first solved using $k = 0$; it is easy to see that this corresponds to setting $E^* = +\infty$. If now k is allowed to increase gradually, a critical value $k = k_1$ would be determined for which the solution would no longer be optimal. This will result in one or more basis changes until the solution is again optimal. After this, k can again be increased until a new critical value $k = k_2$ is obtained, etc.

EXERCISE: Prove the latter procedure is the first parametric linear programming method in disguise. Develop other alternatives based on § 24-3. Why is E^* instead of E used above?

It is probably worth while, however, instead of choosing to increase k gradually, to choose a number of discrete values in advance. The solution will generate a number of different pairs of E^* and $\bar{V}$ values that can be used to spot points on the curve. A plot of E^* against k can be used to determine what new k values to use if a better spacing of E^* values is desired.

Case III: V Is General. Since V is positive (semi-) definite, it can, by a suitable linear transformation, be reduced to Case II; hence this procedure can be used in general to effect a solution to the problem. Alternatively, a general quadratic programming procedure such as that developed by Markowitz [1956-1] or by Wolfe [1959-1] may be used, combined with a parametric programming method for the right-hand side (see § 11-3). However, an analogue of (8) using an E^* term weighted by a parameter k is recommended.

EXERCISE: Combine methods for solving quadratic programs and parametric programs as given in § 24-4 and § 11-3 to solve the minimum-variance problem.

25-2. SCHEDULING TO MEET AN UNCERTAIN DEMAND

Let us consider a simple case: A factory has 100 items on hand which may be shipped to an outlet at the cost of \$1 apiece to meet an uncertain demand d. In the event that the demand should exceed the supply, it is necessary to meet the unsatisfied demand by purchases on the local market at \$2 apiece. The equations that the system must satisfy are

$$(1) \qquad 100 = x + y \qquad\qquad (x, y, v, s \geq 0)$$
$$d = x \quad\;\; + v - s$$
$$C = x \quad\;\; + 2v$$

where $\begin{cases} x = \text{number shipped from the factory,} \\ y = \text{number stored at factory;} \end{cases}$

$\begin{cases} v = \text{number purchased on open market,} \\ s = \text{excess of supply over demand;} \end{cases}$

$\quad d = \text{unknown demand uniformly distributed between 70 and 80;}$

$\quad C = \text{total costs.}$

We view the shipping and purchasing as part of a two-stage process. In the first stage a decision is made consistent with the initial inventory of amounts to ship. In the second stage, the unknown demands occur.

The simple example above belongs to a general class of two-stage problems. In the first stage, $x_j \geq 0$, $u_k \geq 0$ are determined such that

(2)
$$\sum_{j=1}^{n} a_{ij}x_j = b_i \qquad (i = 1, 2, \ldots, m)$$

$$\sum_{j=1}^{n} \bar{a}_{kj}x_j = u_k \qquad (k = 1, 2, \ldots, p)$$

where the initial inventories b_i for $i = 1, 2, \ldots, m$ are known; the $x_j \geq 0$ represent decisions in the first stage resulting in specified quantities u_k being made available for the second stage. For the second stage, the quantities v_k and s_k are determined such that

(3)
$$d_k = u_k + v_k - s_k \qquad (k = 1, 2, \ldots, p)$$

where d_k is the *unknown demand* whose probability distribution is known, v_k is the shortage of supply, and s_k is the excess of supply over demand. The joint probability distribution for $(d_1, d_2, \ldots, d_k)$ may be dependent. Assuming for convenience no purchases on the open market in case of shortage, the total cost is of the form

(4)
$$C = \sum_{j=1}^{n} c_j x_j - \sum_{k=1}^{p} f_k(d_k - v_k) \text{ where } v_k = 0 \text{ if } u_k \geq d_k$$

where c_j is the cost of performing the jth activity and $f_k \geq 0$ is the revenue from satisfying one unit of demand. Thus, it always pays to sell as much of the amount, u_k, supplied as possible so that $(d_k - v_k) = \text{Min } (u_k, d_k)$ and

(5)
$$C = \sum_{j=1}^{n} c_j x_j - \sum_{k=1}^{p} f_k \text{ Min } (u_k, d_k)$$

It is clear that, for any particular choice of x_j and u_k consistent with the first-stage equations, the value of C depends on this choice and on the unknown demand. Hence, for fixed choice of x_j and u_j the expected value of C is given by

(6)
$$\mathscr{E}C = \sum_{j=1}^{n} c_j x_j - \sum_{k=1}^{p} f_k \mathscr{E} \operatorname{Min} (u_k, d_k)$$

Since the expected value of Min (u_k, d_k) depends on u_k, let us denote this function (of u_k) by

(7)
$$\phi_k(u_k) = \mathscr{E} \operatorname{Min} (u_k, d_k)$$

Given the demand distribution of d_k, the function $\phi_k(u_k)$ is easily calculated. Suppose $d_k = 1,\ 2$ with probability $\frac{1}{2}$, $\frac{1}{2}$, respectively, then $\phi_k(u_k)$ is easily determined.

(8)

Amount Supplied (u_k)	Amount Sold $d_k - v_k = \operatorname{Min} (u_k, d_k)$		Expected Value[1] (revenue) $\phi_k(u_k)$ (3)
	where $d_k = 1$ (1)	where $d_k = 2$ (2)	
$u_k = 0$	0	0	0
$0 < u_k < 1$	u_k	u_k	u_k
$u_k = 1$	1	1	1
$1 < u_k < 2$	1	u_k	$1/2 + u_k/2$
$u_k = 2$	1	2	3/2
$2 < u_k$	1	2	3/2

[1] Entries in column (3) are formed by multiplying the entries in column (1) by $p_1 = \frac{1}{2}$, those in column (2) by $p_2 = \frac{1}{2}$, and summing.

In general, to compute $\phi(u) = \mathscr{E} \operatorname{Min} (u, d)$ where d can take on successive values $e_1 \leq e_2, \ldots, \leq e_t$ with probability $p_1, p_2, \ldots, p_t$ and $\sum_{1}^{t} p_i = 1$, we note

(9)
$$\operatorname{Min} (u, d) = u \quad \text{if } d > u$$
$$\operatorname{Min} (u, d) = d \quad \text{if } d \leq u$$

Suppose $e_{r-1} \leq u < e_r$, then (letting Prob denote probability)

$$\phi(u) = u \operatorname{Prob} (d > u) + \operatorname{Prob} (d \leq u) \mathscr{E}(d | d \leq u)$$

whence

(10) $\phi(u) = u(p_r + p_{r+1} + \ldots + p_t) + (e_1 p_1 + e_2 p_2 + \ldots + e_{r-1} p_{r-1})$

$\qquad = u(1 - p_1 - p_2 - \ldots - p_{r-1}) + (e_1 p_1 + e_2 p_2 + \ldots + e_{r-1} p_{r-1})$

where we define, for $r = 1$ in (10), $e_0 = 0$ and $p_0 = 0$. Thus, $\phi(u)$ is a broken-line function starting at the origin with initial slope $s_1 = 1$; at $u = e_1$, the *slope* decreases to $s_2 = 1 - p_1$, etc. (see Fig. 25-2-I).

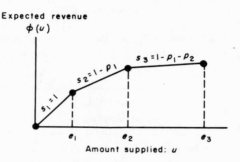

Figure 25-2-I.   Maximum expected revenue is a concave function of the amount supplied.

Referring to our section on convex separable functions, § 24-3, it should be noted that $-\phi(u)$ is *convex* because of the decreasing slopes in Fig. 25-2-I. Indeed, $s_i - s_{i+1} = p_i > 0$. We have therefore shown a result of H. Scarf (informal demonstration to the author).

THEOREM 1:   *The total expected costs under uncertain demand is a convex separable function*

(11) $$\mathscr{E}C = \sum_{j=1}^{n} c_j x_j' - \sum_{k=1}^{p} f_k \phi_k(u_k)$$

where $\phi_k(u_k)$ is a broken-line function whose slope between two successive demands $d_k = e_{r,k}$, and $e_{r+1,k}$ is equal to the probability of exceeding the demand $e_{r,k}$.

THEOREM 2:   *To minimize expected costs, determine $x_j \geq 0$, $u_k \geq 0$, satisfying (2), such that the convex separable function (11) is minimized.*

Continuous Demand Distribution.

To illustrate an example involving a continuous distribution, consider the small two-stage case described earlier in (1). The costs are given by

(12) $$C = x_1 + 2 \,\mathrm{Max}\,(0, d - x_1)$$

where d is uniformly distributed between 70 and 80. The determination of expected costs requires the evaluation of $\mathscr{E} \operatorname{Max} [0, d - x_1]$ as a function of x_1:

$$(13) \qquad \mathscr{E} \operatorname{Max} (0, d - x_1) = \begin{cases} 75 - x_1 & \text{if } 0 \leq x_1 \leq 70 \\ \frac{1}{10} \int_{x_1}^{80} (t - x_1) dt & \text{if } 70 \leq x_1 \leq 80 \\ 0 & \text{if } 80 \leq x_1 \end{cases}$$

whence from (12)

$$(14) \qquad \mathscr{E}C = \begin{cases} 150 - x_1 & \text{if } 0 \leq x_1 \leq 70 \\ x_1 + (80 - x_1)^2/10 & \text{if } 70 \leq x_1 \leq 80 \\ x_1 & \text{if } 80 \leq x_1 \end{cases}$$

It then follows that $\operatorname{Min}_{x_1} \mathscr{E}C = 77.5$ occurs at $x_1 = 75$, i.e., it is best to ship the expected demand in this case.

EXERCISE: Modify the above problem to show that it is not always best to ship the expected demand.

When is it best to ship the expected demand? The following result, due to Madansky [1960-1] (see also Reiter, [1957-1]), is a generalization of earlier results [Theil, 1957-1; Simon, 1956-1], and gives a sufficient condition for the solution of the linear program when the demand is replaced by its expected value also to solve the problem of scheduling to meet uncertain demand. If C can be expressed as $C_1(d, x) + C_2(d)$ where $C_1(d, x)$ is a linear function of d for each x and $C_2(d)$ involves only d and not x, then the x which solves the linear program with d replaced by $\mathscr{E}(d)$ also solves the uncertainty problem.

EXERCISE: Prove this result. Does the example above satisfy the sufficiency condition?

25-3. ON MULTI-STAGE PROBLEMS[2]

The Two-stage Problem with General Linear Structure.

We shall prove a general theorem on convexity for the two-stage problem that forms the inductive step for the multi-stage problem. We shall say a few words about the significance of this convexity later on. The assumed structure of the general two-stage model (of which § 25-2-(2) is a special case) is

$$(1) \qquad \begin{aligned} b_1 &= A_{11}X_1 \qquad\qquad (X_1, X_2 \geq 0) \\ b_2 &= A_{21}X_1 + A_{22}X_2 \\ C &= \phi(X_1, X_2 | E_2) \end{aligned}$$

where A_{ij} are known matrices; b_1 a known vector of initial inventories; b_2 an unknown vector whose components depend on a set of parameters E_2; and C, the cost, depends on X_1, X_2, and E_2.

[2] The material for this section is based on [Dantzig, 1955-1].

We assume the following sequence of events:

(1) $X_1 \geq 0$ is chosen to satisfy $b_1 = A_{11}X_1$. We denote by Ω_1 the set of possible vectors X_1. It is assumed that Ω_1 is nonempty.

(2) E_2 is drawn randomly as a point from a multidimensional sample space S_2 with known probability distribution. E_2 determines b_2.

(3) $X_2 \geq 0$ is chosen to satisfy $b_2 = A_{21}X_1 + A_{22}X_2$. We denote by $\Omega_2 = \Omega_2(X_1|E_2)$ the set of possible vectors X_2. It is assumed that Ω_2 is nonempty, that is to say, there exists at least one such vector whatever be the values of X_1 and E_2 chosen above.[3]

The problem is to select X_1 and later X_2 so that the expected value of C is minimum.

Observing that the nonnegative weighted sum of convex functions is convex and that an expected value is such a sum (or more generally a Stieltjes integral), the following useful lemma results:

LEMMA 1: *If $\phi(X|E)$ is convex in $X \in \Omega$ whatever E be chosen from a sample space S with known probability distribution, then the function $\phi(X) = \mathscr{E}_E \phi(X|E)$ is convex.*

THEOREM 1: *If $\phi(X_1, X_2|E_2)$ is a convex function in $X_1 \in \Omega_1$, $X_2 \in \Omega_2(X_1|E_2)$, then the function*

$$(2) \qquad \phi_0(X_1) = \mathscr{E}_{E_2} [\underset{X_2}{\mathrm{Inf}}\, \phi(X_1, X_2|E_2)]$$

is convex and has the property that $X_1 = X_1^*$ solves the uncertainty problem if

$$\phi_0(X_1^*) = \mathrm{Min}\, \phi_0(X_1)$$

The expectation ($\mathscr{E}$) is taken with respect to the distribution of E_2 and the greatest lower bound (Inf)[4] is taken with respect to all $X_2 \in \Omega_2(X_1|E_2)$.

PROOF:[5] In order to minimize $\mathscr{E}\phi(X_1, X_2|E_2)$, it is clear that, once X_1 has been selected and E_2 determined by chance, X_2 must be selected so that $\phi(X_1, X_2|E_2)$ is minimized for fixed X_1 and E_2. Thus, the cost for *given* X_1 and E_2 is given by

$$(3) \qquad \phi_1(X_1|E_2) = \underset{X_2 \in \Omega_2}{\mathrm{Inf}}\, \phi(X_1, X_2|E_2)$$

The expected cost for a *given* X_1 is then simply the expected value of $\phi_1(X_1|E_2)$ and this we denote by $\phi_0(X_1)$. The optimal choice of X_1 to minimize expected cost is thus reduced to choosing X_1 so as to minimize $\phi_0(X_1)$.

---

[3] This assumption can be interpreted as assuring either that there is enough *fat* in the system or that there are enough *slack* variables in the system so that the set of permanently feasible (X_1, X_2) is not null.

[4] The greatest lower bound instead of minimum is used to avoid the possibility that the minimum value is not attained for any admissible point $X_2 \in \Omega_2$ or $X_1 \in \Omega_1$. In the case where the latter occurs, it should be understood that while there exists no X_i where the minimum is attained, there exists X_i for which values as close to minimum as desired are attained.

[5] This proof is along lines suggested by I. Glicksberg.

There remains only to establish the convexity property. We shall show first that $\phi_1(X_1|E_2)$ for bounded ϕ_1 is convex for X_1 in Ω_1. If true, then applying the lemma, the result that $\phi_0(X_1)$ is convex readily follows. Let us suppose that $\phi_1(X_1|E_2)$ is not convex; then there exist three points X_1', X_1'', X_1''' in Ω_1, $X_1''' = \lambda X_1' + \mu X_1''$, $(\lambda + \mu = 1, 0 \le \lambda \le 1)$ that violate the condition for convexity, i.e.,

(4) $$\lambda\phi_1(X_1'|E_2) + \mu\phi_1(X_1''|E_2) < \phi_1(X_1'''|E_2)$$

or

(5) $$\lambda\phi_1(X_1'|E_2) + \mu\phi_1(X_1''|E_2) = \phi_1(X_1'''|E_2) - \varepsilon_0 \qquad (\varepsilon_0 > 0)$$

For any $\varepsilon_0 > 0$, however, there exist X_2' and X_2'' such that

(6) $$\phi_1(X_1'|E_2) = \phi(X_1', X_2'|E_2) - \varepsilon_1 \qquad (0 \le \varepsilon_1 < \varepsilon_0)$$
$$\phi_1(X_1''|E_2) = \phi(X_1'', X_2''|E_2) - \varepsilon_2 \qquad (0 \le \varepsilon_2 < \varepsilon_0)$$

Setting $X_2''' = \lambda X_2' + \mu X_2''$ we note because of the assumed linearity of the model (1) that $(\lambda X_2' + \mu X_2'') \in \Omega_2(X_1'''|E_2)$ and hence by convexity of ϕ

(7) $$\lambda\phi(X_1', X_2'|E_2) + \mu\phi(X_1'', X_2''|E_2) \ge \phi(X_1''', X_2'''|E_2)$$

whence by (6)

(8) $$\lambda\phi_1(X_1'|E_2) + \mu\phi_1(X_1''|E_2) \ge \phi(X_1''', X_2'''|E_2) - \lambda\varepsilon_1 - \mu\varepsilon_2$$

and by (5)

(9) $$\phi_1(X_1'''|E_2) > \phi(X_1''', X_2'''|E_2) - \lambda\varepsilon_1 - \mu\varepsilon_2 + \varepsilon_0$$

where $0 < \lambda\varepsilon_1 + \mu\varepsilon_2 < \varepsilon_0$, which contradicts the assumption that

$$\phi_1(X_1'''|E_2) = \operatorname*{Inf}_{X_2 \in \Omega_2} \phi(X_1''', X_2|E_2)$$

The proof for unbounded ϕ_1 is omitted; see [Dantzig, 1955-1]. For an illustration of the use of this theorem in solving a linear program under uncertainty, see Chapter 28.

The Multi-stage Problem with General Linear Structure.

The structure assumed is

(10) $$b_1 = A_{11} X_1$$
$$b_2 = A_{21} X_1 + A_{22} X_2$$
$$b_3 = A_{31} X_1 + A_{32} X_2 + A_{33} X_3$$
$$b_4 = A_{41} X_1 + A_{42} X_2 + A_{43} X_3 + A_{44} X_4$$
$$\cdots\cdots\cdots\cdots\cdots\cdots\cdots\cdots\cdots\cdots\cdots\cdots$$
$$b_m = A_{m1} X_1 + A_{m2} X_2 + A_{m3} X_3 + \ldots \quad \ldots + A_{mm} X_m$$
$$C = \phi(X_1, X_2, \ldots, X_m | E_2, E_3, \ldots, E_m)$$

[509]

where b_1 is a known vector; b_i is a chance vector $(i = 2, \ldots, m)$ whose components are functions of a point E_i drawn from a known multidimensional distribution; A_{ij} are known matrices. The sequence of decisions is as follows: X_1, the vector of nonnegative activity levels in the first stage, is chosen so as to satisfy the first-stage restrictions $b_1 = A_{11}X_1$; the values of components of b_2 are chosen by chance by determining E_2; X_2 is chosen to satisfy the second-stage restrictions $b_2 = A_{21}X_1 + A_{22}X_2$, etc., iteratively for the third and higher stages. It is further assumed that:

(a) The components of X_j are nonnegative.
(b) There exists at least one X_j satisfying the jth-stage restraints, whatever be the choice of $X_1, X_2, \ldots, X_{j-1}$ satisfying the earlier restraints or the outcomes $b_1, b_2, \ldots, b_m$.
(c) The total cost C is a convex function in $X_1, \ldots, X_m$ which depends on the values of the sample points $E_2, E_3, \ldots, E_m$.

THEOREM 2: *An equivalent $(m - 1)$-stage programming problem with a convex payoff function can be obtained by dropping the mth-stage restrictions and replacing the convex cost function ϕ by*

(11) $\phi_{m-1}(X_1, X_2, \ldots, X_{m-1}|E_2, \ldots, E_{m-1})$
$$= \mathscr{E} \; \underset{E_m}{\text{Inf}} \; \underset{X_m \in \Omega_m}{} \phi(X_1, X_2, \ldots, X_m|E_2, \ldots, E_m)$$

where Ω_m is the set of possible X_m that satisfy the mth-stage restrictions.

Since the proof of the above theorem is identical to the two-stage case, no details will be given. The fact that a cost function for the $(m - 1)^{\text{st}}$ stage can be obtained from the mth stage is simply a consequence of the fact that optimal behavior for the mth stage is well defined, that is, given any state, $(X_1, X_2, \ldots, X_{m-1})$ at the beginning of this stage, the best possible actions can be determined and the minimum expected cost evaluated. This is a standard technique in "dynamic programming." The reader interested in methods built around this approach is referred to R. Bellman's book on dynamic programming [1957-1].

While the *existence* of convex functions has been demonstrated that permit reduction of an m-stage problem to equivalent $m - 1, m - 2, \ldots,$ one-stage problems, it appears unlikely that such functions can be computed except in very simple cases. The convexity theorem was demonstrated not as a solution to an m-stage problem but only in the hope that it will spur the development of an efficient computational theory for such models. It should be remembered that any procedure that yields a local optimum will be a true (global) optimum if the function is convex. This is important because multidimensional problems in which non-convex functions are defined over non-convex domains lead, as a rule, to local optima and an almost hopeless task, in general, of exploring other parts of the domain for the other extremes [Dantzig and Madansky, 1960-1]. See § 26-3.

The General Two-stage Case.

When the set of possibilities for the chance vector b_2 is $b_2^{(1)}$, $b_2^{(2)}$, . . ., $b_2^{(k)}$ with probabilities $p_1, p_2, \ldots, p_k$, $(\Sigma p_i = 1)$, it is not difficult to obtain a direct linear programming solution for small k, say $k = 3$. Since this type of structure is very special, it appears likely that techniques can be developed to handle large k, which could be used to approximate the solution when b_2 has a general distribution. For $k = 3$, the problem is equivalent to determining vectors X_1 and vectors $X_2^{(1)}$, $X_2^{(2)}$, $X_2^{(3)}$ such that

$$(12) \qquad b_1 = A_{11}X_1$$
$$b_2^{(1)} = A_{21}X_1 + A_{22}X_2^{(1)}$$
$$b_2^{(2)} = A_{21}X_1 \qquad\qquad + A_{22}X_2^{(2)}$$
$$b_2^{(3)} = A_{21}X_1 \qquad\qquad\qquad\qquad + A_{22}X_2^{(3)}$$
$$\mathscr{E}C = \gamma_1 X_1 + p_1\gamma_2 X_2^{(1)} + p_2\gamma_2 X_2^{(2)} + p_3\gamma_2 X_2^{(3)} = z \text{ (Min)}$$

where for simplicity we have assumed a linear objective function. Thus a general two-stage linear program with an uncertain constant vector for the second stage reduces to a linear program of a special structure like (12).

EXERCISE: Develop an algorithm for solving systems like (12) for large k, by dualizing and then using the Decomposition Principle (Chapter 23). Take advantage of the repetitive appearance of A_{22} and γ_2.

25-4. PROBLEMS

1. Prove that the quadratic expression given in § 25-1-(5) is positive semi-definite, i.e., $V \geq 0$.
2. Prove that any quadratic expression Q can by linear transformation be reduced to sum and difference of squares of the new variables. Show that Q cannot be positive definite if it involves differences of squares. (Review.)
3. Show that if Q is positive (semi-) definite, Q is a convex function. (Review.)
4. Show for V and x satisfying § 25-1-(1, 3, 5) and $E \leq E^*$, where E^* is a parameter, that Min V is a monotonically decreasing function of E^* if we allow E^* to take on increasing values.
5. Show above that if Q is any convex function of x, then Min Q is a convex function of E (where E and x satisfy § 25-1-(1, 3).
6. Solve the same problem as § 25-2-(1) using the discrete distribution $d = 70, 71, 72, \ldots, 80$ with probability $1/11$ each.

[511]

7. (a) Solve the transportation problem

Available:

x_{11}	x_{12}	x_{13}	x_{14}	3
2	3	4	1	
x_{21}	x_{22}	x_{23}	x_{24}	2
7	2	5	1	
x_{31}	x_{32}	x_{33}	x_{34}	5
4	3	2	2	

Required: d_1 d_2 d_3 d_4

where the demands are

$$d_1 = 3 \text{ with probability } 1$$
$$d_2 = 3 \quad ,, \qquad ,, \qquad ,,$$
$$d_3 = 2 \quad ,, \qquad ,, \qquad ,,$$
$$d_4 = 2 \quad ,, \qquad ,, \qquad ,,$$

(b) Solve, if

$$d_1 = 2, 3, 4 \text{ with probability } \tfrac{1}{3} \text{ each}$$
$$d_2 = 2, 3, 4 \quad ,, \qquad ,, \qquad ,, \quad ,,$$
$$d_3 = 1, 2, 3 \quad ,, \qquad ,, \qquad ,, \quad ,,$$
$$d_4 = 1, 2, 3 \quad ,, \qquad ,, \qquad ,, \quad ,,$$

Compare this solution with that of 7(a) which uses expected demands in place of the variable demands 7(b).

8. Consider a linear program where all coefficients are subject to uncertainty. Suppose (for $i = 1, 2, \ldots, m$) that

$$\varepsilon_i(x) = \sum_{j=1}^{n} a_{ij}x_j + a_0 \leq 0 \qquad\qquad (x_j \geq 0)$$

$$\varepsilon_0(x) = \sum_{j=1}^{n} a_{0j}x_j = z \text{ (Min)}$$

is desired but, unfortunately, all x_j must be selected *prior* to a random choice of the coefficients a_{ij} whose distributions are, however, known. Denote by $\sigma_i(x)$ the standard error of $\varepsilon_i(x)$. Show that

$$\sigma_i(x) = \left[\sum_{j=1}^{n} \sum_{k=1}^{n} x_j x_k \mathscr{E}(a_{ij} - \bar{a}_{ij})(a_{ik} - \bar{a}_{ik}) \right]^{\frac{1}{2}}$$

[512]

Suppose we solve the program (for $i = 1, 2, \ldots, m$)

$$\bar{\varepsilon}_i(x) + t_i \sigma_i(x) \leq 0 \qquad\qquad (x \geq 0)$$

$$\bar{\varepsilon}_0(x) + t_0 \sigma_0(x) = z \ (\text{Min})$$

where $t_i = 3$, say, means that we have built in a safety factor so that $\bar{\varepsilon}_i(x)$, the expected value of $\varepsilon_i(x)$, is three standard errors below zero. Prove that this is a *convex program*. Apply § 24-1 to solve such a problem. Show by Tchebycheff's inequality that

$$\text{Prob}\left[\varepsilon_i(x) > 0 \right] < \frac{1}{t^2}$$

What is the above probability if $\varepsilon_i(x)$ is approximately normally distributed? Show that if the a_{ij} are independent and normally distributed, then $\varepsilon_i(x)$ is normally distributed.

REFERENCES

Bellman, 1957-1
Bereany, 1963-1
Charnes and Cooper, 1959-1, 1963-1
Charnes, Cooper, and Thompson, 1964-1
Charnes and Lemke, 1954-1
Cramér, 1955-1
Dantzig, 1954-1, 1954-3, 1955-1, 1956-2
Dantzig and Madansky, 1960-1
El Agizy, 1964-1
El-Maghraby, 1959-1, 1960-1
Feller, 1957-1
Ferguson and Dantzig, 1956-1
Freund, 1956-1
Krelle, 1960-1
Kuhn and Tucker, 1950-2
Madansky, 1959-1, 1960-1, 2, 1963-1
Markowitz, 1952-1, 1956-1
Mangasarian, 1964-1
Miller and Wagner, 1964-1
Naslund and Whinston, 1962-1
Neyman, 1950-1
Radner, 1955-1
Reiter, 1957-1
Simon, 1956-1
Sinha, 1963-1
Stigler, 1945-1
Talacko, 1959-1
Theil, 1957-1, 1961-1
Tintner, 1955-1
Tintner, Millham and Sengupta, 1963-1
Vajda, 1958-2
Van den Bogaard, 1960-1
Van Moeseke and Tintner, 1964-1
Vazsonyi, 1955-1
Votaw, 1960-1
Wagner, 1958-2
Wald, 1950-1
Wets, 1964-1
Williams, 1963-1
Wolfe, 1959-1

CHAPTER 26

DISCRETE-VARIABLE EXTREMUM PROBLEMS

Our purpose now is to solve programs involving variables that have integer values. This first section is confined to a general survey; the second section describes Gomory's Method of Integer Forms, which has now replaced the earlier incomplete work in the field; and the third section gives an appreciation of these results by describing a large class of difficult mathematical problems which are reducible to integer programs. In § 26-3-(14) a simple device is given for transforming a discrete-valued variable to an integer-valued variable.

26-1. SURVEY OF METHODS

A number of important scheduling problems, such as the assignment of flights for an airline or the arrangement of stations on an assembly line, require the study of an astronomical number of arrangements to determine which one is "best." The mathematical problem is to find some short-cut way of getting this best assignment without going through all the combinations. By allowing the unknown assignments to vary *continuously* over some range, one can obtain pseudo-solutions in which one or more assignments turn out to be fractions instead of whole numbers. It is common practice to adjust such values to whole numbers. Because mathematical models are often imperfect mirrors of reality, this approach is recommended for most practical problems. But since such procedures can occasionally give far from the best answer, mathematicians have been working on improved techniques.

The purpose of the present section is to review some recent successes using linear programming methods in this difficult area. We shall also say a few words about the functional-equation approach of dynamic programming; one example is presented in which this method provides an efficient algorithm.

To be more explicit, certain classes of problems are combinatorial in nature and easy to formulate, but mathematicians have had only partial success in solving them. These arise often in the form of discrete-variable programming problems, such as:

1. *The empty-containers problem.* A transport company has a large

number of objects for shipment that it places in empty containers of fixed size. What is the least number of containers required ?

2. *The multi-stage machine-scheduling problem.* A machine shop has a large number of different types of tasks to be performed. Each task must be processed first on machine A, then B, then C, . . .; the time required depends on the task. In what order should the processing be done to complete all the tasks in the least time ? [Johnson, 1958-1]

3. *The flight-scheduling problem.* Given a number of sources that must ship specified quantities to a number of destinations, arrange an efficient flight schedule [Markowitz and Manne, 1957-1].

4. *The trim problem.* Newsprint comes in rolls of varying widths that are cut from rolls many times these widths. How are these to be cut to minimize trim ? [Paull and Walter, 1955-1; Eisemann, 1957-1; Land and Doig, 1957-1; Doig and Belz, 1956-1.]

5. *The fixed-charge problem.* See § 26-3.

6. *The traveling-salesman problem.* See § 26-3.

Examples of problems that have yielded to analysis, as we have seen in earlier chapters, are the following:

7. *The assignment problem.* See Chapter 15.

8. *The problem of the shortest route in a network.* See Chapter 17.

The mind seems to have a remarkable facility for scanning many combinations and arriving at what appears to be either a best one or a very good one. The number of possible combinations can be extremely large, however, making it difficult to verify that the choice is, indeed, a good one. Any ideas, therefore, that help verify that a conjectured solution is optimal are of interest. We shall consider the following class of problems:

Find x_j satisfying

$$(1) \qquad \sum_{j=1}^{n} a_{ij}x_j = b_i \qquad\qquad (i = 1, 2, \ldots, m)$$

and

$$(2) \qquad x_j = 0 \text{ or } 1$$

that minimize the linear form

$$(3) \qquad \sum_{j=1}^{n} c_j x_j = z$$

For a programming problem to be discrete, it is not necessary that the variables be 0 or 1. In flight-scheduling problems, for example, the variables that represent the number of flights are required to be nonnegative integers. There exists, however, a very simple device by which such problems can be reduced to the "0 or 1" form if the variables have known upper bounds. Indeed, let x be a variable that can take on only nonnegative integral values and let the integer k be an upper bound for x, so that $x \leq k$; then x can be replaced by the sum

$$x = y_1 + y_2 + \ldots + y_k \qquad (y_j = 0 \text{ or } 1)$$

For this reason the representation (1), (2), and (3) of a discrete programming problem is often referred to as the *standard discrete form*.

An important property of any set of points whose coordinates satisfy equation (2) is that the points are vertices of a convex polyhedral set in n-dimensional space. This is perhaps intuitively obvious since a point such as $(0, 1, 0, \ldots, 1)$ is one of the vertices of the unit n-cube (which of course is convex). As we know in a linear programming problem, if an optimal solution exists, there is one that is an extreme point of feasible solutions. This suggests that, in seeking a solution to the standard discrete problem, we first weaken the hypothesis as follows:

(4) $\qquad$ Replace $\left\{ \begin{array}{c} x_j = 0 \text{ or } x_j = 1 \\ \text{a discontinuous range} \end{array} \right\}$ by $\left\{ \begin{array}{c} 0 \leq x_j \leq 1 \\ \text{a continuous range} \end{array} \right\}$

Because the replacement given in (4) is less restrictive than the condition (2), it follows that the set of feasible solutions to the linear programming problem (1) and (4) forms a convex polyhedral set C that contains the convex polyhedral set C^*, which is the convex hull of the solution points of (1) and (2). It is easy to see, however, that every extreme point (vertex) of C^* is an extreme point of C (see open dots in Fig. 26-1-I); but there may be extreme points of C that are outside of C^* (see closed dots in Fig. 26-1-I). The

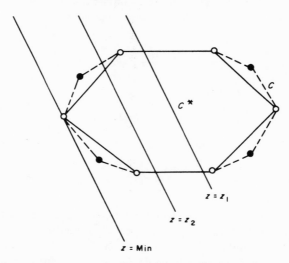

Figure 26-1-I. Schematic representation (two-dimensional case) of the polyhedral set C^* whose vertices are the solutions for a discrete program and of the convex polyhedral set C of solutions for the corresponding continuous problem.

parallel lines in Fig. 26-1-I represent different positions of the hyperplane

$$c_1 x_1 + c_2 x_2 + \ldots + c_n x_n = z = \text{constant}$$

and it is clear that, depending on the values of the c_j, an extreme point corresponding to minimum z may belong to C^* (as in Fig. 26-1-I) or may belong to C and not to C^* [Hoffman and Kruskal, 1956-1].

A remarkable property of the "assignment" problem, and the same holds true for the "shortest-route" problem, is that

(5) $$C^* = C$$

Indeed, this result holds true for a general class of "transportation" problems of which these are special cases. Thus, in the marriage problem (Chapter 15), when we replace the condition $x_{ij} = 0$ or 1 by $0 \leq x_{ij} \leq 1$, we are, in effect, allowing the class of solutions to be extended from the monogamous to the polygamous situation in which sharing mates is possible. The fact that $C^* = C$ states that monogamy will turn out to be the best after all!

The Knapsack Problem.

In certain types of problems, we can get extreme-point solutions for which not all the values of the x_j are either zero or one. When any of the x_j have fractional values, the corresponding extreme points are referred to as *fractional extreme points*. An example of this occurs in the knapsack problem: A person is planning a hike and has decided not to carry more than 70 pounds of various items, such as bed roll, geiger counters (these days), cans of food, etc.

We try to formulate this in mathematical terms. Let a_j be the weight of the jth object and let b_j be its relative value determined by the hiker in comparison with the values of the other objects he would like to have on his trip. Let $x_j = 1$ mean that the jth item is selected, and $x_j = 0$ mean that it is not selected. We express the weight limitation by

(6) $$\sum_{j=1}^{n} a_j x_j \leq 70$$

(7) $$x_j = 0 \text{ or } 1$$

and wish to choose the x_j, so that the total value

(8) $$\sum_{j=1}^{n} b_j x_j = z$$

is a maximum.

Now we can show this pictorially in the plane (Fig. 26-1-II) if one coordinate axis measures weight, a, and the other measures value, b. Each object then is represented by a point having coordinates (a_j, b_j). The problem,

[517]

graphically, is to select a subset of these points that represents the set of items that he carries with him on his hike; the others he rejects. Let us see what type of graphical solution is obtained if the condition $x_j = 0$ or 1 is replaced by the condition that the variables can lie anywhere in the interval from 0 to 1. The latter problem can be solved by regular linear programming methods; indeed, because of its very simple form, it admits an immediate

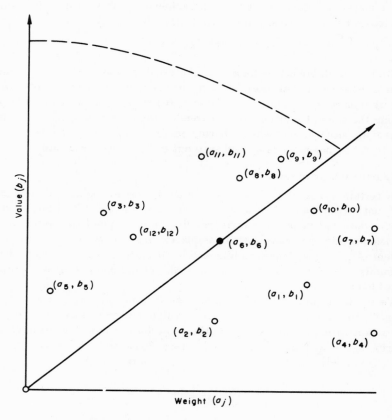

Figure 26-1-II. Graphical solution of the knapsack problem (continuous case).

solution: Rotate clockwise a ray with the origin as pivot point and b axis as starting position. Items corresponding to points swept out by the ray are selected in turn until the sum of their weights exceeds the weight limitation. If upon selection of item j the weight limitation is exceeded, the value x_j is chosen as that fractional part of its weight a_j that would make the sum come exactly to 70 lbs. With the exception of this one item, all the items swept out by the ray have the value $x_j = 1$, while those not swept out have the value $x_j = 0$. It will be noted that this is very close to the kind of solution desired; all the x_j's are either 0 or 1 with the exception of the one that has a fractional value.

Now at this point the natural question is, "What happens if the solution is *rounded*?" The effect of rounding up or down is of course to change the total weight carried to a number different from 70 lbs. If the model is imperfect (in other words, if the hiker really has a limitation of *roughly* 70 lbs) this may be a satisfactory way of getting rid of the fractional solution; this is particularly true if the weight of individual items is small relative to 70 lbs. *For most practical problems, this is probably all that is needed.* Our object here, however, is to explore ways of getting an exact mathematical solution.

The functional-equation approach of dynamic programming (see § 1-4) is the best technique so far devised for the case where there are only a few items and only one kind of limitation. Extensions to two or more limitations—say one on total weight and another on total volume—can be done, but there would be a considerable increase in the amount of computational work. The method consists in ordering the items in any arbitrary way and determining what items would be carried if (a) the selections were restricted to only the first k items, and (b) the weight limitations were $w = 1, 2, \ldots,$ or 70. For example, if $k = 1$ and $w < a_1$ (where a_1 is the weight of the first item), then the item would not be selected; but if $w \geq a_1$, it would be. From this it is easy to decide what the selections would be for the first two items ($k = 2$) for every total weight $w = 1, 2, \ldots, 70$, and then, inductively, for $k = 3, 4, \ldots, n$. To see this, suppose we wish to determine whether we select the $(k + 1)^{\text{st}}$ item if our weight limitation is w when we know how to make the selections for the first k items for any weight $w = 1, 2, \ldots, 70$.

Let $F_k(w)$ be the highest total value that can be obtained with the first k objects under weight limitation w. Then, under the same weight limitation w, the highest total value that can be obtained with first $k + 1$ objects is $F_k(w)$ if the $(k + 1)^{\text{st}}$ object is not selected, but is $b_{k+1} + F_k(w - a_{k+1})$ if the $(k + 1)^{\text{st}}$ object is selected. Hence, the $(k + 1)^{\text{st}}$ object is or is not selected depending on which of these is higher. Thus, not only is the selection for the first $k + 1$ objects determined, but it also is clear that $F_{k+1}(w)$ is given by

$$(9) \quad F_{k+1}(w) = \begin{cases} \text{Max}\,[F_k(w), \quad b_{k+1} + F_k(w - a_{k+1})] & \text{for} \quad w \geq a_{k+1} \\ F_k(w) & \text{for} \quad w < a_{k+1} \end{cases}$$

The procedure is iterated for each w and repeated for $k = 1, 2, \ldots, n$. Although for the functional-equation approach the terms were ordered in an arbitrary way, it is recommended that in a practical application they be ordered initially in sequence corresponding to decreasing b_j/a_j (see Fig. 26-1-II).

[519]

The linear programming approach consists in adding new linear-inequality constraints to the system, so that the fractional extreme points of C in the neighborhood of Max z will be excluded, but the set of extreme points of the convex hull C^* of admissible solutions will be in the new C. The procedure would be complete except that the rules for systematically generating additional constraints require the use of methods discussed in the next section.

DEFINITION: A *cutting plane* is the hyperplane boundary of an added linear inequality constraint. It is thought of as "cutting off" part of the convex of feasible solutions to form a new convex.

Let us suppose, as in Fig. 26-1-II, that the ray swept out items 5, 3, 12, 11, 8, and 9 before the weight limitation was exceeded, but included item 6 just after it was exceeded; then

$$a_5 + a_3 + a_{12} + a_{11} + a_8 + a_9 \qquad < 70$$
$$a_5 + a_3 + a_{12} + a_{11} + a_8 + a_9 + a_6 > 70$$

We wish to exclude the fractional extreme-point solution

(10) $$x_5 = x_3 = x_{12} = x_{11} = x_8 = x_9 = 1, \quad x_6 = f \qquad (0 < f < 1)$$

and $x_j = 0$ for all other j.

It is clear that for an *admissible solution* not all $x_j = 1$ for the seven points $j = 5, 3, 12, 11, 8, 9, 6$, because the weight limitation would be violated. This means that the sum of these variables cannot exceed 6, or

(11) $$x_5 + x_3 + x_{12} + x_{11} + x_8 + x_9 + x_6 \leq 6$$

Since the fractional extreme-point solution (10) does not satisfy this constraint, it is clear that the effect of adding the particular inequality (11) is to exclude this fractional extreme point. Form (8) is maximized under conditions (6) and $0 \leq x_j \leq 1$, but with the constraint (11) added. Again a new fractional extreme point may turn up for the new convex C, and it will be necessary again to seek a condition that will exclude it. For the most part the conditions added will be other partial sums of the x_j similar to (11). However, at times more subtle relations will be required until at last an extreme point is obtained that is admissible. The method discussed in the next section provides a straightforward way to determine these constraints.

Many experiments by the author and others indicate that very often a practical problem can be solved using only such obvious supplementary conditions as (11). In an experiment with a number of randomly chosen traveling-salesman problems involving nine cities, simple upper bounds and so-called simple "loop conditions" on the variables were often sufficient to yield the desired discrete solution [Dantzig, Fulkerson, and Johnson, 1954-1, 1959-1]. To appreciate the power of this procedure it should be noted that, for each nine-city case solved, the tour that minimized the total distance covered was one from among 362,880 ways of touring nine cities and was selected in about two hours of hand-computation time.

26-2. GOMORY'S METHOD OF INTEGER FORMS

In this section we shall present a method due to R. Gomory [1958-1, 2] of automatically generating cutting planes or *integer forms* which gives promise of providing an efficient solution to linear programs in integers in a finite number of steps. This approach has been generalized to the case where some variables are continuous and some are constrained to be integers. This was first done by E. M. L. Beale [1958-1], and by Gomory [1958-3] in a different way, which we follow here.

We begin by giving the method in a precise form and then discuss various ways that it may be relaxed in practice. Our concern is with linear-programming-type problems where, however, some of the variables must have integer values and the others may have fractional values. The former we shall call *integer variables* and the latter *fractional variables*.

PROBLEM: Determine Min v and $y_j \geq 0$ for $j = 1, 2, \ldots, n$ such that v and y_j are integers for a subset J of the indices j and such that

(1)
$$
\begin{aligned}
a_{11} y_1 + a_{12} y_2 + \ldots + a_{1n} y_n &= b_1 \qquad (y_j \geq 0)\\
a_{21} y_1 + a_{22} y_2 + \ldots + a_{2n} y_n &= b_2 \\
&\cdots \cdots \cdots \cdots \cdots \cdots \cdots \cdots \cdots \cdots \cdots \\
a_{m1} y_1 + a_{m2} y_2 + \ldots + a_{mn} y_n &= b_m \\
c_1 y_1 + c_2 y_2 + \ldots + c_n y_n &= v \text{ (Min)}
\end{aligned}
$$

Note that v as well as y_j for $j \in J$ are required to be integers while the remaining variables are allowed to take on fractional values.

The Initial Primal and Dual Systems.

To initiate the algorithm, the problem is first solved ignoring the integer restrictions. Suppose the canonical form obtained on the final iteration is

(2)
$$
\begin{aligned}
\bar{a}_{11} y_1 + \bar{a}_{12} y_2 + \ldots + \bar{a}_{1,n-m} y_{n-m} + y_{n-m+1} &\quad = \bar{b}_1 \\
\bar{a}_{21} y_1 + \bar{a}_{22} y_2 + \ldots + \bar{a}_{2,n-m} y_{n-m} \quad + y_{n-m+2} &\quad = \bar{b}_2 \\
\bar{a}_{m1} y_1 + \bar{a}_{m2} y_2 + \ldots + \bar{a}_{m,n-m} y_{n-m} \quad\quad\quad + y_n &= \bar{b}_m \\
\check{c}_1 y_1 + \check{c}_2 y_2 + \ldots + \bar{c}_{n-m} y_{n-m} &\quad = v - \bar{v}_0
\end{aligned}
$$

where we have assumed, for convenience, $y_{n-m+1}, \ldots, y_n$ as basic variables. Because our solution is optimal, we have for $i = 1, 2, \ldots, m$ and $j = 1, 2, \ldots, n$,

(3)
$$
\bar{b}_i \geq 0, \; \bar{c}_j \geq 0
$$

If we now set

(4) $$y_i = \pi_i \qquad\qquad (i = 1, 2, \ldots, n - m)$$

for all the non-basic variables and solve for basic variables in terms of π_i

(5) $$y_{n-m+k} = \bar{b}_k - \sum_{i=1}^{n-m} \bar{a}_{ki}\pi_i \qquad\qquad (k = 1, \ldots, m)$$

$$v = \bar{v}_0 + \sum_{i=1}^{n-m} \bar{c}_i \pi_k$$

then all the variables $y_1, y_2, \ldots, y_n$ are expressed *parametrically* in terms of π_i.

In the expression for y_j let us now denote by $+\alpha_{ij}$ the coefficient of π_i, by α_{0j} the constant terms, and by α_{i0} the *coefficients* of v. Setting

(6) $$\bar{m} = n - m$$

then the original problem can be cast in the following form:

Find Min v, $y_j \geq 0$, π_i where v and y_j are integers for $j \in J$, such that

(7)
$$y_1 = \alpha_{01} + \alpha_{11}\pi_1 + \ldots + \alpha_{\bar{m}1}\pi_{\bar{m}}$$
$$y_2 = \alpha_{02} + \alpha_{12}\pi_1 + \ldots + \alpha_{\bar{m}2}\pi_{\bar{m}}$$
$$\cdot \qquad \cdot \qquad \cdot \qquad\qquad \cdot$$
$$\cdot \qquad \cdot \qquad \cdot \qquad\qquad \cdot$$
$$\cdot \qquad \cdot \qquad \cdot \qquad\qquad \cdot$$
$$y_n = \alpha_{0n} + \alpha_{1n}\pi_1 + \ldots + \alpha_{\bar{m}n}\pi_{\bar{m}}$$
$$v = \alpha_{00} + \alpha_{10}\pi_1 + \ldots + \alpha_{\bar{m}0}\pi_{\bar{m}}$$

If we set aside the integer restrictions, we can replace (7) by

$$\alpha_{0j} + \sum \alpha_{ij}\pi_i \geq 0 \qquad\qquad (j = 1, 2, \ldots n)$$

$$\alpha_{00} + \sum \alpha_{i0}\pi_i = v \text{ (Min)}$$

and it is clear that the dual problem for (7) becomes

Dual: Find Max x_0 and $x_j \geq 0$ for $j \neq 0$ satisfying

(8)
$$x_0 + \alpha_{01}x_1 + \alpha_{02}x_2 + \ldots + \alpha_{0n}x_n = \alpha_{00}$$
$$\alpha_{11}x_1 + \alpha_{12}x_2 + \ldots + \alpha_{1n}x_n = \alpha_{10}$$
$$\cdot \qquad \cdot \qquad\qquad \cdot \qquad \cdot$$
$$\cdot \qquad \cdot \qquad\qquad \cdot \qquad \cdot$$
$$\alpha_{\bar{m}1}x_1 + \alpha_{\bar{m}2}x_2 + \ldots + \alpha_{\bar{m}n}x_n = \alpha_{\bar{m}0}$$

[522]

Because system (7) is by definition the same as (4), (5), system (8) is the same as (9) below

$$(9) \qquad x_0 \qquad\qquad + \ \bar{b}_1 x_{\overline{m}+1} + \ldots + \ \bar{b}_m x_n = \bar{v}_0$$
$$x_1 \qquad\qquad - \ \bar{a}_{11} x_{\overline{m}+1} - \ldots - \ \bar{a}_{m1} x_n = \bar{c}_1$$

$$x_{\overline{m}} - \bar{a}_{1\overline{m}} x_{\overline{m}+1} - \ldots - \bar{a}_{mm} x_n = \bar{c}_{\overline{m}}$$

which is in canonical form and the basic solution is feasible and optimal ($\bar{b}_i \geq 0$, $\bar{c}_j \geq 0$). The actual order of the variables x_j can be the same as in the primal, and the order of the equations can correspond to the order of the non-basic variables in the primal. We shall assume that this is the case. Moreover, we assume that *the variables of the primal have been previously arranged so that all the integer variables are ahead of the others.* This assumption is not made merely for convenience of exposition; indeed, the finiteness of Gomory's algorithm depends on its being satisfied.

To illustrate, consider the problem of finding Min v, $y_j \geq 0$, where v, y_1, y_2 are integers satisfying

$$(10) \qquad 2y_1 + y_2 + \tfrac{4}{3}y_3 \qquad\quad = \tfrac{13}{3}$$
$$\tfrac{1}{2}y_1 \qquad + \tfrac{3}{4}y_3 + y_4 = \tfrac{9}{4}$$
$$\tfrac{1}{4}y_1 \qquad + \tfrac{4}{3}y_3 \qquad\quad = v + \tfrac{7}{12}$$

If we set $y_1 = \pi_1$, $y_3 = \pi_3$, then

$$(11) \qquad\quad y_1 = \qquad\qquad \pi_1$$
$$y_2 = \qquad \tfrac{13}{3} - 2\pi_1 - \tfrac{4}{3}\pi_3$$
$$y_3 = \qquad\qquad\qquad \pi_3$$
$$y_4 = \qquad \tfrac{9}{4} - \tfrac{1}{2}\pi_1 - \tfrac{3}{4}\pi_3$$
$$v \ = -\tfrac{7}{12} + \tfrac{1}{4}\pi_1 + \tfrac{4}{3}\pi_3$$

where the parameter π_1 is an integer. Ignoring the integer restriction, the dual of (11), is

$$(12) \qquad x_0 \quad + \tfrac{13}{3}x_2 \qquad\quad + \tfrac{9}{4}x_4 = -\tfrac{7}{12}$$
$$x_1 - \quad 2x_2 \qquad\quad - \tfrac{1}{2}x_4 = \tfrac{1}{4}$$
$$- \ \tfrac{4}{3}x_2 + x_3 - \tfrac{3}{4}x_4 = \tfrac{4}{3}$$

Generating New Restrictions.

If the minimizing solution to the primal problem happens to satisfy the integer conditions, this solves the original problem. Thus, if the values of $v = \alpha_{00}$ and $y_j = \alpha_{0j}$ are integers for the integer variables, the basic solution is integral and optimal. If *not*, then the constant term is fractional for at least one expression for an integer variable or for the expression for v as given in (7). In our example, we have two such:

$$(13) \qquad v = -\tfrac{7}{12} + \tfrac{1}{4}\pi_1 + \tfrac{4}{3}\pi_3$$
$$y_2 = \tfrac{13}{3} - 2\pi_1 - \tfrac{4}{3}\pi_3$$

Any such expression can be used to generate a linear inequality (indeed a class of inequalities) which is not satisfied by the current basic solution formed by setting $\pi_i = 0$.

It will be convenient to introduce[1] the symbol $[\alpha_j]^*$ which represents here the greatest *integer* $\leq \alpha_j$; we define

$$(14) \qquad f_j = \alpha_j - [\alpha_j]^* \geq 0$$

to be the *positive proper fractional part of* α_j. For example, if $\alpha_j = \tfrac{4}{3}$, then $[\alpha_j]^* = 1$ and $f_j = \tfrac{1}{3}$; if $\alpha_j = -\tfrac{4}{3}$, then $[\alpha_j]^* = -2$ and $f_j = \tfrac{2}{3}$. We also define the *complement*, $\bar{f}_j$, of the positive fractional part of α_j, as the positive proper fractional part of $-\alpha_j$. It is easy to see that

$$(15) \qquad \bar{f}_j = \begin{cases} 1 - f_j & \text{if } f_j > 0 \\ 0 & \text{if } f_j = 0 \end{cases}$$

THEOREM 1: *If y is an integer variable and $\pi_i \geq 0$ are parameters related by*

$$(16) \qquad y = \alpha_0 + \alpha_1\pi_1 + \ldots + \alpha_{\bar{m}}\pi_{\bar{m}} \qquad\qquad ([\alpha_0]^* < \alpha_0)$$

where $\alpha_i \geq 0$, for $i \neq 0$, then the linear inequality

$$(17) \qquad 1 \leq f_0 + \alpha_1\pi_1 + \ldots + \alpha_{\bar{m}}\pi_{\bar{m}}$$

holds for all π_i generating integral y but is not satisfied by the basic solution generated by $\pi_i = 0$ for $i = 1, \ldots, m$.

PROOF: Since $\alpha_i \geq 0$, and $\pi_i \geq 0$, Min $y \geq \alpha_0$; but the possible values of y are integers, so

$$(18) \qquad y \geq [\alpha_0]^* + 1$$

Subtracting from (16) yields (17). Moreover, writing $y - y^* = [\alpha_0]^* + 1$ where $y^* \geq 0$ is an integer and subtracting from (16) yield

$$(19) \qquad y^* = -\bar{f}_0 + \alpha_1\pi_1 + \ldots + \alpha_{\bar{m}}\pi_{\bar{m}} \qquad\qquad (y^* \geq 0)$$

This is a stronger form of (17) because the new slack variable, y^*, is required to be a *nonnegative integer*.

In our illustrative example

$$(20) \qquad v = -\tfrac{7}{12} + \tfrac{1}{4}\pi_1 + \tfrac{4}{3}\pi_3$$

---

[1] The customary symbol for the largest integer part of a number is a bracket without a star; however, with a star there is less possibility of confusion with ordinary brackets.

where v is an integer variable unrestricted in sign and $\pi_1 \geq 0$, $\pi_3 \geq 0$. (Actually $\pi_1 \geq 0$ is required to be an integer also.) Applying our theorem we have, setting $y^* = y_5$, say

$$(21) \qquad\qquad y_5 = -\tfrac{7}{12} + \tfrac{1}{4}\pi_1 + \tfrac{4}{3}\pi_3 \qquad\qquad (y_5 \geq 0)$$

where $y_5 \geq 0$ is a new integer variable.

System (11) may now be *augmented* by the expression for this new (basic) variable in terms of π_1, π_3. It will be noted that the basic solution generated by setting $\pi_1 = \pi_3 = 0$ is no longer feasible, because $y_5 = -\tfrac{7}{12}$.

It will be also noted that the dual of the augmented system is formed by adding a new variable, say x_5, with coefficients $(-\tfrac{7}{12}, \tfrac{1}{4}, \tfrac{4}{3})$; see (57).[2] The dual is still in canonical form, and its basic solution is feasible but no longer optimal. It will be shown later that the sequence of basic changes required to make it optimal, correspond to a change of the parameters π_i used to represent the y_i.

We may also generate other inequalities by multiplying expression (20) by any integer k, since, if v is an integer, so is kv; thus

$$(22) \qquad\qquad kv = -\frac{7}{12}k + \frac{k}{4}\pi_1 + \frac{4k}{3}\pi_3 \qquad\qquad (k \geq 0)$$

$$y^* = \left[+\frac{7}{12}k\right]^* - \frac{7}{12}k + \frac{k}{4}\pi_1 + \frac{4k}{3}\pi_3 \qquad\qquad (y^* \geq 0)$$

where y^* is an integer.

The knowledge that one or more of the π_i are integers can be used, however, to generate in general new, even stronger inequalities.

THEOREM 2: *If y is an integer variable and the $\pi_i \geq 0$ are integer-valued variables related by*

$$(23) \qquad\qquad y = \alpha_0 + \alpha_1\pi_1 + \ldots + \alpha_{\overline{m}}\pi_{\overline{m}} \qquad\qquad ([\alpha_0]^* < \alpha_0)$$

Then the linear inequality,

$$(24) \qquad\qquad 1 \leq f_0 + f_1\pi_1 + \ldots + f_{\overline{m}}\pi_{\overline{m}}$$

holds for all π_i generating integral y but is not satisfied by the basic solution generated by setting all $\pi_i = 0$.

PROOF: Note that in this theorem the α_i may have either sign, and the π_i are nonnegative integers. Substituting $\alpha_j = f_j + [\alpha_j]^*$ in (23) yields

$$(25) \qquad\qquad \left\{y - [\alpha_0]^* - \sum [\alpha_i]^*\pi_i\right\} = f_0 + f_1\pi_1 + \ldots + f_{\overline{m}}\pi_{\overline{m}}$$

The left member is an integer and $f_j \geq 0$; hence, Theorem 1 may be applied to yield (24) or the stronger form

$$(26) \qquad\qquad y^{**} = -\bar{f}_0 + f_1\pi_1 + f_2\pi_2 + \ldots + f_{\overline{m}}\pi_{\overline{m}} \qquad\qquad (y^{**} \geq 0)$$

where y^{**} is an integer-valued variable.

---

[2] In (57) we have used a stronger condition than (21) by applying Theorem 2.

EXERCISE: Interpret (24) if $f_1 = f_2 = \ldots = f_{\bar{m}} = 0$.

For example, suppose $y \geq 0$ and the $\pi_i \geq 0$ are integer variables related by

$$y = \tfrac{5}{3} + (7/4)\pi_1 - (8/3)\pi_2 + (1/2)\pi_3$$

then a new condition is

$$y^* = -\tfrac{1}{3} + (3/4)\pi_1 + (1/3)\pi_2 + (1/2)\pi_3 \quad (y^* \geq 0 \text{ integer})$$

Another new condition can be generated using $2y$, thus

$$2y = \tfrac{10}{3} + (14/4)\pi_1 - (16/3)\pi_2 + (2/2)\pi_3$$

implies

$$y^{**} = -\tfrac{2}{3} + (1/2)\pi_1 + (2/3)\pi_2 \qquad (y^{**} \geq 0 \text{ integer})$$

A simple extension of these two theorems occurs in the case where some α_i refer to integer parameters π_i, for $i = 1, 2, \ldots, k$, and the remaining parameters may take a fractional value *with the property* all $\alpha_i \geq 0$ (*or all* $\alpha_i \leq 0$) for $i > k$; then the mixed expression

$$(27) \qquad y^* = -\bar{f}_0 + f_1\pi_1 + \ldots + f_k\pi_k + (\alpha_{k+1}\pi_{k+1} + \ldots + \alpha_{\bar{m}}\pi_{\bar{m}})$$

holds for the case $\alpha_i \geq 0$, for all $i > k$, and

$$y^* = -\bar{f}_0 + \bar{f}_1\pi_1 + \ldots + \bar{f}_k\pi_k - (\alpha_{k+1}\pi_{k+1} + \ldots + \alpha_{\bar{m}}\pi_{\bar{m}})$$

holds for the case $\alpha_i \leq 0$ for all $i > k$, for any π_i generating integral y where $y^* \geq 0$, an integer. (This y^* is not the same y^* used earlier.)

In our illustrative example

$$(28) \qquad\qquad y_2 = \tfrac{13}{3} - 2\pi_1 - \tfrac{4}{3}\pi_3$$

where $y_2 \geq 0$, $\pi_1 \geq 0$ are integers and $\pi_3 \geq 0$. Applying the second case, setting $y^* = y_6$, then

$$(29) \qquad\qquad y_6 = -\tfrac{1}{3} + \tfrac{4}{3}\pi_3$$

where $y_6 \geq 0$ is a new integer variable whose expression in terms of the π_i may also be used to augment the system (11) and (21).

If all parameters π_i are integers, then it is interesting to observe that a particularly simple relation exists consisting of a *partial sum* of π_i. This condition is not as strong as earlier ones, since it can be found by combining two known inequalities. Thus for $k = \bar{m}$, (27) implies both

$$(30) \qquad\qquad y^* = -\bar{f}_0 + f_1\pi_1 + \ldots + f_{\bar{m}}\pi_{\bar{m}} \qquad\qquad (y^* \geq 0)$$
$$y^{**} = -f_0 + \bar{f}_1\pi_1 + \ldots + \bar{f}_{\bar{m}}\pi_{\bar{m}} \qquad\qquad (y^{**} \geq 0)$$

where y^* and y^{**} are integers, and we have by adding and setting $y' = y^* + y^{**}$

$$(31) \qquad\qquad y' = -1 + \delta_1\pi_1 + \ldots + \delta_{\bar{m}}\pi_{\bar{m}} \qquad\qquad (y' \geq 0)$$

where $\delta_j = 1$, if $f_j > 0$, and $\delta_j = 0$, if $f_j = 0$. For example, if π_1 and π_3 were both integer variables in (28), then a new relation would be

$$(32) \qquad\qquad y' = -1 + \pi_3$$

It is also interesting to observe that a strong condition can sometimes be generated from an integer variable y, which has an integer value in a solution when all $\pi_i = 0$. For example, suppose

$$(33) \qquad\qquad y = 2 + \tfrac{4}{3}\pi_1 - \tfrac{1}{2}\pi_2$$

where π_1 and π_2 constitute *all* the parameters. Writing

$$(34) \qquad\qquad y - 2 - \pi_1 + \pi_2 = \tfrac{1}{3}\pi_1 + \tfrac{1}{2}\pi_2$$

we note that the left member is integral. Because the right member is nonnegative, we conclude

$$(35) \qquad\qquad y^* = \tfrac{1}{3}\pi_1 + \tfrac{1}{2}\pi_2$$

where $y^* \geq 0$ is an integer. However $y^* = 0$ is *not* possible, because then $\pi_1 = \pi_2 = 0$ and the other integral y_j would have to take on the fractional values of the current basic solution. Hence $y^* = y^{**} + 1 \geq 1$ and

$$(36) \qquad\qquad y^{**} = -1 + \tfrac{1}{3}\pi_1 + \tfrac{1}{2}\pi_2$$

becomes the new restriction. In general, if for some j, $\alpha_{0j} = [\alpha_{0j}]^*$ and $f_i = \alpha_{ij} - [\alpha_{ij}]^* > 0$ for *all* $i \neq 0$, then a new restriction is

$$(37) \qquad\qquad y^{**} = -1 + \sum f_i \pi_i \qquad\qquad (f_i \neq 0)$$

Generating New Conditions for the General Mixed Integer Case.

For problems involving mixed integer and "fractional" variables (variables which may assume fractional values), we must however, in general, be able to generate new inequalities when the coefficients of the fractional variables have either sign. Let

$$(38) \qquad\qquad y = \alpha_0 + \sum_{i=1}^{\overline{m}} \alpha_i \pi_i = \alpha_0 + P - N \qquad\qquad ([\alpha_0]^* < \alpha_0)$$

where P and $-N$ are the partial sums of the positive and negative terms, α_0 is not an integer and y is an integer variable.

If for certain values of π_i, $P - N \geq 0$, then, since $y = \alpha_0 + P - N$ must be an integer so must $f_0 + P - N$; but the latter is strictly positive (for we are assuming that α_0 is non-integral). Hence we must have

$$(39) \qquad\qquad 1 \leq f_0 + P - N$$
$$f_0 \leq P - N$$
$$1 \leq \frac{1}{f_0} P - \frac{1}{f_0} N \leq \frac{1}{f_0} P + \frac{1}{f_0} N$$

If for other values of π_i, $N - P \geq 0$, then $-y = -\alpha_0 + N - P$ is an integer; therefore

(40)
$$1 \leq \bar{f}_0 + N - P$$
$$f_0 \leq N - P$$
$$1 \leq \frac{1}{f_0} N - \frac{1}{f_0} P \leq \frac{1}{f_0} N + \frac{1}{f_0} P$$

Hence for any set of π_i values,

(41)
$$1 \leq \frac{1}{f_0} P + \frac{1}{f_0} N$$

THEOREM 3: *If y is an integer variable, and $\pi_i \geq 0$ satisfy*

(42)
$$y = \alpha_0 + \sum_1^{\overline{m}} \alpha_i \pi_i \qquad \text{where } \alpha_0 > [\alpha_0]^*$$

then

(43)
$$1 \leq \frac{1}{\bar{f}_0}\left(\sum_{I_1} f_i \pi_i + \sum_{I_2} \alpha_i \pi_i \right) + \frac{1}{f_0}\left(\sum_{I_3} \bar{f}_i \pi_i - \sum_{I_4} \alpha_i \pi_i \right)$$

holds for all π_i generating integral y but is not satisfied by the basic solution generated by $\pi_i = 0$. Here

(44)
$$i \in I_1 \text{ if } f_i \leq \bar{f}_0 \text{ and } \pi_i \text{ integral}$$
$$i \in I_2 \text{ if } \alpha_i > 0 \text{ and } \pi_i \text{ fractional}$$
$$i \in I_3 \text{ if } \bar{f}_i < f_0 \text{ and } \pi_i \text{ integral}$$
$$i \in I_4 \text{ if } \alpha_i < 0 \text{ and } \pi_i \text{ fractional}$$

PROOF: If π_i is an integer, set in (42) $\alpha_i = [\alpha_i]^* + f_i$ or $\alpha_i = [\alpha_i]^* + 1 - f_i$ according to whether $f_i < \bar{f}_0$ or $\bar{f}_i < f_0$. Moving all integer terms to the left and calling the left member y', we have

(45)
$$y' = \alpha_0 + \left\{ \sum_{I_1} f_i \pi_i + \sum_{I_2} \alpha_i \pi_i \right\} - \left\{ \sum_{I_3} \bar{f}_i \pi_i - \sum_{I_4} \alpha_i \pi_i \right\}$$

where y' is an integer variable. Identifying (45) with (38), relation (43) corresponds to (41) and the theorem follows.

If we let $y^* \geq 0$ represent the slack in the inequality (43), then the new relation may be written

(46)
$$y^* = -1 + \frac{1}{\bar{f}_0}\left\{ \sum_{I_1} f_i \pi_i + \sum_{I_2} \alpha_i \pi_i \right\} + \frac{1}{f_0}\left\{ \sum_{I_3} \bar{f}_i \pi_i - \sum_{I_4} \alpha_i \pi_i \right\}$$

However, it no longer follows that the added new variable is an integer as was the case with all previous relations that have been developed. (This is too bad because, as we have seen, when y^* is an integer this fact can be

used to advantage to develop, at a later stage, new stronger inequalities.)
To illustrate, suppose

$$(47) \qquad y = \tfrac{5}{3} + \tfrac{3}{5}\pi_1 + \tfrac{4}{2}\pi_2 - \tfrac{9}{7}\pi_3 - \tfrac{5}{2}\pi_4 \qquad\qquad (\pi_j \geq 0)$$

where y, π_1, and π_3 are integers. We may rewrite this

$$(48) \qquad (y - 1 + \pi_3) = \tfrac{2}{3} + \tfrac{3}{5}\pi_1 + \tfrac{4}{2}\pi_2 - \tfrac{2}{7}\pi_3 - \tfrac{5}{2}\pi_4$$

which, if we simply group positive and negative terms, leads to the
inequality

$$(49) \qquad 1 \leq \frac{1}{\tfrac{1}{3}}\,(\tfrac{3}{5}\pi_1 + \tfrac{4}{2}\pi_2) + \frac{1}{\tfrac{2}{3}}\,(\tfrac{2}{7}\pi_3 + \tfrac{5}{2}\pi_4)$$

We may alternatively in (48) set $\tfrac{3}{5}\pi_1 = \pi_1 - \tfrac{2}{5}\pi_1$. Then grouping integer
terms

$$(50) \qquad y - 1 + \pi_3 - \pi_1 = \tfrac{2}{3} + (\tfrac{4}{2}\pi_2) - (\tfrac{2}{5}\pi_1 + \tfrac{2}{7}\pi_3 + \tfrac{5}{2}\pi_4)$$

leads to the inequality

$$(51) \qquad 1 \leq \frac{1}{\tfrac{1}{3}}\,(\tfrac{4}{2}\pi_2) + \frac{1}{\tfrac{2}{3}}\,(\tfrac{2}{5}\pi_1 + \tfrac{2}{7}\pi_3 + \tfrac{5}{2}\pi_4)$$

This is a stronger inequality than (49), because it has a smaller coefficient
of π_1.

Indeed, we may arrange matters, in general, so that the coefficients of
all the integer variables never exceed unity when the constant terms on the
new constraints are unity. To see this, suppose $\pi_i \geq 0$ is an integer; replace
α_i by either $[\alpha_i]^* + f_i$ or $[\alpha_i]^* + 1 - \bar{f}_i$, according to whether $f_i \leq \bar{f}_0$ or
$\bar{f}_i < f_0$. In the first case the coefficient of π_i becomes $f_i/f_0 < 1$ and in the
second case $\bar{f}_i/f_0 \leq 1$.

It is also possible to develop a second type of inequality for the general
case that introduces a *sharper inequality* but increases the size of the system.
Let $i = 1, \ldots, k$ refer to integer variables and $i > k$ to fractional variables.
Set

$$(52) \qquad \bar{y} = \sum_{i>k} \alpha_i \pi_i - \pi^* \qquad\qquad (0 \leq \pi^* \leq 1)$$

where $\bar{y}$ is a new integer variable unrestricted in sign and π^* is the *positive
proper fractional part* of the sum of fractional variable terms; then the new
restriction becomes

$$(53) \qquad y^* = -\bar{f}_0 + \sum_{1}^{k} f_i \pi_i + \pi^* \qquad\qquad (0 \leq \pi^* \leq 1)$$

where y^* is an integer. Since the new restrictions now involve a *bounded*
variable π^*, it is probably better to stay in the primal system rather than pass
to the dual system.

[529]

Iterative Procedure.

Any new restriction

$$(54) \qquad y_t = \alpha_{0t} + \alpha_{1t}\pi_1 + \ldots + \alpha_{\overline{m}t}\pi_{\overline{m}}$$

used to augment the initial system will result in a new variable x_t for the dual system with coefficients α_{it}. The *dual* system is still of course in canonical form but the basic solution is no longer optimal (since $\alpha_{0t} < 0$). Hence, x_t will be introduced into the basis by pivoting on some element α_{rt} in the dual system. This transforms the dual matrix $[\alpha_{ij}]$ into $[\alpha'_{ij}]$.

On the other hand, if we go back to the primal system and introduce a new parameter y_t in place of π_r (by solving equation (54) for π_r in terms of the other π_i and y_t), and substitute in the expressions for y_j and v, then it is easy to see that the matrix $[\alpha_{ij}]$ will also be transformed into $[\alpha'_{ij}]$.

Thus the new dual corresponds to the primal being represented by a set of parameters such that the slack variable of the new restriction becomes a new parameter in place of one of the old parameters. In general, each subsequent dual cycle corresponds to using one of the variables y_j as a new parameter in place of a previous one.

If, after a pivot operation, the dual is still not optimal because some $\alpha_{0t} < 0$, the simplex algorithm is applied until it is. Formally, this corresponds to successively using as "new" restrictions for the primal any existing relation (54) with $\alpha_{0t} < 0$.

EXAMPLE: Find integers Min v, $y_j \geq 0$ satisfying

$$(55) \qquad \begin{aligned} 2y_1 + y_2 + \tfrac{4}{3}y_3 &= \tfrac{13}{3} \\ \tfrac{1}{2}y_1 + \tfrac{3}{4}y_3 + y_4 &= \tfrac{9}{4} \\ \tfrac{1}{4}y_1 + \tfrac{4}{3}y_3 &= v + \tfrac{7}{12} \end{aligned}$$

Fortunately, the system is in optimal canonical form if the integer constraints are set aside. Next, set non-basic variables y_j equal to π_j and represent all variables in terms of π_j. (In the steps below, each y_j used as a parameter is, for convenience, identified by setting $\pi_j = y_j$.)

Primal Cycle 0:

$$(56) \qquad \begin{aligned} y_1 &= \pi_1 \\ y_2 &= \tfrac{13}{3} - 2\pi_1 - \tfrac{4}{3}\pi_3 \\ y_3 &= \pi_3 \\ y_4 &= \tfrac{9}{4} - \tfrac{1}{2}\pi_1 - \tfrac{3}{4}\pi_3 \\ v &= -\tfrac{7}{12} + \tfrac{1}{4}\pi_1 + \tfrac{4}{3}\pi_3 \end{aligned}$$

$$\boxed{y_5 = -\tfrac{7}{12} + \tfrac{1}{4}\pi_1 + \tfrac{1}{3}\pi_3}$$

where the new restriction y_5 is derived from v. We now dualize and optimize:

Dual Cycle 0:

$$(57) \qquad x_0 \quad + \tfrac{13}{3}x_2 \quad\quad + \tfrac{9}{4}x_4 \;\Big|\; - \tfrac{7}{12}x_5 \;\Big| = -\tfrac{7}{12}$$
$$x_1 - \; 2x_2 \quad\quad - \tfrac{1}{2}x_4 \;\Big|\; + \tfrac{1}{4}x_5 \;\Big| = \tfrac{1}{4}$$
$$- \tfrac{4}{3}x_2 + x_3 - \tfrac{3}{4}x_4 \;\Big|\; + \tfrac{1}{3}x_5 \;\Big| = \tfrac{4}{3}$$

● ○ ● ★

Dual Cycle 1:

$$(58) \qquad x_0 + \tfrac{7}{3}x_1 - \tfrac{1}{3}x_2 \quad\quad + \tfrac{13}{12}x_4 \quad\quad = 0$$
$$4x_1 - 8x_2 \quad\quad - \; 2x_4 + x_5 = 1$$
$$- \tfrac{4}{3}x_1 + \tfrac{4}{3}x_2 + x_3 - \tfrac{1}{12}x_4 \quad\quad = 1$$

● ★ ○ ●

This corresponds to eliminating π_1 from the primal, using

$$\pi_5 = y_5 = -\frac{7}{12} + \frac{\pi_1}{4} + \frac{\pi_3}{3}$$

where we have let $y_5 = \pi_5$ be a new parameter; operationally, this is accomplished by *pivoting* on the $\tfrac{1}{4}\pi_1$ term in (56) after first moving the π_5 term to the right-hand side, next to the π_1 term. After pivoting, the pivot equation is dropped. The π_1 terms after elimination are all zero and do not appear. Thus

Primal Cycle 1:

$$(59) \qquad y_1 = \quad \tfrac{7}{3} + 4\pi_5 - \tfrac{4}{3}\pi_3$$
$$y_2 = -\tfrac{1}{3} - 8\pi_5 + \tfrac{4}{3}\pi_3$$
$$y_3 = \quad\quad\quad\quad \pi_3$$
$$y_4 = \tfrac{13}{12} - 2\pi_5 - \tfrac{1}{12}\pi_3$$
$$y_5 = \quad\quad\quad \pi_5$$
$$v = \quad\quad\quad \pi_5 + \quad \pi_3$$

Returning to (58), since the basic solution is not optimal, we perform the indicated pivot step. This yields (except for the boxed column):

Dual Cycle 2:

$$(60) \qquad x_0 + 2x_1 \quad\quad + \tfrac{1}{4}x_3 + \tfrac{17}{16}x_4 \;\Big|\; - \tfrac{3}{4}x_6 \;\Big| = \tfrac{1}{4}$$
$$- 4x_1 \quad\quad + 6x_3 - \tfrac{5}{2}x_4 + x_5 \;\Big|\; \;\Big| = 7$$
$$- \; x_1 + x_2 + \tfrac{3}{4}x_3 - \tfrac{1}{16}x_4 \;\Big|\; + \tfrac{3}{4}x_6 \;\Big| = \tfrac{3}{4}$$

● ○ ● ★

This corresponds to eliminating π_3 from the primal by formally adjoining one of the existing relations, namely,

$$\pi_2 = y_2 = -\tfrac{1}{3} - 8\pi_5 + \tfrac{4}{3}\pi_3$$

and letting $y_2 = \pi_2$ be a new parameter; we can accomplish this by pivoting on the $\frac{4}{3}\pi_3$ term above with respect to (59) (after first moving $\pi_2 = y_2$ to the right). This will eliminate π_3 from the other equations, yielding

Primal Cycle 2:

(61)

$$y_1 = \quad 2 - 4\pi_5 - \quad \pi_2$$
$$y_2 = \quad\quad\quad\quad\quad \pi_2$$
$$y_3 = \quad \tfrac{1}{4} + 6\pi_5 + \quad \tfrac{3}{4}\pi_2$$
$$y_4 = \quad \tfrac{17}{16} - \tfrac{5}{2}\pi_5 - \tfrac{1}{16}\pi_2$$
$$y_5 = \quad\quad\quad \pi_5$$
$$v = \quad \tfrac{1}{4} + 7\pi_5 + \quad \tfrac{3}{4}\pi_2$$

$$\boxed{y_6 = -\tfrac{3}{4} \quad\quad\quad + \tfrac{3}{4}\pi_2}$$

The new column for (60) is derived from the coefficients of x_3 which correspond to $y_3 = \frac{1}{4} + 6\pi_5 + \frac{3}{4}\pi_2$; namely, the new column corresponds to the new restriction $y_6 = -\frac{3}{4} + \frac{3}{4}\pi_2 \geq 0$ shown in (61). Iterating

Dual Cycle 3: (Optimal Integral Solution)

(62)

$$x_0 + \quad x_1 + \quad x_2 + \quad x_3 + \quad x_4 \quad\quad\quad\quad\quad\quad = 1$$
$$- 4x_1 \quad\quad\quad + 6x_3 - \tfrac{5}{2}x_4 + x_5 \quad\quad\quad = 7$$
$$- \tfrac{4}{3}x_1 + \tfrac{4}{3}x_2 + \quad x_3 - \tfrac{1}{12}x_4 \quad\quad\quad + x_6 = 1$$

● ● ●

Primal Cycle 3:

(63)

$$y_1 = 1 - 4\pi_5 - \tfrac{4}{3}\pi_6$$
$$y_2 = 1 \quad\quad\quad + \tfrac{4}{3}\pi_6$$
$$y_3 = 1 + 6\pi_5 + \quad \pi_6$$
$$y_4 = 1 - \tfrac{5}{2}\pi_5 - \tfrac{1}{12}\pi_6$$
$$v = 1 + 7\pi_5 + \quad \pi_6$$

where the optimal solution is found by setting $\pi_5 = \pi_6 = 0$.

Proof of Finiteness of Algorithm. [Gomory, 1958-2, 3.]

For this purpose we regard the initial dual's right-hand side (8) as perturbed by the columns appearing on the left for $j \neq 0$. (See Chapter 10.)

(64)

$$x_0 + \sum_{1}^{n} \alpha_{0j}x_j = \sum_{0}^{n} \alpha_{0j}\varepsilon^j = \alpha_0(\varepsilon)$$

$$\sum_{1}^{n} \alpha_{ij}x_j = \sum_{0}^{n} \alpha_{ij}\varepsilon^j = \alpha_i(\varepsilon) \quad\quad (i = 1, \ldots, \bar{m})$$

[532]

Thus the values of the basic variables become *polynomials* in ε. *It will be assumed that the leading term (i.e., the lowest-power non-zero term) of each* $\alpha_i(\varepsilon)$ *is positive except possibly* $i = 0$.

If the basic variables can be arranged ahead of the non-basic variables as in (9), this assumption is initially satisfied. However, as noted in the paragraph following (9), we require for the convergence proof that x_j corresponding to integer variables y_j *precede* the fractional variables.

EXERCISE: Use artificial variables and the simplex algorithm with perturbation to obtain in the latter case an initial canonical system with the requisite properties, provided one exists. What happens if none exists?

After each augmentation with a supplementary variable (corresponding to a new restriction) we require that the simplex method with perturbation be applied to (64) until it is rendered optimal. We shall refer to this as an *optimal stage*; at such a stage, the coefficients of $\alpha_0(\varepsilon)$ are just the values of v and y_j of a *feasible* solution to the primal, i.e., $\alpha_{0j} \geq 0$ for $j = 1, 2, \ldots, n$. Because we assume that the convex set of feasible solutions to the primal is bounded, the values of the α_{0j} will have, at each such optimal stage, a finite upper bound. If the $k + 1$ leading coefficients $\alpha_{00}, \alpha_{01}, \ldots, \alpha_{0k}$ of $\alpha_0(\varepsilon)$ are all *integers* then the nonnegative coefficients solve the primal and the process terminates. However, if any among the first $k + 1$ are fractional, let $j = j_0$ be the first such. Let $j = n + 1$ be the index of the new column generated from $j = j_0$; then since $\alpha_{0,n+1} < 0$, the new pivot (r, s) is chosen in column $s = n + 1$ and row $r = i$ where $\alpha_{i,n+1} > 0$ and

$$(65) \qquad 0 < \frac{\alpha_r(\varepsilon)}{\alpha_{r,n+1}} = \operatorname*{Min}_{\varepsilon \to 0} \frac{\alpha_i(\varepsilon)}{\alpha_{i,n+1}}$$

Because (64) is in canonical form it is not difficult to show that the choice of pivot is *unique* (see Chapter 10). As a result of the pivot the *new value* of $\alpha_0(\varepsilon)$ is

$$(66) \qquad \alpha_0^*(\varepsilon) = \alpha_0(\varepsilon) - \alpha_r(\varepsilon)(\alpha_{0,n+1}/\alpha_{r,n+1}) > \alpha_0(\varepsilon)$$

For clarity we give again the definition of $j = j_0$ and also define $j = j^*$:

(a) Let $j = j_0$ be the subscript of the first term of $\alpha_0(\varepsilon)$ with non-integral coefficient.

(b) Let $j = j^*$ be the subscript of the first term of $\alpha_0^*(\varepsilon) - \alpha_0(\varepsilon)$ with non-zero coefficient.

THEOREM 4: *Either* $j^* < j_0$ *or* $j^* = j_0$ *and* $\alpha_{0j_0}^* \geq [\alpha_{0j_0}]^* + 1$.

PROOF: The j_0 coefficient of $\alpha_0^*(\varepsilon)$ is

$$(67) \qquad \alpha_{0j_0}^* = \alpha_{0j_0} - \alpha_{rj_0}(\alpha_{0,n+1}/\alpha_{r,n+1})$$

The first non-zero term of $\alpha_0^*(\varepsilon) - \alpha_0(\varepsilon)$ is positive by (66). If it does not occur before $j^* = j_0$, then $\alpha_{rj_0} \geq 0$ (since $\alpha_{0,n+1} < 0$ and the pivot $\alpha_{r,n+1} > 0$, it follows that $\alpha_{r j_0} < 0$ would contradict the inequality in (66)). The remainder of the theorem follows from the relation between

$$(68) \qquad y_{j_0} = \alpha_{0 j_0} + \sum_i \alpha_{i j_0} \pi_i$$

and the new restriction on y^*. *If all π_i are integer parameters*, then

$$(69) \qquad y^* = -\bar{f}_0 + \sum f_i \pi_i$$

where $\alpha_{i j_0} = [\alpha_{i j_0}]^* + f_i$, so that

$$(70) \qquad \alpha_{0 j_0}^* = \alpha_{0 j_0} - \{[\alpha_{r j_0}]^* + f_r\}(-\bar{f}_0/f_r) \geq (\alpha_{0 j_0} + \bar{f}_0) = [\alpha_{0 j_0}]^* + 1$$

which establishes the theorem for this case. *If some π_i are fractional parameters*, we have (46) as the new relation for y^*. In this case $\alpha_{0, n+1} = -1$. If π_r is integral, then

$$(71) \qquad \alpha_{r, n+1} = \text{Min} \left[\frac{f_r}{\bar{f}_0}, \frac{\bar{f}_r}{f_0} \right] < 1$$

where the latter relation was established in the discussion following (51). The remainder of the proof parallels (70) if $\alpha_{r, n+1} = f_r/\bar{f}_0$. On the other hand, if $0 < \alpha_{r, n+1} = \bar{f}_r/f_0 < 1$, then

$$(72) \qquad \alpha_{0 j_0}^* = \alpha_{0 j_0} - \{[\alpha_{r j_0}] + 1 - \bar{f}_r\}(-f_0/\bar{f}_r)$$
$$\geq \alpha_{0 j_0} + (f_0/\bar{f}_r) - f_0 > \alpha_{0 j_0} + 1 - f_0 = [\alpha_{0 j_0}]^* + 1$$

Finally, if π_r is a fractional parameter, then (since $\alpha_{r, j_0} \geq 0$)

$$(73) \qquad \alpha_{r, n+1} = \alpha_{r, j_0}/\bar{f}_0 > 0$$

so that (67) reduces simply to

$$(74) \qquad \alpha_{0 j_0}^* = \alpha_{0j} + \bar{f}_0 = [\alpha_{0j}]^* + 1$$

THEOREM 5: *If the convex of fractional solutions is bounded, then the algorithm is finite.*

PROOF: Suppose, on the contrary, the algorithm is infinite; then $\alpha_0(\varepsilon)$ forms a monotonically increasing sequence. However, the first term must assume some finite integer value after a finite number of iterations and remain unchanged thereafter. Otherwise (because of the assumption of a bounded convex) for some infinite sequence of optimal stages it would take on a set of values increasing toward or attaining some upper bound, and hence, an infinite sequence of non-decreasing fractional values, whose difference tends to zero. By the preceding theorem, *at each optimum stage* a solution is obtained such that the first term of $\alpha_0(\varepsilon)$ which takes on a fractional value, must on the next cycle be at least equal to the next higher integer value. Here $j_0 = j^* = 0$. Hence, the fractional value of one optimal stage and that of the one after the one which follows are separated by at least unity—a contradiction.

Having established that the first term has a constant integer value after p_1 iterations, the second must also after $p_1 + p_2$ iterations. The argument is the same: Since $\alpha_0(\varepsilon)$ is monotonically increasing for sufficiently small ε, it means that after p_1 iterations the second term must be non-decreasing. Because of boundedness of the convex, the values at the end of successive optimum stages must approach or attain a finite upper bound. It cannot take on an infinite set of fractional values because by the preceding theorem it would (because the first component is fixed) on each subsequent stage assume values at least equal to the next higher integer values, etc. The argument may thus be repeated until the first k components which correspond to integer variables are all integers.

Variations.

In practice the selection of the new restriction is not always made by the lowest-index rule; i.e., generated by the integer variable y_j with the lowest index whose value is fractional in a basic solution. Instead, j is often selected so that $-\bar{f}_{0j}$ is minimal. This has sometimes cut down the number of iterations in a number of test runs. If this rule is periodically mixed with the lowest index rule, convergence is still guaranteed. Another device is to impose not one but many new constraints simultaneously. If this is done for our example, the simultaneous imposing of all constraints generated by the integer variables and their multiples yields the required integral solution. If it did not, new simultaneous sets of conditions would have to be imposed and the process repeated. Using perturbation and noting that $\alpha_0^*(\varepsilon)$ is at least as large as before, this variation will converge to a solution in a finite number of steps.

Another weakness of the lowest-index rule is that it requires that v be an integer corresponding to the lowest index. It would be much more satisfactory if v could also be a fractional variable. Gomory has devised special rules to guarantee convergence where v is a fractional variable and all other variables are integers. The proof, however, breaks down in the mixed case if conditions (46) are used. It is not known what happens if (53) are used instead. In practice, of course, the above variants are often used even when v is not an integer.

EXERCISE: If v is a fractional variable and all other variables are integer variables, show for rational coefficients that another form can replace the v form which can be maximized instead and whose value is an integer.

26-3. ON THE SIGNIFICANCE OF SOLVING LINEAR PROGRAMMING PROBLEMS WITH SOME INTEGER VARIABLES

Our purpose is systematically to review and classify problems that can be reduced to linear programs, some or all of whose variables are integer valued [Dantzig, 1960-2]. We shall show that a host of difficult, indeed seemingly impossible, problems of a nonlinear, nonconvex, and combinatorial character are now open for direct attack. The outline for this section is as follows:

I.   General Principles.
    (a) Discussion.
    (b) Dichotomies.
    (c) k-fold Alternatives.
    (d) Selection from Many Pairs of Regions.
    (e) Discrete-variable Problems.
    (f) Nonlinear-objective Problems.
    (g) Conditional Constraints.
    (h) Finding a Global Minimum of a Concave Function.
II.   The Fixed-charge Problem.
III.   The Traveling-salesman Problem.
IV.   The Orthogonal Latin-Square Problem.
V.   Four-Coloring a Map (if possible).

I. General Principles

(a) *Discussion.*   Let us now turn to the main subject, types of problems that are reducible to linear programs some or all of whose variables are integer-valued.

Quite often in the literature, papers appear which formulate a problem in linear programming format *except* for certain side conditions such as $x_1 \cdot x_2 = 0$, or the sum of products of this type, such as $x_1 \cdot x_2 + x_3 \cdot x_4 = 0$, which imply for nonnegative variables that at least one variable of each pair must be zero. Superficially this seems to place the problem in the area of *quadratic programming*. However, the presence of such conditions can change entirely the character of the problem (as we shall see in a moment) and should serve a warning to those who would apply willy-nilly a general nonlinear programming method. If we graph the conditions $x_1 \cdot x_2 = 0$, $x_1 \geq 0$, $x_2 \geq 0$, $x_1 + x_2 \geq 1$, the double lines depict the domain of feasible solutions (see Fig. 26-3-I). It will be noted that this domain has two disconnected parts. If there are many such *dichotomies* in a larger problem, the result can be a domain of feasible solutions with many disconnected parts or connected non-convex regions. For example, k pairs of variables whose products are zero might lead to 2^k disconnected parts. Usual mathematical approaches can guarantee at best a local optimum solution to such problems, i.e., a solution which is optimum only over some connected convex part.

It is well known that in many cases, local optimum solutions could be avoided by the introduction of integer-valued variables, but this fact has been of only passing interest until the recent developments rendered this approach practical. Our purpose here will be to systematize this knowledge.

(b) *Dichotomies.* Let us begin with the important class of problems that have "either-or" conditions. For such a problem to be computationally

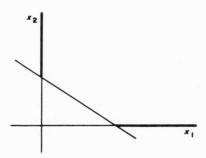

Figure 26-3-I. A disconnected region arising from linear inequalities and conditions like $x_1 x_2 = 0$.

difficult, there must be many sets of such conditions. Let us focus our attention on one of them; say

(1)   *either:* $G(x_1, x_2, \ldots, x_n) \geq 0$

(2)   *or:* $H(x_1, x_2, \ldots, x_n) \geq 0$

must hold for vectors $(x_1, x_2, \ldots, x_n)$ chosen from some set S. We do not exclude the case of both holding if this is possible. For example, a contractor in a bid might stipulate either $x_1 \geq \$10,000$ or $x_1 = 0$. If all bids are nonnegative so that $x_1 \geq 0$, then we can write

(3)   *either:* $x_1 - 10,000 \geq 0$

            or: $-x_1$ ≥ 0

From other considerations it may be known that no bid can exceed \$1,000,000, so that the set S of interest is $0 \leq x_1 \leq 1,000,000$.

We now assume that lower bounds for the functions G and H are known for all vectors $(x_1, x_2, \ldots, x_n)$ in S. If L_G is a lower bound for G and L_H for H, then for $\delta = 1$ the condition

$$G(x_1, x_2, \ldots, x_n) - \delta L_G \geq 0$$

holds for all $(x_1, x_2, \ldots, x_n)$ in S. Similarly for $\delta = 0$ the condition

$$H(x_1, x_2, \ldots, x_n) - (1 - \delta)L_H \geq 0$$

holds for all $(x_1, x_2, \ldots, x_n)$ in S. For our example we would have

(4) $x_1 - 10,000 - \delta(-10,000) \geq 0$

                    $-x_1 - (1 - \delta)(-1,000,000) \geq 0$

The either-or condition (1), (2) can now be replaced by

$$(5) \qquad G(x_1, x_2, \ldots, x_n) - \delta L_G \geq 0 \qquad (\delta = 0, 1)$$

$$(6) \qquad H(x_1, x_2, \ldots, x_n) - (1 - \delta)L_H \geq 0$$

$$(7) \qquad 0 \leq \delta \leq 1$$

where δ is an integer variable. The effect of $\delta = 1$ is to relax the G condition when H holds and that of $\delta = 0$ is to relax H when G holds. If G and H are linear functions, we have reduced the either-or condition to three simultaneous linear inequalities in which the variable δ must be 0 or 1.

A dichotomy can be used to describe an L-shaped region (non-convex): for example, $x_1 \geq 0$, $x_2 \geq 0$, $x_1 \leq 2$, $x_2 \leq 2$, and either $x_1 \leq 1$ or $x_2 \leq 1$. We replace this by

(8)

$$0 \leq x_1 \leq 1 + \delta$$
$$0 \leq x_2 \leq 2 - \delta$$
$$0 \leq \delta \leq 1$$
$$(\delta = 0, 1)$$

If now a problem contains not one but several such pairs of dichotomies (1) and (2), each one would be replaced by a simultaneous set (5), (6), (7) in integer variables δ_i.

(c) *k-fold Alternatives.* More generally suppose that we have a set of conditions

$$(9) \qquad G_1(x_1, x_2, \ldots, x_n) \geq 0$$
$$G_2(x_1, x_2, \ldots, x_n) \geq 0$$
$$\vdots \qquad \qquad \vdots$$
$$G_p(x_1, x_2, \ldots, x_n) \geq 0$$

Suppose a solution is required in which at least k of the conditions must hold simultaneously. We replace (9) by

$$(10) \qquad G_1(x) - \delta_1 L_1 \geq 0$$
$$G_2(x) - \delta_2 L_2 \geq 0$$
$$\vdots \qquad \vdots$$
$$G_p(x) - \delta_p L_p \geq 0$$

where L_i is the lower bound for $G_i(x)$ for $x = (x_1, x_2, \ldots, x_n)$ in S, and δ_i are integer-valued variables satisfying

$$(11) \qquad \delta_1 + \delta_2 + \ldots + \delta_p \leq p - k$$

and

(12) $$0 \le \delta_i \le 1 \qquad\qquad (\delta_i = 0 \text{ or } 1)$$

An example of this type of problem might occur if one wishes to find the minimum over the shaded regions described by $G_1 \ge 0$, $G_2 \ge 0$, $G_3 \ge 0$, and at least two of the conditions $G_4 \ge 0$, $G_5 \ge 0$, $G_6 \ge 0$ as in Fig. 26-3-II.

(d) *Selection from Many Pairs of Regions.* The six-pointed "Star of David" region shown in Fig. 26-3-II (lower part) can best be described as

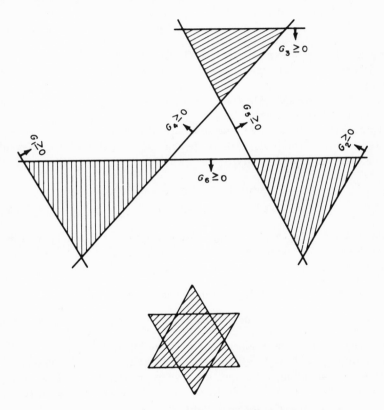

Figure 26-3-II. Examples of non-convex regions representable by a mixed-integer program.

a dichotomy in which a point must be taken from one of two triangles. It is only when there are many such pairs to be chosen at the same time that the problem becomes significant. In general we might have several pairs of regions (R_1, R_1'), (R_2, R_2'), . . ., (R_n, R_n'), and the solution point x must lie in either R_i or R_i' for each i. For each pair R and R' we proceed as follows. Let region R be described by a set of inequalities $G_1(x) \ge 0$, $G_2(x) \ge 0$,

. . ., $G_m(x) \geq 0$, and R' by $H_1(x) \geq 0$, $H_2(x) \geq 0$, . . ., $H_n(x) \geq 0$. The condition that the point must be selected from either the first or the second region can be written

(13)
$$
\begin{aligned}
G_1(x) - \delta L_1 &\geq 0, & H_1(x) - (1 - \delta)L_1' &\geq 0, \\
G_2(x) - \delta L_2 &\geq 0, & H_2(x) - (1 - \delta)L_2' &\geq 0, \\
&\ \ \vdots & &\ \ \vdots \\
G_m(x) - \delta L_m &\geq 0, & H_n(x) - (1 - \delta)L_n' &\geq 0, \\
& 0 \leq \delta \leq 1 & & (\delta = 0 \text{ or } 1)
\end{aligned}
$$

where L_i, L_i' are lower bounds for G_i and H_i. The more general case of selection from several regions can be done by introducing several δ_i as in (11) and (12).

(e) *Discrete-variable Problems.* Suppose that a variable is constrained to take one of several values: $x_1 = a_1$ or $x_1 = a_2$, . . ., or $x_1 = a_k$ and at the same time several other variables are also constrained the same way. It would be a formidable task to test all the combinations. Instead we replace each k-fold dichotomy by

(14)
$$ x_1 = a_1\delta_1 + a_2\delta_2 + \ldots + a_k\delta_k $$

(15)
$$ 1 = \ \ \delta_1 + \ \ \delta_2 + \ldots + \delta_k \qquad (\delta_i = 0 \text{ or } 1) $$

Similarly let $x = (x_1, x_2, \ldots, x_n)$ represent a vector which may only take on specified vector values $x = a^1$ or $x = a^2$ or $x = a^3$ . . . . This may be replaced by

(16)
$$ x = a^1\delta_1 + a^2\delta_2 + \ldots + a^k\delta_k $$

(17)
$$ 1 = \ \ \delta_1 + \ \ \delta_2 + \ldots + \ \ \delta_k \qquad (\delta_i = 0 \text{ or } 1) $$

This device permits the replacement of a nonlinear function $F_{ij} = F_{ij}(x_j)$, in a system $\sum_{j=1}^{n} F_{ij}(x_j) = 0$ for $i = 1, 2, \ldots, m$, by the values of the function corresponding to a sprinkling of representative values of x_j, say $x_j = x_j^r$ where $r = 1, 2, \ldots, k$. In this case the vector takes on the set of values $F_{1j}, F_{2j}, \ldots, F_{mj}$ for each value $x_j = x_j^r$.

(f) *Nonlinear-objective Problems.* Referring to Fig. 26-3-III, suppose the objective form can be written

(18)
$$ \sum_{j=1}^{n} \phi_j(x_j) = z \ (\text{Min}) $$

where ϕ_j is nonlinear and non-convex. Let each $\phi(x)$ be approximated by a broken line function. These define a set of intervals $i = 1, 2, \ldots, k$ of

[540]

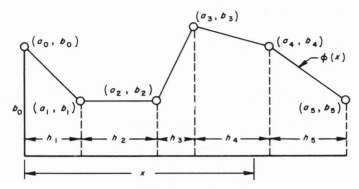

Figure 26-3-III. Converting a non-convex function into a
mixed-integer-programming format.

width h_i and slopes s_i for the approximating chords. We now define y_i as
the amount of overlap of the interval from 0 to x with interval i. Then

$$(19) \qquad x = y_1 + y_2 + \ldots + y_k$$

and $\phi(x)$ is given approximately by

$$(20) \qquad \phi(x) \doteq b_0 + s_1 y_1 + s_2 y_2 + \ldots + s_k y_k$$

where

$$(21) \qquad 0 \leq y_i \leq h_i \qquad\qquad (i = 1, 2, \ldots, k)$$

In the case of *convex* ϕ, the procedure is to replace x and $\phi(x)$ by (19) and
(20) and conditions (21). Here the slopes are monotonically increasing so that

$$(22) \qquad s_1 \leq s_2 \leq \ldots \leq s_k$$

For a fixed x, $\phi(x)$ would be minimum if y_1 is chosen maximum and if for
y_1 maximum, y_2 is chosen maximum, etc. In other words, for the minimizing
solution the y_i's are the overlap of the ith interval with the interval 0 to x,
and all is well. See § 24-3.

However, if $\phi(x)$ is *not convex* as in Fig. 26-3-III, then simple replacement
of x and $\phi(x)$ would result, for fixed x, in those y_i with smaller slopes being
maximized first. In this case the segments that comprise x would be disconnected and our approximation for $\phi(x)$ would no longer be valid. In order to
avoid this, we impose the condition that

$$(23) \qquad \text{either } h_i - y_i = 0 \qquad \text{or } y_{i+1} = 0$$

which implies that unless y_i is maximum, $y_{i+1} = 0$, and if y_i is maximum,
then $y_{i+1} > 0$ is possible. We rewrite this condition

$$(24) \qquad \text{either } y_i - h_i \geq 0 \qquad \text{or } -y_{i+1} \geq 0$$

and then replace it formally by

$$
(25) \quad
\begin{cases}
-y_1 + h_1 \geq 0 \\
y_i - h_i - (-h_i)\delta_i \geq 0 & (i = 1, 2, \ldots, k-1) \\
-y_{i+1} - (-h_{i+1})(1 - \delta_i) \geq 0 \\
\quad 0 \leq \delta_i \leq 1 & (\delta_i = 0 \text{ or } 1)
\end{cases}
$$

Upon substitution of $\delta_i' = 1 - \delta_i$, (25) simplifies to

$$
(26) \quad
\begin{cases}
y_1 \leq h_1 \\
y_i \geq h_i \delta_i' & (i = 1, 2, \ldots, k-1) \\
y_{i+1} \leq h_{i+1}\delta_i' \\
\quad 0 \leq \delta_i' \leq 1 & (\delta_i' = 0 \text{ or } 1)
\end{cases}
$$

which together with (19) and (20) formulates the problem (note that (21) is not required). The above procedure for the non-convex case was discussed in the paper of Markowitz and Manne [1957-1]. The convex case will be found in [Dantzig, 1956-2] and [Charnes and Lemke, 1954-1].

A second method based on (16) is worth noting. Any point on the curve $\phi(x)$ can be represented as a weighted average of two *successive* breakpoints. Hence we may replace x and $\phi(x)$ by

$$
(27) \quad
\begin{cases}
x = \lambda_0 a_0 + \lambda_1 a_1 + \ldots + \lambda_k a_k & (0 \leq \lambda_i) \\
\phi(x) = \lambda_0 b_0 + \lambda_1 b_1 + \ldots + \lambda_k b_k
\end{cases}
$$

$$
(28) \quad 1 = \lambda_0 + \lambda_1 + \ldots + \lambda_k
$$

and then impose the conditions that all $\lambda_i = 0$ except for one pair λ_i and λ_{i+1}. For $k = 4$ this may be expressed by

$$
(29) \quad
\begin{aligned}
\lambda_0 &\leq \delta_0 \\
\lambda_1 &\leq \delta_0 + \delta_1 \\
\lambda_2 &\leq \delta_1 + \delta_2 \\
\lambda_3 &\leq \delta_2 + \delta_3 \\
\lambda_4 &\leq \delta_3 + \delta_4 \\
\lambda_5 &\leq \delta_4
\end{aligned}
$$

where the δ_i are integer-valued variables satisfying

$$
(30) \quad \delta_0 + \delta_1 + \delta_2 + \delta_3 + \delta_4 + \delta_5 = 1 \qquad (\delta_i = 0, 1)
$$

Indeed it will be noted that, when $\delta_{i_0} = 1$ for some $i = i_0$, the inequalities involving λ_{i_0} and λ_{i_0+1} are relaxed but the remainder satisfy $\lambda_i \leq 0$ since their $\delta_i = 0$ by (30).

(g) *Conditional Constraints.* Suppose x and y are functions of several variables. We assume that an upper bound U_x is known for x, and lower bounds L_x and L_y are known for x and y. We wish to impose conditions such as

(31) $$x > 0 \Rightarrow y \geq 0$$

We can write (31) as

(32) $$\text{either } x > 0, y \geq 0 \text{ or } x \leq 0$$

which we rewrite as

(33) $$\begin{cases} x \geq \delta L_x \\ y \geq \delta L_y \\ x \leq (1 - \delta)U_x \end{cases} \qquad (\delta = 0, 1)$$

where the first inequality is written $(\geq)$ instead of $(>)$ because the condition $y \geq 0$ is automatically relaxed for $x = 0$ by selecting $\delta = 1$.

We can now elaborate this method to impose conditions such as

(34) $$x > 0 \Rightarrow u \geq 0$$
$$x < 0 \Rightarrow w \geq 0$$

which may be written as

(35) $$x \geq (1 - \delta_3)L_x$$
$$x \leq (1 - \delta_3)U_x$$
$$x \geq \delta_1 L_x$$
$$u \geq \delta_1 L_u$$
$$x \leq \delta_2 U_x$$
$$w \geq \delta_2 L_w$$
$$\delta_1 + \delta_2 = 1 + \delta_3 \qquad (\delta_i = 0, 1)$$

For example, suppose in a T-period program we wish to complete a specified work load by the *earliest* period possible. Let x_t be the *cumulative sum* of activity levels from the tth period through the last period T, then we wish to arrange matters so that $x_t = 0$ for the smallest t. Note in this case $x_k > 0$ implies $x_s > 0$ for $s < k$. In this case we can define for $t = 1, 2, \ldots, T$,

(36) $$\delta_t = 0 \Rightarrow x_t = 0$$

We may rewrite (36)

(37) $$0 \leq x_t \leq \delta_t U_t \qquad (\delta_t = 0, 1)$$

where U_t is an upper bound for x_t, and then determine Min z where

(38) $$z = \delta_1 + \delta_2 + \ldots + \delta_T$$

(h) *Finding a Global Minimum of a Concave Function.*[3] Suppose the

[3] This application was developed jointly with P. Wolfe.

concave function $Z = Z(x_1, x_2, \ldots, x_n)$ is to be minimized over a region R. If R is convex, this is intrinsically a difficult problem because the concave function could have local minima at many, indeed at *all*, the extreme points of R. We shall in fact assume R convex, for we note that the devices discussed earlier allow us to use a convex domain coupled with integer-valued variables to solve a wide class of problems expressible by either-or conditions. We suppose R to be given, after suitable change in variables, in standard linear programming form

$$(39) \qquad\qquad Ex = e, \qquad x \geq 0$$

where E is a given $m \times n$ matrix and e a given m-component vector.

The concave function Z may be given explicitly or be given implicitly. As an example of the latter, suppose vector y and quantity Z for *fixed* x is given by

$$(40) \qquad\qquad Fy = f + \bar{E}x, \qquad y \geq 0$$
$$\operatorname*{Max}_{y|x} \beta y = Z \text{ (Min)}$$

where $\bar{E}$ and F are given matrices and f and β are given vectors.

EXERCISE: Prove $\operatorname*{Max}_{y|x} \beta y$ is a concave function of x. Prove that $\phi(x) = \operatorname{Min}\{\phi_1(x), \phi_2(x) \ldots\}$ is a concave function if $\phi_i(x)$ is concave for all i.

An illustration having a striking parallel in the real world can be given: Consider a two-move game in which the first player, A, by choosing his activity levels x consistent with (39) modifies the inventory f of his opponent by an amount $\bar{E}x$. The second player, B, by choosing his activity levels y consistent with (40) obtains a payoff βy. A's problem is to choose x so as to minimize the maximum payoff to B.

We shall suppose that Z can reasonably be approximated at all points x in R by the minimum Z of a *finite set of k tangent hyperplanes*,

$$(41) \qquad Z = a_{i1}x_1 + a_{i2}x_2 + \ldots + a_{in}x_n - b_i \quad (i = 1, 2, \ldots, k)$$

to the surface $Z = Z(x)$. The problem reduces to choosing x, Min Z satisfying (39) such that (x, Z) satisfies *at least one* of the conditions

$$(42) \qquad Z - [a_{11}x_1 + a_{12}x_2 + \ldots + a_{1n}x_n - b_1] \geq 0$$
$$Z - [a_{21}x_1 + a_{22}x_2 + \ldots + a_{2n}x_n - b_2] \geq 0$$
$$\cdots\cdots\cdots\cdots\cdots\cdots\cdots\cdots\cdots\cdots\cdots\cdots\cdots$$
$$Z - [a_{k1}x_1 + a_{k2}x_2 + \ldots + a_{kn}x_n - b_k] \geq 0$$

We may rewrite (42) as

$$(43) \qquad Z - [a_{i1}x_1 + a_{i2}x_2 + \ldots + a_{in}x_n] \geq M(1 - \delta_i) \quad (i = 1, 2, \ldots, k)$$
$$\delta_1 + \delta_2 + \ldots + \delta_k = 1 \qquad\qquad (\delta_i = 0, 1)$$

where M is some assumed lower bound for the differences. This solution depends on the approximation of the function $Z = Z(x)$ by k hyperplanes. The solution, given in [Dantzig, 1958-2], for the case where Z is given implicitly by (40), requires finding x, y, Min z, and auxiliary variables $\pi = (\pi_1, \pi_2, \ldots, \pi_m)$ and $\eta \geq 0$, for $j = 1, 2, \ldots, n'$, satisfying

(44)
$$Ex = e, \qquad Fy = f + \bar{E}x, \qquad z = \beta y$$
$$\pi F + \eta - \beta = 0$$
$$\text{either } \eta_j \geq 0 \text{ or } y_j \geq 0$$

where $\pi = (\pi_1, \pi_2, \ldots, \pi_{m'})$ is a row vector, y_j is the jth component of y, and η_j the jth component of η.

EXERCISE: Verify (44).

II. The Fixed-charge Problem.

Earlier we described a problem where a bidder required that the size of the bid satisfies either $x = 0$ or $x \geq a$. In this and many other problems there is an underlying notion of a fixed charge that is independent of the size of the order. In this case $x = a$ represents the break-even point to the bidder. In general, the cost C is characterized by

(45)
$$C = \begin{cases} kx + b & \text{if } x > 0 \\ 0 & \text{if } x = 0 \end{cases}$$

where b is the fixed charge. We may write this in the form

(46) $$C = kx + \delta b \qquad\qquad (\delta = 0, 1)$$

where $x = 0$ if $\delta = 0$, which we impose by

(47) $$x \leq \delta U$$

and

(48) $$0 \leq \delta \leq 1 \qquad\qquad (\delta = 0, 1)$$

where U is some upper bound for x. A discussion of the fixed-charge problem including this device will be found in the paper by W. Hirsch and the author [1954-1].

III. The Traveling-salesman Problem.

The Problem. In what order should a traveling salesman visit n cities to minimize the total distance covered in a complete circuit? We shall give three formulations of this well-known problem. Let $x_{ijt} = 1$ or 0 according to whether the tth directed arc on the route is from node i to node j or not. Letting $x_{ijn+1} \equiv x_{ij1}$, the conditions

(49) $$\sum_i x_{ijt} = \sum_k x_{j,k,t+1} \qquad\qquad (j, t = 1, \ldots, n)$$

[545]

(50) $$\sum_{j,\,t} x_{ijt} = 1 \qquad (i = 1, \ldots, n)$$

(51) $$\sum_{i,\,j,\,t} d_{ij}x_{ijt} = z \ (\text{Min})$$

express (a) that if one arrives at city j on step t, one leaves city j on step $t + 1$, (b) that there is only one directed arc leaving node i, and (c) the length of the tour is minimum. It is not difficult to see that an integer solution to this system is a tour [Flood, 1956-1].

In two papers by Dantzig, Fulkerson, and Johnson [1954-1, 1959-1] the case of a *symmetric distance* $d_{ij} = d_{ji}$ was formulated with only two indices. Here $x_{ji} \equiv x_{ij} = 1$ or 0 according to whether the route from i to j or from j to i was traversed at some time on a route or not. In this case

(52) $$\sum_{i} x_{ij} = 2 \qquad (j = 1, 2, \ldots, n)$$

and

(53) $$\sum_{i,\,j} d_{ij}x_{ij} = z \ (\text{Min})$$

express the condition that the sum of the number of entries and departures for each node is two. Note in this case that no distinction is made between the two possible directions that one could traverse an arc between two cities. These conditions are not enough to characterize a tour even though the x_{ij} are restricted to be integers in the interval

(54) $$0 \leq x_{ij} \leq 1$$

since sub-tours like those in Fig. 26-3-IV also satisfy the conditions. However,

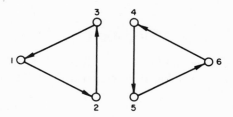

Figure 26-3-IV. Loop conditions are added to rule out sub-tours in the traveling-salesman problem.

if so-called *loop conditions* like

(55) $$x_{12} + x_{23} + x_{31} \leq 2$$

are imposed as added constraints as required, these will rule out integer solutions which are not admissible.

EXERCISE: Construct a fractional solution to (49), (50), (51) that is extremal. Show that any integer solution without sub-tours is a full tour.

A third way to reduce a traveling-salesman problem to an integer program is due to A. W. Tucker [1960-1]. It has less constraints and variables than those above. Let $x_{ij} = 1$ or 0, depending on whether the salesman travels from city i to j or not, where $i = 0, 1, 2, \ldots, n$. Then an optimal solution can be found by finding integers x_{ij}, arbitrary real numbers u_i, and Min z satisfying

(56)
$$\sum_{i=0}^{n} x_{ij} = 1 \qquad\qquad (j = 1, 2, \ldots, n)$$

$$\sum_{j=0}^{n} x_{ij} = 1 \qquad\qquad (i = 1, 2, \ldots, n)$$

$$u_i - u_j + n x_{ij} \leq n - 1 \qquad\qquad (1 \leq i \neq j \leq n)$$

$$\sum_{i=0}^{n} \sum_{j=0}^{n} d_{ij} x_{ij} = z \text{ (Min)}$$

The third group of conditions is violated whenever we have an integer solution to the first two groups that is *not* a tour, for in this case it contains two or more loops with $k < n$ arcs. In fact, if we add all inequalities corresponding to $x_{ij} = 1$ around such a loop *not* passing through city 0, we will cancel the differences $u_i - u_j$ and obtain $nk \leq (n - 1)k$, a *contradiction*. We have only to show for *any tour* starting from $i = 0$ that we can find u_i that satisfies the third group of conditions. Choose $u_i = t$ if city i is visited on the tth step where $t = 1, 2, \ldots, n$. It is clear that the difference $u_i - u_j \leq n - 1$ for all (i, j). Hence the conditions are satisfied for all $x_{ij} = 0$; for $x_{ij} = 1$ we obtain $u_i - u_j + n x_{ij} = (t) - (t + 1) + n = n - 1$.

IV. The Orthogonal Latin-Square Problem.

A latin square consists of n sets of n objects (1), (2), . . ., (n) assigned to an $n \times n$ square array so that no object is repeated in any row or column. Two latin squares are *orthogonal* if the n^2 ordered pairs of corresponding entries are all different; for example

(57)
$$\begin{array}{ccc|ccc}
(1) & (2) & (3) & (2) & (3) & (1) \\
(2) & (3) & (1) & (1) & (2) & (3) \\
(3) & (1) & (2) & (3) & (1) & (2)
\end{array}$$

It was conjectured by Euler that there are no orthogonal latin squares for certain n. After a great deal of research, the case for $n = 10$, for example, was settled[4] in 1959. It has been suggested informally by David Gale that integer programming be tried in this area.

The formulation is straightforward and well known. Let $x_{ijkl} = 0$ or 1 according to whether or not the pair (i, j) is assigned to row k, column l. The condition that each pair (i, j) is assigned to only one location is given by

$$(58) \qquad \sum_{k, l} x_{ijkl} = 1 \qquad (i, j = 1, 2, \ldots, n)$$

The condition that one pair (i, j) is assigned to each location k, l is:

$$(59) \qquad \sum_{i, j} x_{ijkl} = 1 \qquad (k, l = 1, 2, \ldots, n)$$

The condition that i appears only once in the first latin square in column l is given by (60). The condition that j appears only once in the second latin square in column k is given by (61).

$$(60) \qquad \sum_{j, k} x_{ijkl} = 1 \qquad (i, l = 1, 2, \ldots, n)$$

$$(61) \qquad \sum_{i, k} x_{ijkl} = 1 \qquad (j, l = 1, 2, \ldots, n)$$

Similarly the condition that i and j appear only once in the first and second latin square respectively in row k is given by

$$(62) \qquad \sum_{j, l} x_{ijkl} = 1 \qquad (i, k = 1, 2 \ldots, n)$$

$$\sum_{i, l} x_{ijkl} = 1 \qquad (j, k = 1, 2 \ldots, n)$$

It is interesting to note that all pairs of subscripts possible out of four are summed to form the six sets of n^2 equations. For $n = 10$ there are 600 equations which are too many for any integer programming code devised up to 1962 to, handle. However, with some short-cuts introduced, it might become tractable.

V. Four-Coloring a Map (If Possible).

A famous unsolved problem is to prove or disprove that any map *in the plane* can be colored using at most four colors; regions with a boundary in common (other than a point) must have different colors. We shall give two ways to color constructively a particular map, if possible. While this does not

[4] R. C. Bose and S. S. Shukhande proved that Euler's famous conjecture about the non-existence of orthogonal latin squares of certain even orders was false. E. T. Parker has constructed a pair of orthogonal latin squares of order 10. For further information the reader is referred to Abstract 558-27 of the August 1959 Notices of the American Mathematical Society. A non-technical report of their results has appeared in the *Scientific American*, Vol. 201, No. 5, November 1959, pp. 181–188.

contribute to a proof of the truth or falsity of this conjecture, nevertheless an efficient way for solving particular examples on an electronic computer may serve as an aid in finding a counter example.

Without difficulty it can be arranged (as below) so that three regions

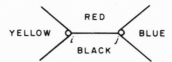

have at most one point in common which will be called a *node*. There will be, accordingly, three arcs leading from any node i to other nodes j. It is well known that if it is possible to four-color a map, then (and this will be true conversely) it is possible (treating the nodes as cities and the arcs as routes between cities) either to tour all the nodes or to make a group of mutually exclusive sub-tours of the cities in several *even* (sub-cycle) loops as in Fig. 26-3-V.

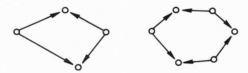

Figure 26-3-V. The four-color problem is equivalent to finding a set of even-order sub-tours.

EXERCISE: Show that the number of arcs is a multiple of 3 and the number of nodes is even.

We may associate with each such even-cycle sub-tour, directed arcs that *reverse their direction* as we pass from node to node. This means the nodes i can be divided into two classes: those which have two arcs pointing away from them and those which have two arcs pointing toward them. Let us set $x_{ij} = 1$, if the directed arc $(i \to j)$ is part of such a sub-tour; otherwise $x_{ij} = 0$. Hence

(63) $$0 \le x_{ij} \le 1$$

It is understood that only arcs (i, j) and variables x_{ij} are considered corresponding to regions that have a boundary in common. All arcs (i, j) that do not correspond to boundaries are omitted in the constraints.

The conditions

(64) $$\sum_j x_{ij} = 2\delta_i \qquad (\delta_i = 0, 1)$$

express the fact there must be two arcs on some sub-tour leading away from node i if $\delta_i = 1$; otherwise there are none. The conditions

$$(65) \qquad \sum_i x_{ij} = 2 - 2\delta_i$$

state there must be two arcs on some sub-tour leading into node i if $\delta_i = 0$, and otherwise none. The three sets of conditions (63), (64), and (65) are those of a *bounded transportation problem* and will be integers (at an extreme point) if the δ_i are integers. This would seem to imply that it is only necessary to assume that the δ_i are integers and the x_{ij} will come out automatically integral in an extremizing solution without further assumptions. However, the wrong choice of integral δ_i could lead to an empty solution set. As an alternative to using an integer programming method to solve this problem, it might be practical to allow the δ_i to vary $0 \leq \delta_i \leq 1$ but to randomly choose various objective forms (since these are open to choice) until an optimal extreme-point solution with integral x_{ij} is obtained.

A second formulation suggested informally by Gomory is straight-forward. Let the regions be $r = 1, 2, \ldots, R$, and let t_r be an integer-valued variable such that

$$0 \leq t_r \leq 3$$

where the four values $t_r = 0, 1, 2, 3$ correspond to the four colors. If regions r and s have a boundary in common, their colors must be different. Hence for each such pair

$$(66) \qquad t_r - t_s \neq 0$$

This may be written in either-or form:

$$(67) \qquad \text{either } t_r - t_s \geq 1 \text{ or } t_s - t_r \geq 1$$

which we may rewrite as

$$(68) \qquad t_r - t_s \geq 1 - 4\delta_{rs} \qquad (\delta_{rs} = 0, 1)$$
$$t_s - t_r \geq -3 + 4\delta_{rs}$$

REFERENCES

Balas, 1964-1
Beale, 1958-1
Charnes and Lemke, 1954-1
Dantzig, 1956-2, 1957-2, 1958-1, 1960-2
Dantzig, Fulkerson, and Johnson, 1954-1, 1959-1
Doig and Belz, 1956-1
Eisemann, 1957-1
Flood, 1956-1
Ford and Fulkerson, 1960-1
Fulkerson, 1956-1
Gale, 1956-1
Gomory, 1958-1, 2, 3, 1960-1
Heller, 1964-1

Hirsch and Dantzig, 1954-1
Hoffman, 1956-1, 1960-1
Hoffman and Kruskal, 1956-1
Johnson, 1958-1, 1965-1
Kruskal, 1956-1
Lambert, 1960-1
Land and Doig, 1957-1
Markowitz and Manne, 1957-1
Miller, Tucker, and Zemlin, 1960-1
Norman, 1955-1
Paull and Walter, 1955-1
Ryser, 1961-1
Saaty, 1955-1
Tucker, 1960-1

Tutte, 1946-1

CHAPTER 27

STIGLER'S NUTRITION MODEL: AN EXAMPLE OF FORMULATION AND SOLUTION

One of the first applications of the simplex algorithm was to the determination of an adequate diet that was of least cost.[1] In the fall of 1947, J. Laderman of the Mathematical Tables Project of the National Bureau of Standards undertook, as a test of the newly proposed simplex method, the first large-scale computation in this field. It was a system with nine equations in seventy-seven unknowns. Using hand-operated desk calculators, approximately 120 man-days were required to obtain a solution.

The particular problem solved was one which had been studied earlier by G. J. Stigler [1945-1], who had proposed a solution based on the substitution of certain foods by others which gave more nutrition per dollar. He then examined a "handful" of the possible 510 ways to combine the selected foods. He did not claim the solution to be the cheapest but gave good reasons for believing that the annual cost could not be reduced by more than a few dollars. Indeed, we shall see that Stigler's solution, when converted from a cost-per-day to a cost-per-year, was only 24 cents higher than the true minimum for the year, which was $39.69 (10.9 cents per day).

27-1. PROBLEMS IN FORMULATING A MODEL

Before launching into the mathematical characteristics of the nutrition problem, it is worthwhile to see just how to develop a "mathematical model." It will be seen to be far from a precise operation, and it is only natural to question the validity of refined techniques for solving what is clearly an approximate model. This situation is typical almost everywhere programming techniques are applied. One should remember, however, that one reason why only the approximate models exist today has been the historic inability of the investigator to solve any large-scale complex model. As the tools for handling these systems increase, so does the desire of the investigator increase to refine his models to take advantage of these new techniques. The next few years will probably see the end of this vicious

---

[1] J. Cornfield of the U.S. Government formulated such a mathematical problem as early as 1940.

circle of the past, in which poor model building justified rapid rough "solutions" and, conversely, the non-existence of methods of accurate solution justified poor model building. It is likely that both model building and solution techniques will begin to reinforce each other in a positive manner.

Stigler's paper [1945-1] provides a very frank discussion of the background of the nutrition model; the greater part of what follows is based upon this source and follows it very closely. In the years since his paper was published, many improvements in the model have been made. However, it is interesting to study some of the typical situations that confront a model builder in the early stages. Stigler began with some findings of nutrition studies:

(1) After certain minimum values of the nutrients are secured, additional quantities yield decreasing (and, in some cases, eventually negative) returns to health.

(2) The optimum quantity of any nutrient depends on the quantities of the other nutrients available.

Diminishing returns are illustrated by the fact that the amount of calcium in the body increases much more slowly than the input of calcium, and that increases of longevity are not proportional to calcium inputs. It appears possible in some cases to substitute one type of nutrition for another type. Stigler cites an example in which it was recommended that 30 micrograms of thiamine be substituted for 100 calories derived from sources other than fats. Another example cited is that a loss of riboflavin accompanies a deficiency of thiamine.

Stigler then turned to another question: How much of various nutrients are required? How do the requirements differ from one individual to another? In resolving this difficulty, he noted that the optimum quantity of calories is known fairly accurately, but that the requirements of other nutrients are known only roughly or not at all. Many minima (to which 50 per cent is usually added as a safety factor) are found by determining the lowest level of input compatible with a stable rate of loss of the nutrient through excreta. The interrelationships among various nutrients are even more obscure, and they are virtually ignored in dietary recommendations. Even the statement of what substances are necessary for health is very complex. Thus, in addition to calcium, the body requires about 13 minerals (some in minute quantities), many kinds of vitamins, a dozen or so types of amino acids, and perhaps many more nutrients yet to be discovered.

The diets developed by Stigler were considerably lower in cost than those developed by others. One of the reasons given is that the other diets included a greater variety of foods as a kind of "insurance" against omitting any of the unknown dietary elements. Another reason is that diet experts do give some weight to social and institutional pressures, particularly where they are not on firm grounds to support alternatives. On the other hand,

Stigler justifies his diet in this regard by citing the National Research Council's belief that these other minerals and vitamins are supplied in adequate amounts automatically when a certain group of common nutrients are obtained from natural foods. Based on considerations of this kind, the first step in setting up a mathematical model was to accept the Council's statement of daily nutritional requirements (given in Table 27-1-I). Note

TABLE 27-1-I

DAILY ALLOWANCES OF NUTRIENTS FOR A MODERATELY ACTIVE MAN
(Weighing 154 pounds)[1]

Nutrient	Daily Allowance
Calories	3,000 $= b_1$ (calories)
Protein	70 $= b_2$ (grams)
Calcium	.8 $= b_3$ (grams)
Iron	12 $= b_4$ (milligrams)
Vitamin A	5,000 $= b_5$ (International Units)
Thiamine (B$_1$)	1.8 $= b_6$ (milligrams)
Riboflavin (B$_2$ or G)	2.7 $= b_7$ (milligrams)
Niacin (nicotinic acid)	18 $= b_8$ (milligrams)
Ascorbic acid (C)	75 $= b_9$ (milligrams)

[1] National Research Council, "Recommended Dietary Allowances," Reprint and Circular Series No. 115, January, 1943.

that only nine of the more common nutrients were used, and the others were assumed to be automatically satisfied. It should also be noted that the requirements (discussed earlier) are rough, and, possibly with the exception of calories, almost any number in a very broad range probably could equally well be justified.

In considering the nutritive values of foods, again we see a similar situation, for the nutritive values of common foods are known only approximately, and that is all that can be known about them. A large margin of uncertainty arises on several scores. For example, the milligrams of ascorbic acid per 100 grams of apples vary with the type of apple:

Jonathan	4.4
McIntosh	2.0
Northern Spy	11.0
Ontario	20.8
Winesap	5.8
Winter Banana	6.6.

The ascorbic acid in milk varies with season. Conditions of storage, such as temperature and length of time in storage, are important factors. The more corn matures, the greater is the amount of vitamin A, but the ascorbic acid content decreases. Long cooking decreases the nutritive value; well-done roasts of beef have roughly 70 per cent of the thiamine, riboflavin, and niacin of raw cuts. Not only is there a considerable variability in foods,

[553]

which conceivably could be taken into account in programming, by introducing probabilistic considerations (as is done in Chapter 25 on uncertainty), but there is also the fact, according to Stigler, that the nutritive values that had been established in 1944 for many foods had been determined by obsolete and inaccurate techniques, or may be just plain wrong for other reasons.

Ignoring these difficulties, a model was set up in which some kind of average nutritive per unit quantity for each food as purchased was developed. If x_j units of the jth food were purchased and each food contained, per unit quantity, a_{ij} units of the ith nutrient, then it was assumed that the individual would receive

$$\sum_{j=1}^{n} a_{ij}x_j$$

units of the ith nutrient, assuming there are no losses due to preparation of the foods. There is also a tacit assumption that there is no interaction between various foods; i.e., the total number of units of a nutrient available in a food is unaffected by the presence of some other food in the diet.

Finally, a list of potential foods was selected for which retail prices were reported by the Bureau of Labor Statistics. The list was not complete since it excluded almost all fresh fruits, many cheap vegetables rich in nutrients, and fresh fish. If these could have been included, it would seem that the minimum cost diet could be reduced by a substantial amount. However, other investigators have found that the optimal choice is quite insensitive to these particular prices due to the presence of certain staples in the optimum diet.

In Table 27-1-II, the coefficients a_{ij} per dollar expenditure are given for an abbreviated list of some 77 types of foods considered by Stigler. He recommended, however, where prices are subject to change because of local and seasonal conditions, and it' is desired to compute not one but several such problems, that the units for measuring the quantity of foods be physical units such as weight, or possibly volume in case of liquids. If this is done, the price data and the nutritive data can be developed independently.

Mathematical Formulation.

The nutrition model may now be set up in linear programming terms. Let the set of possible activities (j) and activity levels x_j be:

Activities	Activity Level
	(unit = one dollar expended per day)
1. Buying the 1st type food (wheat flour)	x_1
2. Buying the 2nd type food (macaroni)	x_2
. . . .	. . .
n. Buying the $n = 77$th type food (strawberry preserves)	x_{77}

[554]

TABLE 27-1-II
Nutritive Values of Common Foods Per Dollar of Expenditure
August 15, 1939

(Abbreviated List of 20 of the 77 Foods)

Nutritive Items (i)

	Commodity[1] (j)	Calories (1,000)	Protein (grams)	Calcium (grams)	Iron (mg.)	Vitamin A (1,000 I.U.)	Thiamine (mg.)	Riboflavin (mg.)	Niacin (mg.)	Ascorbic Acid (mg.)
**	1. Wheat flour (enriched)	44.7	1,411	2.0	365	—	55.4	33.3	441	—
	5. Corn meal	36.0	897	1.7	99	30.9	17.4	7.9	106	—
**	15. Evaporated milk (can)	8.4	422	15.1	9	26.0	3.0	23.5	11	60
*	17. Oleomargarine	20.6	17	.6	6	55.8	.2	—	—	—
**	19. Cheese (Cheddar)	7.4	448	16.4	19	28.1	.8	10.3	4	—
	21. Peanut butter	15.7	661	1.0	48	—	9.6	8.1	471	—
	24. Lard	41.7	—	—	—	.2	—	.5	5	—
**	30. Liver (beef)	2.2	333	.2	139	169.2	6.4	50.8	316	525
	34. Pork loin roast	4.4	249	.3	37	—	18.2	3.6	79	—
*	40. Salmon, pink (can)	5.8	705	6.8	45	3.5	1.0	4.9	209	—
*	45. Green beans	2.4	138	3.7	80	69.0	4.3	5.8	37	862
**	46. Cabbage	2.6	125	4.0	36	7.2	9.0	4.5	26	5,369
*	50. Onions	5.8	166	3.8	59	16.6	4.7	5.9	21	1,184
*	51. Potatoes	14.3	336	1.8	118	6.7	29.4	7.1	198	2,522
**	52. Spinach	1.1	106	—	138	918.4	5.7	13.8	33	2,755
**	53. Sweet potatoes	9.6	138	2.7	54	290.7	8.4	5.4	83	1,912
*	64. Peaches, dried	8.5	87	1.7	173	86.8	1.2	4.3	55	57
*	65. Prunes, dried	12.8	99	2.5	154	85.7	3.9	4.3	65	257
**	68. Lima beans, dried	17.4	1,055	3.7	459	5.1	26.9	38.2	93	—
**	69. Navy beans, dried	26.9	1,691	11.4	792	—	38.4	24.6	217	—

[1] Commodity numbers refer to Stigler's original list. Starred lines refer to a reduced list explained in § 27·2.

Let the set of items (i) be, in this case, the nine different types of nutrients given in Table 27-1-I. Then the only question remaining with regard to formulation of the mathematical model is whether we want to specify that the requirements are met exactly or can be exceeded. In the first case we are considering a problem of the type

$$(1) \qquad \sum_{j=1}^{n} a_{ij}x_j = b_i \qquad\qquad (x_j \geq 0)$$

and in the second case, we are considering a problem of the type

$$(2) \qquad \sum_{j=1}^{n} a_{ij}x_j \geq b_i \qquad\qquad (x_j \geq 0)$$

where we wish to choose x_j to minimize the total cost

$$(3) \qquad z = \sum_{j=1}^{n} x_j$$

It might seem that asking for exact requirements is better than allowing the possibility of exceeding requirements, since getting more than one really needs should be more costly. This reasoning is fallacious, however, since any set of x_j which satisfies (1) automatically satisfies (2) and hence the minimal value of z attained in (2) is certainly no greater than that in (1). *In other words, it is always cheaper (or at least no more costly) to permit an excess over requirements than to insist that requirements be met exactly.*

Often people criticize a plan because they observe what they believe are "wastes." They note that not everybody is busy all the time, or an installation or machine is idle part of the time. They believe a good plan would find some way to put all these people and machines to work constructively. However, one of the first things one learns in programming is that it is not always efficient to try to remove these "defects." For example, putting idle people to work may require that they have tools and materials at their disposal that are badly needed elsewhere. Referring to the footnote of Table 27-2-I, it is seen for the nutrition problem that insistence on no surplus in nutritives would increase the minimum cost per day from 10.9 cents to 13.8 cents, an increase of over 25 per cent.

We shall formulate the nutrition problem allowing surpluses of all nutrients. There is one risk we take in such a procedure; namely, the solution may be a diet which contains an excess of calories or some other nutrient known to be harmful to health.

First, augment the system by introducing slack variables $x_{n+1}, \ldots, x_{n+m}$, yielding

$$(4) \qquad \sum_{j=1}^{n} a_{ij}x_j - x_{n+i} = b_i \qquad\qquad (i = 1, 2, \ldots, m)$$

$$(5) \qquad \sum_{1}^{n} x_j \qquad\qquad = z \text{ (Min)}$$

We now further augment the system by introducing artificial variables $x_{n+m+1}, \ldots, x_{n+2m}$, so that now for $i = 1, 2, \ldots, m$

(6)
$$\sum_{j=1}^{n} a_{ij}x_j - x_{n+i} + x_{n+m+i} = b_i$$

27-2. NUMERICAL SOLUTION OF THE NUTRITION PROBLEM

Solution by Electronic Computer.

The nutrition problem that took 120 man-days to compute in 1948 (using desk computers) can be run in a few minutes on a modern electronic computer. The exact time depends on just how much information one wants to print regarding the problem. In 1953, using an IBM 701 machine, the RAND Simplex Code, and printing out each iteration, the total time was 12 minutes; without printing, the time would have been cut to about one-fourth. If run on a post-1960 computer, the time would be a fraction of a minute.

Since it was desired to compare the minimum cost solutions when exact requirements must be satisfied, § 27-1-(1), and when excesses of requirements are permitted, § 27-1-(2), the instruction code did not allow any slack variable to enter the basic set initially. In 12 iterations Phase I was completed and a basic feasible solution was obtained. On the 16th iteration, Phase II was completed and an optimal feasible solution was obtained for § 27-1-(1). At this point, excess variables were allowed to enter the basic set and an additional 8 iterations were required to obtain an optimal solution for § 27-1-(2). In order to see whether the number of iterations for the latter could be reduced, a second problem was run in which the excess variables were allowed to enter the basic set *at any time*. By some odd coincidence the same set of 24 iterations took place. See Problem 15 for a possible explanation. The results of these computations are summarized in Table 27-2-I and Fig. 27-2-I.

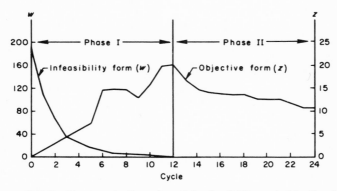

Figure 27-2-I. Decrease in the value of the feasibility and objective forms as a function of iteration in the nutrition problem.

[557]

TABLE 27-2-1

CHANGES IN BASIS ACTIVITIES: VALUES FOR w AND z

Iteration	Calories short	Protein short	Calcium short	Iron short	Vitamin A short	Thiamine short	Riboflavin short	Niacin short	Ascorbic Acid short	Infeasibility Form (w)	Objective Form z (cents)
0	Calories short	Protein short	Calcium short	Iron short	Vitamin A short	Thiamine short	Riboflavin short	Niacin short	Ascorbic Acid short	191.3	0
1	"	"	"	Navy beans	"	"	"	"	Cabbage	110.3	1.4
2	"	"	"	"	"	"	"	"	"	69.6	2.8
3	"	"	"	Salmon	"	Flour	"	Pork roast	"	38.2	4.4
4	"	"	"	"	"	"	"	"	"	27.8	5.6
5	"	"	"	"	"	"	"	"	"	19.5	7.0
6	"	"	"	"	Spinach	Beans	"	"	"	11.0	14.3
7	"	Corn meal	"	"	"	"	"	"	"	7.3	14.6
8	"	"	"	"	"	"	"	"	"	4.2	14.5
9	Lard	"	Evaporated milk	"	Beef liver	"	"	"	"	2.6	13.0
10	"	"	"	"	"	"	"	"	"	1.5	15.6
11	"	"	"	"	"	"	" .	"	"	.2	19.9
12	"	"	"	"	"	Spinach	Lima beans	"	"	—	20.5
13	"	"	"	"	"	"	Flour	"	"	—	16.9
14	"	"	"	"	"	"	"	"	"	—	14.8
15	"	"	"	Peanut butter	"	"	"	"	"	—	14.0
16	"	"	"	"	"	"	"	Potatoes	"	Min $z_1 =$	13.8[1]
17	"	"	"	"	"	"	"	Iron excess	"	—	13.5
18	"	Navy beans	"	Thiamine excess	"	"	"	"	"	—	13.4
19	"	"	"	"	"	"	"	"	"	—	12.8
20	"	Lima beans	"	"	"	"	"	"	"	—	12.7
21	"	Niacin excess	Beef liver	"	Protein excess	"	"	"	"	—	12.7
22	"	"	"	"	"	"	"	"	"	—	11.8
23	Navy beans	"	"	"	"	"	"	"	"	Min $z_2 =$	10.9
24	"	"	"	"	"	"	"	"	"	—	10.9[1]

(Rows 0–11: Phase I; Rows 12–24: Phase II. Basic Activities span the nine "short" columns.)

[1] Min z_1 reached on iteration (16) is the least cost solution without excess nutrients.

Solution by Hand Techniques.

Stigler reduced the list of 77 foods to a list of 15 foods (starred lines in Table 27-1-II) by dropping from the list any food which had, per dollar, no more of each nutrient than did some other food. He effected a further reduction to a list of 9 foods (double starred lines) by dropping any food which had, per dollar, no more of each nutrient than did a mixture of other foods costing a dollar. However, this method can only be used if the nutritional requirements may be exceeded. Where nutritional requirements must be met exactly, this short cut is no longer valid. In Problems 1–5, proofs of these statements are suggested as exercises.

In the final solution for the case where excess nutrients are allowed, nutrients protein, iron, thiamine, and niacin exceeded requirements. With this foreknowledge, it is possible to present here a complete short cut numerical solution of the nutrition problem. To do this, we shall follow Stigler and use the reduced set of 9 foods in place of the 77, and use only 5 of the 9 equations of § 27-1-(2). Equations $i = 2, 4, 6, 8$ (corresponding to the excess slack variables for niacin, thiamine, protein, and iron) have been ignored. The complete computations are given in Table 27-2-II.

It is natural to question any procedure which ignores certain of the restrictions in the problem and solves a smaller problem with fewer than the total number of restraints. In certain cases, however, this approach can be made the basis of a very efficient algorithm. Let us suppose that k equations, each having a slack variable, are ignored in solving a linear programming problem. After solution, the values of the variables of the reduced system may be substituted into these k equations and the values of the omitted slack variables determined. If, by good luck, the values of these slack variables are positive or zero, then it is easy to see that the solution for the restricted system, together with the solution for the slack variables, constitutes an optimal solution for the entire system.

The nutrition problem requires a slight modification in the setup if the simplex multipliers π_i are to be interpreted as the implicit costs of a calorie, a gram of calcium, etc. The c_j represent costs in the model but the $a_{ij} > 0$ are *outputs* of the ith type of nutrient in a unit quantity of the jth food. It is inconvenient in this instance to follow our sign convention that inputs should be positive and outputs negative. In this case, the prices π_i described in Chapters 9 and 12 will turn out to have the wrong sign.

Item	Basic Solution		Wheat Flour (Enriched)	Evaporated Milk	Cheddar Cheese	Beef Liver	Cabbage	Spina
	Variable	Value $\bar{b}_i$	$(j = 1)$	(15)	(19)	(30)	(46)	(52]
Calories	x_{111}	3.0	44.7	8.4	7.4	2.2	2.6	
Calcium	x_{113}	.8	2.0	15.1	16.4	.2	4.0	
Vitamin A	x_{115}	5.0		26.0	28.1	169.2	7.2	91
Riboflavin	x_{117}	2.7	33.3	23.5	10.3	50.8	4.5	1
Ascorbic acid	x_{119}	75.0		60.0		525.0	5369.0	275
Objective form	$(-z)$		1.0	1.0	1.0	1.0	1.0	
Infeasibility form	$(-w)$	−86.5	−80.0	−133.0	−62.2	−747.4	−5387.3	−368
							★	

C

Item	Basic Solution		Wheat Flour (Enriched)	Evaporated Milk	Cheddar Cheese	Beef Liver	Cabbage	Spina
	Variable	Value $\bar{b}_i$	$(j = 1)$	(15)	(19)	(30)	(46)	(52]
Calories	x_{111}	2.9637	44.7	8.3709	7.4	1.9458		−.2
Calcium	x_{113}	.7441	2.0	15.0553	16.4	−.1911		−2.0
Vitamin A	x_{115}	4.8994		25.9195	28.1	168.4960		914.7
Riboflavin	x_{117}	2.6371	33.3	23.4497	10.3	50.3600		11.4
Ascorbic acid	x_{46}	.0140		.0112		.0978	1.0	.5
Objective form	$(-z)$	−.0140	1.0	.9888	1.0	.9022		.4
Infeasibility form	$(-w)$	−11.2444	−80.0	−72.7955	−62.2	−220.6106		−923.9
							●	★

C

Item	Basic Solution		Wheat Flour (Enriched)	Evaporated Milk	Cheddar Cheese	Beef Liver	Cabbage	Spina
	Variable	Value $\bar{b}_i$	$(j = 1)$	(15)	(19)	(30)	(46)	(52]
Calories	x_{111}	2.9649	44.7	8.3776	7.4072	1.9889		
Calcium	x_{113}	.7551	2.0	15.1135	16.4631	.1870		
Vitamin A	x_{52}	.0054		.0283	.0307	.1842		1.0
Riboflavin	x_{117}	2.5756	33.3	23.1241	9.9470	48.2433		
Ascorbic acid	x_{46}	.0112		−.0034	−.0158	.0033	1.0	
Objective form	$(-z)$	−.0166	1.0	.9750	.9850	.8125		
Infeasibility form	$(-w)$	−6.2956	−80.0	−46.6151	−33.817	−50.4191		
			★				●	●

-II

M OF STIGLER'S NUTRITION PROBLEM

Sweet Potatoes (53)	Lima Beans (Dried) (68)	Navy Beans (Dried) (69)	Excess Variables					Artificial Variables				
			(101)	(103)	(105)	(107)	(109)	(111)	(113)	(115)	(117)	(119)
9.6	17.4	26.9	−1.0					1.0				
2.7	3.7	11.4		−1.0					1.0			
290.7	5.1				−1.0					1.0		
5.4	38.2	24.6				−1.0					1.0	
1912.0							−1.0					1.0
1.0	1.0	1.0										
2220.4	−64.4	−62.9	1.0	1.0	1.0	1.0	1.0					
								●	●	●	●	○

Sweet Potatoes (53)	Lima Beans (Dried) (68)	Navy Beans (Dried) (69)	Excess Variables					Artificial Variables				
			(101)	(103)	(105)	(107)	(109)	(111)	(113)	(115)	(117)	(119)
8.6741	17.4	26.9	−1.0				.0005	1.0				−.0005
1.2755	3.7	11.4		−1.0			.0007		1.0			−.0007
38.1359	5.1				−1.0		.0013			1.0		−.0013
3.7975	38.2	24.6				−1.0	.0008				1.0	−.0008
.3561							−.0002					.0002
.6439	1.0	1.0					.0002					−.0002
1.8830	−64.4	−62.9	1.0	1.0	1.0	1.0	−.0034					1.0034
								●	●	○	●	Drop

Sweet Potatoes (53)	Lima Beans (Dried) (68)	Navy Beans (Dried) (69)	Excess Variables					Artificial Variables				
			(101)	(103)	(105)	(107)	(109)	(111)	(113)	(115)	(117)	(119)
8.7478	17.4013	26.9	−1.0		−.0003		.0005	1.0		.0003		−.0005
1.9221	3.7114	11.4		−1.0	−.0022		.0007		1.0	.0022		−.0007
.3150	.0056				−.0011					.0011		
.1778	38.1359	24.6			.0126	−1.0	.0008			−.0126	1.0	−.0008
.1945	−.0029				.0006		−.0002			−.0006		.0002
.4905	.9973	1.0			.0005		.0002			−.0005		−.0002
0.8477	−59.2487	−62.9	1.0	1.0	−.0101	1.0	−.0021			1.0101		1.0021
								○	●	Drop	●	Drop

[561]

TA[BLE]

SIMPLEX SOLUTION TO AN ABBREVIA[TED]

Item	Basic Solution		Wheat Flour (Enriched)	Evaporated Milk	Cheddar Cheese	Beef Liver	Cabbage	Spina[ch]
	Variable	Value $\bar{b}_i$	$(j = 1)$	(15)	(19)	(30)	(46)	(52)
Calories	x_1	.0663	1.0	.1874	.1657	.0445		
Calcium	x_{113}	.6225		14.7386	16.1316	.0980		
Vitamin A	x_{52}	.0054		.0283	.0307	.1842		1.0
Riboflavin	x_{117}	.3668		16.8831	4.4289	$\boxed{46.7616}$		
Ascorbic acid	x_{46}	.0112		−.0034	−.0158	.0033	1.0	
Objective form	$(-z)$	−.0829		.7876	.8193	.7680		
Infeasibility form	$(-w)$	−.9893		−31.6217	−20.5605	−46.8596		
			●			★	●	●

C

Item	Basic Solution		Wheat Flour (Enriched)	Evaporated Milk	Cheddar Cheese	Beef Liver	Cabbage	Spina[ch]
	Variable	Value $\bar{b}_i$	$(j = 1)$	(15)	(19)	(30)	(46)	(52)
Calories	x_1	.0660	1.0	.1714	.1615			
Calcium	x_{113}	.6217		14.7033	$\boxed{16.1224}$			
Vitamin A	x_{52}	.0039		−.0382	.0133			1.0
Riboflavin	x_{30}	.0078		.3610	.0947	1.0		
Ascorbic Acid	x_{46}	.0112		−.0045	−.0161		1.0	
Objective form	$(-z)$	−.0889		.5103	.7466			
Infeasibility form	$(-w)$	−.6217		−14.7033	−16.1224			
			●		★	●	●	●

C

Item	Basic Solution		Wheat Flour (Enriched)	Evaporated Milk	Cheddar Cheese	Beef Liver	Cabbage	Spina[ch]
	Variable	Value $\bar{b}_i$	$(j = 1)$	(15)	(19)	(30)	(46)	(52)
Calories	x_1	.0598	1.0	.0241				
Calcium	x_{19}	.0386		.9120	1.0			
Vitamin A	x_{52}	.0034		−.0503				1.0
Riboflavin	x_{30}	.0042		$\boxed{.2747}$		1.0		
Ascorbic acid	x_{46}	.0118		.0101			1.0	
Objective form	$(-z)$	−.1177		−.1706				
Infeasibility form	$(-w)$							
			●	★	●	○	●	●

(contd.)

OF STIGLER'S NUTRITION PROBLEM

	Lima Beans (Dried) (68)	Navy Beans (Dried) (69)	Excess Variables					Artificial Variables				
			(101)	(103)	(105)	(107)	(109)	(111)	(113)	(115)	(117)	(119)
57	.3893	.6018	.0224					−.0224				
07	2.9329	10.1964	.0447	−1.0	−.0022		.0007	−.0447	1.0	.0022		−.0007
50	.0056				−.0011					.0011		
91	25.1725	4.5604	.7450		.0128	−1.0	.0005	−.7450		−.0128	1.0	−.0005
45	−.0029				.0006		−.0002			−.0006		.0002
48	.6080	.3982	.0224		.0005		.0002	−.0224		−.0005		−.0002
84	−28.1054	−14.7568	−.7897	1.0	−.0105	1.0	−.0012	1.7897		1.0105		1.0012
								Drop	●	Drop	○	Drop

	Lima Beans (Dried) (68)	Navy Beans (Dried) (69)	Excess Variables					Artificial Variables				
			(101)	(103)	(105)	(107)	(109)	(111)	(113)	(115)	(117)	(119)
17	.3653	.5975	−.0231			.0010		.0231			−.0010	
40	2.8801	10.1869	.0432	−1.0	−.0023	.0021	.0007	−.0432	1.0	.0023	−.0021	−.0007
00	−.0936	−.0180	−.0029		−.0011	.0039		.0029		.0011	−.0039	
56	.5383	.0975	.0159			.0003	−.0214	−.0159			−.0003	.0214
49	−.0046	−.0003	−.0001		.0006	.0001	−.0002	.0001		−.0006	−.0001	.0002
89	.1945	.3233	.0101		.0003	.0164	.0002	−.0101		−.0003	−.0164	−.0002
40	−2.8801	−10.1869	−.0432	1.0	.0023	−.0021	−.0007	1.0432		.9977	1.0021	1.0007
								Drop	○	Drop	Drop	Drop

(sible)

	Lima Beans (Dried) (68)	Navy Beans (Dried) (69)	Excess Variables					Artificial Variables				
			(101)	(103)	(105)	(107)	(109)	(111)	(113)	(115)	(117)	(119)
63	.3365	.4954	−.0235	.0100		.0009		.0235	−.0100		.0009	
58	.1786	.6318	.0027	−.0620	−.0001	.0001		−.0027	.0620	.0001	−.0001	
87	−.0960	−.0264	−.0030	.0008	−.0011	.0039		.0030	−.0008	.0011	−.0039	
46	.5214	.0377	.0157	.0059	.0003	−.0214		−.0157	−.0059	−.0003	.0214	
65	−.0017	.0098		−.0010	.0006	.0001	−.0002		.0010	−.0006	−.0001	.0002
74	.0612	−.1484	.0081	.0463	.0004	.0163	.0001	−.0081	−.0463	−.0004	−.0163	−.0001
								1.0000	1.0000	1.0000	1.0000	1.0000
								Drop	Drop	Drop	Drop	

SIMPLEX SOLUTION TO AN ABBRE

Item	Basic Solution		Wheat Flour (Enriched)	Evaporated Milk	Cheddar Cheese	Beef Liver	Cabbage	Sp
	Variable	Value $\bar{b}_i$	$(j = 1)$	(15)	(19)	(30)	(46)	
Calories	x_1	.0594	1.0			−.0876		
Calcium	x_{19}	.0246			1.0	−3.3203		
Vitamin A	x_{52}	.0042				.1830		
Riboflavin	x_{15}	.0153		1.0		3.6407		
Ascorbic acid	x_{46}	.0117				−.0368	1.0	
Objective form	$(-z)$	−.1151				.6210		
Infeasibility form	$(-w)$							
			●	●	○		●	

Item	Basic Solution		Wheat Flour (Enriched)	Evaporated Milk	Cheddar Cheese	Beef Liver	Cabbage	Sp
	Variable	Value $\bar{b}_i$	$(j = 1)$	(15)	(19)	(30)	(46)	
Calories	x_1	.0355	1.0		−.9711	3.1368		
Calcium	x_{69}	.0486			1.9734	−6.5523		
Vitamin A	x_{52}	.0051			.0384	.0556		
Riboflavin	x_{15}	.0086		1.0	−.2707	[4.5396]		
Ascorbic acid	x_{46}	.0112			−.0167	.0185	1.0	
Objective form	$(-z)$	−.1090			.2467	−.1982		
Infeasibility form	$(-w)$							
			●	○		★	●	

Item	Basic Solution		Wheat Flour (Enriched)	Evaporated Milk	Cheddar Cheese	Beef Liver	Cabbage	Sp
	Variable	Value $\bar{b}_i$	$(j = 1)$	(15)	(19)	(30)	(46)	
Calories	x_1	.0295	1.0	−.6910	−.7841			
Calcium	x_{69}	.0610		1.4434	1.5827			
Vitamin A	x_{52}	.0050		−.0122	.0417			
Riboflavin	x_{30}	.0019		.2203	−.0596	1.0		
Ascorbic acid	x_{46}	.0112		−.0041	−.0156		1.0	
Objective form	$(-z)$	−.1087		.0437	.2349			
Infeasibility form	$(-w)$							
			●			●	●	

(contd.)

OF STIGLER'S NUTRITION PROBLEM

t es	Lima Beans (Dried)	Navy Beans (Dried)	Excess Variables					Artificial Variables				
	(68)	(69)	(101)	(103)	(105)	(107)	(109)	(111)	(113)	(115)	(117)	(119)
89	.2908	.4921	−.0249	.0095		.0028		.0249	−.0095		.0028	
60	−1.5525	.5067	−.0494	−.0815	−.0011	.0712		.0494	.0815	.0011	−.0712	
22	−.0005	−.0195	−.0001	.0019	−.0011			.0001	−.0019	.0011		
66	1.8983	.1372	.0571	.0214	.0010	−.0779		−.0571	−.0214	−.0010	.0779	
18	−.0209	.0084	−.0006	−.0012	.0005	.0009	−.0002	.0006	.0012	−.0005	−.0009	.0002
76	.3849	−.1250	.0179	.0500	.0006	.0030	.0001	−.0179	−.0500	−.0006	−.0030	−.0001
								1.0000	1.0000	1.0000	1.0000	1.0000
	★							Drop	Drop	Drop	Drop	

et oes	Lima Beans (Dried)	Navy Beans (Dried)	Excess Variables					Artificial Variables				
	(68)	(69)	(101)	(103)	(105)	(107)	(109)	(111)	(113)	(115)	(117)	(119)
304	1.7985		.0231	.0887	.0010	−.0663		−.0231	−.0887	−.0010	.0663	
366	−3.0638	1.0	−.0974	−.1609	−.0022	.1405	.0001	.0974	.1609	.0022	−.1405	−.0001
343	−.0601		−.0020	−.0012	−.0011	.0028		.0020	.0012	.0011	−.0028	
825	2.3186		.0704	.0435	.0013	−.0972		−.0704	−.0435	−.0013	.0972	
922	.0049		.0002	.0001	.0006	−.0003	−.0002	−.0002	−.0001	−.0006	.0003	.0002
797	.0019		.0057	.0298	.0003	.0206	.0001	−.0057	−.0298	−.0003	−.0206	−.0001
								1.0000	1.0000	1.0000	1.0000	1.0000
	●							Drop	Drop	Drop	Drop	

(timal)

eet toes	Lima Beans (Dried)	Navy Beans (Dried)	Excess Variables					Artificial Variables				
3)	(68)	(69)	(101)	(103)	(105)	(107)	(109)	(111)	(113)	(115)	(117)	(119)
112	.1964		−.0256	.0586	.0001	.0008		.0256	−.0586	−.0001	−.0008	
516	.2827	1.0	.0042	−.0982	−.0002	.0002	.0001	−.0042	.0982	.0002	−.0002	−.0001
427	−.0885		−.0029	−.0018	−.0011	.0039		.0029	.0018	.0011	−.0039	
503	.5107		.0155	.0096	.0003	−.0214		−.0155	−.0096	−.0003	.0214	
950	−.0045		−.0001		.0006	.0001	−.0002	.0001		−.0006	−.0001	.0002
499	.1031		.0088	.0317	.0004	.0164	.0001	−.0088	−.0317	−.0004	−.0164	−.0001
								1.0000	1.0000	1.0000	1.0000	1.0000
	●							Drop	Drop	Drop	Drop	

27-3. PROBLEMS

1. Solve the nutrition problem using the revised simplex algorithm.
2. What are the implicit prices of the nutrients? Comment on the sign of the π_i.
3. What must the price of evaporated milk drop to before it will affect the solution? What food will drop out of the basis?
4. Assuming all other food costs stable, what must be the relationship between the cost of evaporated milk and the cost of the food being dropped out of the basic set for one or the other to be in the solution.
5. Prove that in a nutrition-type problem where all requirements may be exceeded, that the quantity of any food, s, in an optimal solution can be replaced by purchase of an equal number of dollars of another food j, provided $a_{ij} \geq a_{is}$ for all i.
6. Prove, more generally, that the purchase of any food, s, in an optimal solution can be replaced, per dollar of expenditure, by the purchase of λ_1 dollars of food 1, λ_2 dollars of food 2, . . ., λ_r dollars of food r, provided

$$\lambda_1 a_{i1} + \lambda_2 a_{i2} + \ldots + \lambda_r a_{ir} \geq a_{is} \quad (i = 1, 2, \ldots, m)$$
$$\lambda_1 \; + \lambda_2 \; + \ldots + \lambda_r \; = 1$$
$$\lambda_1 \geq 0, \, \lambda_2 \geq 0, \ldots, \lambda_r \geq 0$$

7. Prove for a general linear programming problem:

$$\sum a_{ij} x_j \geq b_i \qquad (x_j \geq 0 \,; i = 1, 2, \ldots, m)$$
$$\sum c_j x_j = z \text{ (Min)}$$

that if, by relabeling, for $k = 1, 2, \ldots, r$ and $i = 1, 2, \ldots, m$

$$\lambda_1 a_{i1} + \lambda_2 a_{i2} + \ldots + \lambda_r a_{ir} \geq a_{is} \qquad (\lambda_k \geq 0)$$
$$\lambda_1 c_1 \; + \lambda_2 c_2 \; + \ldots + \lambda_r c_r \; \leq c_s$$

then an optimal feasible solution exists with $x_s = 0$.
8. Prove that in a nutrition problem where requirements may be exceeded, at least one requirement must be satisfied exactly in an optimal solution.
9. Prove, as a Corollary to Problem 8, that no $x_s > 0$ can occur in an optimal solution if there exists a j satisfying $a_{ij} > a_{is}$ for all i or, more generally, a set $j = 1, 2, \ldots, r$ (by relabeling) satisfying the relations of Problem 6 with strict inequality.
10. Prove for the general linear programming system § 27-1-(2) with a general linear objective that strict inequalities cannot hold for all i in an optimal feasible solution when Min $z \neq 0$. Show, by a counter-example, that this theorem need not be true if Min $z = 0$.
11. Construct an example to show that, if requirements are to be met exactly, then it is possible that there exists an optimal solution with

$x_s > 0$ in spite of the existence of a j satisfying conditions of Problems 5 or 6 above.

12. In solving the nutrition problem, suppose a guess is made as to which slack variables are positive. Suppose the corresponding equations are omitted and an optimal solution is obtained for the resulting system. Suppose finally that substitutions of this optimal solution into the omitted equations yield positive values for their slack variables. Show, by eliminating the basic variables of the restricted system from the omitted equations, that (a) the entire system is reduced to canonical form, (b) the proposed solution to the entire system is a basic solution, and (c) it is an optimal solution.

13. Suppose in Problem 12 that, upon substitution into the omitted equations, one of the corresponding slack variables is negative. Show that one way to eliminate infeasibility is to introduce an artificial variable whose coefficients are the negative of the slack variable, and then proceed to minimize this variable. Generalize this procedure.

14. Show that, by increasing sufficiently the quantity of evaporated milk ($j = 15$), an immediate feasible solution can be obtained for the abbreviated nutrition problems of § 27-2 (see Table 27-2-II).

15. Show by altering the units of a variable that the rule to choose Max $\bar{c}_j > 0$ will choose any j such that $\bar{c}_j > 0$. Illustrate in Table 27-2-II how a change in the units of some variable would have altered the course of calculation. Use this to explain why the introduction of slack variables from the start of the computations could give the same sequence of iterations as their introduction after a minimum was reached without allowing slacks.

REFERENCES

Candler, 1960-1
Fisher and Schruben, 1953-1
Newman, 1955-1

Smith, V. E., 1959-1
Stigler, 1945-1
Waugh, 1951-1

CHAPTER 28

THE ALLOCATION OF AIRCRAFT TO ROUTES UNDER UNCERTAIN DEMAND

28-1. STATEMENT AND FORMULATION

The purpose of this chapter is to illustrate an application of linear programming to the problem of allocating aircraft to routes to maximize expected profits when there is uncertain customer demand. The computational procedure is similar to the fixed demand case with only slightly more computational effort required. After solution of a numerical case we shall compare the allocations with those obtained under the common practice of assuming a fixed demand equal to the expected value. The material for this chapter has been taken, with only minor changes, from the joint papers by Alan Ferguson and the author [Ferguson and Dantzig, 1954-1, 1956-1].

Many business, economic, and military problems have the following characteristics in common: a limited quantity of capital equipment or final product must be allocated among a number of final-use activities, where the level of demand for each of these activities, and hence the payoff, is uncertain; further, once the allocation is made, it is not economically feasible to reallocate because of geographical separation of the activities, or because of differences in form of the final products, or because of a minimum lead time between the decision and its implementation. Examples of such problems are (1) scheduling transport vehicles over a number of routes to meet a demand in some future period and (2) allocating quantities of a commodity at discrete time intervals among several storage or distribution points while the future demand for the commodity is unknown. It is assumed, however, that demand can be forecast or estimated as a distribution of values, each with a specified probability of being the actual value.

The general area where the techniques of this chapter apply may be schematized broadly as problems where

(a) alternative sets of activity levels can be chosen consistent with given resources;
(b) each set of chosen activity levels provides the facilities or stocks to meet an unknown demand whose distribution is assumed known;
(c) profits depend on the costs of the facilities, stocks, and on the revenues from the demand,

[568]

and where the general objective is to determine that set of activity levels that maximizes profits.

Chapter 25, which is based on the paper entitled "Linear Programming under Uncertainty" [Dantzig, 1955-1], forms the theoretical basis for the present chapter. Here we shall illustrate the procedural steps on an example [Ferguson and Dantzig, 1956-1] which, in fact, originally inspired the theoretical work in this area. Thus, little in the way of rigorous theory will be attempted, although each step will be justified intuitively.

The method is explained by the use of a model for routing aircraft. Several types of aircraft are allocated over a number of routes; the monthly demand for service over each route is assumed to be known only as a distribution of probable values. The aircraft are so allocated as to minimize the sum of the cost of performing the transportation, plus the expected value of the revenue lost through the failure to serve all the traffic that actually developed.

For purposes of month-to-month scheduling, an air-transport operator would probably be more willing to make an estimate of the range and general distribution of future travel (or shipment) over his routes than to commit himself to a single expected value. Indeed, he might feel that the optimal assignment should be insensitive to a wide range of demand distribution, and that an assignment based on expected values (as if these were known fixed demands) would be misleading. It is suggested that the reader make sensitivity tests by modifying the demand distributions given in the illustrative example to develop this point. Sensitivity analysis is discussed in § 12-4.

Passenger demand, of course, occurs on a day-by-day or, in fact, on a flight-by-flight basis. The assumed number of passengers per type aircraft per given type flight may be thought of as an ideal number which can be increased slightly by decreasing the amount of air freight and by "smoothing" the demand by encouraging the customers to take open reservations on alternative flights as opposed to less certain reservations on the desired flight. In spite of these possible adjustments, traveler preferences and the inevitable last-minute cancellations do cause loss of seat-carrying capacity. However, the best way to reflect these effects of the daily variations in demand is beyond the scope of this chapter. For our purpose here, either the aircraft passenger capability or the demand may be thought of as adjusted downward to reflect the loss due to daily variations of demand. Our concern will be in over-all monthly variability.

The method employed is simple, and the example used can be solved by hand in an hour or two. Larger problems can be solved with computing machines.

After we formulate the problem, we will (a) briefly indicate the nature of the solution based on *fixed demand* [Ferguson and Dantzig, 1954-1], (b) show the method of solving the problem using stochastic values for demand, and (c) compare the two solutions. Note that the example has been so constructed that the fixed demand is the same as the expected value of the uncertain demand.

A Fixed-demand Example.

The fixed-demand example, used to illustrate the method, assumes a fleet of four types of aircraft, as shown in Table 28-1-I. These aircraft have

TABLE 28-1-I

ASSUMED AIRCRAFT FLEET

Type	Description	Number Available
A	Postwar 4-engine	10
B	Postwar 2-engine	19
C	Prewar 2-engine	25
D	Prewar 4-engine	15

differences in speeds, ranges, payload capacities, and cost characteristics. The assumed routes and expected traffic loads (the distribution of demand will be discussed later) are shown in Table 28-1-II.

TABLE 28-1-II

TRAFFIC LOAD BY ROUTE

Route	Route Miles[1]	Expected Number of Passengers[2]	Price One-way Ticket ($)
(1) N.Y. to L.A. (1-stop)	2,475	25,000	130
(2) N.Y. to L.A. (2-stop)	2,475	12,000	130
(3) N.Y. to Dallas (0-stop)	1,381	18,000	70
(4) N.Y. to Dallas (1-stop)	1,439	9,000	70
(5) N.Y. to Boston (0-stop)	185	60,000	10

[1] *Official Airline Guide*, July, 1954, p. 276. The New York-Los Angeles routes are via Chicago and via Chicago-Denver; the stop en route between New York and Dallas is at Memphis.

[2] This is the expected number of full one-way fares per month to be carried on each route. If a passenger gets off en route and is replaced by another passenger, it is counted as one full fare.

Since this chapter proposes to illustrate the applicability of a method of solving problems in which several realistic elements are considered, it is assumed that not all aircraft can carry their full loads on all routes and that the obtainable utilization varies from route to route. Specifically, Type B is assumed to be able to operate at only 75 per cent payload on Route 3, and Type D at 80 per cent on Route 1; Type C cannot fly either Route 1 or Route 3, and Type B cannot fly Route 1. *Utilization* is defined as the average number of hours of useful work performed per month by each aircraft assigned to a particular route. Utilization of 300 hours per month is assumed on Routes 1 and 2; 285 on Routes 3 and 4; and 240 on Route 5.

The assumed dollar costs per 100 passenger-miles are shown in Table 28-1-III. These do not include any capital costs such as those of the aircraft

TABLE 28-1-III

DOLLAR COSTS

Type of Aircraft	Route				
	(1) N.Y. to L.A. 1-stop ($)	(2) N.Y. to L.A. 2-stop ($)	(3) N.Y. to Dallas 0-stop ($)	(4) N.Y. to Dallas 1-stop ($)	(5) N.Y. to Boston 0-stop ($)
	Dollar Costs Per 100 Passenger-miles				
1—A	0.45	0.57	0.45	0.47	0.64
2—B	—	0.64	0.83	0.63	0.88
3—C	—	0.92	—	0.93	1.13
4—D	0.74	0.61	0.59	0.62	0.81
	Dollar Costs Per Passenger Turned Away[1]				
5—E	130 (13)	130 (13)	70 (7)	70 (7)	10 (1)

[1] Figures shown in parentheses are thousands of dollars lost per 100 passengers turned away. (Throughout this discussion, passengers are measured in units of hundreds.)

and ground facilities; they represent variable costs such as the cost of gasoline, salaries of the crew, and costs of servicing the aircraft.

There is, however, a second kind of "cost." It is the *loss of revenue* when not enough aircraft are assigned to the route to meet the passenger demand. We shall assume that this loss of revenue is the same as the price of a one-way ticket shown in the E row of Table 28-1-III.

Based on the speeds, ranges, payload capacities, and turn-around times, passenger-carrying capabilities were determined. The resultant potential number p_{ij} (in hundreds) of passengers that can be flown per month per aircraft of type i on route j is shown in Table 28-1-IV, as the upper right figure in each box. By multiplying these numbers by the corresponding costs per 100 passenger-miles given in Table 28-1-III and by the number of miles given in Table 28-1-II, the monthly cost per aircraft can also be obtained. This is given in the lower left figure c_{ij} in each box; explicitly, c_{ij} is the cost in thousands of dollars per month per aircraft of type i assigned to the route j. The revenue losses c_{5j}, in thousands of dollars per 100 passengers *not carried*, are given in the E row of Table 28-1-IV; finally, we define $p_{5j} = 1$.[1] The staggered layout of the table was chosen so as to

[1] This will make it easier to state the passenger-balance or "column" equations (2).

TABLE 28-1-IV

PASSENGER-CARRYING CAPABILITIES AND COSTS

Type of Aircraft	Route				
	(1) N.Y. to L.A. 1-stop	(2) N.Y. to L.A. 2-stop	(3) N.Y. to Dallas 0-stop	(4) N.Y. to Dallas 1-stop	(5) N.Y. to Boston 0-stop
	Per Aircraft Per Month				
1—A	$p_{11} = 16$ $c_{11} = 18$	$p_{12} = 15$ $c_{12} = 21$	$p_{13} = 28$ $c_{13} = 18$	$p_{14} = 23$ $c_{14} = 16$	$p_{15} = 81$ $c_{15} = 10$
2—B	*	$p_{22} = 10$ $c_{22} = 15$	$p_{23} = 14$ $c_{23} = 16$	$p_{24} = 15$ $c_{24} = 14$	$p_{25} = 57$ $c_{25} = 9$
3—C	*	$p_{32} = 5$ $c_{32} = 10$	*	$p_{34} = 7$ $c_{34} = 9$	$p_{35} = 29$ $c_{35} = 6$
4—D	$p_{41} = 9$ $c_{41} = 17$	$p_{42} = 11$ $c_{42} = 16$	$p_{43} = 22$ $c_{43} = 17$	$p_{44} = 17$ $c_{44} = 15$	$p_{45} = 55$ $c_{45} = 10$
	Per 100 Passengers Not Carried (Losses)				
5—E	$p_{51} = 1$ $c_{51} = 13$	$p_{52} = 1$ $c_{52} = 13$	$p_{53} = 1$ $c_{53} = 7$	$p_{54} = 1$ $c_{54} = 7$	$p_{55} = 1$ $c_{55} = 1$

identify the corresponding data found in Table 28-2-II; the latter is the *work sheet* upon which the entire problem is solved.

The basic problem is that of determining the number of aircraft of each type to assign to each route consistent with aircraft availabilities, and of determining how much revenue will be lost due to failure of allocated aircraft to meet passenger demand on various routes. Since many alternative allocations are possible, our specific objective will be to find that allocation that minimizes total costs, where costs are defined as operating costs plus lost revenues based on the cost factors given in Table 28-1-III.

This may be formulated mathematically as a linear programming problem. Let x_{ij} denote the unknown quantity of the ith type aircraft assigned to jth route, where $i = 1, 2, \ldots, m - 1$ and $j = 1, 2, \ldots, n - 1$. If x_{in} denotes the surplus or unallocated aircraft, then (1) states that the sum of allocated and unallocated aircraft of each type accounts for the total available aircraft a_i. If x_{mj} denotes the number of passengers in hundreds turned away, then equation (2) states that the sum of passenger carrying capability of each type aircraft allocated to the jth route, $p_{ij}x_{ij}$, plus the unsatisfied demand accounts for the total demand, d_j. Relation (3) states

[572]

that all unknown quantities x_{ij} must be either positive or zero. Finally, if z is total cost, it is the sum of all the individual operating costs of each allocation, $c_{ij}x_{ij}$, plus the revenues lost by unsatisfied demands $c_{mj}x_{mj}$ (see equation (4)).

Fixed-demand Model

Find numbers x_{ij}, and the minimum value of z such that for $i = 1, 2,$ $\ldots, m; j = 1, 2, \ldots, n$:

(1) Row Sums:

$$x_{i1} + x_{i2} + \ldots + x_{in} = a_i \quad (i \neq m)$$

(2) Col. Sums:

$$p_{1j}x_{1j} + p_{2j}x_{2j} + \ldots + p_{mj}x_{mj} = d_j$$

(3)

$$x_{ij} \geq 0$$

(4)

$$\sum_{i=1}^{m} \sum_{j=1}^{n} c_{ij}x_{ij} = z$$

The optimal assignment of aircraft to routes based on fixed demand is a *weighted distribution problem*. The numerical solution shown in Table 28-2-II was obtained using the methods of Chapter 21. The values assigned to the unknowns x_{ij} appear boldfaced in the upper left of each box unless $x_{ij} = 0$ in which case it is omitted; the entire layout takes the form:

$$
\begin{array}{|ll|}
\hline
x_{ij} & \\
 & p_{ij} \\
c_{ij} & \\
\hline
\end{array}
$$

The sums by *rows* of x_{ij} entries in Table 28-2-II equated to availabilities yield equations (1). The sums by *columns* of x_{ij} weighted by corresponding values of p_{ij} equated to demands yield equations (2); the x_{ij} weighted by corresponding c_{ij} and summed over the entire table yields (4). As noted earlier, Table 28-2-II is actually the work sheet upon which the entire problem is solved. Later we shall discuss a revision of this work sheet for solving problems with variable demand. All figures in the table, except for the upper left entries, x_{ij} and values of the so-called "implicit prices" u_i and v_j shown in the margins, are constants which do not change during the course of computation. The values of the variables x_{ij}, u_i, and v_j, however, will change during the course of successive iterations of the simplex method as adapted for this problem. For this reason it is customary to cover the work sheet with clear acetate and to enter the variable information with a grease pencil which can be easily erased; alternatively, a blackboard or semi-transparent tissue paper overlays can be used. The detailed rules for obtaining the optimal solution shown are given in Chapter 21 and will not be repeated here. Instead a more general set of rules for the uncertain demand case will be given which, of course, could be used for the expected demand case.

In Table 28-1-V we have a convenient summary serving to identify and define the numerical data entered in Table 28-2-II and to give the test for optimality.

TABLE 28-1-V

SUMMARY OF NOTATION AND RULES FOR FIXED-DEMAND CASE

(as displayed in Table 28-2-II)

Indices:	$i = 1, 2, \ldots, m - 1$ refers to type of aircraft to which passengers are assigned $i = m$ if passengers are unassigned $j = 1, 2, \ldots, n - 1$ refers to type of route to which an aircraft is assigned $j = n$ if aircraft is unassigned (surplus)
Constants:	a_i = number of available aircraft of type i d_j = expected passenger demand in 100's per month. on route j p_{ij} = passenger-carrying capability in 100's per month per aircraft of type i assigned to route j ($p_{m,j} = 1$ by definition) c_{ij} = costs in 1000's of dollars per month per aircraft of type i assigned to route j (c_{mj} is cost per 100 passengers turned away)
x_{ij} Entries: Omitted x_{ij} Entries:	x_{ij} = number of aircraft of type i assigned to route j (x_{mj} is 100's of passengers turned away) $x_{ij} = 0$ if upper left entry in box is missing
Implicit Prices:	u_i and v_j are determined such that $u_i + p_{ij}v_j = c_{ij}$ for (i, j) boxes corresponding to $x_{ij} > 0$, i.e., non-omitted x_{ij} entries ($u_m = v_n = 0$ by definition)
Test for Optimality:	Solution is optimal if, for all (i, j), the relation $u_i + p_{ij}v_j \leq c_{ij}$ holds

Extension of the Example to Uncertain Demand.

To introduce the element of uncertain demand, we assume not a known fixed demand on each route but a known frequency distribution of demand. The assumed frequency distributions are shown in Table 28-1-VI. Thus on Route 2 (N.Y. to L.A., 2-stop) either 5,000 or 15,000 passengers will want transportation during the month, with probabilities 30 or 70 per cent respectively. The assumed traffic distributions are, of course, hypothetical to illustrate our method. The demand distributions on the five routes vary over wide ranges and have different characteristics; Route 1 is flat, Route 2 is U-shaped, Routes 3, 4, and 5 are unimodular but have differing degrees of concentration about the mode. Route 4 has a distribution with a very long tail that may reflect a realistic traffic situation.

[574]

To illustrate the essential character of the linear programming problem for the case of uncertain demand, let us focus our attention on a single route—say, Route 1—with probability distribution of demand as given in Table 28-1-VI. Let us suppose that aircraft assigned to Route 1 are capable

TABLE 28-1-VI

ASSUMED DISTRIBUTION OF PASSENGER DEMAND

(λ_{hj} = Probability of Demand d_{hj})

Route	Passenger Demand (in hundreds)	Approx. Mean (in hundreds)	Probability of Passenger Demand	Probability of Equaling or Exceeding Demand
(1)	$200 = d_{11}$ $220 = d_{21}$ $250 = d_{31}$ $270 = d_{41}$ $300 = d_{51}$	250	$0.2 = \lambda_{11}$ $0.05 = \lambda_{21}$ $0.35 = \lambda_{31}$ $0.2 = \lambda_{41}$ $0.2 = \lambda_{51}$	$1.0 = \gamma_{11}$ $0.8 = \gamma_{21}$ $0.75 = \gamma_{31}$ $0.4 = \gamma_{41}$ $0.2 = \gamma_{51}$
(2)	$50 = d_{12}$ $150 = d_{22}$	120	$0.3 = \lambda_{12}$ $0.7 = \lambda_{22}$	$1.0 = \gamma_{12}$ $0.7 = \gamma_{22}$
(3)	$140 = d_{13}$ $160 = d_{23}$ $180 = d_{33}$ $200 = d_{43}$ $220 = d_{53}$	180	$0.1 = \lambda_{13}$ $0.2 = \lambda_{23}$ $0.4 = \lambda_{33}$ $0.2 = \lambda_{43}$ $0.1 = \lambda_{53}$	$1.0 = \gamma_{13}$ $0.9 = \gamma_{23}$ $0.7 = \gamma_{33}$ $0.3 = \gamma_{43}$ $0.1 = \gamma_{53}$
(4)	$10 = d_{14}$ $50 = d_{24}$ $80 = d_{34}$ $100 = d_{44}$ $340 = d_{54}$	90	$0.2 = \lambda_{14}$ $0.2 = \lambda_{24}$ $0.3 = \lambda_{34}$ $0.2 = \lambda_{44}$ $0.1 = \lambda_{54}$	$1.0 = \gamma_{14}$ $0.8 = \gamma_{24}$ $0.6 = \gamma_{34}$ $0.3 = \gamma_{44}$ $0.1 = \gamma_{54}$
(5)	$580 = d_{15}$ $600 = d_{25}$ $620 = d_{35}$	600	$0.1 = \lambda_{15}$ $0.8 = \lambda_{25}$ $0.1 = \lambda_{35}$	$1.0 = \gamma_{15}$ $0.9 = \gamma_{25}$ $0.1 = \gamma_{35}$

of taking $100Y_i$ passengers where Y_i is to be determined. Up to 200 units (in hundreds of passengers) of this capability are certain to be used, and revenues from this source (negative costs) will be $13 = k_1$ units (in thousands of dollars) per unit of capability. If $100Y_1 \geq 200$, up to an additional 20 units of this capability will be used with probability $\gamma_{21} = 0.8$. Indeed, 80 per cent of the time the demand will be 220 units or greater, while 20 per cent of the time it will be 200 units; hence, the expected revenue per unit from this increment of capability is $0.8 \times 13 = 10.4$, or $10.4 = k_1\gamma_{21}$ units. On the third increment of 30 units (22,001 to 25,000 seats), the expected revenue is $0.75 \times 13 = 9.8$ or $k_1\gamma_{31}$ units per unit of capability since there is a 25 per cent chance that none of these units of capability will be used and 75 per cent that all will be used. For the fourth increment of 20 units (25,001 to 27,000 seats) of capability, the expected revenue is $0.4 \times 13 = 5.2$ or $k_1\gamma_{41}$ units per unit of capability, while for the fifth increment of 30 units (27,001 to 30,000 seats) it is $0.2 \times 13 = 2.6$ or $k_1\gamma_{51}$ units per unit. For the sixth increment, which is the number of units assigned above the 30,000 seat mark, the expected revenue is $0.0 \times 13 = 0$ per unit, since it is certain that none of these units of capability can be used. It is clear that no assignments above 30,000 seats are worthwhile, and hence the last increment can be omitted. The index $h = 1, 2, 3, 4, 5$ will be used to denote the 1st, 2nd, . . ., 5th increment of demand.

The number of assigned units in each increment, however, can be viewed as an unknown that depends on the *total* (passenger-carrying) capability assigned to route $j = 1$. Thus, if the total assigned is $Y_1 = 210$ units of capability, then the part of this total belonging to the first increment, denoted by y_{11}, is $y_{11} = 200$ and the part belonging to the second increment, denoted by y_{21}, is $y_{21} = 10$. The amounts in the higher increments are $y_{hi} = 0$ for $i = 3, 4, 5$. To review, the passenger-carrying capability Y_j is determined by the number of aircraft assigned to route j, so that

$$(5) \qquad Y_j = p_{1j}x_{1j} + p_{2j}x_{2j} + p_{3j}x_{3j} + p_{4j}x_{4j}$$

On the other hand, Y_j itself breaks down into five increments

$$(6) \qquad Y_j = y_{1j} + y_{2j} + y_{3j} + y_{4j} + y_{5j}$$

for routes $j = 1, 3, 4$, and correspondingly fewer for $j = 2, 5$. Regardless of the total Y_j, the amount y_{hj} belonging to each increment is bounded by the total size b_{hj} of that increment; the latter, however, is simply the change in demand level, so that

$$(7) \qquad \begin{aligned} 0 &\leq y_{1j} \leq d_{1j} &&= b_{1j} \\ 0 &\leq y_{2j} \leq d_{2j} - d_{1j} &&= b_{2j} \\ 0 &\leq y_{3j} \leq d_{3j} - d_{2j} &&= b_{3j} \\ 0 &\leq y_{4j} \leq d_{4j} - d_{3j} &&= b_{4j} \\ 0 &\leq y_{5j} \leq d_{5j} - d_{4j} &&= b_{5j} \end{aligned}$$

Letting

$$(8) \qquad \lambda_{hj} = \text{probability of demand } d_{hj},$$

the total expected revenue from route j is, therefore,

$$(9) \qquad k_j(\gamma_{1j}y_{1j} + \gamma_{2j}y_{2j} + \ldots + \gamma_{5j}y_{5j})$$

where k_j is revenue (in thousands) per 100 passengers carried on route j and, as seen in Table 28-1-VI, the probability, γ_{hj}, of exceeding or equaling demand d_{hj} is related to λ_{hj}, the probability of demand d_{hj}, by

$$(10) \qquad \begin{aligned} 1 = \gamma_{1j} &= \lambda_{1j} + \lambda_{2j} + \lambda_{3j} + \lambda_{4j} + \lambda_{5j} \\ \gamma_{2j} &= \phantom{\lambda_{1j} + {}} \lambda_{2j} + \lambda_{3j} + \lambda_{4j} + \lambda_{5j} \\ \gamma_{3j} &= \phantom{\lambda_{1j} + \lambda_{2j} + {}} \lambda_{3j} + \lambda_{4j} + \lambda_{5j} \\ \gamma_{4j} &= \phantom{\lambda_{1j} + \lambda_{2j} + \lambda_{3j} + {}} \lambda_{4j} + \lambda_{5j} \\ \gamma_{5j} &= \phantom{\lambda_{1j} + \lambda_{2j} + \lambda_{3j} + \lambda_{4j} + {}} \lambda_{5j} \end{aligned}$$

The numerical values of λ_{hj} and γ_{hj} are given in Table 28-1-VI. Applying (9), the total expected revenues for Route 1 are

$$13(1.0y_{11} + .8y_{21} + .75y_{31} + .4y_{41} + .2y_{51})$$

The most important fact to note about this linear form is the decrease in the successive values of the coefficients γ_{hj}. Moreover, this will always be the case whatever the distribution of demand, since the probability of equaling or exceeding a given demand level d_{hj} decreases with increasing values of demand.

＾Suppose now that $y_{11}, y_{21}, \ldots,$ are treated as unknown variables in a linear programming problem subject only to (6) and (7) where the objective is to maximize revenues. Let us suppose further that Y_1 is fixed. It is clear, since the coefficient of y_{11} is largest in the maximizing form (9), y_{11} will be chosen first and made as large as possible consistent with (6) and (7); for the chosen value y_{11}, the next increment y_{21} will be chosen as large as possible consistent with (6) and (7), etc.; as a result, *when the maximum is reached*, the values of the variables $y_{11}, y_{21}, \ldots,$ are precisely the *incremental values* associated with Y_1, which we discussed earlier, (6). Even if passenger capability Y_1 is not fixed, as in the case about to be considered, it should be noted that whatever the value of Y_1, the values of $y_{11}, y_{21}, \ldots,$ which minimize an over-all cost form such as in (14) below, must maximize (9) for $j = 1$ and hence the incremental values of Y_1 will be generated by $y_{11}, y_{21}, \ldots \ldots$

The linear programming problem in the case of uncertain demand is shown by (11), (12), (13), and (14).

Uncertain Demand Model

Find numbers x_{ij} and y_{hj} and the minimum value of z such that for $i = 1, 2, \ldots, m; j = 1, 2, \ldots, n; h = 1, 2, \ldots, r:$

(11) Row Sums: $\qquad x_{i1} + x_{i2} + \ldots + x_{in} = a_i \qquad\qquad (i \neq m)$

(12) Column Sums: $\quad p_{1j}x_{1j} + p_{2j}x_{2j} + \ldots + p_{mj}x_{mj} = y_{1j} + y_{2j} + \ldots + y_{rj} \qquad (j \neq n)$

(13) $\qquad\qquad\qquad x_{ij} \geq 0, \qquad 0 \; y \leq_{hj} \leq b_{hj}$

(14) Expected Costs: $\qquad z = \sum_{i=1}^{m-1} \sum_{j=1}^{n} c_{ij}x_{ij} + \left[R_0 - \sum_{j=1}^{n} k_j \sum_{h=1}^{r} \gamma_{hj}y_{hj} \right]$

Thus expected costs are defined as the total outlays (first term) plus the expected loss of revenue due to shortage of seats (last two terms), where R_0, a constant, is the expected revenue if sufficient seats were supplied for all customers.

For the problem at hand, the bounds, b_{hj}, and the expected revenues, $k_j\gamma_{hj}$, per unit for the "incremental variables" y_{hj} can be computed from probability distributions Table 28-1-VI via (7) and (10).

The numerical values of the constants for the stochastic case are tabulated in Table 28-1-VII.

TABLE 28-1-VII

INCREMENTAL BOUNDS, b_{hj}, AND EXPECTED REVENUES, $k_j\gamma_{hj}$,
PER UNIT OF PASSENGER CARRYING CAPACITY ASSIGNED

Increment h	Route 1		Route 2		Route 3		Route 4		Route 5	
	b_{h1}	$k_1\gamma_{h1}$	b_{h2}	$k_2\gamma_{h2}$	b_{h3}	$k_3\gamma_{h3}$	b_{h4}	$k_4\gamma_{h4}$	b_{h5}	$k_5\gamma_{h5}$
1	200	$k_1 = 13$	50	$k_2 = 13$	140	$k_3 = 7$	10	$k_4 = 7$	580	$k_5 = 1$
2	20	$.8k_1 = 10.4$	100	$.7k_2 = 9.1$	20	$.9k_3 = 6.3$	40	$.8k_4 = 5.6$	20	$.9k_5 = .$
3	30	$.75k_1 = 9.8$	**		20	$.7k_3 = 4.9$	30	$.6k_4 = 4.2$	20	$.1k_5 = .$
4	20	$.4k_1 = 5.2$	**		20	$.3k_3 = 2.1$	20	$.3k_4 = 2.1$	**	
5	30	$.2k_1 = 2.6$	**		20	$.1k_3 = .7$	240	$.1k_4 = .7$	**	

** Only two increments for Route 2 and three increments for Route 5 are needed to describe distribution of demand.

Rules for Computation.

The work sheet for determining the optimal assignment under uncertain demand is shown in Table 28-2-III.

The entries in the x_{ij} boxes and y_{hj} boxes take the form:

To form the new row equations (11), the x_{ij} entries are summed to yield the a_i values given in the aircraft-available column. To form the column equations (12), the x_{ij} entries are multiplied by p_{ij}, the y_{hj} by -1, and summed down to yield zero.

Step 1. To initiate the computation any set of nonnegative values may be assigned to the unknown x_{ij} and y_{hj}, provided they satisfy the equations and thereby constitute a feasible solution.

Step 2. Put a box around any $(m + n - 2)$ of x_{ij} and y_{hj} entries where $m + n$ is the number of row plus column equations. These boxed entries can be arbitrarily selected except that they must have the property that if the fixed values assigned to the other non-boxed variables and the constant terms were *arbitrarily changed to other values*, then the boxed variables would be determined uniquely in terms of the latter. Such a boxed set of variables constitutes, of course, *a basic set of variables*; the array of coefficients associated with this set in the equations (11) and (12) forms a basis (Chapter 8).

Note: One simple way of selecting a basic set is shown in Table 28-2-IV. One x_{ij} entry is arbitrarily selected and boxed in each row corresponding to a row equation (it is suggested that entries be boxed that appear to have a chance of having a positive value in an optimum solution). Next, each y_{hj}, in turn, $h = 1, 2, \ldots$, in a column is assigned its upper bound value b_{hj} until for some $h = h_0$ the column "net" goes negative, in which case a value $y_{hj} < b_{hj}$ for $h = h_0$ is assigned so that the net is zero; the $(h_{0,j})$ entry is then boxed.

Step 3. For (i, j) and (h, j) combinations corresponding to basic entries, compute implicit prices u_i and v_j associated with equations by determining values of u_i and v_j satisfying the equations

$$(15) \qquad\qquad u_i + p_{ij}v_j = c_{ij} \qquad\qquad \text{(for } x_{ij} \text{ basic)}$$

$$(16) \qquad\qquad 0 + (-1)v_j = -k_j\gamma_{hj} \qquad\qquad \text{(for } y_{hj} \text{ basic)}$$

There are always $m + n - 2$ equations (15) and (16) in $m + n - 2$ unknowns u_i and v_j that can be shown easily to have a unique solution (see § 21-1). They can be solved by inspection, for it can be shown that the system is either completely triangular or, at worst, contains subsystems, some triangular and some triangular if one unknown is specified.[2]

Step 4. Compute for all (i, j) and (h, j)

$$(17) \qquad\qquad \bar{c}_{ij} = +c_{ij} - (u_i + p_{ij}v_j)$$

$$(18) \qquad\qquad \bar{c}'_{hj} = +(-k_j\gamma_{hj}) - (0 - v_j)$$

It has been shown in § 5-2 that, if the x_{ij} or y_{hj} value associated with some non-basic entry is changed to

$$(19) \qquad\qquad x_{ij} \pm \theta \quad \text{or} \quad y_{hj} \pm \theta \qquad\qquad (\theta \geq 0)$$

the other non-basic variables remaining fixed, and the basic variables adjusted, then the expected costs z will change to z' where

$$(20) \qquad\qquad z' = z \pm \theta\bar{c}_{ij} \quad \text{or} \quad z' = z \pm \theta\bar{c}'_{hj}$$

Assuming, for generality, that x_{ij} may also be a bounded variable, it pays to increase x_{ij} or y_{hj} if $\bar{c}_{ij}$ or $\bar{c}'_{hj} < 0$, if either is at its upper bound, in which case no increase is allowed; also it pays to decrease x_{ij} or y_{hj} if $\bar{c}_{ij}$ or $\bar{c}'_{hj} > 0$, unless $x_{ij} = 0$ or $y_{hj} = 0$, in which case no *decrease* is allowed.

---

[2] This is the analogue for the weighted distribution problem (11), (12), (13), (14) of the well-known theorem for the standard transportation problem that all bases are triangular. Its proof is similar. See Chapters 14 and 21.

Test for Optimality.

According to the theory of the simplex method with bounded variables (see Chapter 18), if the non-basic variables satisfy the following conditions:

(a) they are all at either their upper or lower bounds,

(b) their corresponding $\bar{c}_{ij}$ and $\bar{c}'_{hj} \geq 0$, if they are at their lower bound, and

(c) their corresponding $\bar{c}_{ij}$ and $\bar{c}'_{hj} \leq 0$ if they are at their upper bound,

then the solution is optimal and the algorithm terminates. Otherwise there are $\bar{c}_{ij}$ or $\bar{c}'_{hj}$ for which (b) or (c) does not hold. In which case an increase or decrease (depending on whether the sign is negative or positive) in the corresponding variable is allowed; we will call these (i, j) or (h, j) combinations *out-of-kilter*; let the largest $\bar{c}_{ij}$ or $\bar{c}'_{hj}$ among them in absolute value be denoted by $\bar{c}_{rs}$ or $\bar{c}'_{rs}$.

Step 5. Leaving all non-basic entries fixed except for the value of the variable corresponding to the (r, s) determined in Step 4, modify the value of x_{rs} (or y_{rs}), if not at its upper bound, to

$$(21) \qquad x_{rs} + \theta \text{ (or } y_{rs} + \theta) \text{ if } \bar{c}_{rs} < 0 \text{ (or } \bar{c}'_{rs} < 0)$$

or, if not at its lower bound, to

$$(22) \qquad x_{rs} - \theta \text{ (or } y_{rs} - \theta) \text{ if } \bar{c}_{rs} > 0 \text{ (or } \bar{c}'_{rs} > 0)$$

where $\theta \geq 0$ is unknown for the moment, and recompute the values of the basic variables as linear functions of θ. Choose the value of $\theta = \theta^*$ at the largest value possible consistent with keeping all basic variables (whose values now depend on θ) between their upper and lower bounds; in the next cycle correct the values of the basic variables on the assumption $\theta = \theta^*$.

Also, if at the value $\theta = \theta^*$ one (or more) of the basic variables attains its upper or lower bound, in the next cycle drop any one of these variables (never drop more than one) from the basic set and box the variable x_{rs} instead. Should it happen that x_{rs} or y_{rs} attains its upper or lower bound at $\theta = \theta^*$, the set of basic variables is the same as before; their values, however, are changed to allow x_{rs} or y_{rs} to be fixed at its new bound.

Start the next cycle of the iterative procedure by returning to Step 3.

28-2. NUMERICAL SOLUTION OF THE ROUTING PROBLEM

For our starting solution in Table 28-2-IV, cycle o, we used for values of x_{ij} the best solution assuming fixed demands equal to the expected values of the distribution[3] shown in Table 28-2-II. These x_{ij} will meet the expected

---

[3] In the humorous parody by Paul Gunther [1955-1] entitled "Use of Linear Programming in Capital Budgeting," *Journal of the Operations Research Society of America*, May, 1955, it will be recalled that Mrs. Efficiency wondered why Mr. O. R. did not start out with a good guess. In this chapter you will note that we followed Mrs. Efficiency's suggestion and have started by guessing at the final solution rather than going through the customary use of artificial variables and a Phase I of the simplex process.

demands so that $Y_j = d_j$, except for Route 5 where there is a deficit of 100 and $Y_5 = 500$ (see § 28-1-(5)). These Y_j are broken down into the incremental values shown below the double line in Table 28-2-IV, cycle 0.

Next, one of the variables in each row is boxed. The selected variables are x_{11}, x_{22}, x_{35}, x_{43}; each appears likely to be in an optimal solution; however, x_{43} has been boxed rather than x_{41}, which may be a better choice. Next, the last positive entry in each column is boxed, i.e., the variables y_{31}, y_{22}, y_{33}, y_{44}, y_{15}. In all there are $m + n - 2 = 9$ boxed variables. The implicit values, u_i and v_j, shown in the table are determined by solving the nine equations:

(1)
$$u_1 + p_{11}v_1 = c_{11} \qquad (p_{11} = 16; c_{11} = 18)$$
$$u_2 + p_{22}v_2 = c_{22} \qquad (p_{22} = 10; c_{22} = 15)$$
$$u_3 + p_{35}v_5 = c_{35} \qquad (p_{35} = 29; c_{35} = 6)$$
$$u_4 + p_{43}v_3 = c_{43} \qquad (p_{43} = 22; c_{43} = 17)$$
$$0 + (-1)v_1 = -k_1\gamma_{31} \qquad (k_1\gamma_{31} = 9.8)$$
$$0 + (-1)v_2 = -k_2\gamma_{22} \qquad (k_2\gamma_{22} = 9.1)$$
$$0 + (-1)v_3 = -k_3\gamma_{33} \qquad (k_3\gamma_{33} = 4.9)$$
$$0 + (-1)v_4 = -k_4\gamma_{44} \qquad (k_4\gamma_{44} = 2.1)$$
$$0 + (-1)v_5 = -k_5\gamma_{15} \qquad (k_5\gamma_{15} = 1.0)$$

This permits the computation of $\bar{c}_{ij}$ and $\bar{c}'_{hj}$ (see § 28-1-(17), (18)). As a check, $\bar{c}_{ij} = 0$ and $\bar{c}'_{hj} = 0$ for (i, j) and (h, j) corresponding to basic variables. The $\bar{c}_{ij}$ or $\bar{c}'_{hj}$ of largest absolute value for those (i, j) or (h, j) that are out-of-kilter is

$$\bar{c}_{24} = 14 - [-76 + 15(2.1)] = +58.5$$

Hence a decrease in the variable x_{24} with adjustments of the basic variables will result in a decrease in the expected costs by an amount of 58.5 units per unit decrease in x_{24}. If $x_{24} = 6$ is changed to $x_{24} = 6 - \theta$, then, in order to satisfy the column 4 equation, the basic variable $y_{44} = 10$ must be modified to $y_{44} = 10 - 15\theta$ (all other variables in column 4 are fixed). Also, to satisfy the row equation 2, $x_{22} = 8$ must be modified to $x_{22} = 8 + \theta$; this in turn causes $y_{22} = 70$ to be changed to $y_{22} = 70 + 10\theta$ in order to satisfy column equation 2. The largest value of θ is $\theta^* = \frac{10}{15}$ at which value $y_{44} = 0$.

The numerical values of the variables appearing in Table 28-2-IV, cycle 1, are obtained from those of Table 28-2-IV, cycle 0, by setting $\theta = \theta^* = \frac{10}{15}$. The variable x_{24} becomes a new basic variable in place of y_{44} which hits its lower bound, zero. Computing the new set of implicit prices the largest $\bar{c}_{ij}$ in absolute value which can increase or decrease according to sign of $\bar{c}_{ij}$ is $\bar{c}_{23} = -23.4$. Changing x_{23} to $5 - \theta$ requires that the variables x_{22}, y_{22}, y_{33} be modified as shown, Table 28-2-IV, cycle 1. The maximum value of θ is $\theta = \theta^* = \frac{20}{14}$ at which value $y_{33} = 0$. The new solution in which x_{23} replaces y_{33} as a basic variable is given in Table 28-2-IV, cycle 2. In Table 28-2-IV,

[581]

cycle 2, the decrease in non-boxed variable x_{41} causes changes in the variables x_{43}, x_{22}, x_{23}, y_{31}, y_{22}. The largest value of $\theta = \frac{9}{16}$, at which value y_{22} hits its *upper bound* $b_{22} = 100$.

In the passage from Table 28-2-IV, cycle 3, to Table 28-2-IV, cycle 4, we have become a little fancy and have taken a "double" step. The maximum increase is $\theta = \frac{80}{29}$ at which point y_{15} hits its upper bound $b_{15} = 580$. It is easy to see that if next the incremental variable y_{25} is increased, $\bar{c}_{32}$ associated with x_{32} should be changed to $\bar{c}_{32} - 29(\gamma_{15} - \gamma_{25})k_5 = +4.5 - 29(1.0 - .9) = +1.6$; therefore, it is economical to increase y_{25} as well as y_{15}. However, it can be shown that signs of $\bar{c}_{32}$ would become negative if the next increment, y_{35}, were considered. The maximum value of $\theta = \theta^* = \frac{100}{29}$.

It will be noted that in the passage from cycle 4 to cycle 5 of Table 28-2-IV, the variable y_{33} is again brought into solution after having been dropped earlier. The maximum value of θ is $\frac{22}{20}$ at which value y_{33} reaches its upper bound, so that the solution, Table 28-2-IV, cycle 5, has the same set of basic variables and hence the same implicit values as Table 28-2-IV, cycle 4. Moreover, the solution is *optimal* since all non-basic variables are either at their upper or lower bounds; those at upper bounds have corresponding $\bar{c}_{ij} \leq 0$ and those at lower bounds have $\bar{c}_{ij} \geq 0$.

In comparing this solution (Table 28-2-IV, cycle 5) with the optimal solution for the fixed-demand case (Table 28-2-II), it is interesting to note that the chief difference appears to be a general tendency to shift the total seats made available on a route to the *mode* of the distribution rather than to the *mean* of the distribution for those distributions with sharp peaks. The total seats made available to routes with flat distributions of demand appear to be at highest level attainable with the residual passenger-carrying potential.

TABLE 28-2-I

COMPARATIVE COSTS OF VARIOUS SOLUTIONS

(*Refer to Table 28-2-IV*)	Expected Revenues for Seats Supplied (1)	Expected Lost Revenues[1] (2)	Operating Costs (3)	Net Expected Cost (Thousands) (2) + (3)
Cycle 0	−6,534	766	900	1,666
Cycle 1	−6,574	726	901	1,627
Cycle 2	−6,607	693	901	1,594
Cycle 3	−6,638	662	899	1,561
Cycle 4	−6,641	659	883	1,542
Cycle 5	−6,659	641	883	1,524

[1] Data in column (2) are obtained by subtracting the expected revenues for seats supplied, column (1), from $R_0 = 7,300$, the expected revenues if an unlimited number of seats were supplied.

To compute the expected costs of the various solutions the first step (see § 28-1-(14)), is to determine what the expected revenues R_0 would be if sufficient seating capacity were furnished at all times to supply all passengers that show up. Referring to Table 28-1-II, it is easy to see that $R_0 = 13(250 + 13(120) + 13(120) + 7(180) + 7(90) + 1(600) = 7,300$ or $\$7,300,000$.

It is seen that the solution presented in Table 28-2-II (the same as the starting solution, Table 28-2-IV, cycle 0, which assumes demands to be exactly equal to the expected values of demand) has a net *expected cost* of $\$1,666,000$. (It is interesting to note that if the demands were not variable, but were fixed and equal to expected demands, the costs would only be $\$1,000,000$ (see Table 28-2-II). The 67 per cent increase in net cost for the variable demand case is due to 13,400 additional passengers (on the average) being turned away because of the distributions of demand assumed.[4]

TABLE 28-2-II

OPTIMAL ASSIGNMENT FOR FIXED DEMAND

Operating Costs and Lost Revenues = $\$1,000,000$

Type of Aircraft	Route						Aircraft Available	Implicit Prices u_i
	(1) N.Y. to L.A. 1-stop	(2) N.Y. to L.A. 2-stop	(3) N.Y. to Dallas 0-stop	(4) N.Y. to Dallas 1-stop	(5) N.Y. to Boston 0-stop	(6) Surplus Aircraft		
(1) A	10 · 16 · 18	15 · 21	28 · 18	23 · 16	81 · 10	0 · 0	10 = a_1	−171
(2) B	**	8 · 10 · 15	5 · 14 · 16	6 · 15 · 14	57 · 9	0 · 0	19 = a_2	−51
(3) C	**	7.8 · 5 · 10	**	7 · 9	17.2 · 29 · 6	0 · 0	25 = a_3	−23
(4) D	10 · 9 · 17	11 · 16	5 · 22 · 17	17 · 15	55 · 10	0 · 0	15 = a_4	−89
(5) E Deficit	1 · 13	1 · 13	1 · 7	1 · 7	100 · 1 · 1	0 · 0	***	0
Demand d_j	250	120	180	90	600	***		
Implicit Prices v_j	11.8	6.6	4.8	4.33	1	0		

** Box not used; aircraft cannot fly range.　*** Row or column has no equation.

[4] For concluding remarks, turn to page 591.

TABLE 28-2-III

WORK SHEET FOR DETERMINING OPTIMAL ASSIGNMENT UNDER UNCERTAIN DEMAND

Type of Aircraft	Route						Aircraft Available	Implicit Prices u_i
	(1) N.Y. to L.A. 1-stop	(2) N.Y. to L.A. 2-stop	(3) N.Y. to Dallas 0-stop	(4) N.Y. to Dallas 1-stop	(5) N.Y. to Boston 0-stop	(6) Surplus Aircraft		
(1) A	x_{11} $p_{11}=16$ $c_{11}=18$	x_{12} 15 21	x_{13} 28 18	x_{14} 23 16	x_{15} 81 10	x_{16} 0 0	10	u_1
(2) B	**	x_{22} 10 15	x_{23} 14 16	x_{24} 15 14	x_{25} 57 9	x_{26} 0 0	19	u_2
(3) C	**	x_{32} 5 10	**	x_{34} 7 9	x_{35} 29 6	x_{36} 0 0	25	u_3
(4) D	x_{41} 9 17	x_{42} 11 16	x_{43} 22 17	x_{44} 17 15	x_{45} 55 10	x_{46} 0 0	15	u_4
Increment (1)	$y_{11} \leq 200$ -1 -13	$y_{12} \leq 50$ -1 -13	$y_{13} \leq 140$ -1 -7	$y_{14} \leq 10$ -1 -7	$y_{15} \leq 580$ -1 -1	**	***	0
(2)	$y_{21} \leq 20$ -1 -10.4	$y_{22} \leq 100$ -1 -9.1	$y_{23} \leq 20$ -1 -6.3	$y_{24} \leq 40$ -1 -5.6	$y_{25} \leq 20$ -1 $-.9$	**	***	0
(3)	$y_{31} \leq 30$ -1 -9.8	**	$y_{33} \leq 20$ -1 -4.9	$y_{34} \leq 30$ -1 -4.2	$y_{35} \leq 20$ -1 $-.1$	**	***	0
(4)	$y_{41} \leq 20$ -1 -5.2	**	$y_{43} \leq 20$ -1 -2.1	$y_{44} \leq 20$ -1 -2.1	**	**	***	0
(5)	$y_{51} \leq 30$ -1 -2.6	**	$y_{53} \leq 20$ -1 $-.7$	$y_{54} \leq 240$ -1 $-.7$	**	**	***	0
Net Implicit Prices v_j	0 v_1	0 v_2	0 v_3	0 v_4	0 v_5	*** 0		

** Box not used because aircraft type cannot fly required range, or fewer increments are needed to describe the distribution of demand on the route.

*** Corresponding row or column has no equation.

TABLE 28-2-IV

Cycle 0

WORK SHEET FOR DETERMINING OPTIMAL ASSIGNMENT UNDER UNCERTAIN DEMAND

$\bar{c}_{24} = +58.4$, $\theta^* = \frac{1}{15}$, Expected Cost = \$1,666,000

Type of Aircraft	Route						Aircraft Available	
	(1) N.Y. to L.A. 1-stop	(2) N.Y. to L.A. 2-stop	(3) N.Y. to Dallas 0-stop	(4) N.Y. to Dallas 1-stop	(5) N.Y. to Boston 0-stop	(6) Surplus Aircraft		Implicit Prices u_i
(1) A	⬜10 16 / 18	15 / 21	28 / 18	23 / 16	81 / 10	0 / 0	10	−139
(2) B	**	⬜8 + θ 10 / 15	5 14 / 16	6 − θ* 15 / 14	57 / 9	0 / 0	19	−76
(3) C	**	7.8 5 / 10	**	7 / 9	⬜17.2 29 / 6	0 / 0	25	−23
(4) D	10 9 / 17	11 / 16	⬜5 22 / 17	17 / 15	55 / 10	0 / 0	15	−91
Increment (1)	200 −1 / −13	50 −1 / −13	140 −1 / −7	10 −1 / −7	⬜500 −1 / −1	**	***	0
(2)	20 −1 / −10.4	⬜70 + 10θ −1 / −9.1	20 −1 / −6.3	40 −1 / −5.6	−1 / −.9	**	***	0
(3)	⬜30 −1 / −9.8	**	⬜20 −1 / −4.9	30 −1 / −4.2	−1 / −.1	**	***	0
(4)	−1 / −5.2	**	−1 / −2.1	⬜10 − 15θ −1 / −2.1	**	**	***	0
(5)	−1 / −2.6	**	−1 / −.7	−1 / −.7	**	**	***	0
Net Implicit Prices v_j	0 9.8	0 9.1	0 4.9	0 2.1	0 1	*** 0		

TABLE 28-2-IV

Cycle 1

WORK SHEET FOR DETERMINING OPTIMAL ASSIGNMENT UNDER UNCERTAIN DEMAND

$\bar{c}_{23} = +23.4$, $\theta^* = \frac{20}{14}$, Expected Cost = \$1,627,000

Type of Aircraft	Route (1) N.Y. to L.A. 1-stop	(2) N.Y. to L.A. 2-stop	(3) N.Y. to Dallas 0-stop	(4) N.Y. to Dallas 1-stop	(5) N.Y. to Boston 0-stop	(6) Surplus Aircraft	Aircraft Available	Implicit Prices u_i
(1) A	$\boxed{10}$ 16 18	15 21	28 18	23 16	81 10	0 0	10	 −139
(2) B	**	$\boxed{8.7+\theta}$ 10 15	$5-\theta^*$ 14 16	$\boxed{5.3}$ 15 14	57 9	0 0	19	 −76
(3) C	**	5 10	**	7 9	$\boxed{17.2}$ 29 6	0 0	25	 −23
(4) D	10 9 17	11 16	$\boxed{5}$ 22 17	17 15	55 10	0 0	15	 −91
Increment (1)	200 −1 −13	50 −1 −13	140 −1 −7	10 −1 −7	$\boxed{500}$ −1 −1	**	***	 0
(2)	20 −1 −10.4	$\boxed{77+10\theta}$ −1 −9.1	20 −1 −6.3	40 −1 −5.6	−1 −.9	**	***	 0
(3)	$\boxed{30}$ −1 −9.8	**	$\boxed{20-14\theta}$ −1 −4.9	30 −1 −4.2	−1 −.1	**	***	 0
(4)	−1 −5.2	**	−1 −2.1	−1 −2.1	**	**	***	 0
(5)	−1 −2.6	**	−1 −.7	−1 −.7	**	**	***	 0
Net Implicit Prices v_j	0 9.8	0 9.1	0 4.9	0 6	0 1	*** 0		

TABLE 28-2-IV

Cycle 2

WORK SHEET FOR DETERMINING OPTIMAL ASSIGNMENT UNDER UNCERTAIN DEMAND

$\bar{c}_{41} = +56.8$, $\theta^* = \frac{9}{16}$, Expected Cost = \$1,594,000

Type of Aircraft	Route (1) N.Y. to L.A. 1-stop	(2) N.Y. to L.A. 2-stop	(3) N.Y. to Dallas 0-stop	(4) N.Y. to Dallas 1-stop	(5) N.Y. to Boston 0-stop	(6) Surplus Aircraft	Aircraft Available	Implicit Prices u_i
(1) A	$\boxed{10}$ 16 18	15 21	28 18	23 16	81 10	0 0	10	-139
(2) B	**	$\boxed{10.1+1.6\theta}$ 10 15	$\boxed{3.6+1.6\theta}$ 14 16	$\boxed{5.3}$ 15 14	57 9	0 0	19	-76
(3) C	**	7.8 5 10	**	7 9	$\boxed{17.2}$ 29 6	0 0	25	-23
(4) D	$10-\theta^*$ 9 17	11 16	$\boxed{5+\theta}$ 22 17	17 15	55 10	0 0	15	-128
Increment (1)	200 -1 -13	50 -1 -13	140 -1 -7	10 -1 -7	$\boxed{500}$ -1 -1	**	***	0
(2)	20 -1 -10.4	$\boxed{91+16\theta}$ -1 -9.1	20 -1 -6.3	40 -1 -5.6	-1 $-.9$	**	***	0
(3)	$\boxed{30-9\theta}$ -1 -9.8	**	-1 -4.9	30 -1 -4.2	-1 $-.1$	**	***	0
(4)	-1 -5.2	**	-1 -2.1	-1 -2.1	**	**	***	0
(5)	-1 -2.6	**	-1 $-.7$	-1 $-.7$	**	**	***	0
Net Implicit Prices v_j	0 9.8	0 9.1	0 6.6	0 6	0 1	*** 0		

TABLE 28-2-IV

Cycle 3

WORK SHEET FOR DETERMINING OPTIMAL ASSIGNMENT UNDER UNCERTAIN DEMAND

$\bar{c}_{32} = +5.5$, $\theta^* = \frac{100}{29}$, Expected Cost = \$1,561,000

Type of Aircraft	Route (1) N.Y. to L.A. 1-stop	(2) N.Y. to L.A. 2-stop	(3) N.Y. to Dallas 0-stop	(4) N.Y. to Dallas 1-stop	(5) N.Y. to Boston 0-stop	(6) Surplus Aircraft	Aircraft Available	Implicit Prices u_i
(1) A	$\boxed{10}$ 16 18	15 21	28 18	23 16	81 10	0 0	10	−139
(2) B	**	$\boxed{11 + .5\theta}$ 10 15	$\boxed{2.7 - .5\theta}$ 14 16	$\boxed{5.3}$ 15 14	57 9	0 0	19	−40
(3) C	**	$7.8 - \theta^*$ 5 10	**	7 9	$\boxed{17.2 + \theta}$ 29 6	0 0	25	−23
(4) D	$\boxed{9.4 - .3\theta}$ 9 17	11 16	$\boxed{5.6 + .3\theta}$ 22 17	17 15	55 10	0 0	15	−71
Increment (1)	200 −1 −13	50 −1 −13	140 −1 −7	10 −1 −1	$\boxed{500 + 29\theta}$ −1 −1	**	***	0
(2)	20 −1 −10.4	100 −1 −9.1	20 −1 −6.3	40 −1 −5.6	−1 −.9	**	***	0
(3)	$\boxed{25 - 2.7\theta}$ −1 −9.8	**	−1 −4.9	30 −1 −4.2	−1 −.1	**	***	0
(4)	−1 −5.2	**	−1 −2.1	−1 −2.1	**	**	***	0
(5)	−1 −2.6	**	−1 −.7	−1 −.7	**	**	***	0
Net Implicit Prices v_j	0 9.8	0 5.5	0 4	0 3.6	0 1	0 0		

TABLE 28-2-IV

Cycle 4

WORK SHEET FOR DETERMINING OPTIMAL ASSIGNMENT UNDER UNCERTAIN DEMAND

$\bar{c}'_{33} = -.9$, $\theta^* = \frac{20}{22}$, Expected Cost = \$1,542,000

Type of Aircraft	Route						Aircraft Available	Implicit Prices u_i
	(1) N.Y. to L.A. 1-stop	(2) N.Y. to L.A. 2-stop	(3) N.Y. to Dallas 0-stop	(4) N.Y. to Dallas 1-stop	(5) N.Y. to Boston 0-stop	(6) Surplus Aircraft		
(1) A	[10] 16 18	15 21	28 18	23 16	81 10	0 0	10	−139
(2) B	**	[12.8] 10 15	[.9] 14 16	[5.3] 15 14	57 9	0 0	19	−40
(3) C	**	[4.3] 5 10	**	7 9	[20.7] 29 6	0 0	25	−18
(4) D	[8.3 − θ] 9 17	11 16	[6.7 + θ] 22 17	17 15	55 10	0 0	15	−71
Increment (1)	200 −1 −13	50 −1 −13	140 −1 −7	10 −1 −7	580 −1 −1	**	***	0
(2)	20 −1 −10.4	100 −1 −9.1	20 −1 −6.3	40 −1 −5.6	20 −1 −.9	**	***	0
(3)	[15 − 9θ] −1 −9.8	**	+22θ* −1 −4.9	30 −1 −4.2	−1 −.1	**	***	0
(4)	−1 −5.2	**	−1 −2.1	−1 −2.1	**	**	***	0
(5)	−1 −2.6	**	−1 −.7	−1 −.7	**	**	***	0
Net Implicit Prices v_j	0 9.8	0 5.5	0 4	0 3.6	0 .8	*** 0		

TABLE 28-2-IV
Cycle 5 (Optimal)
WORK SHEET FOR DETERMINING OPTIMAL ASSIGNMENT UNDER UNCERTAIN DEMAND
Minimum Expected Cost $1,524,000

Type of Aircraft	Route (1) N.Y. to L.A. 1-stop	(2) N.Y. to L.A. 2-stop	(3) N.Y. to Dallas 0-stop	(4) N.Y. to Dallas 1-stop	(5) N.Y. to Boston 0-stop	(6) Surplus Aircraft	Aircraft Available	Implicit Prices u_i
(1) A	[10] 16 18	15 21	28 18	23 16	81 10	0 0	10	−139
(2) B	**	[12.8] 10 15	[.9] 14 16	[5.3] 15 14	57 9	0 0	19	−40
(3) C	**	[4.3] 5 10	**	7 9	[20.7] 29 6	0 0	25	−18
(4) D	[7.4] 9 17	11 16	[7.6] 22 17	17 15	55 10	0 0	15	−71
Increment (1)	200 −1 −13	50 −1 −13	140 −1 −7	10 −1 −7	580 −1 −1	**	***	0
(2)	20 −1 −10.4	100 −1 −9.1	20 −1 −6.3	40 −1 −5.6	20 −1 −.9	**	***	0
(3)	[7] −1 −9.8	**	20 −1 −4.9	30 −1 −4.2	−1 −.1	**	***	0
(4)	−1 −5.2	**	−1 −2.1	−1 −2.1	**	**	***	0
(5)	−1 −2.6	**	−1 −.7	−1 −.7	**	**	***	0
Net Implicit Prices v_j	0 9.8	0 5.5	0 4	0 3.6	0 .8	0		

The successive improvements in the solution, Table 28-2-IV, cycles 0–5, reduced the net expected costs from $1,666,000 to $1,524,000 for the optimal solution.

Thus, the best solution obtained by pretending that demands are fixed at their expected values has a 9 per cent higher expected cost than that for the best solution obtained by using the assumed distributions of demand. It is also seen that very little additional computational effort was required to take account of this uncertainty of demand.

REFERENCES

Dantzig, 1955-1

Ferguson and Dantzig, 1954-1, 1956-1

Gunther, 1955-1

Manne, 1956-2

BIBLIOGRAPHY

Abadie, J. M., 1963-1. "On Decomposition Principle," Operations Research Center, University of California, Berkeley, California, ORC–63–20, 1963.

Abadie, J., and A. C. Williams, 1963-1. "Dual and Parametric Methods in Decomposition," in R. Graves and P. Wolfe (eds.), *Recent Advances in Mathematical Programming*, McGraw Hill Book Company, Inc., New York, 1963.

Ablow, C. M., and Georges Brigham, 1955-1. "An Analog Solution of Programming Problems," *Operations Research*, Vol. 3, No. 4, November, 1955, pp. 388–394.

Agmon, Shmuel, 1954-1. "The Relaxation Method for Linear Inequalities," *Canad. J. Math.*, Vol. 6, No. 3, June, 1954, pp. 382–392.

Allen, R. G. D., 1959-1. *Mathematical Economics*, 2nd ed., Macmillan & Company, Ltd., London, 1959.

Antosiewicz, H. A. (ed.), 1955-1. *Proceedings of the Second Symposium in Linear Programming*, Vols. 1 and 2, National Bureau of Standards and Directorate of Management Analysis, DCS/Comptroller, USAF, Washington, D.C., 1955.

Arrow, K. J., 1951-1. "Alternative Proof of the Substitution Theorem for Leontief Models in the General Case," in T. C. Koopmans (ed.), *Activity Analysis of Production and Allocation*, John Wiley & Sons, Inc., New York, 1951, pp. 155–164.

Arrow, K. J., T. E. Harris, and J. Marschak, 1951-1. "Optimal Inventory Policy," *Econometrica*, Vol. 19, No. 3, July, 1951, pp. 250–272.

Arrow, K. J., L. Hurwicz, and H. Uzawa, 1958-1. *Studies in Linear and Non-Linear Programming*, Stanford University Press, Stanford, California, 1958. 229 pp.

———, 1961-1. "Constraint Qualifications in Maximization Problems," *Naval Res. Logist. Quart.*, Vol. 8, 1961, pp. 175–191.

Arrow, K. J., S. Karlin, and H. Scarf, 1958-1. *Studies in the Mathematical Theory of Inventory and Production*, Stanford University Press, Stanford, California, 1958. 340 pp.

Arrow, K. J., S. Karlin, and P. Suppes (eds.), 1960-1. "Mathematical Methods in the Social Sciences," *Proceedings of the First Stanford Symposium*, Stanford University Press, Stanford, California, 1960. 365 pp.

Balas, E., 1963-1. "Solution of Large-Scale Transportation Problems through Aggregation," Institute of Mathematics, Rumanian Academy of Sciences, Bucharest, Working Paper, November, 1963.

———, 1964-1. "Extension de l'algorithme additif à la programmation en nombres entiens et à la programmation nonlinéaire, *Compt. Rend. Acad. Sci.*, Vol. 258, May 25, 1964, pp. 5136–5139.

Barankin, E. W., and R. Dorfman, 1958-1. *On Quadratic Programming*, University of California Publications in Statistics, Vol. 2, No. 13, University of California Press, Berkeley, California, 1958, pp. 285–318.

Batchelor, James H., 1963-1. *Operations Research, An Annotated Bibliography*, St. Louis Press, St. Louis, Missouri, 1963.

Baumol, William J., 1961-1. *Economic Theory and Operations Analysis*, Prentice-Hall, Inc., Englewood Cliffs, New Jersey, 1961. 438 pp.

Beale, E. M. L., 1954-1. "Linear Programming by the Method of Leading Variables," *Report of the Conference on Linear Programming*, May, 1954, arranged by Ferranti, Ltd., London.

———, 1955-1. "Cycling in the Dual Simplex Algorithm," *Naval Res. Logist. Quart.*, Vol. 2, No. 4, December, 1955, pp. 269–276.

———, 1955-2. "On Minimizing a Convex Function Subject to Linear Inequalities," *J. Roy. Statist. Soc.*, Ser. B, Vol. 17, No. 2, 1955, pp. 173–184.

———, 1958-1. "A Method of Solving Linear Programming Problems When Some but Not All of the Variables Must Take Integral Values," *Statistical Techniques Research Group*, Princeton University, Princeton, New Jersey, approximate date March, 1958.

———, 1959-1. "An algorithm for Solving the Transportation Problem When the Shipping Cost over Each Route Is Convex," *Naval Res. Logist. Quart.*, Vol. 6, No. 1, March, 1959, pp. 43–56.

———, 1959-2. "On Quadratic Programming," *Naval Res. Logist. Quart.*, Vol. 6, No. 3, September, 1959, pp. 227–243.

Beckenbach, E. F., 1948-1. "Convex Functions," *Bull. Amer. Math. Soc.*, Vol. 54, 1948, pp. 439–460.

Beckmann, M. J., 1955-1. "Comparative Studies in Linear Programming and the Giffen Paradox," *Rev. Econ. Studies*, Vol. 23, No. 3, 1955–1956, pp. 232–235.

Beckmann, M. J., C. B. McGuire, and C. Winsten, 1956-1. *Studies in the Economics of Transportation*, The RAND Corporation, Research Memorandum RM-1488, May 12, 1955. 347 pp. Published by the Yale University Press, New Haven, Connecticut, 1956. 232 pp.

Bellman, Richard, 1954-1. *Dynamic Programming of Continuous Processes*, The RAND Corporation, Report R-271, July, 1954.

———, 1957-1. *Dynamic Programming*, Princeton University Press, Princeton, New Jersey, 1957. 342 pp.

———, 1958-1. "On a Routing Problem," *Quart. Appl. Math.*, Vol. 16, No. 1, April, 1958, pp. 87–90.

Bellman, Richard, I. Glicksberg, and O. A. Gross, 1958-1. *Some Aspects of the Mathematical Theory of Control Processes*, The RAND Corporation, Report R-313, January, 1958.

Bellman, R., and W. Karush, 1962-1. "Mathematical Programming and the Maximum Transform," *J. Soc. Indust. Appl. Math.*, Vol. 10, 1962, pp. 550–566.

Bereanu, B., 1963-1. "On Stochastic Linear Programming," *Rev. Math. Pures Appl.*, *Acad. Rep. Populaire Roumaine*, Vol. 8, No. 4, 1963, pp. 683–697.

Berge, Claude, 1962-1. *The Theory of Graphs and Its Applications*, translated by A. Doig, John Wiley & Sons, Inc., New York, 1962, ix + 247 pp.

Bernholtz, B., 1964-1. "A New Derivation of the Kuhn-Tucker Conditions," *Operations Research*, Vol. 12, 1964, pp. 295–299.

Birkhoff, Garrett, 1946-1. "Three Observations on Linear Algebra," *Rev. Univ. Nac. Tucumán, Ser. A.*, Vol. 5, 1946, pp. 147–151.

Blankenship, W. A., 1963-1. "A New Version of the Euclidean Algorithm," *Amer. Math. Monthly*, Vol. 70, 1963.

Blackwell, David, and M. A. Girshick, 1954-1. *Theory of Games and Statistical Decisions*, John Wiley & Sons, Inc., New York, 1954. 355 pp.

Boelter, L. M. K., 1955-1. "Some Reflections on Automation," *Symposium on Electronics and Automatic Production*, San Francisco, California, August, 1955.

Bohnenblust, H. F., S. Karlin, and L. S. Shapeley, 1950-1. "Solutions of Discrete, Two-person Games," in H. W. Kuhn and A. W. Tucker (eds.), *Contributions to the Theory of Games*, Vol. 1, Annals of Mathematics Study No. 24, Princeton University Press, Princeton, New Jersey, 1950, pp. 51–72.

Boldyreff, A. W., 1955-1. "Determination of the Maximal Steady State Flow of Traffic through a Railroad Network," The RAND Corporation, Research Memorandum RM-1532, August 5, 1955, 36 pp. Published in *JORSA*, Vol. 3, No. 4, November, 1955, pp. 443–465.

Borel, Emile, 1921-1. "La théorie du jeu et les équations intégrales à noyau symétrique," *Compt. Rend. Acad. Sci.*, Vol. 173, December 19, 1921, pp. 1304–1308. Translated by Leonard J. Savage in *Econometrica*, Vol. 21, No. 21, No. 1, January, 1953, pp. 97–100.

———, 1924-1. "Sur les jeux où interviennent le hasard et l'habileté des joueurs," *Théorie des probabilités*, Librairie scientifique, Hermann, Paris, 1924, pp. 204–224. Translated by Leonard J. Savage in *Econometrica*, Vol. 21, No. 1, January, 1953, pp. 101–115.

[593]

————, 1927-1. "Sur les systèmes de formes linéaires à déterminant symétrique gauche et la théorie générale du jeu," from "Algèbre et calcul des probabilités," *Compt. Rend. Acad. Sci.*, Vol. 184, 1927, pp. 52–53. Translated by Leonard J. Savage in *Econometrica*, Vol. 21, No. 1, January, 1953, pp. 116–117.

————, 1953-1. Translation of three papers by Borel on the theory of games, with commentary, in "Emile Borel, Initiator of the Theory of Psychological Games and Its Application," by Maurice Fréchet, *Econometrica*, Vol. 21, No. 1, January, 1953, pp. 95–127.

Boulding, K. E., and W. A. Spivey, 1960-1. *Linear Programming and the Theory of the Firm*, The Macmillan Company, New York, 1960. 227 pp.

Bowman, E. H., 1960-1. "Assembly-Line Balancing by Linear Programming," *Operations Research*, Vol. 8, 1960, pp. 385–389.

Bowman, E. H., and R. B. Fetter (eds.), 1959-1. *Analyses of Industrial Operations*, Richard D. Irwin, Inc., Homewood, Illinois, 1959. 485 pp.

Briggs, F. E. A., 1962-1. "A Dual Labelling Method for the Hitchcock Problem," *Operations Research*, Vol. 10, No. 4, July–August, 1962, pp. 507–517.

Brown, G. W., 1951-1. "Iterative Solution of Games by Fictitious Play," in T. C. Koopmans (ed.), *Activity Analysis of Production and Allocation*, John Wiley & Sons, Inc., New York, 1951, pp. 374–376.

Brown, G. W., and T. C. Koopmans, 1951-1. "Computational Suggestions for Maximizing a Linear Function Subject to Linear Inequalities," in T. C. Koopmans (ed.), *Activity Analysis of Production and Allocation*, John Wiley & Sons, Inc., New York, 1951, pp. 377–380.

Cahn, A. S., 1948-1. "The Warehouse Problem," *Bull. Amer. Math. Soc.*, Vol. 54, 1948, p. 1073 (abstract).

Candler, W., 1960-1. "A Short-Cut Method for the Complete Solution of Game Theory and Feed-Mix Problems," *Econometrica*, Vol. 28, No. 3, 1960, pp. 618–639.

Charnes, A., 1952-1. "Optimality and Degeneracy in Linear Programming," *Econometrica*, Vol. 20, No. 2, April, 1952, pp. 160–170. Published in *Operational Res. Quart.*, Vol. 3, No. 3, September, 1952, p. 54 (abstract).

Charnes, A., and W. W. Cooper, 1955-1. "Generalizations of the Warehousing Model," *Operational Res. Quart.*, Vol. 6, 1955, pp. 131–172.

————, 1959-1. "Chance-Constrained Programming," *Management Sci.*, Vol. 6, No. 1, October, 1959, pp. 73–79.

————, 1961-1. *Management Models and Industrial Applications of Linear Programming*, John Wiley & Sons, Inc., New York, 1961.

————, 1963-1. "Deterministic Equivalents for Optimizing and Satisficing under Chance Constraints," *Operations Research*, Vol. 11, No. 1, 1963, pp. 18–39.

Charnes, A., W. W. Cooper, and A. Henderson, 1953-1. *An Introduction to Linear Programming*, John Wiley & Sons, Inc., New York, 1953. 74 pp.

Charnes, A., W. W. Cooper, and K. Kortanek, 1962-1. "A Duality Theory for Convex Programs with Convex Constraints," *Proc. Amer. Math. Soc.*, Vol. 68, 1962, pp. 605–608.

Charnes, A., W. W. Cooper, and B. Mellon, 1952-1. "Blending Aviation Gasolines—A Study in Programming Interdependent Activities in an Integrated Oil Company," *Econometrica*, Vol. 20, No. 2, April, 1952.

Charnes, A., W. W. Cooper, and G. L. Thompson, 1962-1. "Some Properties of Redundant Constraints and Extraneous Variables in Direct and Dual Linear Programming Problems," *Operations Research*, Vol. 10, 1962, pp. 711–723.

————, 1964-1. "Critical Path Analysis Via Chance Constrained and Stochastic Programming," *Operations Research*, Vol. 12, No. 3, May, 1964, pp. 460–470.

Charnes, A., and H. J. Greenberg, 1951-1. "Plastic Collapse and Linear Programming—Preliminary Report," *Bull. Amer. Math. Soc.*, Vol. 57, No. 6, November, 1951, p. 480 (abstract).

Charnes, A., and C. E. Lemke, 1954-1. "Minimization of Non-Linear Separable Convex Functionals," *Naval Res. Logist. Quart.*, Vol. 1, No. 4, December, 1954.

Chung, An-Min, 1963-1. *Linear Programming*, C. E. Merrill, Columbus, Ohio, 1963.

Churchman, C. W., R. L. Ackoff, E. L. Arnoff, et al, 1957-1. *Introduction to Operations Research*, John Wiley & Sons, Inc., New York, 1957. 645 pp.

Ckenery, H. B. and P. G. Clark, 1959-1. *Interindustry Economics*, John Wiley & Sons, Inc., New York, 1959.

Clasen, R. J., 1963-1. "The Linear Logarithmic Programming Problem," The RAND Corporation, Research Memorandum RM–3707–PR, June, 1963.

Cline, R. E., 1963-1. "Representations for the Generalized Inverse of Matrices Partitioned as $A = [U, V]$," in R. Graves and P. Wolfe (eds.), *Recent Advances in Mathematical Programming*, McGraw-Hill Book Company, Inc., New York, 1963 (abstract).

Cornfield, J., W. D. Evans, and M. Hoffenberg, 1947-1. "Full Employment Pattern, 1950," Parts I and II, *Monthly Labor Review*, Vol. 64, February and March, 1947, pp. 163–190, 420–432.

Cottle, R. W., 1963-1. "Symmetric Dual Quadratic Programs," *Quart. Appl. Math.*, Vol. 21, 1963, pp. 237–243.

———, 1963-2. "A Theory of Fritz John in Mathematical Programming," The RAND Corporation, Research Memorandum RM–3858–PR, 1963.

———, 1963-3. "Formal Self-Duality in Nonlinear Programming," Notes on Operations Research I, Operations Research Center, University of California, Berkeley, California, ORC 63–19, 1963.

———, 1964-1. "Non Linear Programs with Positively Bounded Jacobians," Unpublished Ph.D. Thesis, University of California, Berkeley, California, 1964.

———, 1964-2. "A Fundamental Theorem in Quadratic Programming," *J. Soc. Indust. Appl. Math.*, Vol. 12, September, 1964, pp. 663–665.

Courant, R., and D. Hilbert, 1953-1. *Methods of Mathematical Physics*, I, 1st English ed., translated and revised from the German original, Interscience Publishers, Inc., New York, 1953, pp. 164–167.

Cramér, H., 1955-1. *The Elements of Probability Theory and Some of Its Applications*, John Wiley & Sons, Inc., New York, 1955. 281 pp.

Curtes, H. A., 1963-1. "Use of Decomposition Theory in the Solution of the State Assignment Problem of Sequential Machines, *J. Assoc. Computing Mach.*, July, 1963, p. 386.

Dakin, R. J., 1964-1. "A Mixed-Integer Programming Algorithm," Basser Computing Department, School of Physics, The University of Sidney, Technical Report No. 31. September, 1964.

Dantzig, George B., 1948-1. "Programming in a Linear Structure," Comptroller, USAF, Washington, D.C., February, 1948.

———, 1949-1. "Programming of Interdependent Activities, II, Mathematical Model," in T. C. Koopmans (ed.), *Activity Analysis of Production and Allocation*, John Wiley & Sons, Inc., New York, 1951, pp. 19–32; also published in *Econometrica*, Vol. 17, Nos. 3 and 4, July–October, 1949, pp. 200–211.

———, 1951-1. "A Proof of the Equivalence of the Programming Problem and the Game Problem," in T. C. Koopmans (ed.), *Activity Analysis of Production and Allocation*, John Wiley & Sons, Inc., New York, 1951, pp. 330–335.

———, 1951-2. "Application of the Simplex Method to a Transportation Problem," in T. C. Koopmans (ed.), *Activity Analysis of Production and Allocation*, John Wiley & Sons, Inc., New York, 1951, pp. 359–373.

———, 1951-3. "Maximization of a Linear Function of Variables Subject to Linear Inequalities," in T. C. Koopmans (ed.), *Activity Analysis of Production and Allocation*, John Wiley & Sons, Inc., New York, 1951, pp. 339–347.

———, 1954-1. *Notes on Linear Programming: Part XI, Composite Simplex-Dual Simplex Algorithm—I*, The RAND Corporation, Research Memorandum RM-1274, April 26, 1954, 15 pp. Also The RAND Corporation, Paper P-516.

———, 1954-2. *Notes on Linear Programming: Part VII—The Dual Simplex Algorithm*, The RAND Corporation, Research Memorandum RM-1270, July 3, 1954. 10 pp.

———, 1954-3. *Notes on Linear Programming: Parts VIII, IX, X—Upper Bounds, Secondary Constraints, and Block Triangularity in Linear Programming*, The

RAND Corporation, Research Memorandum RM-1367, October 4, 1954. Published in *Econometrica*, Vol. 23, No. 2, April, 1955, pp. 174–183.

———, 1955-1. "Linear Programming under Uncertainty," *Management Sci.*, Vol. 1, 1955, pp. 197–206.

———, 1955-2. *Notes on Linear Programming: Part XIII—Optimal Solution of a Dynamic Leontief Model with Substitution*, The RAND Corporation, Research Memorandum RM-1281-1, April 6, 1955, 13 pp. Published in *Econometrica*, Vol. 23, No. 3, July, 1955, pp. 295–302.

———, 1956-1. "Constructive Proof of the Min-Max Theorem," *Pacific J. Math.*, Vol. 6, No. 1, 1956, pp. 25–33.

———, 1956-2. "Recent Advances in Linear Programming," *Management Sci.*, Vol. 2, No. 2, January, 1956, pp. 131–144.

———, 1957-1. "Thoughts on Linear Programming and Automation," The RAND Corporation, Paper P-824, March 2, 1956, 16 pp. Published in *Management Sci.*, Vol. 3, No. 2, January, 1957, pp. 131–139.

———, 1957-2. "Discrete Variable Extremum Problems," *Operations Research*, Vol. 5, No. 2, April, 1957, pp. 266–277.

———, 1957-3. "On the Status of Multistage Linear Programs," The RAND Corporation, Paper P-1028, February 20, 1957. Published in *Proc. Intern. Statist. Inst.*, Stockholm, Sweden, 1957; also in *Management Sci.*, October, 1959.

———, 1958-1. "On Integer and Partial Integer Linear Programming Problems," The RAND Corporation, Paper P-1410, June 20, 1958.

———, 1959-1. "Inductive Proof of the Simplex Method," The RAND Corporation, Paper P-1851, December 28, 1959. Published in *IBM J. Res. Develop.*, Vol. 4, No. 5, November, 1960, pp. 505–506.

———, 1960-1. "On the Shortest Route through a Network," *Management Sci.*, Vol. 6, No. 2, January, 1960, pp. 187–190.

———, 1960-2. "On the Significance of Solving Linear Programming Problems with Some Integer Variables," *Econometrica*, Vol. 28, No. 1, January, 1960, pp. 30–44.

———, 1960-3. "General Convex Objective Forms," in K. J. Arrow, S. Karlin, and P. Suppes (eds.), *Mathematical Methods in the Social Sciences*, Stanford University Press, Stanford, California, 1960, pp. 151–158.

———, 1960-4. "A Machine-Job Scheduling Model," *Management Sci.*, Vol. 6, 1960, pp. 191–196.

———, 1963-1. "Compact Basis Triangularization for the Simplex Method," in R. Graves and P. Wolfe (eds.), *Recent Advances in Mathematical Programming*, McGraw-Hill Book Company, Inc., New York, 1963.

———, 1964-1. "Linear Control Processes and Mathematical Programming," Operations Research Center, University of California, Berkeley, California, ORC 64-31, December, 1964.

Dantzig, G. B., and R. W. Cottle, 1963-1. "Positive (Semi-) Definite Matrices and Mathematical Programming," Operations Research Center, University of California, Berkeley, California, ORC 63-18, 1963.

Dantzig, G. B., E. Eisenberg, and R. W. Cottle, 1962-1. "Symmetric Dual Nonlinear Programs," Forthcoming *Pacific J. Math.*

Dantzig, George B., Lester R. Ford, Jr., and Delbert R. Fulkerson, 1956-1. "A Primal-Dual Algorithm for Linear Programs," in H. W. Kuhn and A. W. Tucker (eds.), *Linear Inequalities and Related Systems*, Annals of Mathematics Study No. 38, Princeton University Press, Princeton, New Jersey, 1956, pp. 171–181.

Dantzig, George B., and Delbert R. Fulkerson, 1954-1. "Minimizing the Number of Tankers to Meet a Fixed Schedule," *Naval Res. Logist. Quart.*, Vol. 1, No. 3, September, 1954, pp. 217–222.

———, 1956-1, "On the Max-Flow Min-Cut Theorem of Networks," in H. W. Kuhn and A. W. Tucker (eds.), *Linear Inequalities and Related Systems*, Annals of Mathematics Study No. 38, Princeton University Press, Princeton, New Jersey, 1956, pp. 215–221.

Dantzig, George B., Delbert R. Fulkerson, and Selmer M. Johnson, 1954-1. "Solution of a Large-Scale Traveling-Salesman Problem," *JORSA*, Vol. 2, No. 4, November, 1954. pp. 393–410.

———, 1959-1. "On a Linear Programming Combinatorial Approach to the Traveling-Salesman Problem," *Operations Research*, Vol. 7, No. 1, January-February, 1959, pp. 58–66.

Dantzig, G. B., Roy Harvey, and R. McKnight, 1964-1. "Updating the Product Form of the Inverse for the Reversed Simplex Method," Operations Research Center, University of California, Berkeley, California, ORC 64-33, December, 1964.

Dantzig, G. B., and D. L. Johnson, 1964-1. "Maximum Payloads Per Unit Time Delivered Through an Air Network," *Operations Research*, Vol. 12, No. 2, March-April, 1964.

Dantzig, George B., and Albert Madansky, 1960-1. "On the Solution of Two-Stage Linear Programs under Uncertainty," The RAND Corporation, Paper P-2039, July, 1960; also in J. Neyman (ed.), *Proceedings, Fourth Berkeley Symposium on Mathematical Statistics and Probability*, Vol. I, 1961, pp. 165–176.

Dantzig, George B., and William Orchard-Hays, 1953-1. *Notes on Linear Programming: Part V—Alternate Algorithm for the Revised Simplex Method Using Product Form for the Inverse*, The RAND Corporation, Research Memorandum RM-1268, November 19, 1953.

Dantzig, George B., and Alex Orden, 1953-1. *Notes on Linear Programming: Part II— Duality Theorems*, The RAND Corporation, Research Memorandum RM-1265, October 30, 1953.

Dantzig, George B., Alex Orden, and Philip Wolfe, 1954-1. *Notes on Linear Programming: Part I—The Generalized Simplex Method for Minimizing a Linear Form under Linear Inequality Restraints*, The RAND Corporation, Research Memorandum RM-1264, April 5, 1954, 17 pp. Published in *Pacific J. Math.*, Vol. 5, No. 2, June, 1955, pp. 183–195.

Dantzig, G. B., and J. H. Ramser, 1959-1. "The Truck Dispatching Problem," *Management Sci.*, Vol. 6, No. 1, 1959, pp. 80–91.

Dantzig, G. B., and R. M. Van Slyke, 1964-1. "Generalized Upper Bounded Techniques for Linear Programming I, II," Operations Research Center, University of California, Berkeley, California, ORC 64-17, August, 1964, and ORC 64-18, February, 1965.

Dantzig, George B., and A. Wald, 1951-1. "On the Fundamental Lemma of Neyman and Pearson," *Ann. Math. Statist.*, Vol. 22, 1951, pp. 87–93.

Dantzig, George B., and P. Wolfe, 1961-1. "The Decomposition Algorithm for Linear Programming," *Econometrica*, Vol. 29, No. 4, October, 1961.

Debreu, G., 1963-1. "Non-Negative Solutions of Linear Inequalities," Center for Research in Management Science, University of California, Berkeley, California, Technical Report No. 10, June, 1963.

Dennis, J. B., 1959-1. *Mathematical Programming and Electrical Networks*, John Wiley & Sons, Inc., New York, 1959. 185 pp.

Dilworth, R. P., 1950-1. "A Decomposition Theorem for Partially Ordered Sets," *Ann. Math.*, Vol. 51, No. 1, January, 1950, pp. 161–166.

Dines, L. L., and N. H. McCoy, 1933-1. "On Linear Inequalities," *Trans. Roy. Soc. Can., Sect. III*, 1933, pp. 37–70.

Doig, A. G., and M. H. Belz, 1956-1. "Report on Trim Problems for May, 1956," Department of Statistics, University of Melbourne. The report is addressed to Australia Paper Manufacturers, Melbourne, Australia, July 31, 1956.

Doig, A. G., and A. H. Land, 1960-1. "An Automatic Method of Solving Discrete Programming Problems," *Econometrica*, Vol. 28, 1960, pp. 497–520.

Dorfman, R., 1951-1. *Application of Linear Programming to the Theory of the Firm*, University of California Press, Berkeley, California, 1951. 98 pp.

———, 1951-2. "Application of the Simplex Method to a Game Theory Problem," in T. C. Koopmans (ed.), *Activity Analysis of Production and Allocation*, John Wiley & Sons, Inc., New York, 1951, pp. 348–358.

Dorfman, R., P. A. Samuelson, and R. M. Solow, 1958-1. *Linear Programming and Economic Analysis*, McGraw-Hill Book Company, Inc., New York, 1958. 527 pp.

Dorn, W. S., 1963-1. "Nonlinear Programming—A Survey," *Management Sci.*, Vol. 9, 1963, pp. 171–208.

Dorn, W. S., and H. J. Greenberg, 1955-1. *Linear Programming and Plastic Limit Analysis of Structures*, Technical Report No. 7, Carnegie Institute of Technology, Pittsburgh, Pennsylvania, August, 1955. 30 pp.

Dresher, Melvin, 1961-1. *Games of Strategy: Theory and Applications*, Prentice-Hall, Inc., Englewood Cliffs, New Jersey, 1961. 186 pp.

Dresher, Melvin, L. S. Shapley, and A. W. Tucker (eds.), 1964-1. *Advances in Games Theory*, Princeton University Press, Princeton, New Jersey, 1964. 692 pp.

Dresher, Melvin, A. W. Tucker, and Philip Wolfe (eds.), 1957-1. *Contributions to the Theory of Games*, Vol. III, Annals of Mathematics Study No. 39, Princeton University Press, Princeton, New Jersey, 1957. 448 pp.

Duffin, R. J., 1956-1. "Infinite Programs," in H. W. Kuhn and A. W. Tucker (eds.), *Linear Inequalities and Related Systems*, Annals of Mathematics Study No. 38, Princeton University Press, Princeton, New Jersey, 1956, pp. 157–170.

———, 1961-1. "The Extremal Length of a Network," Office of Technical Services, Document No. AD-253 665, 1961.

———, 1962-1. "Dual Programs and Minimum Costs," *J. Soc. Indust. Appl. Math.*, Vol. 10, 1962, pp. 119–123.

Dvoretzky, A., J. Kiefer, and J. Wolfowitz, 1952-1. "The Inventory Problem: I, Case of Known Distributions of Demand; II, Case of Unknown Distributions of Demand," *Econometrica*, Vol. 20, Nos. 2 and 3, 1952, pp. 187–222 and 450–466.

Dwyer, Paul S., 1955-1. "The Solution of the Hitchcock Transportation Problem with the Method of Reduced Matrices," Engineering Research Institute Report, University of Michigan, Ann Arbor, Michigan, December, 1955.

Dzielinski, B. P., and R. E. Gamory, 1963-1. "Lot Size Programming and the Decomposition Principle," *Econometrica*, Vol. 31, 1963, p. 595 (abstract).

Easterfield, Thomas E., 1946-1. "A Combinatorial Algorithm." *J. London Math. Soc.*, Vol. 21, No. 83, Part 3, July, 1946, pp. 219–226.

Edmonds, J., 1962-1. "Covers and Packings in a Family of Sets," *Bull. Amer. Math. Soc.*, Vol. 68, 1962.

Edmondson, J. H., 1951-1. "Proof of the Existence Theorem of an Epsilon Transformation," class exercise dated March 28, 1951, for Department of Agriculture Graduate School course in linear programming given by George B. Dantzig. Copies may be obtained from George B. Dantzig.

Efroymson, M. A., 1962-1. "Some New Algorithms for Linear Programming," presented at Symposium on Mathematical Programming, University of Chicago, Chicago, Illinois, June 18–22, 1962.

Egerváry, E., 1931-1. "Matrixok Kombinatorius Tulajfonságairól," *Matematikai és Fizikai Lapok* No. 38, 1931, pp. 16–28. "On Combinatorial Properties of Matrices," translated by H. W. Kuhn, Paper No. 4, George Washington University Logistics Research Project. Published in *Logistics Papers*, Issue No. 11, Appendix I to Quarterly Progress Report No. 21, November 16, 1954–February 15, 1955, 11 pp.

Eggleston, H. G., 1958-1. "Convexity," Cambridge Tracts in Mathematics and Mathematical Physics, No. 47, Cambridge University Press, Cambridge, 1958.

Eisemann, Kurt, 1957-1. "The Trim Problem," *Management Sci.*, Vol. 3, April, 1957, pp. 279–284.

———, 1964-1. "The Primal-Dual Method for Bounded Variables," *Operations Research*, Vol. 12, No. 1, January–February 1964, pp. 110–121.

———, 1964-2. "The Generalized Stepping Stone Method for the Machine Loading Problem," *Management Sci.*, Vol. 11, No. 1, September, 1964.

Eisemann, Kurt, and J. R. Lourie, 1959-1. "The Machine Loading Problem," IBM 704 Program, IBML. 1, International Business Machines Corporation, IBM Applications Library, New York, 1959.

Eisenberg, E., 1961-1. "Duality in Homogeneous Programming," *Proc. Amer. Math. Soc.*, Vol. 12, No. 5, October, 1961, pp. 783–787.

El Agizy, M., 1964-1. "Programming under Uncertainty with Discrete D.F.," Operations

Research Center, University of California, Berkeley, California, ORC 64-13, July, 1964.

El-Maghraby, S. E., 1959-1. "An Approach to Linear Programming under Uncertainty," *Operations Research*, Vol. 7, March, 1959, pp. 208–216.

——, 1960-1. "Allocation under Uncertainty When the Demand Has Continuous d.f.," *Management Sci.*, Vol. 6, No. 3, April, 1960, p. 270.

——, 1963-1. "An Algorithm for the Solution of the 0–1 Problem of Integer Linear Programming," Yale University, New Haven, Connecticut, 1963.

Everett, H., 1963-1. "Generalized Lagrange Multiplier Method for Solving Problems of Optimum Allocation of Resources," *Operations Research*, Vol. 11, 1963, pp. 399–417.

Fabian, Tibor, 1954-1. "Process Type Analysis of the Iron and Steel Industry, Part IV— Programming Open Hearth Steel Production," Discussion Paper No. 46, Management Sciences Research Project, University of California, Los Angeles, California, November 18, 1954. 12 pp.

——, 1955-1. "Process Analysis of the Iron and Steel Industry: A Model," Research Report No. 47, Management Sciences Research Project, University of California, Los Angeles, California, 1955. Published in *Econometrica*, Vol. 23, No. 3, July, 1955, pp. 347–348 (abstract).

——, 1958-1. "A Linear Programming Model of Integrated Iron and Steel Production," *Management Sci.*, Vol. 4, No. 4, July, 1958, pp. 415–449.

Fan, K., 1953-1. "Minimax Theorems," *Proc. Natl. Acad. Sci. U.S.A.*, Vol. 39, 1953, pp. 42–47.

Farkas, J., 1902-1. "Über die Theorie der einfachen Ungleichungen," *J. Reine Angew. Math.*, Vol. 124, 1902, pp. 1–24.

Feller, William, 1957-1. *An Introduction to Probability Theory and Its Applications*, 2nd ed., Vol. 1, John Wiley & Sons, Inc., New York, 1957. 461 pp.

Fenchel, W., 1953-1. "Convex Cones, Sets, and Functions," in D. W. Blackett's Lecture Notes, Office of Naval Research Logistics Project Report, Department of Mathematics, Princeton University, Princeton, New Jersey, 1953, 74 pp.

Ferguson, Allen R., and G. B. Dantzig, 1954-1. "Notes on Linear Programming: Part XVI—The Problem of Routing Aircraft—a Mathematical Solution," The RAND Corporation, Research Memorandum RM-1369, September 1, 1954; also The RAND Corporation, Paper P-561, published in *Aeronaut. Eng. Rev.*, Vol. 14, No. 4, April, 1955, pp. 51–55.

——, 1956-1. "The Allocation of Aircraft to Routes—An Example of Linear Programming under Uncertain Demand," The RAND Corporation, Paper P-727, December 7, 1956, 41 pp. Published in *Management Sci.*, Vol. 3, No. 1, October, 1956, pp. 45–73.

Fiacco, A. V., N. Smith, and D. Blackwell, 1960-1. "A More General Method for Nonlinear Programming," presented to the 17th National Meeting of O.R.S.A., May 20, 1960.

Fisher, Walter D., and Leonard W. Schruben, 1953-1. "Linear Programming Applied to Feed-Mixing under Different Price Conditions," *J. Farm Econ.*, Vol. 35, No. 4, November, 1953, pp. 471–483.

Flood, Merrill M., 1956-1. "The Traveling Salesman Problem," in J. F. McCloskey and J. M. Coppinger (eds.), *Operations Research for Management*, Vol. II, Johns Hopkins Press, Baltimore, Maryland, 1956, pp. 340–357; also in *Operations Research*, Vol. 4, No. 1, February, 1956, pp. 61–75.

——, 1960-1. "An Alternative Proof of a Theorem of König as an Algorithm for the Hitchcock Distribution Problem," in R. Bellman and Marshall Hall, Jr. (eds.), *Proceedings of Symposia in Applied Mathematics*, Vol. X, *Combinatorial Analysis*, American Mathematical Society, Providence, Rhode Island, 1960, pp. 299–307.

——, 1962-1. "A Symposium on Game Theory," *Behavioral Science*, Vol. 7, No. 1, January, 1962, pp. 1–102.

Ford, Lester R., Jr., and Delbert R. Fulkerson, 1954-1. "Maximal Flow through a Network," The RAND Corporation, Research Memorandum RM-1400, November 19, 1954; also The RAND Corporation, Paper P-605, November 19, 1954. Published in *Canad. J. Math.*, Vol. 8, No. 3, 1956, pp. 399–404.

————, 1957-1. "A Primal-dual Algorithm for the Capacitated Hitchcock Problem," The RAND Corporation, Paper P-827, March 23, 1956; also The RAND Corporation, Research Memorandum RM-1798, September 25, 1956. Published in *Naval Res. Logist. Quart.*, Vol 4, No. 1, March, 1957, pp. 47–54.

————, 1958-1. "Constructing Maximal Dynamic Flows from Static Flows," *Operations Research*, Vol. 6, May, 1958, pp. 419–433.

————, 1958-2. "Suggested Computation for Maximal Multi-Commodity Network Flows," The RAND Corporation, Paper P-1114, March 27, 1958. Published in *Management Sci.*, Vol. 5, No. 1, October, 1958, pp. 97–101.

————, 1960-1. *Flows in Networks*, The RAND Corporation, Report R-375, December 20, 1960. Published by Princeton University Press, Princeton, New Jersey, 1962.

Forsythe, G. E., 1953-1. "Solving Linear Algebraic Equations Can be Interesting," *Bull. Amer. Math. Soc.*, Vol. 59, No. 4, July, 1953, pp. 299–329.

————, 1955-1. "Computing Constrained Minima with Lagrange Multipliers," *J. Soc. Indust. Appl. Math.*, Vol. 3, No. 4, December, 1955, pp. 173–178.

Foulkes, J., 1955-1. "Linear Programming and Structural Design," in H. A. Antosiewicz (ed.), *Proceedings of the Second Symposium in Linear Programming*, Vol. 2, National Bureau of Standards and USAF, Washington, D.C., 1955, pp. 177–184.

Fourier, Jean Baptiste Joseph, 1826-1. "Solution d'une question particulière du calcul des inégalités," 1826, and extracts from "Histoire de l'Académie," 1823, 1824, Oeuvres II, pp. 317–328.

Fox, L., 1954-1. "Practical Solution of Linear Equations and Inversion of Matrices," in Olga Taussky (ed.), *Contributions to the Solution of Systems of Linear Equations and the Determination of Eigenvalues*, Applied Mathematics Series 39, National Bureau of Standards, Washington, D.C., September, 1954, pp. 1–54.

Frank, M., and P. Wolfe, 1956-1. "An Algorithm for Quadratic Programming," *Naval Res. Logist. Quart.*, Vol. 3, 1956, pp. 95–110.

Frederick, F. P., 1964-1. *Experience with the Staged-Pivot, Product Form Algorithm*, Booner and Moore Associates, Inc., Huston, Texas, July, 1964.

Freimer, M., and S. Dreyfus, 1961-1. "A New Approach to the Duality Theory of Mathematical Programming," MIT Lincoln Laboratory, Lexington, Massachusetts, Report 55G-0036, May, 1961.

Freund, R. J., 1956-1. "The Introduction of Risk into a Programming Model," *Econometrica*, Vol. 24, No. 3, July, 1956, pp. 253–263.

Frisch, Ragnar, 1957-1. "Linear Dependencies and a Mechanized Form of the Multiplex Method for Linear Programming," *Memorandum*, Universitetets Socialokonomiske Institutt, Oslo, University Institute of Economics, September, 1957.

Fulkerson, D. R., 1956-1. "Note on Dilworth's Decomposition Theorem for Partially Ordered Sets," *Proc. Amer. Math. Soc.*, Vol. 7, 1956, pp. 701–702.

————, 1961-1. "A Network Flow Computation for Project Cost Curves," *Management Sci.*, Vol. 7, No. 2, January, 1961, pp. 167–178.

————, 1961-2. "An Out-of-Kilter Method for Minimal-Cost Flow Problems," *J. Soc. Indust. Appl. Math.*, Vol. 9, No. 1, March, 1961, pp. 18–27.

————, 1962-1. "Tentative Formulation of the Multiplex Method for the Case of a Large Number of Basic Variables," Institute of Economics, University of Oslo, March, 1962.

Fulkerson, D. R., 1964-1. "Expected Critical Path Lengths in PERT Networks," The RAND Corporation, Research Memorandum, RM-437-PR, 1964.

Fulkerson, D. R., and G. B. Dantzig, 1955-1. "Computations of Maximal Flows in Networks," *Naval Res. Logist. Quart.*, Vol. 2, No. 4, December, 1955, pp. 277–283.

Fulkerson, D. R., and P. Wolfe, 1962-1. "An Algorithm for Scaling Matrices," Notes on Linear Programming and Extensions, Part 28, The RAND Corporation, Research Memorandum, RM-2956-PR, February, 1962.

Gaddum, J. W., 1952-1. "A Theorem on Convex Cones with Applications to Linear Inequalities," *Proc. Amer. Math. Soc.*, Vol. 3, 1952, pp. 957–960.

Gaddum, J. W., A. J. Hoffman, and D. Sokolowsky, 1954-1. "On the Solution of the

BIBLIOGRAPHY

Caterer Problem," *Naval Res. Logist. Quart.*, Vol. 1, No. 3, September, 1954, pp. 223–229.

Gainen, Leon, 1955-1. "Linear Programming in Bid Evaluations," in H. A. Antosiewicz (ed.), *Proceedings of the Second Symposium in Linear Programming*, Vol. 2, National Bureau of Standards and Directorate of Management Analysis, DCS/Comptroller, USAF, Washington, D.C., pp. 29–38.

Gale, David, 1951-1. "Convex Polyhedral Cones and Linear Inequalities," in T. C. Koopmans (ed.), *Activity Analysis of Production and Allocation*, John Wiley & Sons, Inc., New York, 1951, Chapter XVII, pp. 287–297.

———, 1956-1. "Neighboring Vertices on a Convex Polyhedron," in H. W. Kuhn and A. W. Tucker (eds.), *Linear Inequalities and Related Systems*, Annals of Mathematics Study No. 38, Princeton University Press, Princeton, New Jersey, 1956, pp. 255–263.

———, 1960-1. *The Theory of Linear Economic Models*, McGraw-Hill Book Company, Inc., New York, 1960. 330 pp.

———, 1962-1. "On the Number of Faces of a Convex Polytope," Department of Mathematics, Brown University, Technical Report No. 1, 1962.

Gale, David, H. W. Kuhn, and A. W. Tucker, 1950-1. "On Symmetric Games," in H. W. Kuhn and A. W. Tucker (eds.), *Contributions to the Theory of Games*, Vol. 1, Annals of Mathematics Study No. 24, Princeton University Press, Princeton, New Jersey, 1950, pp. 81–87.

———, 1951-1. "Linear Programming and the Theory of Games," in T. C. Koopmans (ed.), *Activity Analysis of Production and Allocation*, John Wiley & Sons, Inc., New York, 1951. Also The RAND Corporation, Report R-193, June, 1951.

Garvin, Walter W., 1960-1. *Introduction to Linear Programming*, McGraw-Hill Book Company, Inc., New York, 1960, 281 pp.

Garvin, Walter W., H. W. Crandall, J. B. John, and R. A. Spellman, 1957-1. "Applications of Linear Programming in the Oil Industry," *Management Sci.*, Vol. 3, No. 4, July, 1957, pp. 407–430.

Gass, Saul I, 1964-1. *Linear Programming: Methods and Applications*, 2nd ed., McGraw-Hill Book Company, Inc., New York, 1964, 280 pp.

Gass, Saul I., and T. L. Saaty, 1955-1. "The Computational Algorithm for the Parametric Objective Function," *Naval Res. Logist. Quart.*, Vol. 2, No. 1, June, 1955, pp. 39–45.

Gassner, Betty J., 1964-1. "Cycling in the Transportation Problem," *Naval Res. Logist. Quart.*, Vol. 11, No. 1, March, 1964.

Gauss, Karl Friedrich, 1826-1. "Theoria Combinationis Observationum Erroribus Minimis Obnoxiae," *Werke*, Vol. 4, *Supplementum*, Göttingen, 1826, pp. 55–93.

Gauthier, J. M., 1961-1. "Le principle de décomposition de Dantzig et Wolfe," Groupe de Travail, Mathématiques des Programmes Economiques, March 13, 1961.

Geary, R. C., and M. D. McCarthy, 1964-1. *Elements of Linear Programming, with Economic Applications*, Charles Griffin and Company Limited, London, 1964.

Gerstenhaber, Murray, 1951-1. "Theory of Convex Polyhedral Cones," in T. C. Koopmans (ed.), *Activity Analysis of Production and Allocation*, John Wiley & Sons, Inc., New York, 1951, Chapter XVIII, pp. 298–316.

———, 1958-1. "A Solution Method for the Transportation Problem," *J. Soc. Indust. Appl. Math.*, Vol. 6, No. 4, 1958, pp. 312–316.

Gilmore, P. C., 1963-1. "Optimal and Sub-Optimal Algorithms for the Quadratic Assignment Problem," *J. Soc. Indust. Appl. Math.*, Vol. 10, No. 2, June, 1963, pp. 305–313.

Gilmore, P. C., and R. E. Gomory, 1961-1. "A Linear Programming Approach to the Cutting Stock Problem," I.B.M. Watson Research Center, Research Report, RC-408, March, 1961; also Part I, *Operations Research*, Vol. 9, 1961, pp. 849–859, Part II, *Operations Research*, Vol. 11, No. 6, 1963, pp. 863–887.

———, 1964-2. "Sequencing, a One State Variable Machine: A Solvable Case of the Travelling Salesman Problem," I.B.M. Watson Research Center, Research Paper, RC-1103, January, 1964.

Glicksman, M. A., 1963-1. *Linear Programming and Theory of Games*, John Wiley & Sons, Inc., New York, 1963.

Glover, F., 1964-2. "Generalized Cuts in Diophantine Programming," Graduate School of Industrial Administration, Carnegie Institute of Technology, October, 1964.

Goldman, A. J., 1956-1. "Resolution and Separation Theorems for Polyhedral Convex Sets," in H. W. Kuhn and A. W. Tucker (eds.), *Linear Inequalities and Related Systems*, Annals of Mathematics Study No. 38, Princeton University Press, Princeton, New Jersey, 1956, pp. 41–51.

Goldman, A. J., and A. W. Tucker, 1956-1. "Polyhedral Convex Cones," *Ibid.*, pp. 19–39.

———, 1956-2. "Theory of Linear Programming," *Ibid.*, pp. 53–97.

Goldstein, Leon, 1952-1. "Problem of Contract Awards," in Alex Orden and Leon Goldstein (eds.), *Symposium on Linear Inequalities and Programming*, Project SCOOP, No. 10, Planning Research Division, Director of Management Analysis Service, Comptroller, USAF, Washington, D.C., April, 1952, pp. 147–154.

Goldstein, A. A., and B. R. Kripke, 1964-1. "Mathematical Programming by Minimizing Differentiable Functions," *Numer. Math.*, Vol. 6, 1964, pp. 47–48.

Gol'shteyn, E. G., and D. B. Yudin, 1961-1. "Concerning One Class of Problems in Planning the National Economy," English translation Office of Technical Service, Document No. JPRS:11175.

Gomory, R. E., 1958-1. "Essentials of an Algorithm for Integer Solutions to Linear Programs," *Bull. Amer. Math. Soc.*, Vol. 64, No. 5, 1958.

———, 1958-2. "An Algorithm for Integer Solutions to Linear Programs," Princeton-IBM Mathematics Research Project, Technical Report No. 1, November 17, 1958.

———, 1958-3. "An Algorithm for the Mixed Integer Problem," The RAND Corporation, Paper P-1885, February 22, 1960, and Abstract 553-190, "Extension of an Algorithm for Integer-Solutions to Linear Programs," *Amer. Math. Soc. Notices*, Vol. 6, No. 1, Issue 36, February, 1959, p. 52.

———, 1960-1. "All-Integer Programming Algorithm," I.B.M. Research Center, Yorktown Heights, New York, RC 189, January, 1960.

———, 1965-1. "On the Relation Between Integer and Noninteger Solutions to Linear Programs," *Proc. Natl. Acad. Sci. U.S.A.*, Vol. 53, No. 2, pp. 260–265.

Gomory, R. E., and W. J. Baumol, 1960-1. "Integer Programming and Pricing," *Econometrica*, Vol. 28, No. 3, 1960.

Gomory, R. E. and T. C. Hu, 1964-1. "Synthesis of a Communication Network," *J. Soc. Indust. Appl. Math.*, Vol. 12, No. 2, June, 1964.

———, 1960-1. "Multi-terminal Network Flows," IBM Research Report, RC318, 1960. 30 pp.

———, 1960-2. "An Application of Generalized Linear Programming to Network Flows," IBM Research Report, 1960. 50 pp.

Gordan, P., 1873-1. "Über die Auflösung linearer Gleichungen mit reelen Coefficienten," *Math. Ann.*, Vol. 6, 1873, pp. 23–28.

Graves, R., 1963-1. "Parametric Linear Programming," in R. Graves and P. Wolfe (eds.), *Recent Advances in Mathematical Programming*, McGraw-Hill Book Company, Inc., New York, 1963.

Graves, Robert L., and Philip Wolfe (eds.), 1963-1. *Recent Advances in Mathematical Programming*, McGraw-Hill Book Company, Inc., New York, 1963.

Greene, J. H., K. Chatto, C. R. Hicks, and C. B. Cox, 1959-1. "Linear Programming in the Packing Industry," *J. Indust. Eng.*, Vol. 10, No. 5, September-October, 1959, pp. 364–372.

Gross, O., 1959-1. "The Bottleneck Assignment Problem," The RAND Corporation, Paper P-1630, March 6, 1959, presented at the RAND Symposium on Mathematical Programming (Linear Programming and Extensions), March 16–20, 1959.

———, 1962-1. "A Linear Program of Prager's," Notes on Linear Programming and Extensions, Part 60, The RAND Corporation, Research Memorandum RM-2993-PR, April, 1962.

Gunther, Paul, 1955-1. "Use of Linear Programming in Capital Budgeting," *JORSA*, Vol. 3, No. 2, May, 1955, pp. 219–224.

Hadley, G., 1964-1. *Nonlinear and Dynamic Programming*, Addison-Wesley Publishing Co., Reading, Massachusetts, Inc., 1964.

Hadley, G., and M. A. Simonnard, 1959-1. "A Simplified Two-Phases Technique for the Simplex Method," *Naval Res. Logist. Quart.*, September, 1959.

Hakimi, S. L., "On Simultaneous Flows in a Communication Network," Office of Technical Services Document No. AD-267 090, 1961.

Haldi, J., 1962-1. "Solving Fixed Charge Problems by Means of Integer Programming," Graduate School of Business, Stanford University, Stanford, California, May, 1962.

Halmos, P. R., and Herbert E. Vaughan, 1950-1. "The Marriage Problem," *Amer. J. Math.*, Vol. 72, No. 1, January, 1950, pp. 214–215.

Hanson, M. A., 1964-1. "Duality and Self-Duality in Mathematical Programming," *J. Soc. Indust. Appl. Math.*, Vol. 12, No. 2, June, 1964, pp. 446–449.

Hartley, H. O., 1959-1. "Nonlinear Programming by the Simplex Method," *Econometrica*, Vol. 29, 1959, pp. 223–237.

Hartley, H. O., and R. R. Hocking, 1963-1. "Convex Programming by Tangential Approximation," *Management Sci.*, Vol. 9, 1963, pp. 600–612.

Hartley, H. O., and L. D. Loftsgard, 1958-1. "Linear Programming with Variable Restraints," *J. Sci.*, Iowa State College, Ames, Iowa, Vol. 33, No. 2, November, 1958, pp. 161–172.

Heady, E. O., and W. Candler, 1958-1. *Linear Programming Methods*, Iowa State College Press, Ames, Iowa, 1958, 597 pp.

Healy, W. C., Jr., 1964-1. "Multiple Choice Programming," *Operations Research*, Vol. 12, 1964, pp. 122–138.

Heller, I., 1964-1. "On Linear Programs Equivalent to the Transportation Problem," *J. Soc. Indust. Appl. Math.*, Vol. 12, No. 1, March, 1964, pp. 31–42.

Heller, I., and C. B. Tompkins, 1956-1. "An Extension of a Theorem of Dantzig's, Paper 14," in H. W. Kuhn and A. W. Tucker (eds.), *Linear Inequalities and Related Systems*, Annals of Mathematics Study No. 38, Princeton University Press, Princeton, New Jersey, 1956, pp. 247–254.

Henderson, A., and R. Schlaifer, 1954-1. "Mathematical Programming," *Harvard Business Rev.*, Vol. 32, May-June, 1954, pp. 73–100.

Herrmann, C. C., and J. F. Magee, 1953-1. "Operations Research for Management," *Harvard Business Rev.*, Vol. 31, No. 4, July-August, 1953, pp. 100–112.

Heyman, J., 1951-1. "Plastic Design of Beams and Plane Frames for Minimum Material Consumption," *Quart. Appl. Math.*, Vol. 8, No. 4, January, 1951, pp. 373–381.

Hicks, J. R., 1960-1. "Linear Theory," *The Economic Journal* (Quarterly Journal of the Royal Economic Society), London, Vol. LXX, No. 280, December, 1960, pp. 671–709.

Hills, R., 1961-1. "An Electrical Analogue for Solving Transportation Problems," *Intern. J. Production Res.*, Vol. 1, No. 1, November, 1961, pp. 56–62.

Hirsch, Warren M., and George B. Dantzig, 1954-1. "The Fixed Charge Problem," The RAND Corporation, Paper P-648, December 1, 1954.

Hirsch, W. M., and A. J. Hoffman, 1961-1. "Extreme Varieties, Concave Functions and the Fixed Charge Problem," *Communications on Pure and Applied Math.*, Vol. 19, No. 3, August, 1961, pp. 355–369.

Hitchcock, Frank L., 1941-1. "The Distribution of a Product from Several Sources to Numerous Localities," *J. Math. Phys.*, Vol. 20, 1941, pp. 224–230.

Hoffman, A. J., 1953-1. "Cycling in the Simplex Algorithm," National Bureau of Standards, Report No. 2974, December 16, 1953. 7 pp.

———, 1956-1. "Systems of Distinct Representatives and Linear Programming," *Amer. Math. Monthly*, Vol. 63, 1956, pp. 455–460.

———, 1960-1. "Some Recent Applications of the Theory of Linear Inequalities to Extremal Combinatorial Analysis," in R. Bellman and Marshall Hall, Jr. (eds.), *Proceedings of Symposia in Applied Mathematics*, Vol. X, *Combinatorial Analysis*, American Mathematical Society, Providence, Rhode Island, 1960, pp. 113–127.

———, 1963-1. "On Abstract Dual Linear Programs," I.B.M. Watson Research Center, Research Note NC-214, March, 1963.

Hoffman, A. J., and R. E. Gomory, 1962-1. "Finding Optimum Combinations," *Intern. Sci. Technol.*, July, 1962, pp. 26–33.

BIBLIOGRAPHY

Hoffman, A. J., and J. G. Kruskal, 1956-1. "Integral Boundary Points of Convex Polyhedra," in H. W. Kuhn and A. W. Tucker (eds.), *Linear Inequalities and Related Systems*, Annals of Mathematics Study No. 38, Princeton University Press, Princeton, New Jersey, 1956, pp. 223–246.

Hoffman, A. J., and H. W. Kuhn, 1956-1. "On Systems of Distinct Representatives," *Ibid.*, pp. 199–206; also in *Amer. Math. Monthly*, Vol. 63, 1956, pp. 455–460.

Hoffman, A. J., M. Mannos, D. Sokolowsky, and N. Wiegmann, 1953-1. "Computational Experience in Solving Linear Programs," *J. Soc. Indust. Appl. Math.*, Vol. 1, No. 1, 1953, pp. 17–33.

Hoffman, A. J., and H. M. Markowitz, 1963-1. "A Note on the Shortest Path, Assignment, and Transportation Problems," *Naval Res. Logist. Quart.*, Vol. 10, No. 4, December, 1963.

Houthakker, H. S., 1959-1. "The Capacity Method of Quadratic Programming," in P. Wolfe (ed.), *The RAND Symposium on Mathematical Programming*, The RAND Corporation, Report R-351, March 16–20, 1959.

Hu, T. C., 1961-1. "Parallel Sequencing and Assembly Line Problems," *Operations Research*, Vol. 9, No. 6, November-December, 1961, pp. 841–848.

———, 1961-2. "The Maximum Capacity Route Problem," *Operations Research*, Vol. 9, No. 6, November-December, 1961, pp. 898–900.

———, 1963-1. "Multi-Comodity Network Flow," I.B.M. Watson Research Center, Research Report RC-865, January, 1963, and *Operations Research*, Vol. 11, 1963, pp. 344–360.

———, 1964-1. "On the Feasibility of Simultaneous Flows in Networks," *Operations Research*, Vol. 12, March-April, 1964.

Hu, T. C., and W. Prager, 1958-1. "Network Analysis of Production Smoothing," Division of Applied Mathematics, Brown University, Providence, Rhode Island, March, 1958.

Huard, P., 1963-1. "Dual Programs," in R. Graves and P. Wolfe (eds.), *Recent Advances in Mathematical Programming*, McGraw-Hill Book Company, Inc., New York, 1963.

———, 1964-1. "Résolution des programmes mathématiques à constraintes nonlinéaires par la méthode des centres," Electricité de France, Direction des Etudes et Recherches, May, 1964.

———, (ed.), 1964-2. "Mathématiques des programmes économiques," *Collection des Monographies de Recherche Opérationnelle*, No. 1, publiées par l' AFIRO, Dunod, Paris, 1964.

Iri, M., 1960-1. "A New Method of Solving Transportation Network Problems," *J. Operations Res. Soc. Japan*, Vol. 3, No. 1 and 2, October, 1960, pp. 27–87.

Ivanescue, P. L., 1963-1. "Some Network Flow Problems Solved with Pseudo-Boolean Programming," Institute of Mathematics, Rumanian Academy, Bucharest, December, 1963.

———, 1964-1. "Programmation polynomial en nombers entiers," *Compt. Rend. Acad. Sci.*, Paris, Vol. 258, January, 1964, pp. 424–427.

Jackson, J. R., 1957-1. "Simulation Research on Job Shop Production," *Naval Res. Logist. Quart.*, Vol. 1, No. 4, December, 1957, p. 287.

Jacobs, W. W., 1954-1. "The Caterer Problem," *Naval Res. Logist .Quart.*, Vol. 1, No. 2, June, 1954, pp. 154–165.

———, 1955-1. "Military Applications of Linear Programming," in H. A. Antosiewicz (ed.), *Proceedings of the Second Symposium in Linear Programming*, Vol. 2, National Bureau of Standards and Directorate of Management Analysis, DCS/Comptroller, USAF, Washington, D.C., 1955, pp. 1–27.

Jewell, W. S., 1957-1. "Warehousing and Distribution of a Seasonal Product," in E. H. Bowman and R. B. Fetter (eds.), *Analyses of Industrial Operations*, 1959, pp. 129–135; also in *Naval Res. Logist. Quart.*, Vol .4, No. 1, March, 1957, pp. 29–34.

———, 1958-1. "Optimal Flow Through Networks," Interim Technical Report No. 8, on

Fundamental Investigations in Methods of Operations Research, Massachusetts Institute of Technology, Cambridge, Massachusetts, 1958.

——, 1960-1. "Optimal Flow Through Networks with Gains," presented at Second International Conference on Operations Research, Aix-en-Provence, France, 1960.

——, 1960-2. "A Classroom Example of Linear Programming," *Operations Research*, Vol. 8, No. 4, 1960, pp. 565–570.

John, F., 1948-1. "Extremum Problems with Inequalities as Subsidiary Conditions," *Studies and Essays* (Courant Anniversary Volume), Interscience Publishers, Inc., New York, 1948, pp. 187–204.

Johnson, E., 1965-1. "Network Flows, Graphs and Integer Programming," Operations Research Center, University of California, Berkeley, California, ORC 65-1.

Johnson, S., 1958-1. "Discussion: Sequencing n Jobs on Two Machines with Arbitrary Time Lags: Alternate Proof and Discussion of General Case," The RAND Corporation, Paper P-1526, October, 1958. Published in *Management Sci.*, Vol. 5, No. 3, April, 1959.

Joksch, H. C., 1964-1. "Programming with Fractional Linear Objective Functions," The Mitre Corporation, presented at the joint CORS-ORSA Meeting at Montreal, May 28, 1964.

Jordan, W., 1920-1. *Handbuch der Vermessungskunde*, Vol. 1, J. B. Metclersche Buchhandlung, Stuttgart, 7th ed., 1920, p. 36; also in 5th ed., 1904, Vol. 1, pp. 81–83, 100–105.

Kalaba, R. E., and M. L. Juncosa, 1956-1. "Optimal Design and Utilization of Communication Networks," *Management Sci.*, Vol. 3, No. 1, 1956, pp. 33–44.

Kantorovich, L. V., 1939-1. "Mathematical Methods in the Organization and Planning of Production," Publication House of the Leningrad State University, 1939. 68 pp. Translated in *Management Sci.*, Vol. 6, 1960, pp. 366–422.

——, 1942-1. "On the Translocation of Masses," *Compt. Rend. Acad. Sci., U.R.S.S.*, 37, 1942, pp. 199–201.

——, 1963-1. *Calcul économique et utilisation des resources*, translated from the Russian, Dunod, Paris, 1963.

Kantorovich, L. V., and M. K. Gavurin, 1949-1. "The Application of Mathematical Methods to Problems of Freight Flow Analysis" (translation), *Akademii Nauk SSSR*, 1949.

Karlin, Samuel, 1959-1. *Mathematical Methods and Theory in Games, Programming, and Economics*, Vols. 1 and 2, Addison-Wesley Publishing Company, Inc., Cambridge, Massachusetts, 1959.

Karush, W., 1963-1. "Duality and Network Flow," System Development Corporation, TM-1042-201-00, March 15, 1963.

Kaufmann, A., 1962-1. "Méthodes et modeles de la recherche opérationnelle," Dunod, Paris, 1962; translated *Methods and Models in Operations Research*, Prentice Hall, Englewood Cliffs, New Jersey, 1963.

Kawaratani, T. K., R. J. Ullman, and G. B. Dantzig, 1960-1. "Computing Tetraethyllead Requirements in the Linear Programming Format," The RAND Corporation, Research Memorandum RM-2425, April 1, 1960; also The RAND Corporation, Paper P-1545, June 26, 1959. Published in *Operations Research*, Vol. 8, No. 1, January-February, 1960.

Kelley, J. E., Jr., 1960-1. "The Cutting Plane Method for Solving Convex Programs," *J. Soc. Indust. Appl. Math.*, Vol. 8, No. 4, December, 1960, pp. 703–712.

——, 1961-1. "Critical-Path Planning and Scheduling; Mathematical Basis," *Operations Research*, Vol. 9, May, 1961, pp. 296–320.

Kelly, R. J., and W. A. Thompson, Jr., 1963-1. "Quadratic Programs in Real Hilbert Space," *J. Soc. Indust. Appl. Math.*, Vol. 11, No. 4, December, 1963, pp. 1063–1070.

Kemeny, J. G., J. C. Snell, and G. L. Thompson, 1957-1. *Introduction to Finite Mathematics*, Prentice-Hall, Inc., Englewood Cliffs, New Jersey, 1957. 372 pp.

Kendall, David G., 1960-1. "On Definite Doubly-Stochastic Matrices and Birkhoff's Problem III," *J. London Math. Soc.*, Vol. 35, Part 1, No. 137, January, 1960. pp. 81–84.

Klee, Victor, 1964-1. "A String Algorithm for Shortest Paths in Directed Networks," *Operations Research*, Vol. 12, No. 3, May-June, 1964.

———, 1964-2. "Convex Polytopes and Linear Programming," Mathematics Research Laboratory, Boeing Scientific Research Laboratories, Mathematical Note No. 366, August, 1964.

König, Dines, 1936-1. *Theorie der endlichen und unendlichen Graphen*, Akad. Verl. M.B.H., Leipzig, 1936, and Chelsea Publishing Company, New York, 1950. 258 pp.

Koopmans, T. C., 1947-1. "Optimum Utilization of the Transportation System," *Proceedings of the International Statistical Conferences*, 1947, Washington, D.C. (Vol. 5 reprinted as Supplement to *Econometrica*, Vol. 17, 1949.)

———, (ed.), 1951-1. *Activity Analysis of Production and Allocation*, John Wiley & Sons, Inc., New York, 1951. 404 pp.

———, 1951-2. "Analysis of Production as an Efficient Combination of Activities," in T. C. Koopmans (ed.), *Activity Analysis of Production and Allocation*, John Wiley & Sons, Inc., New York, 1951, pp. 33–97.

Koopmans, T. C., and S. Reiter, 1951-1. "A Model of Transportation," in T. C. Koopmans (ed.), *Activity Analysis of Production and Allocation*, John Wiley & Sons, Inc., New York, 1951, pp. 222–259.

Krelle, W., 1960-1. "Linear Programming under Uncertainty," *Econometrica*, Vol. 28, 1960, pp. 664–665 (abstract).

Kruskal, J. B., Jr., 1956-1. "On the Shortest Spanning Subtree of a Graph and the Traveling Salesman Problem," *Proc. Amer. Math. Soc.*, Vol. 7, 1956, pp. 48–50.

Kuenne, R., 1963-1. *The Theory of General Economic Equilibrium*, Princeton University Press, Princeton, New Jersey, 1963.

Kuhn, H. W., 1955-1. "The Hungarian Method for the Assignment Problem," *Naval Res. Logist. Quart.*, Vol. 2, 1955, pp. 83–97.

———, 1956-1. "Solvability and Consistency for Linear Equations and Inequalities," *Amer. Math. Monthly*, Vol. 63, No. 4, April, 1956, pp. 217–232.

Kuhn, H. W., and A. W. Tucker (eds.), 1950-1. *Contributions to the Theory of Games*, Vol. 1, Annals of Mathematics Study No. 24, Princeton University Press, Princeton, New Jersey, 1950.

———, 1950-2. "Nonlinear Programming," in Jerzy Neyman (ed.), *Proceedings of the Second Berkeley Symposium on Mathematical Statistics and Probability*, University of California Press, Berkeley, California, 1950, pp. 481–492; also in *Econometrica*, Vol. 19, No. 1, January, 1951, pp. 50–51 (abstract).

——— (eds.), 1953-1. *Contributions to the Theory of Games*, Vol. II, Annals of Mathematics Study No. 28, Princeton University Press, Princeton, New Jersey, 1953.

———, 1955-1. "Games, Theory of," *Encyclopaedia Britannica*, Vol. 10, 1958, pp. 5–10.

——— (eds.), 1956-1. *Linear Inequalities and Related Systems*, Annals of Mathematics Study No. 38, Princeton University Press, Princeton, New Jersey, 1956. 322 pp.

——— (eds.), 1956-2. "A Bibliography on Linear Inequalities and Related Systems," *Ibid.*, pp. 305–322.

———, 1958-1. "John von Neumann's Work in the Theory of Games and Mathematical Economics," *Bull. Amer. Math. Soc.*, Vol. 64, No. 3, Part 2, May, 1958, pp. 100–122.

Künzi, H. P., and W. Krelle, 1962-1. *Nichtlineare Programmierung*, Springerverlag, Berlin, Göttingen-Heidelberg, 1962.

Künzi, H. P. and W. Oettli, 1963-1. "Integer Quadratic Programming," in R. Graves and P. Wolfe, *Recent Advances in Mathematical Programming*, McGraw-Hill Book Company, Inc., New York, 1963.

Lambert, F., 1960-1. "Programmes linéaires mixtes," *Cahiers Centre d'Études Rech. Opér.*, Brussels, 1960.

Land, A. H., 1963-1. "A Problem of Assignment with Inter-Related Costs," *Operations Research*, Vol. 14, No. 2, June, 1963, pp. 185–199.

Land, A. H., and A. G. Doig, 1957-1. "An Automatic Method of Solving Discrete Programming Problems" (unpublished work, prepared as part of a project for the British Trading Company, Ltd., at the London School of Economics and Political Science).

Lawler, E. L., 1963-1. "The Quadratic Assignment Problem," *Management Sci.*, Vol. 9, 1963, p. 586.

Lehman, R. S., 1954-1. "On the Continuous Simplex Method." The RAND Corporation, Research Memorandum RM-1386, 1954.

Lemke, C. E., 1954-1. "The Dual Method of Solving the Linear Programming Problem," *Naval Res. Logist. Quart.*, Vol. 1, 1954, pp. 36–47.

———, 1961-1. "The Constrained Gradient Method of Linear Programming," *J. Soc. Indust. Appl. Math.*, Vol. 9, No. 1, March, 1961, pp. 1–17.

Leontief, Wassily, 1951-1. *The Structure of American Economy, 1919–1931*, Oxford University Press, New York, 1951.

Lesourne, J., 1960-1. *Technique économique gestion industrielle*, 2nd ed., Dunod, Paris, France, 1960, pp. 408–476.

Lewis, Robert E., 1955-1. "Top Management Looks at Linear Programming and Inventory Management," *Proceedings of the Linear Programming and Inventory Management Seminar*, Methods Engineering Council, Pittsburgh, Pennsylvania, September 15–16, 1955, pp. B-1 to B-8.

Lourie, Janice R., 1964-1. "Topology and Computation of the Generalized Transportation Problem," *Management Sci.*, Vol. 11, No. 1, September, 1964.

Luce, R. Duncan, and Howard Raiffa, 1957-1. *Games and Decisions, Introduction and Critical Survey*, John Wiley & Sons, Inc., New York, 1957. 509 pp.

Macguire, C. B., 1963-1. "Some Extensions of the Dantzig-Wolfe Decomposition Scheme," Center for Research in Management Science, University of California, Berkeley, California, Working Paper No. 66, March, 1963.

Madansky, Albert, 1959-1. "Some Results and Problems in Stochastic Linear Programming," The RAND Corporation, Paper P-1596, January 19, 1959.

———, 1960-1. "Inequalities for Stochastic Linear Programming Problems," *Management Sci.*, Vol. 6, No. 2, January, 1960.

———, 1960-2. "Methods of Solution of Linear Programs under Uncertainty," The RAND Corporation, Paper P-2132, November 8, 1960.

———, 1963-1. "Dual Variables in Two-Stage Linear Programming under Uncertainty," *J. Math. Anal. Appl.*, Vol. 6, February, 1963, pp. 98–108.

Maghout, K., G. Comes, and N. Steinberg, 1962-1. "Généralisation à n dimensions du problème de transport," *Revue Française de Recherche Opérationelle*, Vol. 6, No. 22, First quarter, 1962, pp. 21–34.

Malinvaud, E., 1963-1. "Decentralized Procedures for Planning," Center for Research in Management Science, University of California, Berkeley, California, Technical Report No. 15, 1963.

Mangasarian, O. L., 1962-1. "Duality in Nonlinear Programming," *Quart. Appl. Math.*, Vol. 20, 1962, pp. 300–302.

———, 1964-1. "Nonlinear Programming Problems with Stochastic Objective Functions," *Management Sci.*, Vol. 10, No. 2, January, 1964.

Mangasarian, O. L., and J. Ponstein, 1963-1. "Minimax and Duality in Nonlinear Programming," Shell Development Company, Emeryville, California, P-1182, 1963.

Manne, Alan S., 1956-1. *Scheduling of Petroleum Refinery Operations*, Harvard University Press, Cambridge, Massachusetts, 1956. 185 pp.

———, 1956-2. "An Application of Linear Programming to the Procurement of Transport Aircraft," *Management Sci.*, Vol. 2, No. 2, January, 1956, pp. 190–191 (abstract).

———, 1960-1. "On the Job-Shop Scheduling Problem," *Operations Research*, Vol. 8, 1960, pp. 219–223.

———, 1961-1. *Economic Analysis for Business Decisions*, McGraw-Hill Book Company, Inc., New York, 1961.

Marcus, M., 1960-1. "Some Properties of Doubly Stochastic Matrices," *Amer. Math. Monthly*, Vol. 67, No. 3, March, 1960, pp. 215–221.

Markowitz, Harry M., 1952-1. "Portfolio Selection," *The Journal of Finance*, Vol. 7, No. 1, March, 1952.

————, 1954-1. *The Nature and Applications of Process Analysis*, The RAND Corporation, Research Memorandum RM-1254, May 24, 1954.

————, 1954-2. "Concepts and Computing Procedures for Certain X_{ij} Programming Problems," in H. A. Antosiewicz (ed.), *Proceedings of the Second Symposium in Linear Programming*, Vol. 2, National Bureau of Standards and Directorate of Management Analysis, DCS/Comptroller, USAF, Washington, D.C., 1955, pp. 509–565; also The RAND Corporation, Paper P-602, November 19, 1954.

————, 1956-1. "The Optimization of a Quadratic Function Subject to Linear Constraints," The RAND Corporation, Research Memorandum RM-1438, February 21, 1955; also The RAND Corporation, Paper P-637, June 27, 1955. Published in *Naval Res. Logist. Quart.*, Vol. 3, 1956.

————, 1959-1. *Portfolio Selection: Efficient Diversification of Investments*, John Wiley & Sons, Inc., New York, 1959. 344 pp.

Markowitz, Harry M., and A. S. Manne, 1957-1. "On the Solution of Discrete Programming Problems," *Econometrica*, Vol. 25, No. 1, January, 1957, p. 19.

Marschak, J., 1962-1. "Computation, Decomposition, and Internal Pricing," Center for Research in Management Science, University of California, Berkeley, California, Working Paper No. 56, December, 1962.

Martin, G. T., 1963-1. "An accelerated Euclidean Algorithm for Integer Linear Programming," in R. Graves and P. Wolfe (eds.), *Recent Advances in Mathematical Programming*, McGraw-Hill Book Company, Inc., New York, 1963.

Massé, Pierre, 1946-1. *Les réserves et la régulation de l'avenir dans la vie économique*, Vol. I, *Avenir déterminé*, Vol. II, *Avenir aléatoire*, Librairie scientifique, Hermann, Paris, 1946.

————, 1963-1. *Le choix des investiments*, 2nd ed., Dunod, Paris. Translated as *Optimal Investment Decisions*, Prentice Hall, Englewood Cliffs, New Jersey, 1963.

Massé, Pierre, and R. Gibrat, 1957-1. "Applications of Linear Programming to Investments in the Electric Power Industry," *Management Sci.*, Vol. 3, No. 1, January, 1957, pp. 149–166.

Maynard, Harold B., 1955-1. "Putting New Management Tools to Work," *Proceedings of the Linear Programming and Inventory Management Seminar*, Methods Engineering Council, Pittsburgh, Pennsylvania, September 15–16, 1955.

McIlroy, M. D., 1962-1. "Transportation Problems with Distributed Loads," Bell Telephone Laboratories, Inc., Murray Hill, New Jersey, July, 1962.

McKinsey, J. C. C., 1952-1. *Introduction to the Theory of Games*, The RAND Corporation, Report R-228, July, 1952; also published by McGraw-Hill Book Company, Inc., New York, 1952. 371 pp.

Miller, C. E., 1960-1. "The Simplex Method for Local Separable Programming," Standard Oil Company of California, August, 1960.

————, 1963-1. "The Simplex Method for Local Separable Programming," in R. Graves and P. Wolfe (eds.), *Recent Advances in Mathematical Programming*, McGraw-Hill Book Company, Inc., 1963.

Miller, C. E., A. W. Tucker, and R. A. Zemlin, 1960-1. "Integer Programming Formulation of Traveling Salesman Problems," *J. Assoc. Comput. Mach.*, Vol. 7, No. 4, October, 1960.

Miller, L. B., and H. M. Wagner, 1964-1. "Chance Programming with Joint Constraints," Graduate School of Business, Stanford University, Technical Report No. 9, October, 1964.

Mills, Harlan D., 1956-1. "Marginal Values of Matrix Games and Linear Programs," in H. W. Kuhn and A. W. Tucker (eds.), *Linear Inequalities and Related Systems*, Annals of Mathematics Study No. 38, Princeton University Press, Princeton, New Jersey, 1956, pp. 183–193.

————, 1960-1. "Equilibrium Points in Finite Games," *J. Soc. Indust. Appl. Math.*, Vol. 8, No. 2, June, 1960, pp. 397–402.

Minkowski, H., 1896-1. *Geometrie der Zahlen*, B. G. Teubner, Leipzig and Berlin, 1910. 256 pp. First printing, 1896; also reprinted by Chelsea Publishing Company, New York, 1953.

BIBLIOGRAPHY

Minty, George J., 1962-1. "On an Algorithm for Solving Some Network-Programming Problems," *Operations Research*, Vol. 10, No. 3, May-June, 1962, pp. 403–405.

Monroe, Arthur Eli, 1924-1. *Early Economic Thought; Selections from Economic Literature Prior to Adam Smith*, Harvard University Press, Cambridge, Massachusetts, 1924. 400 pp.

Moore, E. F., 1957-1. "The Shortest Path Through a Maze," unpublished mimeographed report, Bell Telephone Laboratories, 16 pp.

Morgenstern, Oskar, 1949-1. "The Theory of Games," *Sci. American*, Vol. 180, No. 5, May, 1949, pp. 22–25.

——— (ed.), 1954-1. *Economic Activity Analysis*, John Wiley & Sons, Inc., New York, 1954. 554 pp.

Morin, George, 1955-1. "More Effective Production Planning with Linear Programming," Paper F from *Proceedings of the Linear Programming and Inventory Management Seminar*, Methods Engineering Council, Pittsburgh, September 15–16, 1955.

Motzkin, T. S., 1936-1. *Beiträge zur Theorie der linearen Ungleichungen*, Jerusalem, 1936 (Doctoral Thesis, University of Zurich).

———, 1952-1. "The Multi-index Transportation Problem," *Bull. Amer. Math. Soc.*, Vol. 58, No. 4, 1952, p. 494 (abstract).

———, 1956-1. "The Assignment Problem," *Proceedings of the Sixth Symposium in Applied Mathematics*, McGraw-Hill Book Company, Inc., New York, 1956, pp. 109–125.

Motzkin, T. S., H. Raiffa, G. L. Thompson, and R. M. Thrall, 1953-1. "The Double Description Method," in H. W. Kuhn and A. W. Tucker (eds.), *Contributions to the Theory of Games*, Vol. II, Annals of Mathematics Study No. 28, Princeton University Press, Princeton, New Jersey, 1953, pp. 51–73.

Motzkin, T. S., and I. J. Schoenberg, 1954-1. "The Relaxation Method for Linear Inequalities," *Canad. J. Math.*, Vol. 6, 1954, pp. 393–404.

Mueller-Merbach, H., 1964-2. "A Parametric Linear Programming Approach for the Project Cost Curves," Operations Research Center, University of California, Berkeley, California, Working Paper, 1964.

———, 1964-3. "The Symmetric Product Form of the Revised Simplex Method," Operations Research Center, University of California, Berkeley, California, July, 1964.

Munkres, James, 1957-1. "Algorithms for the Assignment and Transportation Problems," *J. Soc. Indust. Appl. Math.*, Vol. 5, No. 1, March, 1957, pp. 32–38.

Naslund, Bertil, and Whinston, A., 1962-1. "A Model of Multi-Period Investment under Uncertainty," *Management Sci.*, Vol. 8, No. 2, January, 1962, pp. 184–200.

Natrella, Joseph V., 1955-1. "New Applications of Linear Programming," presented at the Annual Meeting of the Association for Computing Machinery, Philadelphia, Pennsylvania, September 14–16, 1955; also in *Computers and Automation*, Vol. 4, No. 11, p. 22, Item 48, 1955 (abstract).

Nelson, Richard R., 1957-1. "Degeneracy in Linear Programming: A Simple Geometric Interpretation," *Rev. Econ. Statist.*, Vol. 39, 1957, pp. 402–407.

Newman, P., 1955-1. "Some Calculations on Least-Cost Diets Using the Simplex Method," *Bulletin*, Oxford University Institute of Statistics, Oxford, England, September, 1955, Vol. 17, pp. 303–320.

New York Times, 1959-1. "Russian Assails Soviet Economics," by Harry Schwartz, *The New York Times*, May 29, 1959.

Neyman, J., 1950-1. *First Course in Probability and Statistics*, Vol. 1, Henry Holt & Company, Inc., New York, 1950, 350 pp.

Neyman, J., and E. S. Pearson, 1936-1. "Contributions to the Theory of Testing Statistical Hypotheses," *Statist. Res. Mem.*, Parts I and II, 1936, 1938.

Norman, R. Z., 1955-1. "On the Convex Polyhedra of the Symmetric Traveling Salesman Problem," *Bull. Amer. Math. Soc.*, Vol. 61, No. 6, November, 1955, p. 559 (abstract).

Norman, R. Z., and M. O. Roben, 1958-1. "An Algorithm for a Minimum Cover of a Graph," *Notices Amer. Math. Soc.* 5, 36, 1958.

[609]

Orchard-Hays, W., 1954-1. *A Composite Simplex Alorithm—II*, The RAND Corporation, Research Memorandum RM-1275, May, 1954.

———, 1955-1. *RAND Code for the Simplex*, The RAND Corporation, Research Memorandum RM-1440, February 7, 1955.

———, 1956-1. "Evolution of Computer Codes for Linear Programming." The RAND Corporation, Paper P-810, March 14, 1956, pp. 22–24.

Orchard-Hays, W., Leola Cutler, and Harold Judd, 1956-1. "Manual for the RAND IBM Code for Linear Programming on the 704," The RAND Corporation, Paper P-842, May 16, 1956, pp. 24–26.

Orden, Alex, 1952-1. "Application of the Simplex Method to a Variety of Matrix Problems," in Alex Orden and Leon Goldstein (eds.), *Symposium on Linear Inequalities and Programming*, Project SCOOP, No. 10, Planning Research Division, Director of Management Analysis Service, Comptroller, USAF, Washington, D.C., April, 1952.

———, 1956-1. "The Transshipment Problem," *Management Sci.*, Vol. 2, No. 3, April, 1956, pp. 276–285.

Orden, Alex, and L. Goldstein (eds.), 1952-1. *Symposium on Linear Inequalities and Programming*, Project SCOOP, No. 10, Planning Research Division, Director of Management Analysis Service, Comptroller, USAF, Washington, D.C., April, 1952.

Parisot, G. R., 1961-1. "Résolution numérique approchée du problème de programmation linéaire par application de la programmation logarithmique," Université de Lille, France, Thèse Numéro d'Ordre 52, March, 1961.

Paull, A. E., and John R. Walter, 1955-1. "The Trim Problem: An Application of Linear Programming to the Manufacture of Newsprint Paper," *Econometrica*, Vol. 23, No. 3, July, 1955, p. 336 (abstract).

Phipps, C. G., 1952-1. "Maxima and Minima Under Restraint," *Amer. Math. Monthly*, Vol. 59, No. 4, April, 1952, pp. 230–235.

Pollack, Maurice, 1961-1. "Solutions of the Kth Best Route through a Network—A Review," *J. Math. Anal. Appl.*, Vol. 3, No. 3, December, 1961, pp. 547–559.

Poussin, M. Ch. J. de la Vallée, 1911-1. "Sur la méthode de l'approximation minimum," *Ann. Soc. Sci. de Bruxelles*, 35, 1911, pp.1–16.

Prager, William, 1956-1. "On the Caterer Problem," *Management Sci.*, Vol. 3, No. 1, October, 1956, pp. 15–23; *Management Sci.*, Vol. 3, No. 2, January, 1957, p. 209 (abstract).

———, 1957-1. "A Generalization of Hitchcock's Transportation Problem," *J. Math. Phys.* (M.I.T.), Vol. 36, No. 2, July, 1957, pp. 99–106.

———, 1963-1. "A Structural Method for Computing Project Cost Polygons," *Management Sci.*, Vol. 9, No. 3, April, 1963, pp. 394–404.

Pyne, Insley B., 1956-1. "Linear Programming on an Electronic Analogue Computer," AIEE Transactions Annual, 1956; also Reeves Instrument Corporation, Technical Article Reprint No. 110.

Radner, Roy, 1955-1. "The Linear Team: An Example of Linear Programming under Uncertainty," in H. A. Antosiewicz (ed.), *Proceedings of the Second Symposium in Linear Programming*, Vol. 2, National Bureau of Standards and Directorate of Management Analysis, DCS/Comptroller, USAF, Washington, D.C., 1955, pp. 381–396.

———, 1959-1. "The Application of Linear Programming to Team Decision Problems," *Management Sci.*, Vol. 5, January, 1959, pp. 143–150.

Raiffa, H., G. L. Thompson, and R. M. Thrall, 1952–1. "An Algorithm for the Determination of all Solutions of a Two-person Zero-sum Game with a Finite Number of Strategies (Double Descriptive Method)," in A. Orden and Leon Goldstein (eds.), *Symposium on Linear Inequalities and Programming*, Project SCOOP, No. 10, Planning Research Division, Director of Management Analysis Service, Comptroller, USAF, Washington, D.C., April, 1952, pp. 100–114.

Reisch, E., and L. Eisgruber, 1960-1. "Bibliography of Linear Programming and Its Application to Agricultural Economic Problems," mimeographed report (probably available from Purdue University), 1960, 30 pp.

Reiter, S., 1957-1. "Surrogates for Uncertain Decision Problems: Minimal Information for Decision Making," *Econometrica*, Vol. 25, 1957, pp. 339–345.

Riley, Vera, and Saul I. Gass, 1958-1. *Linear Programming and Associated Techniques; a Comprehensive Bibliography on Linear, Nonlinear and Dynamic Programming*, Johns Hopkins Press, Baltimore, Maryland, 1958, 613 pp.

Ritter, K., 1962-1. "Ein Verfahren zur Lösung parameterabhängiger, nicht-linearer Maximum-Probleme," *Unternehmensforschung*, Vol. 6, 1962, pp. 149–166.

Robinson Julia, 1951-1. "An Iterative Method of Solving a Game," *Ann. Math.*, Vol. 54, No. 2, September, 1951, pp. 296–301.

Rockafellar, R. T., 1963-1. "Convex Functions and Dual Extremum Problems," Ph.D. Dissertation, Harvard University, Cambridge, Massachusetts, 1963.

―――, 1964-1. "A Combinatorial Algorithm for Linear Programs in the General Mixed Form," *J. Soc. Indust. Appl. Math.*, Vol. 12, No. 1, March, 1964, pp. 215–225.

Rosen, J. B., 1960-1. "Gradient Projection Method for Non-Linear Programming, Part I, Linear Constraints," *J. Soc. Indust. Appl. Math.*, Vol. 8, No. 1, 1960, pp. 181–217. "Part II, Non-Linear Constraints," preprint Shell Development Company, New York, Paper P-954, January, 1961.

―――, 1961-1. "The Gradient Projection Method for Non-Linear Projection, Part II," *J. Soc. Indust. Appl. Math.*, Vol. 9, 1961, pp. 514–532.

―――, 1963-1. "Convex Partition Programming," in R. Graves and P. Wolfe (eds.), *Recent Advances in Mathematical Programming*, McGraw-Hill Book Company, Inc., New York, 1963.

―――, 1963-2. "Primal Partition Programming for Block Diagonal Matrices," Computer Science Division, School of Humanities and Sciences, Stanford University, Stanford, California, Technical Report No. 32, November, 1963.

Roubalt, M., 1963-1. "Étude d'un algorithme de résolution pour les programmes non lineaires convexes," Thesis, Faculté des Sciences, Université de Paris, Paris, France, June, 1963.

Ryser, H. J., 1963-1. *Combinatiorial Mathematics*, The Carus Mathematical Monographs, No. 14. The Mathematical Association of America Publisher, distributed by John Wiley & Sons, Inc., New York, 1963, 154 pp.

Saaty, T. L., 1955-1. "The Number of Vertices of a Polyhedron," *Amer. Math. Monthly*, Vol. 65, No. 5, May, 1955, pp. 327–331.

―――, 1959-1. *Mathematical Methods of Operative Research*, McGraw-Hill Book Company, Inc., New York, 1959, 421 pp.

Salveson, M. E., 1953-1. "A Computational Technique for the Fabrication Scheduling Problem," Management Sciences Research Project, University of California, Los Angeles, California, 1953.

Samuelson, P. A., 1955–1. "Linear Programming and Economic Theory," in H. A. Antosiewicz (ed.), *Proceedings of the Second Symposium in Linear Programming*, Vol. 2, National Bureau of Standards and Directorate of Management Analysis, DCS/Comptroller, USAF, Washington, D.C., 1955, pp. 251–272.

Sasieni, M. W., A. Yaspan, and L. Friedman, 1959–1. *Operations Research: Methods and Problems*, John Wiley & Sons, Inc., New York, 1959, 316 pp.

Schelling, T. C., 1960–1. *The Strategy of Conflict*, Harvard University Press, Cambridge, Massachusetts, 1960.

Shapley, L. S., 1959–1. "On Network Flow Functions," The RAND Corporation, Research Memorandum RM-2338, March, 1959, and The RAND Corporation, Paper P-2185, January 9, 1961; also in *Naval Res. Logist. Quart.*, Vol. 8, No. 2, June, 1961.

―――, 1961-1. "On Network Flow Functions," The RAND Corporation, Paper P-2185, January, 1961.

Shapley, L. S., and R. N. Snow, 1950–1. "Basic Solutions of Discrete Games," in H. W. Kuhn and A. W. Tucker (eds.), *Contributions to the Theory of Games*, Vol. 1, Annals of Mathematics Study No. 24, Princeton University Press, Princeton, New Jersey, 1950, pp. 27–35.

Shetty, C. M., 1959-1. "A Solution to the Transportation Problem with Non-Linear Costs," *Operations Research*, Vol. 7, No. 5, September-October, 1959, pp. 571–580.

Shubik, Martin, 1959-1. *Strategy and Market Structure; Competition, Oligopoly, and the Theory of Games*, John Wiley & Sons, Inc., New York, 1959.

———, (ed.), 1964-1. *Game Theory and Related Approaches to Social Behaviour*, John Wiley & Sons, Inc., New York, 1964.

Simon, H. A., 1956-1. "Dynamic Programming under Uncertainty with a Quadratic Criterion Function," *Econometrica*, Vol. 24, 1956, pp. 74–81.

Simonnard, M., 1962-1. *Programmation linéaire*, Dunod, Paris, 1962, 420 pp.

Simonnard, M. A., and G. F. Hadley, 1959-1. "Maximum Number of Iterations in the Transportation Problem," *Naval Res. Logist. Quart.*, Vol. 6, 1959.

Sinden, F. W., 1963-1. "Duality in Convex Programming and in Projective Space," *J. Soc. Indust. Appl. Math.*, Vol. 11, No. 3, September, 1963, pp. 535–552.

Sinha, S. M., 1963-1. "Stochastic Programming," Operations Research Center, University of California, Berkeley, ORC 63-22, August 19, 1963.

Slater, M., 1950-1. "Lagrange Multipliers Revisited," *Cowles Commission Discussion Papers*, Math. 403, November, 1950; The RAND Corporation, Research Memorandum RM-676, August, 1951.

Smith, D. M., and W. Orchard-Hays, 1963-1. "Computational Efficiency in Product Form LP Codes," in R. Graves and P. Wolfe (eds.), *Recent Advances in Mathematical Programming*, McGraw-Hill Book Company, Inc,1963.

Smith, V. E., 1959-1. "Linear Programming Models for the Determination of Palatable Human Diets," *J. of Farm Econ.*, Vol. 41, No. 2, May, 1959, pp. 272–283.

Solow, R. M., 1952-1. "On the Structure of Linear Models," *Econometrica*, Vol. 20, No. 1, January, 1952, pp. 29–46.

Spivey, W. A., 1963-1. *Linear Programming*, The Macmillan and Company, New York, 1963.

Spurkland, S., 1963-2. "Error Control," Norwegian Computer Center, LP-Note 8, Blindern, Norway, October, 1963.

Stiefel, E., 1960-1. "Note on Jordan Elimination, Linear Programming and Tchebycheff Approximation," *Numer. Math.*, Vols. 2 and 4, 1960.

Stiemke, E., 1915-1. "Über positive Lösungen homogener linearer Gleichungen," *Math. Ann.*, Vol. 76, 1915, pp. 340–342.

Stigler, George J., 1945-1. "The Cost of Subsistence," *J. Farm Econ.*, Vol. 27, No. 2, May, 1945, pp. 303–314.

Stoer, J., 1964-1. "On a Duality Theorem in Non-Linear Programming," *Numer. Math.*, Vol. 6, 1964, pp. 55–58.

Stokes, R. W., 1931-1. "A Geometric Theory of Solution of Linear Inequalities," *Trans. Amer. Math. Soc.*, Vol. 33, 1931, pp. 782—805.

Swanson, E. R., 1955-1. "Integrating Crop and Livestock Activities in Farm Management Activity Analysis," *J. Farm Econ.*, Vol. 37, No. 5, December, 1955, pp. 1249–1258.

Symonds, G. H., 1955-1. *Linear Programming: The Solution of Refinery Problems*, Esso Standard Oil Company, New York, 1955.

———, 1955-2. "Mathematical Programming as an Aid to Decision Making," *Advanced Management*, Vol. 20, No. 5, May, 1955, pp. 11–17.

Szwarc, W., 1963-2. "The Mixed Integer Linear Programming Problem When the Integer Variables are Zero or One," Graduate School of Industrial Administration, Carnegie Institute of Technology, May, 1963.

Talacko, J. V., 1959-1. "On Stochastic Linear Inequalities," *Trabajos Estadist.*, Vol. 10, 1959, pp. 89–112.

Theil, H., 1957-1. "A Note on Certainty Equivalence in Dynamic Planning," *Econometrica*, Vol. 25, 1957, pp. 346–349.

———, 1961-1. "Some Reflections on Static Programming under Uncertainty," *Weltwirtschaftliches Archiv*, Vol. 87, 1961, pp. 124–138.

Theil, H., and C. van de Panne, 1960-1. "Quadratic Programming as an Extension of Classical Quadratic Maximization," *Management Sci.*, Vol. 7, 1960, pp. 1–20.

Thrall, R. M., 1955-1. "Some Results in Non-linear Programming," The RAND Corporation, Research Memorandum RM-909, August 6, 1952, 17 pp.; also in H. A. Antosiewicz (ed.), *Proceedings of the Second Symposium in Linear Programming*, Vol. 2, National Bureau of Standards and Directorate of Management Analysis, DCS/Comptroller, USAF, Washington, D.C., 1955, pp. 471–493.

Tintner, G., 1955-1. "Stochastic Linear Programming with Application to Agricultural Economics," in H. A. Antosiewicz (ed.), *Proceedings of the Second Symposium in Linear Programming*, Vol. 1, National Bureau of Standards and Directorate of Management Analysis, DCS/Comptroller, USAF, Washington, D.C., 1955, pp. 197–228.

Tintner, G., C. Millham, and J. K. Sengupta, 1963-1. "A Weak Duality Theorem for Stochastic Linear Programming," *Unternehmensforschung*, Vol. 7, 1963, pp. 1–8.

Tompkins, C. B., 1955-1. "Projection Methods in Calculation," in H. A. Antosiewicz (ed.), *Proceedings of the Second Symposium in Linear Programming*, Vol. 2, National Bureau of Standards and Directorate of Management Analysis, DCS/Comptroller, USAF, Washington, D.C., 1955, p. 425–448.

———, 1957-1. "Some Methods of Computational Attack on Programming Problems, Other Than the Simplex Method," *Naval Res. Logist. Quart.*, Vol. 4, No. 1, March, 1957, pp. 95–96.

Tornqvist, L., 1961-1. "On Distribution Function for Quantities Related to Networks," *Bull. Intern. Statist. Inst.*, Vol. 38, Part 4, 1961, pp. 609–612.

Totschek, R., and R. C. Wood, 1961-1. "An Investigation of Real-Time Solution of the Transportation Problem," *Journal of A.C.M.*, April, 1961, p. 230.

Tucker, A. W., 1950-1. "Linear Programming and Theory of Games," *Econometrica*, Vol. 18, No. 2, April, 1950, p. 189.

———, 1955-1. "Linear Inequalities and Convex Polyhedral Sets," in H. A. Antosiewicz (ed.), *Proceedings of the Second Symposium in Linear Programming*, Vol. 2, National Bureau of Standards and Directorate of Management Analysis, DCS/Comptroller, USAF, Washington, D.C., 1955, pp. 569–602.

———, 1956-1. "Dual Systems of Homogeneous Linear Relations," in H. W. Kuhn and A. W. Tucker (eds.), *Linear Inequalities and Related Systems*, Annals of Mathematics Study No. 38, Princeton University Press, Princeton, New Jersey, 1956, pp. 3–18.

———, 1957-1. "Linear and Nonlinear Programming," *Operations Research*, Vol. 5, No. 2, April, 1957, pp. 244–257.

———, 1960-1. "On Directed Graphs and Integer Programs," IBM Mathematical Research Project, Technical Report, Princeton University, Princeton, New Jersey, 1960.

———, 1960-2. "A Combination Equivalence of Matrices," in R. Bellman and Marshall Hall, Jr. (eds.), *Proceedings of Symposia in Applied Mathematics*, Vol. X, *Combinatorial Analysis*, American Mathematical Society, Providence, Rhode Island, 1960, pp. 129–140.

———, 1960-3. "Solving a Matrix Game by Linear Programming," *IBM J. Res. Develop.*, Vol. 4, No. 5, November, 1960, pp. 507–517.

———, 1963-1. "Combinatorial Theory Underlying Linear Programs," in R. Graves and P. Wolfe (eds.), *Recent Advances in Mathematical Programming*, McGraw-Hill Book Company, Inc., New York, 1963.

Tucker, A. W., and R. D. Luce (eds.), 1959-1. *Contributions to the Theory of Games*, Princeton University Press, Princeton, New Jersey, 1959.

Tutte, W. T., 1946-1. "On Hamiltonian Circuits," *J. London Math. Soc.*, Vol. 21, Part 2, No. 82, April, 1946, pp. 98–101.

USAF, 1954-1, Hq., Comptroller, Computational Division. "The Application of Linear Programming Techniques to Air Force Problems," December 17, 1954, 27 pp.

Uzawa, Hirofumi, 1958-1. "The Kuhn-Tucker Theorem in Concave Programming," in Kenneth J. Arrow, Leonid Hurwicz, and Hirofumi Uzawa (eds.), *Studies in Linear and Non-Linear Programming*, Stanford University Press, Stanford, California, 1958.

————, 1960-1. "Market Mechanisms and Mathematical Programming," *Econometrica*, Vol. 28, No. 4, October, 1960, pp. 872–881.

Vajda, S., 1956-1. *The Theory of Games and Linear Programming*, John Wiley & Sons, Inc., New York, 1956. 106 pp.
————, 1958-1. *Readings in Linear Programming*, John Wiley & Sons, Inc., New York, 1958, and Sir Isaac Pitman & Sons Ltd., London, 1958. 99 pp.
————, 1958-2. "Inequalities in Stochastic Linear Programming." *Bull. Internat. Statist. Inst.*, Vol. 36, 1958, pp. 357–363.
————, 1961-1. *Mathematical Programming*, Addison-Wesley Publishing Company, Inc., Reading, Massachusetts, 1961. 310 pp.
————, 1963-1. "Pourquoi est-il nécessaire de developper les méthodes actuelles de planification mathématique?" *Econometrica*, Vol. 31, 1963, pp. 257–259 (abstract).
van den Bogaard, P. J. M., 1960-1. "On the Static Theory of Certainty Equivalence," International Center for Management Science, Rotterdam, Report 6010, 1960.
van de Panne, C., and Andrew Whinston, 1963-1. "The Simplex and Dual Method for Quadratic Programming," International Center for Management Science, Rotterdam, Report 6314 (ICMS No. 28), April, 1963.
van Moeseke, P., and G. Tintner, 1964-1. "Base Duality Theorem for Stochastic and Parametric Linear Programming," *Unternehmensforschung*, Vol. 8, 1964, pp. 75–79.
van Slyke, R., 1963-1. "Monte Carlo Methods and the PERT Problem," *Operations Research*, Vol. 11, No. 5, September-October, 1963, pp. 839–860.
van Slyke, R., and Roger Wets, 1962-1. "On Diagonalization Methods in Integer Programming," Operations Research Center, University of California, Berkeley, California, RR 27, 1962.
Vazsonyi, Andrew, 1955-1. "Optimizing a Function of Additively Separated Variables Subject to a Simple Restriction," in H. A. Antosiewicz (ed.), *Proceedings of the Second Symposium in Linear Programming*, Vol. 2, National Bureau of Standards and Directorate of Management Analysis, DCS/Comptroller, USAF, Washington, D.C., 1955, pp. 453–469.
————, 1958-1. *Scientific Programming in Business and Industry*, John Wiley & Sons, Inc., New York, 1958, 474 pp.
Veinott, A. F., Jr., and H. M. Wagner, 1962-1. "Optimum Capacity Scheduling, I and II," *Operations Research*, Vol. 10, 1962, pp. 518–546.
Ville, Jean A., 1938-1. "Sur la théorie générale des jeux où intervient l'habileté des joueurs,"*Applications aux jeux de hasard* by Emile Borel and Jean Ville, Tome 4, Fascicule 2, in *Traité du calcul des probabilités et de ses applications*, by Emile Borel, 1938, pp. 105–113.
von Neumann, John, 1928-1. "Zur Theorie de Gesellschaftsspiele," *Math. Ann.*, Vol. 100, 1928, pp. 295–320. Translated by Sonya Bargmann in A. W. Tucker and R. D. Luce (eds.), *Contributions to the Theory of Games*, Vol. IV, Annals of Mathematics Study No. 40, Princeton University Press, Princeton, New Jersey, 1959, pp. 13–42.
————, 1937-1. "Über ein ökonomisches Gleichungssystem und ein Verallgemeinerung des Brouwerschen Fixpunktsatzes," *Ergebnisse eines mathematischen Kolloquiums*, No. 8, 1937. Translated in *Rev. Econ. Studies*, Vol. 13, No. 1, 1945–46, pp. 1–9.
————, 1947-1. "On a Maximization Problem" (manuscript), Institute for Advanced Study, Princeton, New Jersey, November, 1947.
————, 1948-1. "A Numerical Method for Determination of the Value and Best Strategies of a Zero-Sum, Two-Person Game," Institute for Advanced Study, Princeton, New Jersey, 1948.
————, 1953-1. "A Certain Zero-Sum Two-Person Game Equivalent to the Optimal Assignment Problem," in H. W. Kuhn and A. W. Tucker (eds.), *Contributions to the Theory of Games*, Vol. 2, Annals of Mathematics Study No. 28, Princeton University Press, Princeton, New Jersey, 1953, pp. 12–15.
————, 1954-1. "A Numerical Method to Determine Optimum Strategy," *Naval Res. Logist. Quart.*, Vol. 1, No. 2, 1954.
von Neumann, John, and Oskar Morgenstern, 1944-1. *Theory of Games and Economic*

BIBLIOGRAPHY

Behavior, Princeton University Press, Princeton, New Jersey, 1944; 2nd ed., 1947; 3rd ed., 1953.

Votaw, D. F., Jr., 1955-1. "Programming under Conditions of Uncertainty," in H. A. Antosiewicz (ed.), *Proceedings of the Second Symposium in Linear Programming*, Vol. 2, National Bureau of Standards and Directorate of Management Analysis, DCS/Comptroller, Washington, D.C., 1955, pp. 187–195.

———, 1960-1. "Statistical Programming," *Ann. Math. Statist.*, Vol. 31, No. 4, December, 1960, pp. 1077–1083.

Votaw, D. F., Jr., and A. Orden, 1952-1. "Personnel Assignment Problem," in Alex Orden and Leon Goldstein (eds.), *Symposium on Linear Inequalities and Programming*, Project SCOOP, No. 10, Planning Research Division, Director of Management Analysis Service, Comptroller, USAF, Washington, D.C., April, 1952, pp. 155–163.

Wagner, H. M., 1957-1. "A Linear Programming Solution to Dynamic Leontief Type Models," *Management Sci.*, Vol. 3, April, 1957, pp. 234–254.

———, 1958-1. "The Dual Simplex Algorithm for Bounded Variables," *Naval Res. Logist. Quart.*, Vol. 5, No. 3, September, 1958, pp. 257–261.

———, 1958-2. "On the Distribution of Solutions in Linear Programming Problems," *J. Amer. Statist. Assoc.*, Vol. 53, March, 1958, pp. 161–163.

———, 1959-1. "On a Class of Capacitated Transportation Problems," *Management Sci.*, Vol. 5, No. 3, April, 1959, pp. 304–318.

Wald, Abraham, 1935-1. "Über die eindeutige positive Lösbarkeit der neuen Produktions Gleichungen"; also "Über die Produktions Gleichungen der ökonomischen Wertlehre," *Ergebnisse eines mathematischen Kolloquiums*, No. 6, 1935, pp. 12–18, and No. 7, 1936, pp. 1–6.

———, 1950-1. *Statistical Decision Functions*, John Wiley & Sons, Inc., New York, 1950. 170 pp.

Walras, Leon, 1874-1. "Eléments d'économie politique pure ou théorie de la richesse sociale," 1st fasc, Vol. 8, Lausanne, Paris, and Basel, 1874, 208 pp. For other references on Walras, see Dorfman, Samuelson, and Solow, 1958-1.

Warga, J., 1963-1. "A Convergent Procedure for Convex Programming," *J. Soc. Indust. Appl. Math.*, Vol. 11, No. 3, September, 1963, pp. 579–587. See also pp. 588–593.

Waugh, F. V., 1951-1. "The Minimum-Cost Dairy Feed," *J. Farm Econ.*, Vol. 33, No. 3, August, 1951, pp. 299–310.

———, 1958-1. "Alligations, Forerunner of Linear Programming," *J. Farm Econ.*, Vol. 40, 1958, pp. 89–101.

Wbell, J. R., and W. H., Marlow, 1961-1. "On an Industrial Programming Problem of Kantorovich," *Management Sci.*, Vol. 8, 1961, pp. 13–17.

Wegner, P., 1960-1. "A Nonlinear Extension of the Simplex Method," *Management Sci.*, Vol. 7, 1960, pp. 43–55.

Wets, Roger, 1964-1. "Programming under Uncertainty, the Complete Problem," Boeing Scientific Research Laboratory, October, 1964.

Weyl, H., 1935-1. "Elementare Theorie der konvexen Polyeder," *Comment. Math. Helv.*, Vol. 7, 1935, pp. 290–306. Translated in H. W. Kuhn and A. W. Tucker (eds.), *Contributions to the Theory of Games*, Vol. 1, Annals of Mathematics Study No. 24, Princeton University Press, Princeton, New Jersey, 1950, pp. 3–18.

Whinston, A., 1962-1. "Price Coordination in Decentralized Systems," ONR Research Memorandum No. 99 (ditto), Carnegie Institute of Technology, Graduate School of Business Administration, Pittsburgh, June, 1962.

———, 1964-1. "A Decomposition Algorithm for Quadratic Programming," Cowles Foundation for Research in Economics, Yale University, Cowles Foundations Discussion Paper No. 172, June, 1964.

White, W. B., S. M. Johnson, and G. B. Dantzig, 1958-1. "Chemical Equilibrium in Complex Mixtures," *J. Chem. Phys.*, Vol. 28, No. 5, May, 1958, pp. 751–755. See also Dantzig, Johnson and White, "A Linear Programming Approach to the Chemical Equilibrium Problem," *Management Sci.*, Vol. 5, No. 1, October, 1958, pp. 38–43.

[615]

BIBLIOGRAPHY

Wilde, D. J., 1962-1. "Differential Calculus in Nonlinear Programming," *Operations Research*, Vol. 10, 1962, pp. 764–773.

Williams, A. C., 1960-1. "The Method of Continuous Coefficients," Socony Mobile Oil Company, Part I, Report No. ECC 60.3, March 1, 1960; Part II, Report No. ECC 60.4, March 21, 1960.

————, 1962-1. "A Treatment of Transportation Problems by Decomposition," *J. Soc. Indust. Appl. Math.*, Vol. 10, No. 1, January-March, 1962, pp. 35–48.

————, 1963-1. "A Stochastic Transportation Problem," *Operations Research*, Vol. 11, No. 5, 1963, pp. 759–770.

Williams, John D., 1954-1. *The Compleat Strategyst*, The RAND Corporation Research Studies, McGraw-Hill Book Company, Inc., New York, 1954.

Witzgall, C., 1963-1. "An All-Integer Programming Algorithm with Parabolic Constraints," Argonne National Laboratory, Argonne, Illinois; also published in *J. Soc. Indust. Appl. Math.*, Vol. 11, No. 4, December, 1963, pp. 855–871.

Wolfe, Philip, 1957-1. "Computational Techniques for Non-Linear Programs," Princeton University Conference, Princeton, New Jersey, March, 1957.

————, 1959-1. "The Simplex Method for Quadratic Programming," *Econometrica*, Vol. 27, No. 3, July, 1959.

———— (ed.), 1959-2. *The RAND Symposium on Mathematical Programming*, The RAND Corporation, Report R-351, March 16–20, 1959.

————, 1960-1. "Accelerating the Cutting Plane Method for Non-Linear Programming," The RAND Corporation, Paper P-2010, August, 1960; also in the *J. Soc. Indust. Appl. Math.*, Vol. 9, No. 3, September, 1961, pp. 481–488.

————, 1961-1. "A Duality Theorem for Nonlinear Programming," *Quart. Appl. Math.*, Vol. 19, 1961, pp. 239–244.

————, 1961-2. "An Extended Composite Algorithm for Linear Programming," The RAND Corporation, Paper P-2373, July, 1961.

————, 1961-3. "Accelerating the Cutting Plane Method for Non-Linear Programming," *J. Soc. Indust. Appl. Math.*, Vol. 9, No. 3, September, 1961, pp. 481–488.

————, 1962-1. "Some Simplex-Like Nonlinear Programming Procedures," *Operations Research*, Vol. 10, 1962, pp. 438–447.

————, 1963-1. "Methods of Nonlinear Programming," in R. Graves and P. Wolfe (eds.), *Recent Advances in Mathematical Programming*, McGraw-Hill Book Company, Inc., New York, 1963.

————, 1963-2. "A Technique for Resolving Degeneracy in Linear Programming," *J. Soc. Indust. Appl. Math.*, Vol. 11, No. 2, June, 1963, pp. 205–211.

Wolfe, P. and L. Cutler, 1963-1. "Experiments in Linear Programming," in R. Graves and P. Wolfe (eds.), *Recent Advances in Mathematical Programming*, McGraw-Hill Book Company, Inc., New York, 1963.

Wolfe, P. and G. B. Dantzig, 1962-1. "Linear Programming in a Markov Chain," *Operations Research*, Vol. 10, 1962, pp. 702–710.

Wollmer, Richard, 1964-1. "Removing Arcs from a Network," *Operations Research*, Vol. 12, No. 6, November-December, 1964.

Wood, Marshall K., 1948-1. "Scientific Planning Techniques," Project SCOOP, Discussion Paper Number 1-DU, Planning Research Division, Directorate of Program Standards and Cost Control. Comptroller, USAF, Washington, D.C., August, 1948, p. 6A.

Wood, Marshall K., and G. B. Dantzig, 1949-1. "The Programming of Interdependent Activities: General Discussion," in T. C. Koopmans, *Activity Analysis of Production and Allocation*, John Wiley & Sons, Inc., New York, 1951, pp. 15–18; also in *Econometrica*, Vol. 17, Nos. 3 and 4, July-October, 1949, pp. 193–199.

Wood, Marshall K., and M. A. Geisler, 1951-1. "Development of Dynamic Models for Program Planning," in T. C. Koopmans (ed.), *Activity Analysis of Production and Allocation*, John Wiley & Sons, Inc., New York, 1951, pp. 189–192.

Zoutendijk, G., 1960-1. *Methods of Feasible Directions*, Elsevier Publishing Company, New York, 1960. 126 pp.

SUBJECT INDEX

Activity, 2, 6, 433
definition of, 32
level of, 2, 32
permanently feasible, 499
variable coefficients of, 433
with one control parameter, 440–444
with several control parameters, 444–445
Activity analysis, 6, 19
(*See also* Linear programming assumptions)
Allocation of aircraft to routes, 568–591
fixed-demand case in the problem of, 570–574
formulation of the problem of, 568–578
uncertain-demand case in the problem of, 574–577
numerical solution of, 580–590
Allocation with surplus and deficit, 322–329
example of, with slack, 326–329
as a transportation problem, 323
Alternative
k-fold, 538–540
theorem of, for a matrix, 21, 139
(*See also* Dichotomies)
Ambitious industrialist example, 260–262
Arc of a graph, 352
slack, 421
Assignment problem, 247, 310, 316–322, 515, 517
definition of, 316
degeneracy in, 318–319
equivalence of transportation problem and, 319–321
reduction of, to a linear program, 318n
typical uses of the, 321–322
(*See also* Allocation of aircraft to routes; Distribution problems)
Automation, 1
relation of, to mathematical programming, 10–11
Average
weighted, 47

Basic solution, 22
definition of, 81
degenerate, 81, 99
feasible, optimal, 95
to the transportation problem, 302–303, 386–387
to the transshipment problem, 346, 386–387

in using the upper-bounding technique, 372
initial feasible, to the capacitated transportation problem, 378–379
to the weighted transportation problem, 415–417
(*See also* Feasible solutions)
Basis
complementary, in quadratic programming, 493
complementary primal and dual, 241–242
inverse of, 198, 210
product form of, 200
of a linear program, 81
number of, 235
relationship between tree and, 356
triangular, 303, 325, 340
of a vector space, 181
(*See also* Matrix; Systems of linear equations; Vector)
Blending problem examples, 42–50, 63–64, 160–161
application of the simplex method to, 110
gasoline, 443–444
Block-pivoting, 201–202

Cannery example, 2–3, 35–42
(*See also* Transportation problem)
Canonical form (*see* Systems of linear equations)
Capacitated system, 370
Caterer problem, 366
Center of gravity, 47, 92, 161
Chain-decomposition theorem, 342, 388
Chain in a graph, 353
Changes in constraint constants, 269
Changes in cost coefficients
for basic activities, 270
for nonbasic activities, 267
Changes in input-output coefficients
for basic activities, 271–272
for nonbasic activities, 267–268
Chemical equilibrium problem, 481–482
Circling, 25, 100n, 210, 228, 231
examples of, using simplex algorithm, 228–230
in transportation problems, 307–308
(*See also* Degeneracy)
Coefficients
input-output, 35

NAME INDEX

[625]

PUBLISHED RAND BOOKS

Akhmanova, O. S., R. M. Frumkina, I. A. Mel'chuk, and E. V. Paducheva. *Exact Methods in Linguistic Research*. Translated from the Russian by David G. Hays and Dolores V. Mohr. Berkeley and Los Angeles: University of California Press, 1963.

Arrow, Kenneth J., and Marvin Hoffenberg. *A Time Series Analysis of Inter-industry Demands*. Amsterdam: North-Holland Publishing Company, 1959.

Baker, C. L., and F. J. Gruenberger. *The First Six Million Prime Numbers*. Madison, Wisc.: The Microcard Foundation, 1959.

Baum, Warren C. *The French Economy and the State*. Princeton, N.J.: Princeton University Press, 1958.

Bellman, Richard. *Adaptive Control Processes: A Guided Tour*. Princeton, N.J.: Princeton University Press, 1961.

Bellman, Richard. *Dynamic Programming*. Princeton, N.J.: Princeton University Press, 1957.

Bellman, Richard. *Introduction to Matrix Analysis*. New York: McGraw-Hill Book Company, Inc., 1960.

Bellman, Richard (ed.). *Mathematical Optimization Techniques*. Berkeley and Los Angeles: University of California Press, 1963.

Bellman, Richard, and Kenneth L. Cooke. *Differential-Difference Equations*. New York: Academic Press, 1963.

Bellman, Richard, and Stuart E. Dreyfus. *Applied Dynamic Programming*. Princeton, N.J.: Princeton University Press, 1962.

Bellman, Richard E., Harriet H. Kagiwada, Robert E. Kalaba, and Marcia C. Prestrud. *Invariant Imbedding and Time-Dependent Transport Processes*, Modern Analytic and Computational Methods in Science and Mathematics, Vol. 2. New York: American Elsevier Publishing Company, Inc., 1964.

Bellman, Richard E., and Robert E. Kalaba. *Quasilinearization and Nonlinear Boundary-value Problems*, Modern Analytic and Computational Methods in Science and Mathematics, Vol. 3. New York: American Elsevier Publishing Company, Inc., 1965.

Bellman, Richard E., Robert E. Kalaba, and Marcia C. Prestrud. *Invariant Imbedding and Radiative Transfer in Slabs of Finite Thickness*, Modern Analytic and Computational Methods in Science and Mathematics, Vol. 1. New York: American Elsevier Publishing Company, Inc., 1963.

Bergson, Abram. *The Real National Income of Soviet Russia Since 1928*. Cambridge, Mass.: Harvard University Press, 1961.

Bergson, Abram, and Hans Heymann, Jr. *Soviet National Income and Product, 1940–48*. New York: Columbia University Press, 1954.

Boehm, Barry W., *ROCKET: RAND's Omnibus Calculator of the Kinematics of Earth Trajectories*. Englewood Cliffs, N.J.: Prentice-Hall, Inc., 1964.

Brodie, Bernard. *Strategy in the Missile Age*. Princeton, N.J.: Princeton University Press, 1959.

Buchheim, Robert W., and the Staff of The RAND Corporation. *New Space Handbook: Astronautics and Its Applications*. New York: Vintage Books, A Division of Random House, Inc., 1963.

Chapman, Janet G. *Real Wages in Soviet Russia Since 1928*. Cambridge, Mass.: Harvard University Press, 1963.

Dantzig, G. B. *Linear Programming and Extensions*. Princeton, N.J.: Princeton University Press, 1963.

Davison, W. Phillips. *The Berlin Blockade: A Study in Cold War Politics*. Princeton, N.J.: Princeton University Press, 1958.

Dinerstein, H. S. *War and the Soviet Union: Nuclear Weapons and the Revolution in Soviet Military and Political Thinking.* New York: Frederick A. Praeger Inc., 1959.

Dinerstein, H. S., and Leon Gouré. *Two Studies in Soviet Controls: Communism and the Russian Peasant; Moscow in Crisis.* Glencoe, Ill.: The Free Press, 1955.

Dole, Stephen H. *Habitable Planets for Man.* New York: Blaisdell Publishing Company, Inc., 1964.

Dole, Stephen, and Isaac Asimov. *Planets for Man.* New York: Random House, Inc., 1964.

Dorfman, Robert, Paul A. Samuelson, and Robert M. Solow. *Linear Programming and Economic Analysis.* New York: McGraw-Hill Book Company, Inc., 1958.

Dresher, Melvin. *Games of Strategy: Theory and Applications.* Englewood Cliffs, N.J.: Prentice-Hall, Inc., 1961.

Dubyago, A. D. *The Determination of Orbits.* Translated by R. D. Burke, G. Gordon, L. N. Rowell, and F. T. Smith. New York: The Macmillan Company, 1961.

Edelen, Dominic G. B. *The Structure of Field Space: An Axiomatic Formulation of Field Physics.* Berkeley and Los Angeles: University of California Press, 1962.

Fainsod, Merle. *Smolensk under Soviet Rule.* Cambridge, Mass.: Harvard University Press, 1958.

Ford, L. R., Jr., and D. R. Fulkerson. *Flows in Networks.* Princeton, N.J.: Princeton University Press, 1962.

Gale, David. *The Theory of Linear Economic Models.* New York: McGraw-Hill Book Company, Inc., 1960.

Galenson, Walter. *Labor Productivity in Soviet and American Industry.* New York: Columbia University Press, 1955.

Garthoff, Raymond L. *Soviet Military Doctrine.* Glencoe, Ill.: The Free Press, 1953.

George, Alexander L. *Propaganda Analysis: A Study of Inferences Made from Nazi Propaganda in World War II.* Evanston, Ill.: Row, Peterson and Company, 1959.

Goldhamer, Herbert, and Andrew W. Marshall. *Psychosis and Civilization.* Glencoe, Ill.: The Free Press, 1953.

Gouré, Leon. *Civil Defense in the Soviet Union.* Berkeley and Los Angeles: University of California Press, 1962.

Gouré, Leon. *The Siege of Leningrad.* Stanford, Calif.: Stanford University Press, 1962.

Gruenberger, F. J., and D. D. McCracken. *Introduction to Electronic Computers.* New York: John Wiley & Sons, Inc., 1963.

Halpern, Manfred. *The Politics of Social Change in the Middle East and North Africa.* Princeton, N.J.: Princeton University Press, 1963.

Harris, Theodore E. *The Theory of Branching Processes.* Berlin, Germany: Springer-Verlag, 1963; Englewood Cliffs, N.J.: Prentice-Hall, Inc., 1964.

Hastings, Cecil, Jr. *Approximations for Digital Computers.* Princeton, N.J.: Princeton University Press, 1955.

Hearle, Edward F. R., and Raymond J. Mason. *A Data Processing System for State and Local Governments.* Englewood Cliffs, N.J.: Prentice-Hall, Inc., 1963.

Hirshleifer, Jack, James C. DeHaven, and Jerome W. Milliman. *Water Supply: Economics, Technology, and Policy.* Chicago: The University of Chicago Press, 1960.

Hitch, Charles J., and Roland McKean. *The Economics of Defense in the Nuclear Age.* Cambridge, Mass.: Harvard University Press, 1960.

Hoeffding, Oleg. *Soviet National Income and Product in 1928.* New York: Columbia University Press, 1954.

Hsieh, Alice L. *Communist China's Strategy in the Nuclear Era.* Englewood Cliffs, N.J.: Prentice-Hall, Inc., 1962.

Janis, Irving L. *Air War and Emotional Stress: Psychological Studies of Bombing and Civilian Defense.* New York: McGraw-Hill Book Company, Inc., 1951.

Johnson, John J. (ed.). *The Role of the Military in Underdeveloped Countries.* Princeton, N.J.: Princeton University Press, 1962.

Johnstone, William C. *Burma's Foreign Policy: A Study in Neutralism.* Cambridge, Mass.: Harvard University Press, 1963.

Judd, William R. (ed.). *State of Stress in the Earth's Crust.* New York: American Elsevier Publishing Company, Inc., 1964.

Kecskemeti, Paul. *Strategic Surrender: The Politics of Victory and Defeat.* Stanford, Calif.: Stanford University Press, 1958.

Kecskemeti, Paul. *The Unexpected Revolution: Social Forces in the Hungarian Uprising.* Stanford, Calif.: Stanford University Press, 1961.

Kershaw, Joseph A., and Roland N. McKean. *Teacher Shortages and Salary Schedules.* New York: McGraw-Hill Book Company, Inc., 1962.

Kramish, Arnold. *Atomic Energy in the Soviet Union.* Stanford, Calif.: Stanford University Press, 1959.

Krieger, F. J. *Behind the Sputniks: A Survey of Soviet Space Science.* Washington, D.C.: Public Affairs Press, 1958.

Leites, Nathan. *On the Game of Politics in France.* Stanford, Calif.: Stanford University Press, 1959.

Leites, Nathan. *The Operational Code of the Politburo.* New York: McGraw-Hill Book Company, Inc., 1951.

Leites, Nathan. *A Study of Bolshevism.* Glencoe, Ill.: The Free Press, 1953.

Leites, Nathan, and Elsa Bernaut. *Ritual of Liquidation: The Case of the Moscow Trials.* Glencoe, Ill.: The Free Press, 1954.

Liu, Ta-Chung, and Kung-Chia Yeh. *The Economy of the Chinese Mainland: National Income and Economic Development, 1933–1959.* Princeton, N.J.: Princeton University Press, 1964.

Lubell, Harold. *Middle East Oil Crises and Western Europe's Energy Supplies.* Baltimore, Maryland: The Johns Hopkins Press, 1963.

Markowitz, H. M., B. Hausner, and H. W. Karr. *SIMSCRIPT: A Simulation Programming Language.* Englewood Cliffs, N.J.: Prentice-Hall, Inc., 1963.

McKean, Roland N. *Efficiency in Government through Systems Analysis: With Emphasis on Water Resource Development.* New York: John Wiley & Sons, Inc., 1958.

McKinsey, J. C. C. *Introduction to the Theory of Games.* New York: McGraw-Hill Book Company, Inc., 1952.

Mead, Margaret. *Soviet Attitudes toward Authority: An Interdisciplinary Approach to Problems of Soviet Character.* New York: McGraw-Hill Book Company, Inc., 1951.

Melnik, Constantin, and Nathan Leites. *The House without Windows: France Selects a President.* Evanston, Ill.: Row, Peterson and Company, 1958.

Moorsteen, Richard. *Prices and Production of Machinery in the Soviet Union, 1928–1958.* Cambridge, Mass.: Harvard University Press, 1962.

Newell, Allen (ed.). *Information Processing Language-V Manual.* Englewood Cliffs, N.J.: Prentice-Hall, Inc., 1964.

O'Sullivan, J. J. (ed.). *Protective Construction in a Nuclear Age.* 2 vols. New York: The Macmillan Company, 1961.

Pincus, J. A. *Economic Aid and International Cost Sharing.* Baltimore, Maryland: The Johns Hopkins Press, 1965.

Quade, Edward S. (ed.). *Analysis for Military Decisions.* Chicago: Rand McNally & Company; Amsterdam: North Holland Publishing Company, 1964.

The RAND Corporation. *A Million Random Digits with 100,000 Normal Deviates.* Glencoe, Ill.: The Free Press, 1955.

Rush, Myron. *The Rise of Khrushchev.* Washington, D.C.: Public Affairs Press, 1958.

Rush, Myron. *Struggle for Power: Political Succession in the USSR.* New York: Columbia University Press, 1965.

Scitovsky, Tibor, Edward Shaw, and Lorie Tarshis. *Mobilizing Resources for War: The Economic Alternatives.* New York: McGraw-Hill Book Company, Inc., 1951.

Selin, Ivan. *Detection Theory.* Princeton, N.J.: Princeton University Press, 1965.

Selznick, Philip. *The Organizational Weapon: A Study of Bolshevik Strategy and Tactics.* New York: McGraw-Hill Book Company, Inc., 1952.

Shanley, F. R. *Weight-Strength Analysis of Aircraft Structures.* New York: McGraw-Hill Book Company, Inc., 1952.

Smith, Bruce Lannes, and Chitra M. Smith. *International Communication and Political Opinion: A Guide to the Literature.* Princeton, N.J.: Princeton University Press, 1956.

Sokolovskii, V. D. *Soviet Military Strategy.* Translated and annotated by H. S. Dinerstein, L. Gouré, and T. W. Wolfe. Englewood Cliffs, N.J.: Prentice-Hall, Inc., 1963.

Speier, Hans. *Divided Berlin: The Anatomy of Soviet Political Blackmail.* New York: Frederick A. Praeger Inc., 1961.

Speier, Hans. *German Rearmament and Atomic War: The Views of German Military and Political Leaders.* Evanston, Ill.: Row, Peterson and Company, 1957.

Speier, Hans, and W. Phillips Davison (eds.). *West German Leadership and Foreign Policy.* Evanston, Ill.: Row, Peterson and Company, 1957.

Tanham, G. K. *Communist Revolutionary Warfare: The Viet Minh in Indochina.* New York: Frederick A. Praeger Inc., 1961.

Trager, Frank N. (ed.). *Marxism in Southeast Asia: A Study of Four Countries.* Stanford, Calif.: Stanford University Press, 1959.

Whiting, Allen S. *China Crosses the Yalu: The Decision To Enter the Korean War.* New York: The Macmillan Company, 1960.

Williams, J. D. *The Compleat Strategyst: Being a Primer on the Theory of Games of Strategy.* New York: McGraw-Hill Book Company, Inc., 1954.

Wolf, Charles, Jr. *Foreign Aid: Theory and Practice in Southern Asia.* Princeton, N.J.: Princeton University Press, 1960.

Wolfe, Thomas. *Soviet Strategy at the Crossroads.* Cambridge, Mass.: Harvard University Press, 1964.

Forthcoming

Gruenberger, F. J. *Problems for Computer Solution.* New York: John Wiley & Sons, Inc.

Meyer, J. R., J. F. Kain, and M. Wohl. *The Urban Transportation Problem.* Cambridge, Mass.: Harvard University Press.